Study Guide

STATISTICS FOR MANAGEMENT AND ECONOMICS, THIRD EDITION

William Mendenhall
University of Florida

James E. Reinmuth
University of Oregon

Prepared by

Robert Beaver
University of California, Riverside

DUXBURY PRESS

North Scituate, Mass. *Belmont, California*
A division of Wadsworth Publishing Company, Inc.

Duxbury Press
North Scituate, Massachusetts
A Division of Wadsworth Publishing Company, Inc.

L.C. Cat. Card No.: 77-22411
ISBN 0-87872-166-5

Printed in the United States of America

3 4 5 6 7 8 9 10 _____ 82 81 80 79

CONTENTS

PREFACE

The study of statistics differs from the study of many other college subjects. Not only must the student absorb a set of basic concepts and applications, he must also acquire a new language.

Understanding the meaning of words employed in the study of a subject is a prerequisite to the mastery of concepts. Such understanding offers little difficulty in many branches of the physical, social, and biological sciences; many terms related to these disciplines occur in the curricula of the public schools, in the news media, in periodicals, and in everyday conversation. In contrast, few students encounter the language of probability and statistical inference before embarking on an introductory college-level study of the subject. However, for a student of business and economics, familiarization with this language and a working knowledge of the methods of probability and statistical inference are minimal requirements for mastering the complexities of economic forecasting, production control, and marketing research.

This study guide attempts to lead the student through the language and concepts necessary for a mastery of the material in *Statistics for Management and Economics* by Mendenhall and Reinmuth (Duxbury Press, 1978). The intent of both the study guide and the textbook it accompanies is to present a study of probability and statistical inference, relate the information given to problems in business and economics through examples and exercises, and supplement the material with some statistical methods of special interest within the fields of business and economics.

Although the study guide is intended to be a supplement to the textbook, *Statistics for Management and Economics* by Mendenhall and Reinmuth, it can be used effectively by itself in certain instances. For the graduate student or individual seeking a quick but thorough review of the elements of business and economic statistics, the study guide alone provides a valuable aid.

A study guide with answers is intended to be an individual student study aid. The subject matter is presented in an organized manner that incorporates continuity with repetition. For the most part, the chapters bear the same titles and order as the textbook chapters. Within each chapter, the material both summarizes and reexplains the essential concepts from the corresponding textbook chapter. This gives the student more than one perspective on each topic and, hopefully, enhances his understanding of the material.

At appropriate points in each chapter, the student will encounter a set of Self-Correcting Exercises in which problems relating to new material are presented. Terse, stepwise solutions to these problems are found at the back of the study guide and can be referenced by the student at any intermediate point in the solution of each problem, or used as a stepwise check on any final answer. These exercises not only provide the student with the answers to specific problems, but also reinforce the stepwise logic required to arrive at a correct solution to each problem.

With the exception of Chapters 14 and 15, further sets of exercises can be found at the end of each chapter. These exercises are provided for the student who feels that additional individual practice is needed in solving the kinds of problems found within each chapter. At this point, having been given stepwise solutions to the Self-Correcting Exercises, the student is now presented only with final answers to these problems. Hopefully, when the student's answer disagrees with that given in the study guide, he can recalculate and compare the solutions to similar Self-Correcting Exercises and then find his error. If the answer given disagrees with the student's only in decimal accuracy, this difference can be taken to be due only to rounding error at various stages in the calculations.

When the study guide is used as a supplement, the textbook chapter should be read first. Then the student should study the corresponding chapter within the study guide. Key words, phrases, and numerical computations have been left blank for the student to insert his response. The answers are presented in the page margins. These should be covered until the student has supplied his response. One should bear in mind that in some instances, more than one answer may be appropriate for a given blank. It is left to the reader to determine whether his answer is synonymous with the answer given within the margin.

Since perfection is something to be desired, we ask that the reader who has located an error kindly bring it to our attention.

Additional preparation for this study guide was provided by Michael A. Flynn for P.S. Associates, Sterling, Massachusetts.

Chapter 1

INTRODUCTION

1.1 The Population and the Sample (1.1, 1.2)

1. Business statistics involves the use of _____ *dota* ___ to predict, estimate, and ultimately, make ___*decision*___ in the presence of ___*uncertainty*___.

   sample data
   decisions
   uncertainty

2. A specified number of objects or bits of ___*data*___ drawn from a much larger body of data is called a ___*sample*___, while the body of data from which it is drawn is called the ___*population*___.

   information
   sample
   population

3. "Population" refers to ___*data*___ and not to people.

   data *or* measurements

4. *Population* and *sample* have specific definitions: A ___*sample*___ is the set representing all measurements of interest to the _____. A ___*sample*___ is a subset of measurements selected from the ___*population*___ of interest.

   population
   investigator
   sample
   population

5. Usually, one is primarily interested in the (population, sample). Because it is generally impractical to observe or measure every element in the population, one selects a ___*sample*___ with the hope that it is representative of the underlying ___*population*___.

   population

   sample
   population

6. In discussing a sample or population, it is important to distinguish between the *objects* measured and the *measurements* themselves. "Experimental units" and "elements of the sample" refer to the (objects, measurements). However, when the textbook uses the terms "population" or "sample," it means the ___*measurement*___ made on the objects.

   objects

   measurements

7. The preferences of eligible voting stockholders at a corporation's annual meeting is a population of interest to the board of directors of that corporation. An inference about the characteristics of this population can be obtained from information contained in a ___*sample*___. The inference will involve a(n) ___*decision*___ concerning the characteristics of the ___*population*___.

   sample
   decision *or* estimate
   population

8. An experiment was conducted by the owner of a taxi company to determine the tire wear after 10,000 miles of use of the tires of a particular manufacturer. Ten of the manufacturer's tires were placed on the right rear wheels of ten different taxis. The measurements of the amounts of

sample
population

inference

tread on the ten tires after 10,000 miles use represent a _Sample_ drawn from the conceptual (sample, population) of measurements of the amounts of tread on all tires of the manufacturer after 10,000 miles of use under similar circumstances. The information contained in the sample of ten tire wear measurements is to be used to make an _inference_ about the conceptual population from which the sample was drawn.

1.2 The Parts of a Statistical Problem (1.3, 1.4)

inferences
population
sample

five

question; population

definition of the population
specification of the question
sample
design
sampling
money; time
selected; information

maximum; minimum
analysis
method
information

inference; population

goodness
reliability; most

reliability

1. The objective of statistics is to make _inference_ about certain characteristics of a _population_ based on information contained in a _sample_.

2. The objective of statistics can be achieved by successfully completing each of the _five_ (give number) parts of a statistical problem.

3. The first part of a statistical problem is the clear specification of the _question_ to be answered, and the definition of the _population_ of interest. Notice that the first part of a statistical problem itself consists of two steps, which must be done in the correct order: The (specification of the question, definition of the population) must follow, and be determined by, the (specification of the question, definition of the population).

4. The second part of a statistical problem is deciding how the _sample_ will be selected. This second part, also called the _design_ of the experiment, or the _sampling_ procedure, is important because data cost _time_ and _money_, and because the way the sample is _selected_ will affect the amount of _info_ per observation. The object is to plan experiments and surveys so that they yield the (minimum, maximum) information at (minimum, maximum) cost.

5. The third part of a statistical problem is the collection and _analysis_ of the sample data. It is important to use the appropriate _test_ of data analysis to properly extract the _info_ from the data.

6. The fourth part of a statistical problem is using the sample data to make an _inference_ about the _population_. Here it is important to choose the best inference- or decision-making procedure from the many available for the problem at hand.

7. The final part of a statistical problem is measuring the _reliability_ or _goodness_ of the inference. This is perhaps the (most, least) important contribution of statistics to the problem of business decision making. Every inference, whether it be an estimate, or prediction, or decision, should be accompanied by a measure of its _goodness_.

1.3 Summary (1.5)

inferences; population
sample

1. The objective of statistics is to make _inferences_ about a _population_ based on information contained in a _sample_. In order for the

resulting inferences to be meaningful, it is important that the sample be selected from the population of ___*interest*___ .

2. Statistics is a theory of ___*info*___ which utilizes applied ___*math*___ .
3. Statistics is concerned with the design of ___*sampling*___ or _____ procedures, the ___*analysis*___ of data, and the procedures for making ___*inferences*___ about a ___*population*___ of measurements from information contained in a ___*sample*___ .
4. The business statistician is concerned with developing and using procedures for ___*design*___ , ___*analysis*___ , and ___*inference*___ making that will provide the best inferences for a given expenditure.
5. In addition to making the best inferences, the statistician is also concerned with measuring the ___*goodness*___ or ___*reliability*___ of the inference-making procedure.
6. It is essential that the business statistician effectively ___*communicate*___ his experimental conclusions to management.

interest
information; mathematics
experiments; sampling
analysis
inferences; population
sample
design; analysis; inference
goodness; reliability
communicate

Chapter 2

USEFUL MATHEMATICAL NOTATION

2.1 Introduction (2.1)

1. To fulfill the objective of statistics, we must extract ___*data*___ from
   measurements contained in a (sample, population) drawn from the
   ___*population*___ of interest.

   information
   sample
   population

2. Formulas for analyzing this information are often expressed in summation
   notation, which is a shorthand way of instructing us to add the sample
   measurements, or numbers calculated from the sample measurements.

3. To understand summation notation, we must also know something
   about two basic algebraic concepts. One of these is functional notation,
   which provides a compact way of specifying a relationship between sets of
   elements. The other concept is the idea of a numerical ___*sequence*___,
   which is used to order the elements of a set.

   sequence

4. Functional notation is essential because we will often wish to sum some
   function of the sample measurements. Numerical sequences are important
   because we must know which sample measurements are to be summed.

2.2 Functional Notation (2.2)

1. A ___*set*___ is a collection of specific things such as particular
   objects or numbers. If we have two sets of elements, there could be many
   different rules defining correspondences or ___*relations*___ between the
   elements of the first set and the elements of the second.

   set

   relationships

2. A function consists of ___*2*___ (give number) sets of elements and a
   specified ___*relationship*___ between the elements of the sets such that for
   each element in the first set there corresponds exactly ___*one*___ (give
   number) element in the second set.

   two
   correspondence or
   relationship; one

3. A function can be displayed graphically showing the elements of the first

and second sets as points inside respective enclosures and the rule of association indicated by joining associated points (elements) with lines. Here is an example.

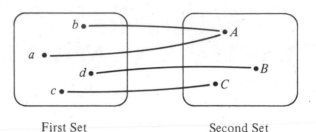

First Set   Second Set

4. The preceding visualized function might also be exhibited as a collection of "ordered pairs." In each pair, the *right* member is an element of the **first** second set, and *no two* pairs have the same (first, second) element. Thus the function represented above can also be displayed as the collection **ordered** $\{(a,A),(b,A),(d,B),(c,C)\}$ of ___ordered___ pairs. Though two of these pairs have the same second element, we note that no two of these **first** pairs have the same ___first___ element.

5. A third manner of representing a function is to employ the mathematical **functional notation** shorthand or symbolism called ___functional notation___. Thus the element of the second set which corresponds to the element x of the first is denoted by an expression of the type, $f(x)$.

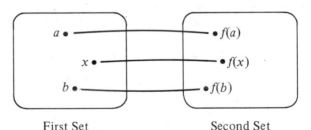

First Set   Second Set

When y is the element of the second set corresponding to a typical element x of the first set, we indicate the relationship by writing

$f(x)$
$$y = \underline{f(x)}.$$

In the applications of functional notation in this book, the sets will usually, but not always, consist of numbers.

6. In those cases in which the sets consist of numbers, the relationship between their respective elements will consist of an equation. However, by itself, functional notation only indicates the existence of a functional relationship, not the specific nature of the relationship.

7. *Example:*

Write down the collection of ordered pairs represented in functional notation by:

$$f(x) = x^2, \qquad x = 1, 2, 3$$

Solution:

$\{(1, 1), (2, \underline{\hspace{0.3cm} 4 \hspace{0.3cm}}), (\underline{\hspace{0.3cm} 3 \hspace{0.3cm}}, \underline{\hspace{0.3cm} 9 \hspace{0.3cm}})\}$. Here the first set is the set of numbers $\{1, 2, 3\}$, while the second set is the set of numbers $\{\underline{\hspace{0.3cm} 1 \hspace{0.3cm}}, \underline{\hspace{0.3cm} 4 \hspace{0.3cm}}, \underline{\hspace{0.3cm} 9 \hspace{0.3cm}}\}$.

$4; 3; 9$

$1; 4; 9$

8. *Example:*

$$f(y) = 2y^2 - 3y + 1, \qquad y = 0, 1, 2, 3$$

Supply each of the following functional values:

$f(0) = \underline{\hspace{0.3cm} 1 \hspace{0.3cm}}$ 1

$f(1) = \underline{\hspace{0.3cm} 0 \hspace{0.3cm}}$ 0

$f(2) = \underline{\hspace{0.3cm} 3 \hspace{0.3cm}}$ 3

$f(3) = \underline{\hspace{0.3cm} 10 \hspace{0.3cm}}$ 10

This function is the collection of ordered pairs:

$$\{(0,1), (1, \underline{\hspace{0.3cm} 0 \hspace{0.3cm}}), (\underline{\hspace{0.3cm} 2, 3 \hspace{0.3cm}}), (\underline{\hspace{0.3cm} 3, 10 \hspace{0.3cm}})\}$$

$0; 2,3; 3,10$

9. *Some Useful Functions*

a. Functions of the type $f(x) = (1/2)^x, x = 0, 1, 2, \ldots, n$, are used in later chapters. We shall be consistent with mathematical convention and define a^0 to be 1 ($a^0 = 1$) if a is not zero. Thus, if $f(x) = (1/2)^x$, then $f(0) = \underline{\hspace{0.3cm} 1 \hspace{0.3cm}}$. Also, $f(2) = \underline{\hspace{0.3cm} \frac{1}{4} \hspace{0.3cm}}$ and $f(4) = \underline{\hspace{0.3cm} \frac{1}{16} \hspace{0.3cm}}$. The letter used to represent a typical value from the first set (here we have used the letter x) is often called the "independent variable." The quantity $y = f(x)$ is then said to be the "dependent variable," since the value assumed by $f(x)$ depends on the value used for x.

$1; 1/4; 1/16$

b. The factorial function $f(n) = n!, n = 1, 2, \ldots$, is used in the expression of certain important probability distributions. Again we follow mathematical convention and define $f(0) = 0!$ to be 1 ($0! = 1$). To complete the definition of $n!$, we require that $n! = n(n-1)!$ for $n = 1, 2, 3, \ldots$. Thus,

$1! = (1)(0)! = \underline{\hspace{0.3cm} 1 \hspace{0.3cm}}$ 1

$2! = (2)(1)! = \underline{\hspace{0.3cm} 2 \hspace{0.3cm}}$ 2

$3! = (3)(2)! = 3 \cdot 2 \cdot 1 = \underline{\hspace{0.3cm} 6 \hspace{0.3cm}}$ 6

$4! = (4)(3)! = 3 \cdot 2 \cdot 1 \ = \underline{\hspace{0.3cm} 24 \hspace{0.3cm}}$ $4 \cdot 3 \cdot 2 \cdot 1; 24$

$n! = n(n-1)(n-2) \ldots 3 \cdot 2 \cdot 1$

10. *Examples:*

The student should not be disturbed if letters other than x are used to represent independent variables or if symbols other than $f(x)$ are used to represent dependent variables. Supply each missing entry in the following table:

	Value of Independent Variable	Formula for Dependent Variable	Value of Dependent Variable	
3	a. $x = 2$	$f(x) = x^2 - 1$	$f(2)$ =	_3_
-1	b. $y = -1$	$g(y) = 2y + 1$	$g(-1)$ =	_-1_
8	c. $x = 2$	$f(x) = 3^x - 1$	$f(2)$ =	_8_
0	d. $t = 0$	$f(t) = 3^t - 1$	$f(0)$ =	_0_
6	e. $u = 3$	$h(u) = u!$	$h(3)$ =	_6_
2	f. $u = 0$	$h(u) = u! + 1$	$h(0)$ =	_2_
x_5	g. $i = 5$	$g(i) = x_i$	$g(5)$ =	_x_5_

2.3 Numerical Sequences (2.3)

1. A set of objects $x_1, x_2, x_3, \ldots$ that is ordered so that one can identify the first, second, etc., elements of the set is called a _sequence_. The objects $x_1, x_2, x_3, \ldots$ are usually _number_ and are called the _elements_ of the sequence.

   sequence
   numbers
   elements

2. Sequences arise quite naturally in statistics. For example, a sample of measurements is a sequence because the measurements are obtained in a definite order.

3. Elements of a sequence (are, are not) arranged in order of magnitude. All that is required is that each element have a definite _order_ in the sequence.

   are not
   position

4. _functional notation_ provides a shorthand notation for the elements of a sequence because a numerical sequence can be thought of as a function with the positive integers $(1, 2, 3, 4, \ldots)$ as the independent variable. So when the elements of a sequence correspond to the functional values of $f(y)$ for $y = 1, 2, 3, \ldots$, then y is often called a _position_ variable, since the value given to y determines the position of the element $f(y)$ in the sequence.

   Functional notation
   position

   Example:
   Find a formula expressing the typical element of the sequence

   $$3, 6, 9, 12, \ldots$$

   as a function of its position in the sequence.
   Solution:
   We note that the element in the first position is $3(1)$, the element in the second position is $3(2)$, the third is $3(3)$, etc. Hence a formula expressing the typical element as a function of its position is

   $$f(y) = 3y, \qquad y = 1, 2, 3, \ldots$$

   3y

5. But while the elements of many sequences can be determined simply from a formula that has the position variable (y in the above example) as its independent variable, not all important sequences are of this type, espe-

cially in statistics. In statistics, most numerical sequences of interest are sets of measurements obtained by sampling or experimentation. Were it possible to know the value of a measurement simply by knowing the order in which the measurement was taken, it would be a very unusual (and nonrandom) sample indeed!

6. Statisticians generally work with sequences of measurements and therefore need a convenient way of referring to the first, second, . . . , or last measurement observed. Suppose that a statistician was working with measurements concerning the construction costs per mile for 10 different sections of an interstate highway. Wishing to use the variable c to designate "cost," he would probably write c_1 (c-sub-one) to designate the cost for the first section, c_2 to designate the cost for the second section, and so on. Thus, he would refer to his measurements as

$$c_1, c_2, c_3, \ldots, c_9, c_{10}$$

In this case, we could write a typical element of this sequence as

$$f(i) = c_i$$

using i as the _position_ variable. Then $f(3) = c_3$ would be the cost of the third section.

position

2.4 Summation Notation (2.4)

1. Consider the expression

$$\sum_{y=2}^{4} f(y)$$

a. The Greek letter Σ (upper case sigma) is an instruction to perform the operation of _addition_ .

addition

b. $f(y)$ is the yth term of the sequence $\{f(1), f(2), f(3), \ldots\}$ and is called the _typical element_ of summation.

typical element

c. The notation "$y = 2$" found below the symbol Σ indicates two things.
   i. The letter y is to be used as the position variable or the *variable of summation*.
   ii. The first term in the sum is to be $f(2)$, the second term in the above sequence.
   The number of the first term in the sum is usually referred to as the *lower limit of summation*. In this case the lower limit of summation is _2_ .

2

d. The number 4 above the symbol Σ indicates that the last term in the

upper

sum is to be $f(4)$. In general this number is called the <u>upper</u>
limit of summation.

e. The total expression $\displaystyle\sum_{y=2}^{4} f(y)$ is the instruction to add the second,

third and fourth terms of the sequence $\{f(1), f(2), \ldots\}$

2. *Example:*
Evaluate

$$\sum_{y=1}^{4} y^2$$

Solution:

$$\sum_{y=1}^{4} y^2 = 1^2 + 2^2 + 3^2 + 4^2$$

9; 16

$$= 1 + 4 + \underline{\quad 9 \quad} + \underline{\quad 16 \quad}$$

30

$$= \underline{\quad 30 \quad}$$

3. *Example:*
Evaluate

$$\sum_{y=2}^{4} (y + 2)$$

Solution:

$$\sum_{y=2}^{4} (y + 2) = (2 + 2) + (3 + 2) + (4 + 2)$$

5; 6

$$= 4 + \underline{\quad 5 \quad} + \underline{\quad 6 \quad}$$

15

$$= \underline{\quad 15 \quad}$$

4. One must pay close attention to parentheses in problems involving summations. Notice the difference between the next two problems.

a. $\displaystyle\sum_{x=1}^{3} (x^2 - 1) = (1^2 - 1) + (2^2 - 1) + (3^2 - 1) =$ __11__   11

b. $\displaystyle\sum_{x=1}^{3} x^2 - 1 = (1^2 + 2^2 + 3^2) - 1 =$ __13__   13

In problem a. the typical element of summation is $(x^2 - 1)$ which means that within each term one is subtracted from x^2. In problem b. the typical element of summation is x^2, so that after summing, one is sub-

tracted from $\displaystyle\sum_{x=1}^{3} x^2$. The placement or absence of a set of parentheses

is crucial in defining the typical element of summation.

5. *Examples:*

Evaluate the following summations.

a. $\displaystyle\sum_{x=3}^{5} (x^2 + 2x) = 15 +$ __24__ $+$ __35__ $=$ __74__ $24; 35; 74$

b. $\displaystyle\sum_{z=1}^{3} 1/3\,z + 10 = (1/3 + 2/3 + 3/3) +$ __10__ $=$ __12__ $10; 12$

c. $\displaystyle\sum_{i=1}^{4} (i^2 - i + 1) = 1 + 3 +$ __7__ $+$ __13__ $=$ __24__ $7; 13; 24$

d. $\displaystyle\sum_{j=1}^{4} (j^2 - j) + 1 = (0 + 2 + 6 + 12) + 1 =$ __21__   21

Notice that any symbol can be used as a valid variable of summation. In fact the letters i and j are very commonly used as position variables in statistical problems.

6. *Example:*

The following measurements represent the cost in cents of 5 different 7 oz. aerosol cans of deodorant: $y_1 = 119, y_2 = 98, y_3 = 79, y_4 = 89, y_5 = 95$

Using these values, evaluate the following summations.

a. $$\sum_{i=1}^{5} y_i$$

b. $$\sum_{i=1}^{5} y_i \Big/ 5$$

c. $$\sum_{i=1}^{5} (y_i - 96)$$

d. $$\sum_{i=1}^{5} (y_i - 96)^2$$

e. $$\sum_{i=1}^{5} y_i^2 - \left(\sum_{i=1}^{5} y_i \right)^2 \Big/ 5$$

Solution:

a. In each of these five summation problems the letter i is used as a position variable to designate the ith measurement (cost) in the group of five measurements. Therefore,

$$\sum_{i=1}^{5} y_i = y_1 + y_2 + y_3 + y_4 + y_5$$

$$= 119 + 98 + 79 + 89 + 95$$

$$= \underline{480}$$

480

b. From part a, $\sum_{i=1}^{5} y_i = 480$, so that $\sum_{i=1}^{5} y_i \Big/ 5 = 480/5 = \underline{96}$

96

c. This problem can be solved directly as

$$\sum_{i=1}^{5} (y_i - 96) = (119 - 96) + (98 - 96) + (79 - 96) + (89 - 96)$$

$$+ (95 - 96)$$

$$= 23 + 2 - 17 - \underline{7} - \underline{1}$$

$$= \underline{0}$$

7; 1

0

d. Using the results of part c,

$$\sum_{i=1}^{5} (y_i - 96)^2 = (23)^2 + (2)^2 + (-17)^2 + (-7)^2 + (-1)^2$$

$$= \underline{872}$$

872

e. To compute this summation, we first need to find $\sum_{i=1}^{5} y_i^2$.

$$\sum_{i=1}^{5} y_i^2 = (119)^2 + (98)^2 + (79)^2 + (89)^2 + (95)^2$$

$$= \underline{46952}$$

46952

With the result of part a,

$$\sum_{i=1}^{5} y_i^2 - \left(\sum_{i=1}^{5} y_i\right)^2 / 5 = 46952 - (\underline{480})^2/5$$

480

$$= 46952 - 46080$$

$$= \underline{872}$$

872

(It is no accident that the answers to parts d and e are identical.)

2.5 Summation Theorems (2.5)

1. *Theorem 1*

$$\sum_{x=1}^{n} c = nc$$

nc

We say that c is a __constant__ because c does depend upon the __variable__ of __summation__

constant

variable; summation

One may encounter sums with a lower limit of summation different from 1. A useful device for arriving at the correct answer in this case is illustrated by the example $\sum_{x=4}^{10} 5$.

10; 3

a. Now $\sum_{x=1}^{10} 5$ has __16__ terms while $\sum_{x=1}^{3} 5$ has __3__ terms.

b. But $\sum_{x=4}^{10} 5 = \sum_{x=1}^{10} 5 - \sum_{x=1}^{3} 5$

7; 35

c. $\sum_{x=4}^{10} 5$ has __7__ terms and hence $\sum_{x=4}^{10} 5 = (10-3)5 = \underline{35}$

2. Theorem 2

$c \sum_{x=1}^{n} f(x)$

$$\sum_{x=1}^{n} cf(x) = \underline{\dfrac{c\sum_{x=1}^{n} f(x)}{}}$$

An equivalent form of this rule is

$c \sum_{i=1}^{n} x_i$

$$\sum_{i=1}^{n} cx_i = \underline{\dfrac{c\sum_{i=1}^{n} x_i}{}}$$

Thus,

25; 150

$$\sum_{x=1}^{3} 25x = (\underline{25}) \sum_{x=1}^{3} x = \underline{150}$$

3. Theorem 3

$\sum_{x=1}^{n} g(x)$

$$\sum_{x=1}^{n} [f(x) + g(x)] = \sum_{x=1}^{n} f(x) + \underline{\sum_{x=1}^{n} g(x)}$$

$\sum_{x=1}^{n} f(x) - \sum_{x=1}^{n} g(x)$

$$\sum_{x=1}^{n} [f(x) - g(x)] = \underline{\sum_{x=1}^{n} f(x) - \sum_{x=1}^{n} g(x)}$$

Thus,

$$\sum_{x=1}^{6} (x - 5) = \sum_{x=1}^{6} x - \underline{\sum_{x=1}^{6} 5}$$

$$= \underline{\quad 21 \quad} - \underline{30}$$

$$= \underline{\quad -9 \quad}$$

$$\sum_{x=1}^{6} 5$$

$21; 6(5)$

-9

Rules given in 1, 2, and 3 may be used in combination, as in the following example.

4. *Example:*
Evaluate

$$\sum_{x=1}^{5} (3x^2 + 5x - 2)$$

Solution:
a. Using rule 3,

$$\sum_{x=1}^{5} (3x^2 + 5x - 2) = \sum_{x=1}^{5} 3x^2 + \sum_{x=1}^{5} 5x - \sum_{x=1}^{5} 2$$

b. The first two terms can be simplified using rule 2 to give

$$\sum_{x=1}^{5} (3x^2 + 5x - 2) = 3 \sum_{x=1}^{5} x^2 + 5 \sum_{x=1}^{5} x - \sum_{x=1}^{5} 2$$

c. Finally, using rule 1 to simplify $\sum_{x=1}^{5} 2 = 5(2)$, we have

$$\sum_{x=1}^{5} (3x^2 + 5x - 2) = 3 (\underline{\quad 55 \quad}) + 5 (\underline{\quad 15 \quad}) - 10$$

$$= \underline{\quad 230 \quad}$$

$55; 15$

230

5. *Example:*

Evaluate

$$\sum_{x=1}^{5} (x - 4)^2$$

Solution:

a. If the element of summation is not written as a simple sum or difference of terms, it may be possible to convert it to a sum or difference by algebraic manipulation.

b. The typical element of summation is $(x - 4)^2$. But $(x - 4)^2 = x^2 - 8x + 16$, so that

$$\sum_{x=1}^{5} (x - 4)^2 = \sum_{x=1}^{5} (x^2 - 8x + 16)$$

$$= \sum_{x=1}^{5} x^2 - 8 \sum_{x=1}^{5} x + 5(16)$$

$$= \underline{\quad 55 \quad} - 8(\underline{\quad 15 \quad}) + \underline{\quad 80 \quad}$$

$$= \underline{\quad 15 \quad}$$

55; 15; 80

15

6. *Example:*

Using summation theorems, rewrite the following summation as sums or differences of terms.

$$\sum_{i=1}^{n} (y_i - c)^2$$

Solution:

a. Following the technique given in Number 5, the typical element of summation is $(y_i - c)^2$ which when algebraically squared equals $(y_i^2 - 2cy_i + c^2)$.

b. Using the summation theorems, write

$$\sum_{i=1}^{n} (y_i - c)^2 = \sum_{i=1}^{n} (y_i^2 - 2cy_i + c^2)$$

$$= \sum_{i=1}^{n} y_i^2 - 2c \cdot \sum_{i=1}^{n} \underline{y_i} + \underline{nc^2} \qquad\qquad y_i; nc^2$$

c. Note that until the values of $y_1, y_2, \ldots, y_n$ and c are given, we cannot proceed any further with this problem.

7. *Example:*

Use the results of Number 6 to find $\sum_{i=1}^{5} (y_i - 3)^2$ if $y_1 = 2, y_2 = 4, y_3 = 1,$

$y_4 = 3, y_5 = 4.$

Solution:

a. From Number 6,

$$\sum_{i=1}^{5} (y_i - 3)^2 = \sum_{i=1}^{5} y_i^2 - 6 \sum_{i=1}^{5} y_i + 5(9).$$

Therefore we need to find $\sum_{i=1}^{5} y_i^2$ and $\sum_{i=1}^{5} y_i.$

b. $\quad \sum_{i=1}^{5} y_i^2 = 2^2 + 4^2 + 1^2 + 3^2 + 4^2 = \underline{46} \qquad\qquad 46$

$\quad \sum_{i=1}^{5} y_i = 2 + 4 + 1 + 3 + 4 = \underline{14} \qquad\qquad 14$

c. Collecting results we have

$$\sum_{i=1}^{5} (y_i - 3)^2 - 46 - 6(14) + \underline{45} \qquad\qquad 45$$

$$= \underline{7} \qquad\qquad 7$$

Although this method seems slow and sluggish and you would rather

use $\sum_{i=1}^{5} (y_i - 3)^2$ directly for this problem, when the number of observations, n, is larger than 5 and the measurements are not small whole numbers, the simplified form of the summation will prove to be easier to use.

2.6 Summary (2.6)

1. We have considered certain special topics and mathematical concepts essential for a thorough understanding of probability distributions.

sets; rule

second

first

independent

dependent

2. A function consists of two ___set___ of elements and a ___rule___ which associates one and only one element of the (first, second) set with each of the elements in the ___first___ set. In the formula $y = f(x)$, x is called the (dependent, independent) variable and y is called the ___dependent___ variable.

3. In the expression

$$\sum_{x=1}^{n} f(x)$$

variable

element

n

x is called the position variable or ___variable___ of summation and $f(x)$ is called the ___element___ of summation. This expression is the indicated sum of ___n___ (give number) terms. It is important to remember the summation formulas:

nc

a. $$\sum_{x=1}^{n} c = \underline{\quad nc \quad}$$

$$c \sum_{x=1}^{n} f(x)$$

b. $$\sum_{x=1}^{n} cf(x) = \underline{\quad \sum_{x=1}^{n} f(x) \quad}$$

$$\sum_{x=1}^{n} f(x) \pm \sum_{x=1}^{n} g(x)$$

c. $$\sum_{x=1}^{n} [f(x) \pm g(x)] = \underline{\quad \sum_{x=1}^{n} f(x) \pm \sum_{x=1}^{n} g(x) \quad}$$

These formulas can be used in combination when the typical element of summation is the sum or difference of several terms.

Exercises

1. $f(x) = 2x + 3$. Find $f(4)$.   11
2. $g(t) = t^2 - 2$. Find $g(0)$ and $g(4)$.
   -1 14

3. $h(x) = x!$ Find $h(0)$ and $h(4)$.

4. $g(u) = u!$ Find $g(0) + g(4)$.

5. $f(y) = 3y - 2u$. Find $f(u)$.

6. $G(u) = 3u^3 - 2u$. Find $G(a)$.

7. $h(y) = 2(1/3)^y$. Find $h(0)$ and $h(2)$.

8. $h(y) = 2(1/3)^y$. Find $\sum_{y=1}^{3} h(y)$.

9. $g(x) = 2x^2 - 5$. Find $\sum_{x=1}^{4} g(x)$.

10. Evaluate $\sum_{x=1}^{10} 3$.

11. Expand $\sum_{i=3}^{6} (x_i - a)$.

12. Express the following in a more compact form by using summation notation:

$$(x_3 - m)^2 + (x_4 - m)^2 + (x_5 - m)^2 + (x_6 - m)^2$$

13. $\sum_{u=1}^{3} (3x + u!) = $ _____

14. $\sum_{x=0}^{3} \dfrac{(.75)}{x! (3 - x)!} = $ _____

15. Evaluate $\sum_{i=7}^{14} 4$.

16. Evaluate $\sum_{x=7}^{8} 4x$.

17. If $\sum_{i=1}^{25} y_i = 50$, find $\sum_{i=1}^{25} (2y_i - 3)$.

18. If $\sum_{i=1}^{25} y_i = 50$ and $\sum_{i=1}^{25} y_i^2 = 250$, find $\sum_{i=1}^{25} (y_i - 10)^2$.

19. $f(u) = 2u^2 - 3u + 5$. Find $f(1/x)$.

20. $F(u) = 2u^2 - 3/u$ and $g(v) = 1/v$. Find $F[g(v)]$.

Use the following set of measurements to answer exercises 21–27.

i	1	2	3	4	5	6	7	8	9	10
y_i	-1	2	1	0	4	-3	1	6	-5	-2

21. $\displaystyle\sum_{i=1}^{10} y_i$

22. $\displaystyle\sum_{i=1}^{10} y_i^2$

23. $\displaystyle\sum_{i=3}^{8} (y_i - 4)$

24. $\displaystyle\sum_{i=1}^{10} (y_i - 5)^2$

25. $\displaystyle\sum_{i=1}^{10} y_i/10$

26. $\displaystyle\sum_{i=1}^{5} (y_i^2 - y_i)$

27. $\displaystyle\sum_{i=1}^{10} y_i^2 - \left(\sum_{i=1}^{10} y_i\right)^2 \Big/ 10$

Chapter   3

DESCRIBING DISTRIBUTIONS OF MEASUREMENTS

3.1 Introduction (3.1)

1. Having reviewed some essential mathematics, we return to the objective of modern statistics, which is to make _____ about a _____ based on information contained in a _____ .   inferences; population sample

2. This objective creates a need for methods of describing sets of data so that: (1) we can better understand the data and the phenomena they measure; and (2) so that we will be able to make a descriptive statement—that is, an inference—about a population based on sample data.

3. Methods for describing sets of numerical measurements are the subject matter of _____ statistics.   descriptive

4. The methods of descriptive statistics fall into one of two categories: _____ methods and _____ methods.   graphical; numerical

5. The graphical methods discussed in this chapter include _____, _____ and _____. The numerical methods emphasize measures of _____ tendency such as the _____, median, and _____, and measures of _____ or dispersion such as the _____, quartiles, _____ and _____ _____.   histograms tables; charts central; mean mode; variability range; variance standard deviation

6. In addition to these specific descriptive methods, the chapter also reviews the idea of a relative frequency distribution, the ways in which graphical methods can be misleading, the use of Tchebysheff's Theorem and the Empirical Rule to construct a mental picture of the frequency distribution, and a shortcut way to calculate the variance or standard deviation of a set of measurements.

3.2 Frequency Distributions (3.2)

1. Graphical methods are designed to present a set of measurements in pictorial form so as to give the reader an adequate visual description of the measurements.

2. Let us begin discussion of graphical methods by examining the following sample data. The numbers of correct responses on a brand recognition test consisting of 30 items, recorded for 25 respondents, were:

25	29	23	27	25
23	22	25	22	28
28	24	17	24	30
19	17	23	21	24
15	20	26	19	23

30
15

equal

5
measurements
larger

15; 8; 2

18.5-20.49
20.5-22.49; 22.5-24.49;
24.5-26.49; 26.5-28.49; none
point
classes

class frequency
f_i

relative frequency

f_i/n

n

1

3. The highest score in the sample is _____ (give number), and the lowest score is _____.

4. To determine how the remaining scores are distributed between 15 and 30, we divide this interval into an arbitrary number of (equal, unequal) subintervals. As a general rule of thumb, the interval from 15 to 30 could be divided into from _____ (give number) to 20 subintervals depending on the number of _____ available. Larger amounts of data require a (larger/smaller) number of subintervals. In order to obtain 8 subintervals, a suitable subinterval width can be determined by dividing 30 – 15 = _____ by _____. The integer _____ (give number) would seem to provide a satisfactory subinterval width for the above data.

5. Utilizing the subinterval boundaries 14.5-16.49, 16.5-18.49, _____, _____, _____, _____, _____, and 28.5-30.49, we guarantee that (all, none) of the measurements will fall on a _____ of division. Thus each measurement falls into only one of the subintervals or _____.

6. a. The number of measurements falling in a particular class, e.g., class i, is called the _____ _____ and is designated by the symbol _____.

   b. Of the total number of measurements, the fraction falling in each class is called the class _____ _____. If there are a total of n measurements, the formula for the relative frequency in the ith class would be:

   relative frequency = _____

   c. Given n measurements that have been divided into k classes or subintervals, it is always true that

   i. $\sum_{i=1}^{k} f_i = $ _____

   ii. $\sum_{i=1}^{k} f_i/n = $ _____

These facts can be used to check your tabulations of data for histograms.

7. We can now tally the given measurements and record the class frequencies
in a table. Fill in the missing information.

Tabulation of Data for Histogram

Class (i)	Class Boundaries	Tally	Class Frequency (f_i)	Class Relative Frequency (f_i/n)
1	14.5–16.49	I		
2	16.5–18.49			
3	18.5–20.49			
4	20.5–22.49			
5	22.5–24.49			
6	24.5–26.49			
7	26.5–28.49			
8	28.5–30.49	II		

1; 1/25
II; 2; 2/25
III; 3; 3/25
III; 3; 3/25
JHT II; 7; 7/25
IIII; 4; 4/25
III; 3; 3/25
2; 2/25

8. The tabulation can be presented graphically, using a _____
_____ (with class frequency plotted on the vertical axis) or a
_____ _____ _____ (with class relative
frequency plotted on the vertical axis) to describe the data. The two histograms are identical except for _____ _____. In a
(relative) frequency histogram, the rectangle over each class interval i is
_____ to the class (relative) frequency.

frequency
histogram
relative frequency histogram

vertical scale

proportional

9. a. Study the following frequency histogram based on our data.

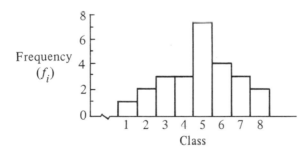

b. Complete the following relative frequency histogram for the same data.

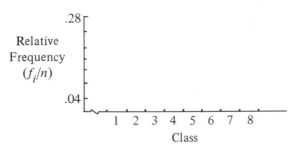

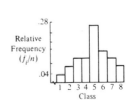

6/25; 24

5/25
20
14/25; 56

2/25; 8

frequency histogram
increases
population

5/25; 20
would

distribution
horizontal

fraction

probability

identical

7/25

3/25

22/25

16/25

13/25

c. When completed, a. and b. should appear identical except for vertical scale.

10. With reference to the tabulated data, consider the following question:
   a. What fraction of the respondents had scores less than or equal to 20? _____ or _____%
   b. What fraction of the respondents had scores greater than 26? _____ or _____%
   c. What fraction of the respondents had scores between 20.5 and 26.5? _____ or _____%
   d. Suppose one of the 25 respondents were selected at random. What is the chance (or "probability") that his or her score is equal to or greater than 29? _____ or _____%

11. Though we have been discussing the scores of 25 respondents, we are presumably interested in the population of all consumers from which that sample was selected. Our sample frequency histogram provides information about the population _____ _____. As the number of measurements in the sample (increases, decreases), the sample histogram should resemble the _____ histogram more and more. Thus, to estimate the fraction of respondents in the entire population that would have scores greater than 26, we could use our sample histogram, estimating this fraction to be _____ or _____%. It is likely that our estimate (would, would not) differ from the true population fraction.

12. A relative frequency histogram is often called a relative frequency _____, because it displays the manner in which the data are distributed along the abscissa or _____ axis of the graph.

13. The rectangular bars above the class intervals in the relative frequency histogram can be given two interpretations:
   a. The height of the bar above the ith class would represent the _____ of the observations falling in the ith class.
   b. The height of the bar above the ith class would also represent the _____ that a measurement drawn at random from this sample will belong to the ith class.

14. If every member of the population were included in the sample, then the population and sample histograms would be (different, identical).

15. *Example:*
   Complete the following statements based on the tabulated data in 6.
   a. The probability that a measurement drawn at random from this data will fall in the interval 22.5 to 24.5 is _____.
   b. The probability that a measurement drawn at random from this data will fall in the interval 26.5 to 28.5 is _____.
   c. The probability that a measurement drawn at random from this data will be greater than 18.5 is _____.
   d. The probability that a measurement drawn at random from this data will be less than 24.5 is _____.
   e. The probability that a measurement drawn at random from this data will be greater than 18.5 and less than 24.5 is _____.

16. *Example:*

The following data represent the burning times for an experimental lot of hand grenade fuses measured to the nearest tenth of a second:

5.2	3.8	5.7	3.9	3.7
4.2	4.1	4.3	4.7	4.3
3.1	2.5	3.0	4.4	4.8
3.6	3.9	4.8	5.3	4.2
4.7	3.3	4.2	3.8	5.4

Tabulate the missing entries below, and then construct a relative frequency histogram for these data.

Tabulation of Data

Class	Class Boundary	Tally	Frequency	Relative Frequency
1	2.45–2.94	I	1	.04
2	2.95–3.44			
3	3.45–3.94			
4	3.95–4.44			
5	4.45–4.94			
6	4.95–5.44			
7	5.45–5.94			

III; 3; 12
JHH I; 6; .24
JHH II; 7; .28
IIII; 4; .16
III; 3; .12
I; 1; .04

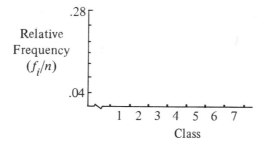

Relative Frequency (f_i/n)

.28

.04

1 2 3 4 5 6 7

Class

17. Complete the following statements based on the preceding tabulated data.

a. The probability that a measurement drawn at random from this sample is greater than 4.45 is _____.

8/25

b. The probability that a measurement drawn at random from this sample is less than 3.45 is _____.

4/25

c. An estimate of the probability that a measurement drawn at random from this population would be in the interval 3.45 to 4.45 is _____.

13/25

18. Recall the principles for constructing a frequency distribution.

a. The first step is to determine the _____ of _____,

number; classes

uniformity
5; 20
width
smallest
classes

equal

boundaries
impossible

depending on the amount and _____ of the data. It is usually best to have from _____ to _____ (give numbers) classes.

b. The second step is to determine the class _____, by dividing the difference between the largest and _____ measurements by the number of _____, and then adjusting the resulting quotient to obtain a convenient figure. With the possible exception of the lowest and highest classes, all classes should be of _____ width.

c. The third step is to locate the class _____. Class boundaries should be chosen so that it is (impossible, likely) that a measurement will fall on a boundary.

Self-Correcting Exercises 3A

1. The following data are the ages in years of the employees of a recently organized small manufacturing firm.

51	32	31	33	23	52
23	21	55	34	38	32
49	35	26	29	50	34
30	19	41	39	41	27
25	21	18	36	35	28
44	44	59	28	23	46
27	37	42	32	43	30

a. Find the range of these data.
b. Using about 10 intervals of equal width, set up class boundaries to be used in the construction of a frequency distribution and complete the tabulation of the data.
c. Construct a frequency histogram for these data.
d. For these same data construct a frequency histogram utilizing about 6 intervals.
e. Which histogram presents the data in the more meaningful way?

2. The following are the annual rates of profit on stockholders equity after taxes in percent for 32 industries.

10.6	10.8	14.8	10.8
12.5	6.0	10.7	11.0
14.6	6.0	12.8	10.1
7.9	5.9	10.0	10.6
10.8	16.2	18.4	10.7
10.6	13.3	8.7	15.4
6.5	10.1	8.7	7.5
11.9	9.0	12.0	9.1

a. Construct a relative frequency histogram for these data utilizing 7 intervals of length 2, beginning at 5.55.

Using your histogram (or tabulation) answer the following questions.

b. What is the probability that an industry drawn at random from this distribution has a rate of profit greater than 15.55%?

c. What is the probability that an industry drawn at random has a rate of profit less than 9.55%?

d. What is the probability that an industry drawn at random has a rate of profit greater than 9.55% but less than 15.55%?

3.3   More on Graphical Methods (3.3, 3.4)

1. A statistical table is a _____ or subdivided frequency distribution comparing the (relative) frequencies for samples drawn from two or more different populations. The populations may be different periods, regions, divisions, companies, etc. The classifications or subdivisions must be _____ within each sample to permit cross analysis.

    classified

    identical

2. The three most commonly used statistical charts are the _____ chart, the _____ chart, and the _____ chart.

    bar
    line; pie

3. Bar charts, line charts, and pie charts are designed to serve as visual _____ of data. Bar charts and pie charts are pictorial _____ _____. Line charts are usually plots of points which trace some variable over _____.

    summarizations
    frequency histograms
    time

4. Bar charts are most useful in representing the total amount of some quantity for each of a given number of years or for each of a group of categories.

5. *Example:*

The following data represent the total sales and domestic sales for the ABC Company over the years 1972–76.

Sales (thousands of dollars)					
	1972	*1973*	*1974*	*1975*	*1976*
Domestic	250	300	350	390	400
Total	300	350	500	520	600

Construct a bar chart to depict these data.

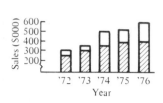

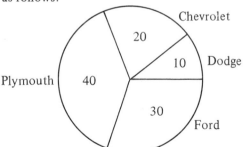

frequency

total

proportion

1.71

75

pie

360

360

360 $\frac{30}{100}$ = 108

6. Since a bar chart is a _____ histogram, the height of each bar represents the _____ sales for the year of interest. Furthermore, the amount of each bar which is shaded is equal to the _____ of that year's sales which were domestic.
   a. Since total sales for 1973 were $600,000 as compared to 1973 sales of $350,000, the 1973 bar is _____ times as high as the 1973 bar.
   b. Since domestic sales for 1975 were $390,000 while total sales were $520,000, the proportion of the 1975 bar which is shaded, indicating domestic sales, is _____ %.

7. A _____ chart illustrates how a single total quantity is divided into a group of categories.

8. *Example:*
   During 1970, the Avis Taxi Company purchased 30 Fords, 20 Chevrolets, 40 Plymouths, and 10 Dodges. A pie chart displaying this information would appear as follows:

Automobiles purchased by the Avis Taxi Company during 1970

9. The primary usefulness of a pie chart is that it allows the reader to see how much of the total is represented by each subdivision of the total.

10. Since the angular portions of a circular pie chart must sum to _____ (give number) degrees, each subdivision is represented by a portion whose central angle contains _____ X (subdivision total/grand total) degrees. Thus, the number of Fords purchased by Avis in 1970 is represented by a sector whose central angle contains _____ degrees.

11. The charts produced by graphical descriptive techniques must be inter-

preted with care, or the wrong conclusions may result. It is especially easy to mislead a careless reader by breaking, shrinking, or stretching the _____ of a graph. To protect oneself, always examine the _____ of measurement on graphs and charts carefully.

axes
scales

Self-Correcting Exercises 3B

1. The following data supplied by the Bureau of Labor Statistics gives the total civilian labor force and those employed during the years 1970–76.

	Civilian Labor Force (in millions)						
	1970	*1971*	*1972*	*1973*	*1974*	*1975*	*1976*
Employed	78.6	79.1	81.7	84.4	85.9	84.8	87.5
Total Labor Force	82.8	84.1	86.5	88.7	91.0	92.6	94.8

   a. Construct a bar chart to depict these data.
   b. Suppose that, for political reasons, you wanted to make the drop in employment due to the recession in 1975 look as large and dramatic as possible. Construct a bar chart that distorts the information in order to achieve that goal.

2. The following data are the number of persons employed during 1972 according to the following occupational groups.

Group	*Millions Employed*
White collar	39.1
Blue collar	28.6
Service worker	11.0
Farm worker	3.1
Total	81.8

Construct a pie chart to depict these data.

3.4 Numerical Descriptive Measures (3.5)

1. The chief advantage to using a graphical method is its rapid visual representation of the data.
2. But many times we are restricted to reporting our data verbally. In this case a _____ method of description cannot be used.
3. However, the greatest disadvantage of a graphical method for describing data is its unsuitability for making _____. This is because it is

graphical

inferences

difficult to give a measure of goodness or reliability for graphical inferences.

4. Therefore, we turn to *numerical descriptive* measures. We seek a set of
numbers that characterizes the frequency distribution of the measurements and at the same time will be useful in making inferences.

5. We will distinguish between numerical descriptive measures for a population and those associated with a set of sample measurements. A numerical
descriptive measure calculated from all the measurements in a population

parameter

statistics

is called a (<u>statistic, parameter</u>). Those numerical descriptive measures calculated from sample measurements are called _____.

3.5 Measures of Central Tendency (3.6)

1. Measures of central tendency are designed to measure the center of a

frequency distribution

mean *or* arithmetic mean

_____ _____.

2. The _____ of a set of n measurements $y_1, y_2, y_3, \ldots, y_n$ is
defined as the sum of the measurements divided by n. That is, the mean is

average

$\bar{y}; \mu$

the arithmetic _____ of a set of measurements. The symbol
_____ is used to designate the sample mean while _____ (the
Greek letter mu) is used to designate the population mean. The formula
for the sample mean, in summation notation, is:

$$\frac{\sum\limits_{i=1}^{n} y_i}{n}$$

$$\bar{y} = \underline{\hspace{2cm}}$$

The sample mean can be shown to have very desirable properties for
making inferences about the population mean. In fact, we will use $\bar{y}$ to

μ

estimate or predict _____.

3. *Example:*
Find the mean of the following measurements:

$$2, 5, 7, 10, 11, 13$$

Solution:

48

a. $\displaystyle\sum_{i=1}^{6} y_i = \underline{\hspace{2cm}}$

$\dfrac{48}{6}$

b. $\bar{y} = \dfrac{\displaystyle\sum_{i=1}^{n} y_i}{n} = \dfrac{(\underline{\hspace{1.5cm}})}{(\underline{\hspace{1.5cm}})}$

8

$\bar{y} = \underline{\hspace{2cm}}$

4. In addition to being an easily calculated measure of central tendency, the mean is also easily understood by all users. The calculation of the mean utilizes all of the measurements and can always be found exactly.

5. One disadvantage of using the mean to measure central tendency is well-known to any student who has had to pull up one low test score: the mean (is, is not) greatly affected by extreme values.   is

6. One might be unwilling to accept the average property value of $75,000 for a given area as an acceptable measure of the middle property value if it were known that (a) the property value of a residence owned by a millionaire was included in the calculation and (b) excluding his residence, the property values ranged from $15,000 to $30,000. A more realistic measure of central tendency in this situation might be the property value such that half of the property values are less than this value and half are greater than this value. This leads us to a second measure of central tendency.

7. The _____ of a set of n measurements $y_1, y_2, \ldots, y_n$, is that   median
   value of y that falls in the middle when the measurements are arranged in
   order of _____. If n is an even number, the median is the value   size *or* magnitude
   of y halfway between the two middle values.

8. *Example:*
   Find the median of the following measurements:

   $$5, 3, 2, 7, 4$$

   Solution:
   a. Arranging the measurements in order of magnitude, we have

   $$2, 3, 4, 5, 7$$

   b. Therefore the median (or middle measurement) is _____.   4

9. *Example:*
   Find the median of the following set of measurements:

   $$10, 8, 13, 14, 9, 8$$

   Solution:
   Arranging the measurements in order of magnitude, we have

   $$8, 8, 9, 10, 13, 14$$

   Since $n = 6$ is even, the median is given as

   $$\text{median} = \frac{9 + 10}{2}$$

   $$= 9.5$$

10. *Example:*

Find the mean and median of the following data:

$$5, 7, 8, 10, 10, 11, 13, 14$$

Solution:

a. To find $\bar{y}$, the sample mean, we calculate

78

$$\sum_{i=1}^{8} y_i = \underline{\hspace{2cm}}$$

$\dfrac{78}{8}$; 9.75

$$\bar{y} = \frac{\displaystyle\sum_{i=1}^{8} y_i}{n} = \frac{(\underline{\hspace{1.5cm}})}{(\underline{\hspace{1.5cm}})} = \underline{\hspace{2cm}}$$

b. To find the median, we note that the measurements are already arranged in order of magnitude and that $n = 8$ is even. Therefore, the median is given as

10; 10

$$\text{median} = \frac{(\underline{\hspace{1.5cm}}) + (\underline{\hspace{1.5cm}})}{2}$$

10

$$= \underline{\hspace{2cm}}$$

11. In the last example the mean and the median gave reasonably close numerical values as measures of central tendency for the data. However, if the measurement $y_9 = 30$ were added to the eight measurements

12
10
mode

given, the recalculated mean would be $\bar{y} = \underline{\hspace{2cm}}$, but the median would remain at $\underline{\hspace{2cm}}$.

12. The $\underline{\hspace{2cm}}$ of a set of n measurements $y_1, y_2, y_3, \ldots, y_n$, is defined to be the value of y occurring with the greatest frequency.

13. *Example:*

Find the mode of the following measurements:

$$1, 2, 3, 3, 5, 6, 8$$

Solution:

3
3

The measurement which occurs with the greatest frequency is $\underline{\hspace{2cm}}$; therefore, the mode is $\underline{\hspace{2cm}}$.

14. The mode is generally not a good measure of central tendency, since data may be grouped in such a way that the greatest frequencies occur nowhere near the central area of the distribution. The mode may not even be unique because the greatest frequency can occur at more than one value.

15. In summary, the _____ is the statistic describing the most frequent outcome; the _____ is the center measurement of a group of measurements arranged in order of magnitude; the _____ is, in a physical sense, the "center of gravity" of a set of measurements.

> mode
> median
> mean *or* arithmetic mean

16. If the values of a measured variable that are equidistant from the mean occur with equal frequency, the resulting frequency distribution is said to be _____.

> symmetric

17. When the distribution of a group of measurements is symmetric, the mean and median (and, if the distribution is also mound-shaped, the mode) are _____. A distribution which is not symmetric is said to be _____.

> equal *or* identical
> skewed

18. A distribution that is skewed to the right is said to have _____ skewness. In this case, the mode is (larger, smaller) than the median, which in turn is _____ than the mean.

    A distribution that is skewed to the left is said to have _____ skewness. In this case, the _____ is smaller than the median, which in turn is smaller than the _____ .

> positive
> smaller
> smaller
> negative
> mean
> mode

3.6 Measures of Variability (3.7)

1. Having found measures of central tendency, we next consider a measure of the variability or _____ of the data. A measure of variability is necessary since a measure of central tendency alone does not adequately describe the data.

> dispersion

2. Consider these two sets of data:

a. $x_1 = 9$
$x_2 = 10$ $\bar{x} =$ _____
$x_3 = 11$

> 10

b. $y_1 = 1$
$y_2 = 10$ $\bar{y} =$ _____
$y_3 = 19$

> 10

c. Both of these sets of data have a mean equal to _____; however, the second set of measurements displays (less, more) variability about the mean than does the first set.

> 10
> more

3. We have already used the simplest measure of variation, the range. The range of a set of n measurements, $y_1, y_2, \ldots, y_n$, is defined to be the difference between the largest and _____ measurements.

> smallest

4. *Example:*
Two sets of data are given below. Find the range for each set of data.
a. Set I:

23	73	34	74
28	29	26	17
88	8	52	49
37	96	32	45
81	62	23	62

96; 8; 88

Range = _____ - _____ = _____

b. Set II:

8.8	6.7	7.1	2.9
9.0	0.2	1.2	8.6
6.3	6.4	2.1	8.8

9.0; 0.2; 8.8

Range = _____ - _____ = _____

variability *or* dispersion

5. By examining the following distributions, it is apparent that although the range is an easily calculated measure of _____, it alone is not adequate to describe the variability. Both distributions have the same _____ but display different _____.

range; variability *or* dispersion

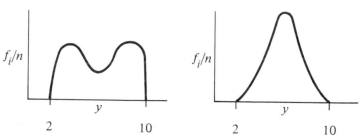

6. In looking for a more sensitive measure of variability, we extend the concept of the median as follows:

a. Let $y_1, y_2, y_3, \ldots, y_n$ be a set of n measurements arranged in order of magnitude: The pth _____ is that value of y such that $p\%$ of the measurements are _____ than y and $(100 - p)\%$ are _____ than y.

percentile
less
greater

b. The 25th percentile is called the lower quartile while the 75th percentile is called the upper quartile.

7. Percentiles are more sensitive than the _____ in measuring variability, but have the disadvantage that several percentiles must be calculated to provide an adequate description of the data.

range

8. We base the next important measure of variability on the dispersion of the data about the sample mean, $\bar{y}$. Define the quantity $(y_i - \bar{y})$ as the deviation of the ith measurement from the mean. Large deviations indicate (more, less) variability in the data than do small deviations.

more

9. We could utilize these deviations in various ways.

a. If we attempt to use either the sum or the average of the n deviations, we find that both are equal to _____. This is easily shown to be true in general as follows:

0

$$\sum_{i=1}^{n} (y_i - \bar{y}) = \sum_{i=1}^{n} y_i - \sum_{i=1}^{n} \bar{y}$$

$$= \sum_{i=1}^{n} y_i - n\bar{y}$$

$$= \sum_{i=1}^{n} y_i - \underline{\hspace{2cm}}$$

$$\sum_{i=1}^{n} y_i$$

$$= \underline{\hspace{2cm}}$$

0

Since the average is simply the sum divided by n, it too equals _____.

0

b. To avoid a zero sum, we could use the average of the absolute values of the deviations. This measure is not difficult to calculate, but one cannot easily give a measure of its goodness in inference making.

c. Instead, we base our measure of variability or dispersion on the sum of the *squared* deviations.

10. The _____ (denoted by the symbol _____) of a population of N measurements is defined as the average of the squares of the deviations of the measurements about the population mean _____ (give symbol). The formula for the population variance is

variance; σ^2

μ

$$\sigma^2 = \underline{\hspace{3cm}}$$

$$\frac{1}{N} \sum_{i=1}^{N} (y_i - \mu)^2$$

11. But we typically only have a sample of measurements from the population. When we try to use this formula to calculate an estimate of the population variance σ^2, using $\bar{y}$ for μ, the average of the squared deviations for a sample of size n tends to (over, underestimate) σ^2. However, the quantity

underestimate

$$s^2 = \frac{1}{n-1} \sum_{i=1}^{n} (y_i - \bar{y})^2$$

has the average value σ^2 in repeated sampling, and thus s^2 is appropriately called the sample _____. This leads to the following definition.

variance

12. Given a set of n measurements $y_1, y_2, \ldots, y_n$, the _____ _____ is

sample
variance

$$s^2 = \frac{\sum_{i=1}^{n} (y_i - \bar{y})^2}{n-1}$$

13. *Example:*

Calculate the sample mean and variance for the following data:

4, 2, 3, 5, 6

Solution:

y_i	$y_i - \bar{y}$	$(y_i - \bar{y})^2$
4	0	0
2	-2	4
3	-1	1
5	1	1
6	2	4
$\Sigma y_i = $ _____	$\Sigma (y_i - \bar{y}) = $ _____	$\Sigma (y_i - \bar{y})^2 = $ _____

20; 0; 10

a. $\displaystyle \bar{y} = \frac{\sum_{i=1}^{n} y_i}{n} = \frac{(20)}{(5)} = $ _____

4

b. $\displaystyle s^2 = \frac{\sum_{i=1}^{n} (y_i - \bar{y})^2}{n - 1} = \frac{(\quad)}{(\quad)} = $ _____

$\dfrac{10}{4}$; 2.5

c. We note that a shorter and simpler method will be introduced in a following section for the calculation of the numerator of s^2, which is

$$\sum_{i=1}^{n} (y_i - \bar{y})^2.$$

14. Computing the variance of a set of measurements results in a quantity measured in the _____ of the original units. To return this quantity to the original units, we find the _____ _____ of the sample variance, s^2

square
square
root

15. The _____ _____ _____, s, of a set of n measurements is the positive square root of the sample variance. Thus,

sample standard deviation

$$s = \sqrt{s^2} = \underline{\quad\quad}.$$

$$\sqrt{\frac{\sum_{i=1}^{n} (y_i - \bar{y})^2}{n - 1}}$$

16. From Example 13, the standard deviation is found to be

$$s = \sqrt{s^2} = \sqrt{2.5} = \underline{\hspace{3cm}}$$

1.58

Self-Correcting Exercises 3C

1. Fifteen brands of breakfast cereal were judged by nutritionists according to four criteria: taste, texture, nutritional value and popularity with the buying public. Each brand was rated on a 0–5 scale for each criterion and the sum of the four ratings reported. (A high score with respect to the maximum of 20 points indicates a good evaluation of the brand.)

9	8	16	17	10
15	12	6	12	13
10	13	19	11	9

   a. Find the mean and the median scores for these data. Compare their values.
   b. Why would the mode be inappropriate in describing these data?
   c. Calculate the range of these scores.
   d. Calculate the standard deviation of these scores. (As an intermediate check on your calculations, remember that the sum of the deviations must be zero.)

2. The number of daily arrivals of cargo vessels at a west coast port during an 11/ day period are given below.

3	2	0
5	4	4
2	3	2
7	1	

   a. Calculate the mean and standard deviation of the number of arrivals per day during this 11 day period.
   b. Compare the mean and the median for these data.

3.7 The Practical Significance of the Standard Deviation (3.8)

1. The standard deviation is used to describe the variability of a set of measurements through Tchebysheff's Theorem and the Empirical Rule.
2. *Tchebysheff's Theorem:* Given a number k greater than or equal to _____ (give number) and a set of n measurements $y_1, y_2, \ldots, y_n$, at least _____ (give quantity) of the measurements will lie within _____ (give number) standard deviations of their mean.

1

$1 - 1/k^2$

k

   a. The importance of this theorem is due to the fact that it applies to any

μ

$\bar{y}$; s

more

0
3/4
8/9
99/100

42

_____ set of measurements. We could then refer to a population using the population mean, _____, and the population
standard deviation, σ, or we could refer to a sample from a given
population using _____ and _____, the sample mean and
sample standard deviation.

b. Since this theorem applies to any set of measurements, it is of necessity
a conservative theorem. It is very important to reiterate that usually
(more, less) than $(1 - 1/k^2)$ of the measurements will lie within k
standard deviations of the mean.

3. Complete the following chart for the values of k given:

k	Interval $\bar{y} \pm ks$	Interval contains at least the fraction $(1 - 1/k^2)$
1	$\bar{y} \pm s$	_____
2	$\bar{y} \pm 2s$	_____
3	$\bar{y} \pm 3s$	_____
10	$\bar{y} \pm 10s$	_____

4. *Example:*
The mean and variance of a set of $n = 20$ measurements are 35 and 25,
respectively. Use Tchebysheff's Theorem to describe the distribution of
these measurements.
Solution:
Collecting pertinent information we have:

$$\bar{y} = 35$$

$$s^2 = 25$$

$$s = \sqrt{25} = 5$$

a. At least 3/4 of the measurements lie in the interval $35 \pm 2(5)$ or 25
to 45.
b. At least 8/9 of the measurements lie in the interval $35 \pm 3(5)$ or 20
to 50.
c. At least 15/16 of the measurements lie in the interval $35 \pm 4(5)$ or
15 to 55.

5. *Example:*
If the mean and variance of a set of $n = 50$ measurements are 42 and 36,
respectively, describe these measurements using Tchebysheff's Theorem.
Solution:
Pertinent information: $\bar{y} = $ _____

$$s^2 = \underline{\hspace{3cm}}$$

$$s = \sqrt{s^2} = \underline{\hspace{2.5cm}}$$

a. _____ _____ 3/4 of the measurements lie in the

interval _____ ± 2(_____) or _____ to _____ .

b. _____ _____ 8/9 of the measurements lie in the

interval _____ ± 3(_____) or _____ to _____ .

c. _____ _____ 15/16 of the measurements lie in the

interval _____ ± 4(_____) or _____ to _____ .

6. *Empirical Rule:* Given a distribution of measurements which are approximately bell-shaped, the interval

   a. $\mu \pm \sigma$ contains approximately _____% of the measurements,

   b. $\mu \pm 2\sigma$ contains approximately _____% of the measurements,

   c. $\mu \pm 3\sigma$ contains approximately _____% of the measurements.

This rule holds reasonably well for any set of measurements that possesses a distribution that is mound-shaped. A bell-shaped or mound-shaped distribution is taken to mean that the distribution has the properties associated with the normal distribution whose graph is given in your text and elsewhere in this study guide.

7. *Example:*

A random sample of 100 cans of tomato sauce, designed to weigh 8 oz., was taken from a production line and individual weights measured. The mean and variance of these measurements were 7.8 oz. and 0.36 oz.^{2}, respectively. Assuming the measurements produced a mound-shaped distribution, describe these measurements using the Empirical Rule.

Solution:

First find the intervals needed.

k	$\bar{y} \pm ks$	$\bar{y} - ks$	to	$\bar{y} + ks$
1	$\bar{y} \pm s$	_____	to	_____
2	$\bar{y} \pm 2s$	_____	to	_____
3	$\bar{y} \pm 3s$	_____	to	_____

Then approximately

   a. _____% of the measurements lie in the interval _____

      to _____ ,

   b. _____% of the measurements lie in the interval _____

      to _____ ,

   c. _____% of the measurements lie in the interval _____

      to _____ .

When n is small, the distribution of measurements (would, would not) be mound-shaped and as such the Empirical Rule (would, would not) be appropriate in describing this data. Since Tchebysheff's Theorem applies to any set of measurements it can be used regardless of the size of n.

Answer column (right margin):

36

6

At least
42; 6; 30; 54

At least
42; 6; 24; 60

At least
42; 6; 18; 66

68

95

99.7

7.2; 8.4
6.6; 9.0
6.0; 9.6

68; 7.2
8.4
95; 6.6
9.0
99.7; 6.0
9.6
would not
would not

3.8 A Short Method for Calculating the Variance (3.9)

1. The calculation of

$$s^2 = \frac{\sum\limits_{i=1}^{n} (y_i - \bar{y})^2}{n-1}$$

requires the calculation of the quantity

$$\sum_{i=1}^{n} (y_i - \bar{y})^2.$$

To facilitate this calculation, we introduce the identity

$$\sum_{i=1}^{n} (y_i - \bar{y})^2 = \sum_{i=1}^{n} y_i^2 - \frac{\left(\sum\limits_{i=1}^{n} y_i \right)^2}{n}$$

2. This computation requires the ordinary arithmetic sum of the measurements,

$$\sum_{i=1}^{n} y_i$$

and the sum of the squares of the measurements,

$$\sum_{i=1}^{n} y_i^2$$

3. Note the distinction between

$$\sum_{i=1}^{n} y_i^2 \text{ and}$$

$$\left(\sum_{i=1}^{n} y_i \right)^2 \quad \text{used in 3.8(1).}$$

a. To calculate

$$\sum_{i=1}^{n} y_i^2$$

we *first square* each measurement and *then sum* these squares.

b. To calculate

$$\left(\sum_{i=1}^{n} y_i \right)^2$$

we *first sum* the measurements and *then square* this sum.

4. *Example:*

Calculate s^2 for 3.6(13).

Solution:

Display the data in the following way, finding Σy_i and Σy_i^2.

a.

y_i	y_i^2
2	4
3	9
4	16
5	25
6	36
$\Sigma y_i = 20$	$\Sigma y_i^2 = 90$

b. Calculate

$$\Sigma (y_i - \bar{y})^2 = \Sigma y_i^2 - \frac{(\Sigma y_i)^2}{n}$$

$$= 90 - \frac{(20)^2}{5}$$

$$= 90 - \frac{400}{5}$$

$$= 90 - 80$$

$$= 10$$

c. Then

$$s^2 = \frac{\sum\limits_{i=1}^{n} (y_i - \bar{y})^2}{n - 1} = \frac{10}{4} = 2.5$$

5. *Example:*
Calculate the mean and variance of the following data:

$$5, 6, 7, 5, 2, 3$$

Solution:
Displaying the data in tabled form we have:

y_i	y_i^2
5	25
6	_____
7	_____
5	_____
2	_____
3	_____
$\Sigma y_i =$ _____	$\Sigma y_i^2 =$ _____

36
49
25
4
9

28; 148

Then

a. $\bar{y} = \dfrac{\sum\limits_{i=1}^{n} y_i}{n} = \dfrac{(\underline{\hspace{2cm}})}{(\underline{\hspace{2cm}})} = \underline{\hspace{2cm}}$

$\dfrac{28}{6}$; 4.67

b. $\sum\limits_{i=1}^{n} (y_i - \bar{y})^2 = \Sigma y_i^2 - \dfrac{(\Sigma y_i)^2}{n}$

148; 28

$$= \underline{\hspace{2cm}} - \frac{(\underline{\hspace{2cm}})^2}{6}$$

$$= \underline{\hspace{2cm}} - \frac{(\underline{\hspace{2cm}})}{6}$$

148; 784

$$= \underline{\hspace{2cm}} - \underline{\hspace{1.5cm}}$$

148; 130.67

$$= \underline{\hspace{2cm}}$$

17.33

Therefore,

$$s^2 = \frac{\sum_{i=1}^{n} (y_i - \bar{y})^2}{n - 1} = \frac{(\underline{\hspace{1.5cm}})}{(\underline{\hspace{1.5cm}})} = \underline{\hspace{2cm}}$$

$$\frac{17.33}{5} ; 3.47$$

Self-Correcting Exercises 3D

1. Using the breakfast cereal data from Self-Correcting Exercises 3C, problem 1, calculate the sample variance utilizing the shortcut formula to calculate the required sum of squared deviations. Verify that the values of the variance (and hence the standard deviation) found using both calculational forms are identical.
2. Follow the instructions in 1 using the data from problem 2, Self-Correcting Exercises 3C.
3. If a person were concerned about accuracy due to rounding of numbers at various stages in computation, which formula for calculating

$$\sum_{i=1}^{n} (y_i - \bar{y})$$ would be preferred?

a. $$\sum_{i=1}^{n} (y_i - \bar{y})^2$$ or

b. $$\sum_{i=1}^{n} y_i^2 - \frac{\left(\sum_{i=1}^{n} y_i\right)^2}{n}$$

Defend your choice of either part a or b.

3.9   Estimating the Mean and Variance for Grouped Data (3.10)

1. When published data are listed only in terms of the frequency of measurements within various classes, the usual formulas cannot be used to compute the mean and variance of the data.
2. Nevertheless, the mean and variance for grouped data can be approximated by the formulas

$$\bar{y} \approx \sum_{i=1}^{k} \frac{f_i m_i}{n}$$

and

$$s^2 \approx \frac{\sum_{i=1}^{k} f_i m_i^2 - \left(\sum_{i=1}^{k} f_i m_i\right)^2 / n}{n-1}$$

where m_i is the _____ of class i, f_i is the _____ of measurements within class i, k is the number of _____, and n is the total number of _____.

midpoint; frequency
classes
measurements

3. *Example:*

The number of defective electrical components produced in an assembly operation has been recorded for each of the past 30 days. The results are summarized in the following frequency histogram.

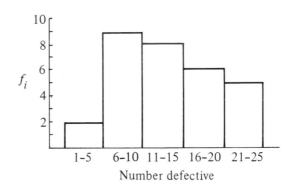

Estimate $\bar{y}$ and s^2, the mean and variance of the number of defectives produced each day by the assembly operation.

Solution:

Complete the following table.

Class	Class Boundaries	f_i	m_i	$f_i m_i$	$f_i m_i^2$	
1	1–5	2	3	6	18	
2	6–10	_____	8	_____	_____	9; 72; 576
3	11–15	8	_____	_____	_____	13; 104; 832
4	16–20	_____	18	_____	_____	6; 108; 1944
5	21–25	5	23	115	_____	2645
	Totals	_____		_____	6015	30; 405

The mean of the grouped data can be approximated by

$$\bar{y} \approx \frac{\sum\limits_{i=1}^{5} f_i m_i}{30} = \frac{\underline{\hspace{1cm}}}{30}$$

405

$$= \underline{\hspace{1.5cm}}$$

13.5

while the variance is approximated by

$$s^2 = \frac{\sum\limits_{i=1}^{5} f_i m_i^2 - \left(\sum\limits_{i=1}^{5} f_i m_i\right)^2 \Big/ 30}{29}$$

$$= \frac{6015 - (\underline{\hspace{1cm}})^2/30}{29}$$

405

$$= \frac{6015 - \underline{\hspace{1cm}}}{29}$$

5467.5

$$= \frac{\underline{\hspace{1cm}}}{29}$$

547.5

$$= \underline{\hspace{1.5cm}}$$

18.879

4. In order to apply the formulas for approximating the mean and variance of grouped data, we (do, do not) need to assume that classes are of equal width. The approximations obtained are reliable only if the class _____ are approximately equal to the _____ of the measurements within each class.

do not
midpoints
arithmetic mean

5. Using the class midpoints to represent the average value within a class tacitly implies that no class should be open-ended since the midpoint of such a class would not be defined.

Self-Correcting Exercises 3E

1. The following frequency distribution has been published by an airline to indicate the number of separate air journeys taken during the past year by 20 randomly selected passengers.

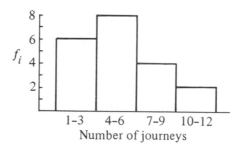

Approximate the average, $\bar{y}$, and the standard deviation, s, of the number of journeys during the past year for the passengers of the airline using the formulas for grouped data.

2. The number of traffic accidents during a one-week period at a dangerous intersection was recorded for 50 weeks. The following tabulation has resulted.

Number of accidents /wk	Frequency
0	10
1	18
2	13
3	6
4	2
5	1

a. Find the mean and standard deviation of the number of accidents per week during this 50-week period.
b. In this particular case will the mean and standard deviation found in a. be approximations or exact values of $\bar{y}$ and s?

3.10 Linear Transformations of Data (3.11)

1. When one wishes to make comparisons between two sets of measurements, both sets must be recorded in the same _____ of measure.

units *or* scale

2. The _____ Theorem allows one to transform the mean, variance, and standard deviation from one set of measurements into the mean, variance, and standard deviation of a second set of measurements, where the second set of measurements have been obtained by a _____ transformation of the first set.

3. *The Coding Theorem:*
If $\bar{y}$ and s_y^2 are the mean and variance of a set of n measurements y_1, y_2, $y_3, \ldots, y_n$, and if the linear transformation $x_i = a + by_i$ is applied to each measurement, the mean of the transformed measurements is

$$\bar{x} = a + b\bar{y}$$

and the transformed variance is

$$s_x^2 = b^2 s_y^2$$

4. *Example:*
During the month of June 1970, the daily high temperatures in Cairo averaged 25 degrees centigrade with a variance of 50. What are the mean and variance of the June 1970 temperatures in Cairo in Fahrenheit degrees?
Solution:
From a basic formula of physical science, we know that

$$\text{Fahrenheit degrees} = 32 + \frac{9}{5}\,(\text{centigrade degrees}).$$

Applying the Coding Theorem, the mean and variance in Fahrenheit degrees are found by letting $a = $ _____ and $b = $ _____. Thus, the transformed mean is _____ + _____ $(25) = $ _____ degrees Fahrenheit, and the transformed variance is ($\underline{\hspace{1.5cm}}$)^2 $(50) = $ _____.

5. *Example:*
To simplify calculations a student subtracted 100 from each of his observations and then divided the resulting value by 10. If the mean and standard deviation of the transformed values were 6.3 and 1.6 respectively, what are the mean and standard deviation of the original measurements?
Solution:
Let x_i represent the transformed value of the original measurement and y_i represent the original measurement. Then the original and transformed values are related by the formula

$$y_i = \underline{\hspace{1.5cm}} + \underline{\hspace{1.5cm}}\, x_i$$

From the problem we know that $\bar{x} = $ _____ and $s_x = $ _____.
Using the Coding Theorem with a slight notational change, we see that

---

Coding

linear

32; 9/5
32; 9/5; 77
9/5
162

100; 10

6.3; 1.6

a. $\bar{y} = 100 + 10\bar{x}$

$= 100 + 10(6.3)$

163

$= \underline{\hspace{2cm}}$

b. $s_y = 10\, s_x$

$= 10(1.6)$

16

$= \underline{\hspace{2cm}}$

The mean and standard deviation of the original measurements are $\bar{y} = 163$ and $s_y = 16$.

Self-Correcting Exercises 3F

1. It is reported that the average height of men in a European country is 171.7 centimeters with a standard deviation of 6.6 cm. If one inch equals 2.54 centimeters what would the mean and standard deviation of these heights be if measured in inches?
2. If the mean and standard deviation of a set of measurements were given as $\bar{y} = 10.2$ gal. and $s_y = 1.6$ gal., what would the mean and standard deviation be in liters if one U.S. gallon equals 3.785 liters?
3. A set of measurements has values recorded to the nearest tenth in which the values all lie between 160.0 and 170.0.
    a. What system of coding would be useful to reduce the arithmetic work involved in calculating the mean and standard deviation for these data?
    b. What would be the relationship between the mean and standard deviation of the original data and the coded data?

3.11   Summary (3.12)

inferences
sample
graphical; numerical

histogram; distribution

mean

1. The objective of statistics is to make _____ about a population based on information contained in a _____.
2. Sets of numbers can be described by _____ or _____ descriptive measures.
3. The graphical method utilizes a frequency _____ or _____ to show how the data are distributed. The frequency histogram is an excellent method for characterizing a population, but is unsuitable for inference making.
4. Numerical descriptive methods attempt to provide a set of numbers that will create a mental picture of the distribution of the data. Two of the most useful numerical descriptive measures are the mean and the standard deviation. The _____ locates the center or average of the dis-

tribution of measurements, while the _____ _____
measures the variability of the data.

standard deviation

5. The standard deviation can be meaningfully interpreted as a measure of
   variability using _____ Theorem or the _____ Rule.

Tchebysheff's; Empirical

Exercises

1. The following set of data represents the gas mileage for each of 20 cars
   selected randomly from a production line during the first week in March.

18.1	16.3	18.6	18.7
15.2	19.9	20.3	22.0
19.7	17.7	21.2	18.2
20.9	19.7	19.4	20.2
19.8	17.2	17.9	19.6

   a. What is the range of these data?
   b. Construct a relative frequency histogram for these data using subinter-
      vals of width 1.0. (You might begin with 15.15.)
   c. Based on the histogram in part b:
      i. What is the probability that a measurement selected at random from
         these data will fall in the interval 17.15 to 21.15?
      ii. What is the estimated probability that a measurement taken from the
          population would be greater than 19.15?
   d. Arrange the measurements in order of magnitude beginning with 15.2.
   e. What is the median of these data?
   f. The _____ th percentile would be any number lying between
      16.3 and 17.2.
   g. The _____ th percentile would be any number lying between
      19.9 and 20.2.
   h. Calculate $\bar{y}, s^2$, and s for these data. (Remember to use the shortcut
      method.)
   i. Do these data conform to Tchebysheff's Theorem? Support your
      answer by calculating the fractions of the measurements lying in the
      intervals $\bar{y} \pm ks$ for $k = 1, 2, 3$.
   j. Does the Empirical Rule adequately describe these data?

2. A life insurance company randomly sampled 25 new policy holders and
   for each recorded the number of children claimed by the policy holder.
   The data are shown below.

2	0	2	1	3
3	1	1	3	2
1	0	7	0	2
0	0	0	4	1
4	3	2	2	5

a. What is the range of these data?
b. Calculate the median.
c. What is the mode?
d. Calculate $\bar{y}$, s^2, and s for these data.
e. Construct a relative frequency histogram for these data using classes of width 1.0. (You might begin with –0.5.)
f. Assuming the above sample is representative of all the company's policy holders,
   i. what is the probability a policy holder has no more than 1 child?
   ii. what is the probability a policy holder has 3 or more children?
g. Can the Empirical Rule be applied to these data? Explain.
3. The annual sales for a small variety store for the years 1968 through 1972 are listed below.

	1968	1969	1970	1971	1972
Cash	21,000	25,000	32,000	40,000	38,000
Credit	34,000	35,000	45,000	45,000	40,000

a. Construct a bar graph to depict the store's total sales volume for the five-year period.
b. Construct a bar graph to depict simultaneously the store's cash sales and credit sales over the five-year period.
4. The proposed 1975 federal budget dollar in terms of receipts and expenditures was presented using the following figures.

Receipts

Individual income taxes		$ .42
Corporation income taxes		.16
Social insurance receipts		.28
From employees	$.14	
From employers	$.14	
Excise taxes		.06
Borrowing		.03
Other		.05
Total		$1.00

Expenditures

Benefit payments to individuals	$ .37
Grants to states and localities	.17
National defense	.29
Net interest	.07
Other federal operations	.10
Total	$1.00

Depict the proposed budget using two separate pie charts.
5. The investment portfolio of pension funds of the employees of the Mallon Company for 1960 and 1970 are listed.

Type of Asset	1960	1970
Common stocks	$600,000	$690.000
Preferred stocks	120,000	115.000
Industrial bonds	120,000	345.000
Government bonds	300,000	690.000
Real estate mortgages	60,000	460.000

Construct two separate pie charts to depict the Mallon Company's portfolio composition, one to depict the composition in 1960. the other to depict the composition in 1970.

6. The SME Company sells men's and women's clothing on the export market. Their primary export business is with Australia, Great Britain, and West Germany. Over the past five years, the dollar volume of their business with these three countries has been:

Year	Australia	Great Britain	West Germany
1970	$200,000	$250,000	$150,000
1971	210,000	240,000	130,000
1972	210,000	250,000	170,000
1973	270,000	250,000	220,000
1974	310,000	230,000	250,000

Construct a bar graph to depict simultaneously SME's sales in these three countries over the past five years.

7. The carrying capacities of 100 barrels of crude oil designed to hold 42 gallons, are measured and found to have a mean of 42.5 gallons and a variance of .66, respectively.
   a. Use Tchebysheff's Theorem to describe these measurements.
   b. Assuming that the capacities have approximately a normal distribution, use the Empirical Rule to describe the data.
8. The lifetime of a particular television tube is known to be approximately mound-shaped with mean 900 hours and standard deviation 90.
   a. If one classifies as "substandard" any tube whose length of life is less than 810 hours, what percentage of tubes will be "substandard"?
   b. What percentage of tubes will have lifetimes between 810 and 1080 hours? Hint: Use the symmetry of the normal distribution; ½ of 68% of the measurements lie one standard deviation to the left or to the right of the mean, and ½ of 95% of the measurements lie two standard deviations to the left or to the right of the mean.
9. For mound-shaped or approximately normal data, one can use the range as a check on the computation of s, the standard deviation.
   a. Since 95% of the measurements are expected to fall within two standard deviations of their mean, the range should equal approximately how many standard deviations?
   b. Therefore to check the calculation of s, one can divide the range by _____ and compare this quantity with s.
   c. Use this method to check the calculation of s in the following:

    i. Exercise 1

    ii. Section 3.6(13)

    iii. Section 3.8(5)

d. Since extreme measurements are more likely to be observed in large samples, we can adjust this approximation to s by dividing the range by a divisor that depends on sample size, n. A rule of thumb to use in approximating s by using the range is presented in the following table:

n	Divide Range by
5	2.5
10	3
25	4
100	5

e. Compute s for the data in Section 3.6(13). Approximate s as in d. and compare these two values.

10. A certain company operates a fleet of 40 cars to be used for executive business trips. The fuel consumptions in miles per gallon range from 8.5 to 12.3. In presenting this data in the form of a histogram, suppose you had decided to use 0.5 m.p.g. as the width of your class interval.

    a. How many intervals would you use?

    b. Give the class boundaries for the first and the last classes.

11. A machine designed to dispense cups of instant coffee will dispense on the average μ oz., with standard deviation $\sigma = .7$ oz. Assume that the amount of coffee dispensed per cup is approximately mound-shaped. If 8 oz. cups are to be used, at what value should μ be set so that approximately 97.5% of the cups filled will not overflow?

12. A pharmaceutical company wishes to know whether an experimental drug being tested in its laboratories has any effect on systolic blood pressure. Fifteen subjects, randomly selected, were given the drug and the systolic blood pressures in millimeters recorded.

115	161	142
172	148	123
140	108	152
123	129	133
130	137	128

    a. Approximate s using the method described in part 9d.

    b. Calculate y and s for the data.

    c. Find values for the points a and b such that at least 75% of the measurements fall between a and b.

    d. Would Tchebysheff's Theorem be valid if the approximated s (part a) were used in place of the calculated s (part b)?

    e. Would the Empirical Rule apply to this data?

13. Approximate s using the rule in Exercise 9d, and then calculate $\bar{y}$, s^2, and s for the following data: 5, 4, 6, 5, 5. Compare the estimated value of s with the computed value of s.

14. Calculate $\bar{y}$, s^2, and s and use Tchebysheff's Theorem to describe the following data:

$$-1, \quad 4, \quad 0, \quad 2, \quad 3, \quad 2, \quad 1, \quad 2, \quad 0, \quad 1$$

15. It is known that a population has a mean and standard deviation of 50 and 7, respectively.
    a. What fraction of the measurements would lie in the interval 43 to 57?
    b. If the population is mound-shaped, approximately what fraction of the measurements would lie in the interval 36 to 64?

16. A lumbering company interested in the lumbering rights for a certain tract of slash pine trees is told that the mean diameter of these trees is 14 inches with a standard deviation of 2.8 inches. Assume the distribution of diameters is approximately normal.
    a. What fraction of the trees will have diameters between 8.4 inches and 22.4 inches?
    b. What fraction of the trees will have diameters greater than 16.8 inches?

17. If the mean duration of television commercials on a given network is one minute, 15 seconds, with a standard deviation of 25 seconds. what fraction of these commercials would run longer than two minutes, five seconds? Assume that duration times are approximately normally distributed.

18. Calculate $\bar{x}$, s^2, and s for the following data:

12	16
15	18
14	15
11	14
19	15

19. Generate a new set of measurements $y_1, y_2, \ldots, y_n$, from the $x_1, x_2, \ldots, x_n$ given in Exercise 18 as follows: Let $y_i = x_i - 10$.
    a. Calculate $\bar{y}$, s_y^2, s_y.
    b. Does $\bar{y} = \bar{x} - 10$?
    c. Does $s_y^2 = s_x^2$?
    d. Does $s_y = s_x$?

20. The high temperatures recorded for 20 consecutive days in Rome, Italy, during the month of May 1970 were (in centigrade degrees):

$$18, \quad 17, \quad 18, \quad 21, \quad 20, \quad 22, \quad 25, \quad 23, \quad 19, \quad 20$$
$$21, \quad 19, \quad 18, \quad 21, \quad 23, \quad 26, \quad 27, \quad 25, \quad 22, \quad 24$$

a. Compute the mean and variance of the 20 temperature recordings in centigrade degrees. Then use the Coding Theorem to find the mean and variance of the temperature recordings in terms of Fahrenheit degrees.
b. Transform each of the 20 temperature recordings from centigrade degrees to Fahrenheit degrees. Then find the mean and variance of the 20 Fahrenheit recordings. Compare the results obtained in part a and in part b.

Chapter 4

PROBABILITY

4.1 Introduction (4.1)

1. As always, the objective of statistics is to make _____ about a population based on information contained in a sample. However, a sample provides only partial information about the _____.

2. _____ enables us to use the partial information contained in a set of _____ data to infer the nature of the larger set of data, the _____.

3. Suppose we make an assumption about a population. Probability can help us make an inference or decision concerning the _____ of that assumption by using the partial _____ contained in a sample drawn from that population. Given the assumption we are making about the _____, probability helps us determine how _____ are the sample measurements. For example, if it is rather unlikely that we would observe the sample that actually has been collected if the assumption were true, then we would presumably infer that the assumption is _____.

inferences

population
Probability
sample
population

correctness *or* accuracy
information

population
probable *or* likely

incorrect *or* false

4.2 The Sample Space (4.2)

1. Data (or measurements or observations) are collected either by _____ of uncontrolled events in nature or by controlled _____ in the laboratory.

2. An _____ is defined as the process by which an observation (or measurement) is obtained. An experiment (<u>must, need not</u>) produce a numerical value.

3. A population may be conceptually generated by repeating an _____ a large number of times.

4. Each experiment may result in one or more outcomes, called _____ , which are denoted by capital letters.

observation
experimentation
experiment
need not

experiment

events

one

compound events

eight

E_3; HTH
E_4; HTT
E_5; THH
E_6; THT
E_7; TTH
E_8; TTT

compound
E_4; E_6
E_7
simple
E_1

$M_2M_3M_1$; $M_3M_1M_2$
$M_3M_2M_1$
$M_2M_3M_1$
simple
$M_2M_1M_3$
Venn diagram

sample points

5. A *simple event* is defined as one of the outcomes of a single repetition of the experiment. Simple events are denoted by the symbol E with a subscript.

6. An experiment will result in exactly _____ (give number) of the simple events.

7. Events which can be decomposed into simpler events are called

_____ _____.

8. Consider the experiment in which three coins are tossed. Let H denote a head and T denote a tail. There are _____ (give number) simple events. Complete the following table of the simple events E_1, E_2, etc. generated by this experiment of tossing three coins.

Event	Coin 1	Coin 2	Coin 3
E_1	H	H	H
E_2	H	H	T

9. In the experiment, the event "observe exactly two tails" is a _____ event because it is composed of the simple events _____, _____, and _____ (give symbols). On the other hand, the event "observe no tails" is a _____ event because it is composed of exactly one simple event, namely _____.

10. Suppose that the experiment involves ranking three applicants M_1, M_2, and M_3, in order of their abilities to do a certain job. The sample points could then be symbolized by $(M_1M_2M_3)$, $(M_1M_3M_2)$, $(M_2M_1M_3)$, (_____), (_____), and (_____). The compound event that applicant M_2 will be ranked first comprises the two sample points $(M_2M_1M_3)$ and (_____). The event that applicant M_2 will be ranked first *and* applicant M_1 will be ranked second is a _____ event which contains only the single sample point (_____).

11. A _____ _____ graphically portrays an experiment by displaying the simple events in the experiment as points in the diagram. These points are called _____ _____.

12. In the space on page 57, draw the Venn diagram for the three-coin-toss experiment.

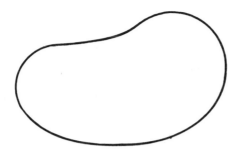

13. The set of all sample points for an experiment is called the _____ _____ and is represented by the symbol _____ . We say that S is the _____ of all sample points.

14. We can now define an _____ as a specific collection of sample points.

15. A sample point is included in a particular event if the occurrence of the (sample point, event) implies the occurrence of the (sample point, event).

16. By definition, the performance of an _____ will result in the occurrence of one and only one sample point, and an _____ will occur if any sample point in that event occurs.

17. Let A be the event "observe no tails," B be the event "observe at least two tails," and C be the event "observe an odd number of tails" in the three-coin-toss experiment. Represent A, B, C in a Venn diagram in the space below.

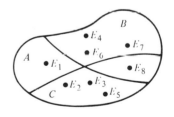

18. If an experiment is repeated a large number of times, N, and the event A is observed n_A times, then the probability of A, denoted by _____ (give symbol), is _____ (give algebraic expression). This practical view of the meaning of probability is called the _____ _____ concept of probability.

19. The probability $P(E_i)$ of any event E_i in a sample space S is subject to two very important requirements:

    a. _____ $\leqslant P(E_i) \leqslant$ _____ (give numbers), for all i

    b. $\sum_S P(E_i) =$ _____ (give number), where $\sum_S$ means to

---

sample
space; S
totality
event

sample point; event
experiment
event

$P(A)$
n_A/N
relative
frequency

0; 1
1

sum

_____ the sample point probabilities over all the points in S.

sum
sample points *or*
simple events

20. The probability of an event A is equal to the _____ of the probabilities of the _____ _____ in A.

21. If the three-coin-toss experiment is performed with three fair coins, so that on any given toss a head is exactly as likely as a tail, then each event $E_1, E_2, \ldots, E_8$ is equally likely. If this is true, then

1/8

$$P(E_1) = P(E_2) = \cdots = P(E_8) = \text{_____} \text{ (give number)}$$

22. Similarly, the probability of the event C "observe an odd number of tails" is given by (fill in sample points)

$E_2; E_3; E_5; E_8$

$$P(C) = P(\text{\_\_\_\_\_}) + P(\text{\_\_\_\_\_}) + P(\text{\_\_\_\_\_}) + P(\text{\_\_\_\_\_})$$

Hence,

$\dfrac{1}{8} + \dfrac{1}{8} + \dfrac{1}{8} + \dfrac{1}{8} = \dfrac{1}{2}$

$$P(C) = \text{_____}$$

23. Calculating the probability of an event by summing the probabilities of the sample points requires the following five steps:

Define
List
decomposed
sample space
probabilities
$\sum_S P(E_i) = 1$

a. _____ the experiment.
b. _____ the simple events associated with the experiment, and test each to make certain they cannot be _____. This defines the _____ _____.
c. Assign reasonable _____ to the sample points in the sample space S, making certain that _____ (give algebraic requirements).

sample
points
summing
A

d. Define A, the event of interest, as a specific collection of _____ _____.
e. Find $P(A)$ by _____ the probabilities of the sample points in _____.

4.3 Compound Events (4.3)

compound

1. Most events of interest to statisticians are _____ events, which are formed by a composition of two or more simple events. Composition takes place in the form of unions and/or intersections.

union

2. If A and B are two events in a sample space S, then the _____ of A and B is the event containing all the sample points in A or B or both, and is denoted by _____ (give symbol).

$A \cup B$
either
both
intersection

3. $A \cup B$ is the event that _____ event A or event B occurs or that _____ A and B occur.
4. If A and B are two events in a sample space S, then the _____

of A and B is the event composed of all sample points that are in both A and B, and is symbolized by _____ or _____ (give symbols).

5. The intersection AB is the event that _____ A and B occur.

6. Refer to the three-coin-toss experiment. For each of the symbols below, indicate which events $E_1, E_2, \ldots, E_8$ are included, and then shade the Venn diagram to portray the symbol.

a. $A \cup B =$ (in simple events) _____ .

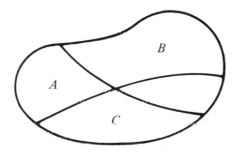

b. BC (or $B \cap C$) = _____ .

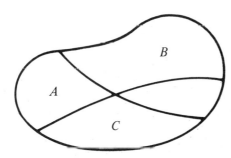

c. AC (or $A \cap C$) = _____ .

$AB; A \cap B$

both

E_1, E_4, E_6, E_7, E_8

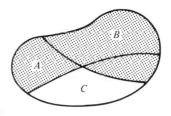

E_8

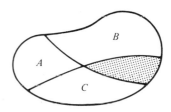

none of E_i are in both A and C

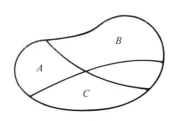

7. In each of the Venn diagrams below, express symbolically the event represented by the shaded area. In each case, the sample space S comprises all sample points within the rectangle.

a.

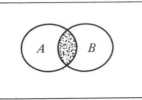

AB or A ∩ B

Symbol _____

b.

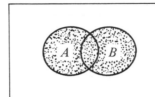

A ∪ B

Symbol _____

c.

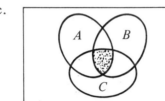

ABC or A ∩ B ∩ C

Symbol _____

d.

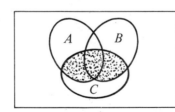

AC ∪ BC
or
(A ∩ C) ∪ (B ∩ C)

Symbol _____

8. In each of the Venn diagrams below shade in the event symbolized.
   a. Symbol: A ∪ B.

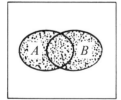

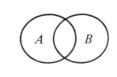

b. Symbol: *BC*

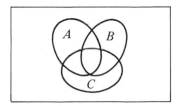

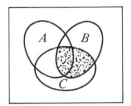

c. Symbol: $AE_1 \cup AE_2$

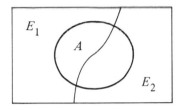

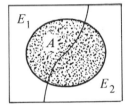

d. Note that $E_1 \cup E_2 = S$ and $AE_1 \cup AE_2 = $ _____.

9. *Example:*

A researcher proposed the following experiment to assess public attitudes toward racial minorities. In the experiment, a person is shown four photographs—1, 2, 3 and 4—of armed robberies that have been committed and is asked to select what he considers to be the two worst crimes. All four robberies have essentially the same features and involve the same amount of money. However, 1 and 2 are robberies committed against nonwhite victims. In 3 and 4, the victims are white. If the person shows no bias in his selection, find the probabilities associated with the following events:

    A: the selection includes pictures 1 and 2.
    B: the selection includes picture 3.
    C: both *A* and *B* occur.
    D: either *A* or *B* or both occur.

Solution:

The experiment consists of selecting two pictures out of four. Listing the possible outcomes, we have the following distinct pairs.

Sample point	E_1	E_2	E_3	E_4	E_5	E_6
Pair	(1,2)	(1,3)	(1,4)	(2,3)	(2,4)	(___)

3,4

1/6

E_1

E_1; 1/6

3/6

0

4/6

If there is no bias in selection, each sample point would be assigned probability equal to _____ .

a. The event A consists of the sample point _____ . Hence,

$$P(A) = P(\underline{\hspace{2cm}}) = \underline{\hspace{2cm}}$$

b. The event B consists of the sample points E_2, E_4, and E_6. Then

$$P(B) = \underline{\hspace{2cm}}$$

c. The event C is the intersection of A and B and consists of the sample point that includes pictures 1 and 2 and at the same time includes picture 3. Since no sample points satisfy these conditions,

$$P(C) = P(AB) = \underline{\hspace{2cm}}$$

d. The event D is the union of the events A and B and consists of those sample points which include picture 3 and the sample point that includes pictures 1 and 2. Hence $A \cup B$ consists of the sample points E_1, E_2, E_4 and E_6 and

$$P(D) = P(A \cup B) = \underline{\hspace{2cm}}$$

Self-Correcting Exercises 4A

1. A lot containing six items is comprised of 4 good items and 2 defective items. Two items are selected at random for testing.
   a. List the sample points for this experiment.
   b. Define the following events:
      A: at least one item is defective.
      B: exactly one item is defective.
      C: no more than one item is defective.
   List the sample points in each of these three events.
   c. Suppose that each item in the lot of six has an equal chance of being selected. Find $P(A), P(B)$, and $P(C)$.
2. A hospital administrator reported that four births had taken place at the hospital during the last twenty-four hours. If we consider only the sex of these four newborn children, recording M for a male child and F for a female child, there are sixteen sex combinations possible.
   a. List these sixteen outcomes in terms of sample points, beginning with E_1 as the outcome (FFFF).
   b. Define the following events in terms of the sample points $E_1 \ldots E_{16}$.
      A: two boys and two girls are born.
      B: no boys are born.
      C: at least one boy is born.
      D: either A or B or both occur.

      E: both B and C occur.
      F: either A or C or both occur.
   c. If the sex of a newborn baby is just as likely to be male as female, find
      the probabilities associated with the six events listed in part b.
3. Imagine a coin that is so thick that one is just as likely to obtain a toss
   that lands on edge (G) as it is a head (H) or tail (T). That is, G, H, and T
   each occur one-third of the time. Suppose that two such coins are tossed.
   a. List the sample points for this experiment.
   b. Define the following events in terms of sample points:
      A: no edges (G's) are observed.
      B: at least one head (H) is observed.
      C: both coins show the same result (i.e., TT, HH, or GG).
   c. Find the probabilities of A, B, C, $A \cup C$, BC.
   d. Draw a Venn diagram of the sample space. Show events A, B, and C in
      the diagram. Shade in the space corresponding to $B \cup C$.
4. In quality control on taste and texture, it is common to have a taster
   compare a new batch of a food product with one having the desired properties. Three new batches are independently tested against the standard
   and classified as having the desired properties H or not having the desired
   properties N.
   a. List the sample points for this experiment.
   b. If in fact all three new batches are no different from the standard, all
      sample points in part a should be equally likely. If this is the case, find
      the probabilities associated with the following events:
      A: exactly one batch is declared as not having the desired properties.
      B: batch number one is declared to have the desired property.
      C: all three batches are declared to have the desired property.
      D: at least two batches are declared to have the desired property.
   c. Using the information in parts a and b, find the probabilities for $A \cup D$
      and BD.

4.4 Event Relations (4.4)

1. Two events, A and B, may be related in three important ways. Events
   A and B may be _____, _____, or _____
   exclusive.   complementary; independent;
                                                                                 mutually

2. The complement of an event, A, is the collection of all sample points
   that (are, are not) in the sample space S but (are, are not) in A.   are; are not
   The complement of A is denoted by the symbol _____. $\overline{A}$

3. It is always true that $P(A) + P(\overline{A}) = $ _____. Using this fact, simple   1
   algebra yields the very useful result:

   $$P(A) = 1 - \text{_____}$$ $P(\overline{A})$

4. *Example:*
   Suppose that 10% of the fuses in a large lot of electrical fuses are defective. A packet of three fuses will be obtained by packaging three fuses

selected at random from the lot. Let A be the event that at least two of the three fuses will be defective. It can be shown that the probability that at most one of the fuses will be defective is .972. Find $P(A)$.

Solution:

one

.972; .028

$\overline{A}$ is the event that at most _____ of the fuses will be defective. Thus $P(\overline{A}) =$ _____ and $P(A) =$ _____.

5. Before introducing the concept of independence of events, we must first consider conditional probability. Let A and B be two events defined on a sample. Suppose you are told that event A has occurred. Given that information, what *now* is the probability that event B has occurred?

6. The probability of event B, given that event A has occurred, is called the _____ _____ of B given A, symbolized by

conditional probability

$P(B|A)$

_____.

$P(AB)/P(A)$

7. By definition, $P(B|A) =$ _____,

8. Similarly, the probability of event A, given that event B has occurred, is called the conditional probability of _____ given _____, and is symbolized by _____.

$A; B$

$P(A|B)$

9. *Example:*

Five applicants, all equally qualified, are being considered for a managerial position. There are three males and two females among the applicants. Define the following events:

        A: female number one is selected.

        B: a female is selected.

If the selection is done at random, find $P(A)$ and $P(A|B)$.

Solution:

1/5

The unconditional probability, $P(A) =$ _____. We can find $P(A|B)$ in one of two ways.

a. *Direct enumeration.* If B has occurred, then we need only consider the two female applicants as comprising the new restricted sample space.

1/2

   Hence $P(A|B) =$ _____.

1/5

2/5

b. *Calculation.* By definition, $P(A/B) = P(AB)/P(B)$. $P(AB) =$ _____;
$P(B) =$ _____; hence

1/2

$$P(A|B) = P(AB)/P(B) =$$ _____

10. If either $P(A|B) = P(A)$ or $P(B|A) = P(B)$, the events A and B are

independent

_____, since the probability of the occurrence of A is unaffected by the knowledge that B has occurred. If $P(A|B) \neq P(A)$,

dependent

we say that events A and B are _____.

a. *Example:*

Are the events A and B defined in 9 independent?

Solution:

We found that $P(A) = 1/5$ and $P(A|B) = 1/2$. Since $P(A) \neq P(A|B)$,

are not

the events (are, are not) independent.

b. *Example:*

You hold ticket number 7 in an office lottery in which ten tickets

numbered 1 through 10 were sold. The winning ticket is drawn at random from those sold. You are told that an odd number was drawn. Does this information increase the probability that you have won?
Solution:
Define the events.

A: number 7 is drawn.
B: an odd number is drawn.

Then $P(A) =$ _____ and $P(A|B) =$ _____ . The events A and B are _____ and the probability that you have won is now doubled. | 1/10; 1/5 dependent

11. Events A and B which have no sample points in common are said to be _____ _____ . Thus A and B are mutually exclusive when the set AB is _____ . The probability of an event is the _____ of the probabilities assigned to its sample points. Thus, if A and B are mutually exclusive, then $P(AB) =$ _____ . Events A and $\overline{A}$ (are, are not) mutually exclusive. | mutually exclusive / empty / sum / 0 / are

12. *Example:*
In a marketing research survey an individual is first classified as belonging to one of the following age groups:

G_1: 25 years of age or younger.
G_2: older than 25 but not older than 40.
G_3: older than 40 but not older than 60.
G_4: over 60 years of age.

These groups (are, are not) mutually exclusive. Hence the probability that a person will be categorized as simultaneously belonging to two groups will be _____ . | are / zero

4.5 Two Probability Laws and Their Use (4.5)

1. Given two events A and B, the probability of the intersection AB is given by the _____ Law of Probability. It states that | Multiplicative

$$P(AB) = P(A) \underline{\hspace{2cm}}$$ | $P(B|A)$

or equivalently that

$$P(AB) = \underline{\hspace{2cm}} P(A|B)$$ | $P(B)$

2. If A and B are independent events, $P(AB) =$ _____ | $P(A)P(B)$

3. The probability of the event $A \cup B$ is given by the _____ Law of Probability, which states that | Additive

$P(A) + P(B) - P(AB)$

$$P(A \cup B) = \text{_____}$$

4. If A and B are mutually exclusive, then

0

$$P(AB) = \text{_____}$$

and

$P(A) + P(B)$

$$P(A \cup B) = \text{_____}$$

5. *Examples:*

In the following Venn diagrams the ten sample points shown are equally likely. Thus, to each sample point is assigned the probability _____.

1/10

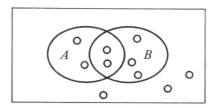

7/10
2/10
5/10
2/5
5/10
independent

a. $P(A \cup B) =$ _____
b. $P(AB) =$ _____
c. $P(B) =$ _____
d. $P(A|B) =$ _____
e. $P(\bar{B}) =$ _____
f. A and B are (independent, dependent).

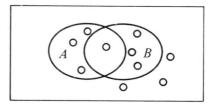

7/10
1/10
4/10
1/4
dependent

a. $P(A \cup B) =$ _____
b. $P(AB) =$ _____
c. $P(A) =$ _____
d. $P(A|B) =$ _____
e. A and B are (independent, dependent).

6. *Example:*

The personnel files for the Quick Sales Agency lists its 150 employees as follows:

	Years Employed with Quick Sales		
	A (0-5)	B (6-10)	C (11 or more)
D: Not a college graduate	10	20	20
E: College graduate	40	50	10

If *one* personnel file is drawn at random from Quick's personnel files, calculate the probabilities requested below:

a. $P(A) = $ _____   1/3

b. $P(E) = $ _____   2/3

c. $P(BD) = $ _____   2/15

d. $P(C|E) = $ _____   1/10

e. $P(A \cup E) = $ _____   11/15

f. $P(A|C) = $ _____   0

g. A and E are (independent, dependent).   dependent

Self-Correcting Exercises 4B

1. Refer to Self-Correcting Exercises 4A, problem 2.
   a. Rewrite events D, E, and F in terms of the events A, B and C.
   b. List the sample points in the following events: AB, $B \cup C$, $AC \cup BC$, $\overline{C}$, $\overline{AC}$.
   c. Using the results of part 2c in Exercises 4A, calculate $P(A \cup B)$, $P(\overline{C})$, $P(\overline{BC})$.
   d. Calculate $P(A|C)$. Are A and C mutually exclusive? Are A and C independent?
   e. Calculate $P(B|C)$. Are B and C independent? Mutually exclusive?
2. Two hundred corporate executives in the Los Angeles area were interviewed. They were classified according to the size of the corporation they represented and their choice as to the most effective method for reducing air pollution in the Los Angeles basin. (Data are fictitious.)

	Corporation Size		
	A (Small)	B (Medium)	C (Large)
D: Car pooling	20	15	20
E: Bus expansion	30	25	11
F: Gas rationing	3	8	4
G: Conversion to natural gas	10	7	5
H: Anti-pollution devices	12	20	10

Suppose that one executive is chosen at random to be interviewed on a television broadcast.

   a. Calculate the following probabilities and describe each probability in terms of the above problem: $P(A)$, $P(F)$, $P(AF)$, $P(A \cup G)$, $P(AD)$, $P(\overline{F})$.
   b. Calculate $P(A|F)$, $P(A|D)$. Are A and F independent? Mutually exclusive? Are A and D independent? Mutually exclusive?
3. The selling style of a temperamental salesman is strongly affected by his

success or failure in his preceding attempt to sell. If he has just made a sale his confidence and effectiveness rise and the probability of selling to his next prospect is 3/4. When he fails to sell, his manner is fearful and the probability of his selling to his next prospect is only 1/3. Suppose that the probability that he will sell to his first contact on a given day is 1/2. Find the probability of the event A, that he makes at least two sales on his first three contacts on a given day.

4. An investor holds shares in three independent companies which, according to his business analyst, should show an increase in profit per share with probabilities .4, .6 and .7 respectively. Assume that the analyst's estimates for the probabilities of profit increases are correct.

    a. Find the probability that all three companies show increases for the coming year.

    b. Find the probability that none of the companies show a profit.

    c. Find the probability that at least one company shows a profit.

4.6 Bayes' Law (4.6)

conditional

1. Bayes' Law gives a formula for the computation of a _____ probability, $P(B|A)$, when the conditional probabilities _____ and

$P(A|B)$

_____ and the marginal probabilities $P(B)$ and _____ are

$P(A|\bar{B}); P(\bar{B})$

known. The computational formula for Bayes' Law is

$$P(B|A) = \frac{P(A|B)\, P(B)}{P(A|B)\, P(B) + P(A|\bar{B})\, P(\bar{B})}$$

posterior

2. The probability $P(B|A)$ is called the _____ probability of event

event A

B given _____.

prior

3. The simple or marginal probabilities $P(B)$ and $P(\bar{B})$ are called the _____ probabilities of events B and $\bar{B}$, respectively.

4. *Example:*

An oil wildcatter must decide whether or not to hire a seismic survey before deciding whether or not to drill for oil on a plot of land. Given that oil is present, the survey will indicate a favorable result with probability .8; if oil is not present, a favorable result will occur with probability .3. The wildcatter figures the probability is .5 that oil is present on the plot of land. Determine the effectiveness of the survey by computing the probability that oil is present given a favorable seismic survey outcome.

Solution:

Define the events.   *F:* a favorable seismic outcome results.

                      O: oil is actually present.

                      $\bar{O}$: oil is not present.

    a. We want to find

        $P(O|F) =$ _____ / _____

$P(F|O)P(O); P(F|O)P(O)$
$+ P(F|\bar{O})P(\bar{O}).$

    b. $P(F|O) =$ _____, $P(F|\bar{O}) =$ _____

.8; .3

c. Since $P(O) =$ _____, then $P(\bar{O}) = 1 - P(O) =$ _____.

d. Thus, $P(O|F) =$ _____.

.5; .5

8/11

5. *Example:*

Each item coming off a given production line is inspected by either Inspector 1 or Inspector 2. Inspector 1 inspects about 60% of the production items while Inspector 2 inspects the rest. Inspector 1, who has been at his present job for some time, will not find 1% of the defective items he inspects. Inspector 2, who is newer on the job, misses about 5% of the defective items he inspects. If an item which has passed an inspector is found to be defective, what is the probability that it was inspected by Inspector 1?

Solution:

Define the following events.

D: a defective item is passed by an inspector.

A: Inspector 1 inspected the item.

$\bar{A}$: Inspector 2 inspected the item.

a. The following information is available.

$P(A) = .6$	$P(\bar{A}) =$ _____
$P(D|A) =$ _____	$P(D|\bar{A}) =$ _____

.4

.01; .05

b. We want to find

$$P(A|D) = \frac{P(A)\,P(D|A)}{P(A)\,P(D|A) + P(\bar{A})\,P(D|\bar{A})}$$

c. $P(A)\,P(D|A) = (.6)\,(.01) =$ _____

$P(\bar{A})\,P(D|\bar{A}) = (.4)\,(.05) =$ _____

d. Then $P(A|D) = .006/(.006 + .020) =$ _____

.006

.020

.23

4.7 Counting Sample Points (4.7)

1. When the sample space is (small, large), the probabilities associated with events of interest can usually be determined by direct counting of the relevant sample points.

2. But when the number of sample points is large, we resort to shortcut methods for counting sample points.

3. Whenever we have a large-sample space, S, with N equally probable sample points, and an event, A, with n_A sample points in it, the probability of A is given by the simple formula

$$P(A) =$$ _____

small

n_A/N

mn rule

mn

48

rst
permutations

P^n_r
$n!/(n-r)!$

$n!$

$n!$

4. This section reviews the counting rules that permit us to determine (in the above example) n_A and N.

5. The first of these, the _____ _____, applies to situations in which we must determine the number of ways in which pairs of objects can be formed when the objects are selected, one each, from two different groups.

6. The rule states that with m elements $a_1, a_2, \ldots, a_m$ and n elements $b_1, b_2, \ldots, b_n$, we can form _____ pairs that contain one element from each group.

7. *Example:*
   In the Ajax Corporation's management trainee program, each trainee spends three months in each of the corporation's four divisions: marketing, production, finance, and personnel. At the end of each three-month rotation, an evaluation must be completed for each trainee. If there are twelve trainees in the program, how many trainee evaluations must be completed?
   Solution:
   There are 4 divisions and 12 trainees. An evaluation will be completed following each trainee's rotation through each division. Hence, $4 \cdot 12 = $ _____ evaluations will be completed.

8. This rule can be extended to as many groups as needed, provided that one element is selected from each group. For example, the number of triplets that can be formed by choosing one element from each of three groups where there are r elements in the first group, s in the second, and t in the third is _____.

9. Our second counting rule concerns _____, which are ordered arrangements of some number, say r, of distinct objects.

10. The number of ways of ordering n distinct objects taken r at a time is designated by the symbol _____ and is given by the formula

    _____.

11. Notice that when we wish the number of all possible ordered arrangements of all n objects, that n and r are equal and the formula becomes

    $$P^n_n = \underline{\hspace{2cm}}$$

12. This is, in fact, a special application of the *mn* rule, for there are n ways to fill the first position in the ordered arrangement. But that means that only $n-1$ objects remain to fill the second position, and $n-2$ to fill the third. We thus proceed until there is only one element left to fill the last, or nth, position. Hence,

    $$P^n_n = n(n-1)(n-2) \ldots (2)(1) = \underline{\hspace{2cm}}$$

13. *Example:*
    Thirteen company employees have been found equally qualified for promotion to a particular job. It has been decided to choose five of the

employees for assignment to a sequential promotion list by lottery. These lucky five will then be promoted as vacancies occur in the order they are listed. How many different promotion lists are possible?
Solution:
Notice that *order* is important in the arrangement. The arrangement *ABCDE* is not the same as the arrangement *DCEAB,* particularly if you are Mr. D. There are, in this example, _____ ways to fill the first place on the promotion list, _____ ways to fill the second, _____ ways to fill the third, and _____ and _____ ways to fill the fourth and fifth positions, respectively. Hence, the answer is

13
12
11; 10; 9

$$P_5^{13} = 13!/8! = 13 \cdot 12 \cdot 11 \cdot 10 \cdot 9 = \underline{\hspace{1cm}}$$

154440

14. However, order is not always so important. Often we care only about the number of different combinations of objects. For example, *ABCDE* and *DCEAB* would be considered the same combination when the order of the elements can be disregarded.
15. The number of combinations of n objects taken r at a time is denoted by the symbol _____ and is given by the formula _____.

$C_r^n \ or \binom{n}{r}; n!/r!(n-r)!$

16. *Example:*
Refer to the previous example. Suppose that instead of a promotion list, the lottery will be used to select 5 of the 13 for immediate promotion. How many combinations of 5 promotees are possible?
Solution:
We can apply the formula for counting combinations.

$$n = \underline{\hspace{1cm}} \ \text{and} \ r = \underline{\hspace{1cm}}$$

13; 5

The answer is given by

$$C_5^{13} = \frac{13!}{5!8!} = \frac{13 \cdot 12 \cdot 11 \cdot 10 \cdot 9}{5 \cdot 4 \cdot 3 \cdot 2 \cdot 1} = \underline{\hspace{1cm}}$$

1287

17. Here are the diagnostic clues for deciding which counting rule to use:
   a. One of the three counting rules probably applies if the sample point is identified by a _____ number of characteristics.

   fixed

   b. The _____ rule probably applies if the characteristics are taken _____ each from two or more sets. On the other hand, the permutation and combination rules apply to the selection of characteristics from _____ set (s).

   mn
   one

   one

   c. The _____ rule applies if the characteristics are chosen from a single set and each arrangement of a specific set of characteristics corresponds to a new sample point.

   permutations

   d. The _____ rule applies if the characteristics are selected

   combinations

from a single set and reordering the characteristics does not produce another sample point.

Self-Correcting Exercises 4C

1. In a manufacturing plant, Machine I produces 40% of the output while Machine II produces the remaining 60%. 1.5% of Machine I's output is defective and 2.0 of Machine II's output is defective. One unit of the day's production run is examined and proves to be defective. What is the probability that it was produced on Machine I?

2. A stereo components retailer is advertising a sale plan which allows a customer to build a high-fidelity system for $500 by choosing one of four receivers, one of five turntables, one of three cassette decks, and one of six sets of speakers. The dealer's cost of one model within each category of equipment is such that he will lose money if a customer includes that model in his system selection. That is, there is one brand of receiver, one brand of turntable, etc., that will cause a loss to the store if a customer selects it. Assume that customers choose components at random. What is the probability that the dealer will make a profit on any particular sale?

3. There are six new advertising accounts that the manager of an advertising agency must assign to his six new account executives. In how many different ways can the six accounts be assigned?

4. A company makes six different models of camp stoves. A magazine advertisement is being prepared, and the layout provides space for displaying only four of the camp stoves. It has already been decided that two particular models, the most expensive one and a medium-priced model whose sales have been lagging, will definitely appear in the layout. If the other stove models are selected at random, how many different layouts are possible?

4.8 Subjective Probability (4.8)

1. When an experiment can be repeated many times, we can assign a probability, $P(E_i)$, to a particular event in accordance with the _____ _____ concept of probability. That is, we regard $P(E_i)$, the probability of event E_i, as the _____ of times that E_i will occur in a long series of _____ of the experiment.

relative frequency
fraction
repetitions

subjective

2. But experiments that cannot be repeated require a _____ evaluation of the probabilities of an event. One must rely on his or her experience and judgment in assigning probabilities to the sample points.

3. Probabilities assigned to events that are acquired subjectively and based

on experience are called _____ _____ or, sometimes, personal probabilities.

subjective probabilities

4. The existence of both the subjective and the relative frequency concepts
of probability leads us to view any probability, $P(E_i)$, as a _____
of one's _____ in the outcome of a particular event, E_i.

measure
belief

5. That is, we assign a number to each sample point E_i as a measure of our
belief that the sample point E_i will occur when the experiment is conducted _____ time (s).

one

4.9 Random Variables (4.9)

1. An _____ is the process by which an observation (or measurement) is obtained.

experiment

2. Most experiments produce _____ data, or data that can be
quantified by assigning _____ to represent categories. Consequently, we are particularly interested in experiments that produce
numerically valued outcomes.

numerical
numbers

3. The variable y which is measured in an experiment is called a
_____ _____ if the value that y assumes is a
chance or random event.

random variable

4. The particular value that y assumes is a chance or random event if
that value cannot be predicted with absolute _____ in
advance of the experiment.

certainty

5. A random variable y can assume many values, each with its own
associated probability. The set of all these possible outcomes of y, and
their associated probabilities, is called the _____ _____
for y.

probability distribution

4.10 Summary (4.10)

1. An experiment is the process of obtaining an _____. The outcomes of an experiment are called _____. An event which cannot be decomposed is called a _____ event. To each simple
event we assign a _____ _____. The totality S of
sample points for a given experiment is the
_____ for that experiment.

observation
events
simple
sample point
sample
space

2. An _____ is a collection of sample points.

event

3. Probabilities assigned to the sample points must meet the requirements

$$\sum_{\text{all } i} P(E_i) = \underline{\hspace{2cm}}, \text{ and } \underline{\hspace{2cm}}$$

$1; 0 \leqslant P(E_i) \leqslant 1$

4. The probability of an event A is the _____ of the probabilities

sum

sample points

S

intersections; unions
AB
both; $A \cup B$
A ; B

multiplicative; additive
intersection
union

independent
complementary
mutually
exclusive
$P(A|B)$
$P(AB)/P(B)$

independent.

sample

posterior
Bayes'

mn

permutation

combination
Probability

random variable

assigned to the _____ _____ in *A*. For the *special case* where the sample points are assigned equal probability (equally likely), *P(A)* will equal the number of sample points in *A* divided by the number of sample points in _____. (Counting the sample points can be simplified by using combinatorial mathematics.)

5. A second method for calculating the probability of an event is the event-composition approach. Events may be combined in two ways, by forming _____ and _____. The intersection of two events, *A* and *B*, denoted by the symbol, _____, is the set of all sample points that are in _____ *A* and *B*. The union, denoted by the symbol _____, is the set of all sample points either in _____ or in _____ or in both *A* and *B*.

6. The probability of an event composition can be obtained by using the _____ and _____ laws of probability. The multiplicative law gives the probability for an _____. The additive law gives the probability for a _____.

7. Events *A* and *B* may be related in various ways. Thus, *A* and *B* may be complementary, mutually exclusive, or _____. *A* and *B* are _____ if *B* comprises all points of the sample space which are not in *A*. If *AB* contains no sample points, then *A* and *B* are _____ _____. The conditional probability of event *A* given that *B* has occurred is indicated by the symbol _____. By definition, *P(A|B)* = _____. The laws of probability simplify when the events are mutually exclusive or independent. If *P(A|B)* = *P(A)*, then *A* and *B* are _____.

8. Probability is important in the study of statistics because it provides the mechanism necessary for making inferences. Thus one must be able to calculate the probability of the _____ in order to make an inference about the population.

9. When events *A* and *B* occur in that order, the computed probability *P(A|B)* is called the _____ probability of *A* given event *B*, and can be calculated using _____ Law.

10. The number of ways in which pairs of objects can be formed when the objects are selected, one each, from two different groups is given by the _____ rule.

11. The number of ways of ordering *n* distinct objects taken *r* at a time is given by the _____ rule.

12. The number of different groupings of *n* objects taken *r* at a time, without regard to order, is given by the _____ rule.

13. _____ can be viewed as a measure of one's belief in the outcome of a particular event.

14. A variable *y* is a _____ _____ if the values that *y* assumes, corresponding to the various outcomes of an experiment, are chance or random events.

Exercises

1. Assume that probabilities have been assigned to all the points in a sample space; tell how you would find the probability of an event A.
2. The probabilities associated with a sample space must satisfy two requirements. State these requirements.
3. State:
   a. How you would tell whether events A and B are independent.
   b. How you would tell whether events A and B are mutually exclusive.
4. Suppose that an experiment requires the ranking of three applicants A, B, and C in order of their abilities to do a certain job. The sample points could then be symbolized by the ordered triplets ABC, BAC, etc.
   a. The event A that applicant A will be ranked first comprises which of the sample points?
   b. The event B that applicant B will be ranked third comprises which of the sample points?
   c. List the points in $A \cup B$.
   d. List the points in AB.
   e. If equal probabilities are assigned to the sample points show whether or not events A and B are independent.
5. An investor is considering investing in three investment opportunities A, B, and C. The probability each investment "pays off" is $P(A) = .5$, $P(B) = .4$, and $P(C) = .6$. Assuming the performances of the investments are independent of one another, find:
   a. The probability all investments will pay off.
   b. The probability two of the three investments will pay off.
   c. The probability at least one of the investments pays off.
6. The owner of a camera shop knows from experience that 5% of all cameras produced by the Osaka Company prove to be defective. If the owner purchases five cameras from the Osaka Company, find the probability none are defective.
7. The owner of the camera shop mentioned in Exercise 6 has been sent five cameras by the Osaka Company, but, unknown to the owner, one of the cameras is defective. Suppose the store owner tests the cameras one at a time.
   a. What is the probability he discovers the defective camera on the first test?
   b. As a time saving measure, suppose the store owner tests only 40% of the cameras in shipments sent to him by manufacturers. If he adopts this rule with the Osaka shipment, what is the probability the defective camera is found in testing?
   c. Is the fact that 5% of all cameras produced by the Osaka Company are defective of any assistance in solving parts a and b? Explain.
8. Suppose $P(A) = 1/2$ and $P(B) = 1/4$. Find $P(AB)$ if:
   a. A and B are independent.
   b. A and B are mutually exclusive.
9. Suppose $P(A) = 1/3$, $P(B) = 1/4$ and $P(A|B) = 1/2$. Find $P(A \cup B)$.

10. Suppose that independent events A and B have nonzero probabilities. Show that A and B cannot be mutually exclusive.

11. An antique dealer had accumulated a number of small items including a valuable stamp collection and a solid gold vase. To make room for new stock he distributed these small items among four boxes. Without revealing which items were placed in which box, the dealer stated that the stamp collection was included in one box and the gold vase in another. The four boxes were sealed and placed on sale, each at the same price. A certain customer purchased two boxes selected at random from the four boxes. What is the probability that he acquired
    a. the stamp collection?
    b. the vase?
    c. at least one of these bonus items?

12. The sample space for a given experiment is comprised of the simple events E_1, E_2, E_3, and E_4. Let the compound events A, B, and C be defined by the relationships

$$A = E_1 \cup E_2, \quad B = E_1 \cup E_4, \quad C = E_2 \cup E_3$$

Construct a Venn diagram showing the events E_1, E_2, E_3, E_4, A, B, and C.

13. Refer to Exercise 12. Probabilities are assigned to the simple events as indicated in the following table.

Simple event	E_1	E_2	E_3	E_4
Assigned probability	1/3	1/3	1/6	—

    a. Supply the missing entry in the table.
    b. Find $P(A)$ and $P(AB)$.
    c. Find $P(A|B)$ and $P(A|C)$.
    d. Find $P(A \cup B)$ and $P(A \cup C)$.

14. Refer to Exercise 12.
    a. Which pairs of the events A, B, and C are mutually exclusive?
    b. Which pairs of the events A, B, and C are independent?

15. A large commercial bank has branch banks located throughout five western states. The 120 branch banks are categorized below according to the state in which they are located and the number of years they have been in operation.

	State				
	Washington	Oregon	California	Nevada	Idaho
Under 5	11	9	17	3	6
5–10	12	5	23	4	3
Over 10	7	6	10	3	1

A bank is selected at random from among the 120 branch banks.
    a. Find the probability that the bank is located in Washington.
    b. Find the probability that the bank has been in operation less than five years.

    c. Find the probability that the bank has been in operation at least five years.

    d. Find the probability that the bank is in California or has been in operation over 10 years, or both.

    e. Find the probability that the bank has been in operation at least five years or is located in Oregon or both.

    f. Find the probability that the bank is located in Washington and has been in operation at least 10 years.

    g. Given that the bank has been in operation less than five years, find the probability that it is located in Idaho.

    h. Given that the bank is located in California, find the probability that it has been in operation 10 years or less.

    i. Find the probability that the bank is located outside of California.

16. A random sample of size five is drawn from a large production lot with fraction defective 10%. The probability that this sample will contain no defectives is .59. What is the probability that this sample will contain at least one defective?

17. In an article in a local newspaper it was stated that if the probability of destroying an attacking plane were .15 at each of five defense barriers, and if an attacking plane had to pass all five barriers to get to the target, then the probability of destroying the plane before it passed all five barriers would be .75. Is the newspaper correct in its conclusion? Explain.

18. To test the competence of a diamond salesman, a dealer requires the salesman to select the three most valuable gems from a collection of ten gems, and to specify which of these is first, which is second, and which is third in order of value. Suppose that the salesman is totally lacking in ability to rank gems in order of value.

    a. What is the probability that the salesman will achieve total success?

    b. What is the probability that at least one of the three most valuable gems will be included among the three selected by the salesman?

19. A factory operates an eight-hour day shift. Five machines of a certain type are used. If one of these machines breaks down, it is set aside and repaired by a crew operating at night. Suppose the probability that a given machine suffers a breakdown during a day's operation is 1/5.

    a. What is the probability that no machine breakdown will occur on a given day?

    b. What is the probability that two or more machine breakdowns will occur on a given day?

20. Income in a neighborhood is approximately normally distributed (bell-shaped) with mean and standard deviation equal to $4600 and $500, respectively. If two wage earners are selected randomly from the neighborhood, give the probability that both will have incomes in excess of $5100 per year.

21. An oil prospector will drill a succession of holes in a given area to find a productive well. The probability that he is successful on a given trial is .2.

a. What is the probability that the third hole drilled is the first which locates a productive well?

b. If his total resources allow the drilling of no more than three holes, what is the probability that he locates at least one productive well?

22. Suppose that two defective refrigerators have been included in a shipment of six refrigerators. The buyer begins to test the six refrigerators one at a time.

a. What is the probability that the last defective refrigerator is found on the fourth test?

b. What is the probability that no more than four refrigerators must be tested before locating both of the defective refrigerators?

23. An individual is to be selected at random from a given population. Let T be the event that this individual has tuberculosis and E be the event that his X-ray examination indicates (rightly or wrongly) that he has tuberculosis. Suppose that we know the following probabilities:

$$P(T) = .001, \quad P(E|T) = .90, \quad P(E|\bar{T}) = .01$$

a. State in words what is meant by $P(E|\bar{T})$.

b. Noting that $E = ET \cup E\bar{T}$, calculate $P(E)$.

c. Calculate $P(T|E)$, and state in words what is implied about the proper interpretation of the X-ray examination.

24. Construction firm A must be awarded at least two jobs within a week to maintain employment for its basic personnel. It has submitted bids for each of three jobs of type I and for each of two jobs of type II. The winning firms will be announced within the crucial week. Suppose that firm A has probability 1/2 of being awarded a given job of type I and probability 3/4 of being awarded a given job of type II. The decisions will be made independently. What is the probability that firm A will be able to continue the employment of its basic personnel?

25. Construction firm B is considering bidding on a construction job to build an apartment building. They feel they will win the contract to build the apartment with probability 3/4 if construction firm C does not submit a bid, but the probability that they will win the contract if C does submit a bid on the job is 1/3. What is the probability that firm B will win the contract, given that C bids on 30% of the construction jobs?

Chapter 5

RANDOM VARIABLES AND PROBABILITY DISTRIBUTIONS

5.1 Random Variables: How They Relate to Statistical Inference (5.1)

1. An _____ is the process of collecting a measurement (or an observation). Usually the process yields a _____ measurement that varies randomly from sample point to sample point.

    experiment
    numerical

2. Such a measurement is called a _____ _____ if the value it assumes is a chance or random event.

    random variable

3. When an experiment is repeated many times and a large body of data is obtained, a _____ is generated.

    population

4. We seldom ever measure every member of the population. Instead, we obtain a small set of measurements called a _____, and use the information therein to describe or make _____ about the _____.

    sample
    inferences
    population

5. In order to use a sample of measurements to make inferences about a population of interest, we must know the _____ associated with each value of the random variable. That is, we must know the _____ _____ of the random variable, which represents the theoretical _____ histogram for the population of numerical measurements.

    probability

    probability distribution
    frequency

6. Suppose that y is a random variable defined on a sample space. The phrase "defined on a sample space" means that y takes values associated with sample points that are outcomes of an _____.
One and only one value of the random variable y is associated with each _____ in the sample space.

    experiment

    point

7. The values that the random variable y may assume form one set and the sample points another. Therefore, the random variable y is said to be a numerically valued _____.

    function

8. Suppose that a sample of one hundred people was randomly drawn from a population of voters, and the number favoring candidate Jones was recorded. This process defines an _____. The number of voters in the sample favoring candidate Jones is an example of a _____ _____.

    experiment
    random
    variable

9. Suppose that of the 100 voters in the sample, 60 favored Jones. This would not necessarily imply that Jones will win because one could obtain 60 or more in the *sample* favorable to Jones even though only half or less of the voting *population* favor him. In fact the crucial question is, "What is the probability that 60 or more of the 100 voters in the sample are favorable to Jones when actually just 50% or less of the voting population will vote for him?"

10. To answer this question, we need to investigate the probabilistic behavior of the random variable y, the number of favorable voters in a sample of 100 voters. The set of values that a random variable y may assume and the probability, $p(y)$, associated with each value of y define a _____ _____. Before we can use a random variable to make inferences about a population, we must study some basic characteristics of probability distributions.

probability distribution

5.2 Classification of Random Variables (5.2)

1. Random variables are divided into two classes according to the values the random variable can assume. If a random variable y can take on only a finite or a countable infinity of distinct values, it is classified as a _____ random variable. If a random variable y can take on all of the values associated with the points on a line interval, then y is called a _____ random variable.

discrete

continuous

2. It is necessary to make the above distinction between the discrete and continuous cases because the probability distributions require different mathematical treatment. In fact, calculus is a prerequisite to any complete discussion of continuous random variables. Arithmetic and elementary algebra are all we need to develop discrete probability distributions.

3. The probabilities associated with each value of a _____ random variable can be assigned so that the probabilities sum to _____ (give number). This (is, is not) possible with continuous random variables.

discrete
1
is
continuous

4. The following would be examples of _____ random variables:
   a. The time required to complete a clerical operation.
   b. The height of a tree on a tree farm.
   c. The amount of ore produced by a given mining operation.

continuous

5. The following would be examples of _____ random variables:
   a. The number of voters favoring a political candidate in a given precinct.
   b. The number of defective bulbs in a package of 20 bulbs.
   c. The number of errors in an income tax return.
   Notice that discrete random variables are basically counts and the phrase *the number of* can be used to identify a discrete random variable.

discrete

6. Classify the following random variables as discrete or continuous:
   a. The number of consumers who correctly identify a brand from an advertising jingle. _____
   b. The number of building permits issued in a community during a given month. _____

discrete

discrete

c. The number of productive oil wells in Southern California. _____   discrete
d. The juice content of six Valencia oranges. _____   continuous
e. Time to failure for an electronic system. _____   continuous
f. The amount of radiation given off by X-ray equipment. _____   continuous
g. The number of defects in one square yard of carpeting. _____   discrete

5.3 Probability Distributions for Discrete Random Variables (5.3)

1. In simplest mathematical terms, the probability distribution for a discrete random variable y consists of the pairs $[y_i, p(y_i)]$ where y_i is one of the possible values of y and $p(y_i)$ is its corresponding probability.
2. In practice, the probability for a discrete random variable can be represented by a _____ , a _____ , or a _____   formula; table; graph
that gives the probability associated with each value of the random variable.
3. Suppose an investor records whether the value per share of a stock rises R or drops D over a three-day period. If the stock is just as likely to rise as it is to drop, let us find the probability distribution for y, the number of days that the stock shows a rise. Let us list the sample points associated with this experiment as follows:

Simple event	Day 1	2	3
E_1	R	R	R
E_2	D	R	R
E_3	R	D	R
E_4	R	R	D
E_5	D	D	R
E_6	___	___	___
E_7	R	D	D
E_8	D	D	D

$D; R; D$

a. Since the stock is just as likely to rise as it is to drop for any given day, each of the 8 sample points is equally likely. Therefore we assign
$P(E_i) =$ _____ .   1/8
b. There are four possible values y can assume, namely $y =$ _____ ,   0
_____ , _____ , _____ . The value $y = 0$ will occur only   1; 2; 3
if the simple event _____ occurs, so that the probability that E_8
y equals zero is

$$p(0) = P(\underline{\qquad}) = \underline{\qquad}$$ E_8; 1/8

The value $y = 1$ will occur only if one of the simple events E_5, E_6 or
_____ occurs. Then, E_7

$E_7; 3/8$

$3/8; 1/8$

$$p(1) = P(E_5) + P(E_6) + P(\underline{\qquad}) = \underline{\qquad}$$

In like manner we find $p(2) =$ _____ and $p(3) =$ _____.

4. We can display the probability distribution for y in one of 3 ways:
   a. by listing opposite each value of y its probability $p(y)$ in a table,
   b. graphically as a probability histogram by plotting $p(y)$ against y,
   c. and by supplying a formula (function) together with the possible values of y.

For our problem the tabular presentation would be:

y	$p(y)$
0	_____
1	_____
2	_____
3	_____

1/8
3/8
3/8
1/8

while the probability histogram would be:

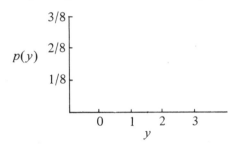

5. The formula for this probability distribution is

$$p(y) = \frac{3!}{y!\,(3-y)!}\,(\tfrac{1}{2})^3 \quad y = 0, 1, 2, 3$$

This formula will be explained in chapter 6.

6. A probability distribution for a discrete random variable must satisfy two requirements:
   a. For any possible value of y,

$$\underline{\qquad} \leqslant p(y) \leqslant \underline{\qquad}$$

$0; 1$

1

   b. $\qquad \sum_{y} p(y) =$ _____

Verify that the probability distribution we have just found satisfies these two requirements.

7. *Example:*

A product recognition experiment required a subject to classify a set of prints according to whether he did or did not recognize the product described in an advertising layout. Suppose that a subject can correctly identify each print with probability $p = .7$, that sequential classifications are independent events, and that he is presented with $n = 3$ prints to classify. We are interested in y, the number of correct classifications for the three prints.

Solution:

a. This experiment is analogous to tossing three unbalanced coins where correctly classifying a print corresponds to the observation of a head in the toss of a single coin. Each classification results in one of two outcomes, correct or incorrect. The total number of sample points in the sample space is _____ .

8

b. Let *IIC* represent the sample point for which the classification of the first and second prints is incorrect and the third is correct. Complete the listing of all sample points in the sample space.

Sample Points		Sample Points	
E_1	*III*	E_5	*CII*
E_2	*IIC*	E_6	*CCI*
E_3	*ICI*	E_7	_____
E_4	*ICC*	E_8	*CCC*

CIC

c. The sample point E_2 is an *intersection* of three independent events. That is,

$$E_2 = IIC$$

Applying the multiplicative law of probability,

$$P(E_2) = P(IIC) = P(I)P(I)P(C) = (.3)(.3)(.7)$$

$$= .063$$

Similarly, $P(E_1) =$ _____ $; P(E_3) =$ _____ . Calculate the probabilities for all sample points in the sample space.

.027; .063

$P(E_1) =$ _____	$P(E_5) =$ _____	.027; .063
$P(E_2) = .063$	$P(E_6) =$ _____	.147
$P(E_3) =$ _____	$P(E_7) =$ _____	.063; .147
$P(E_4) =$ _____	$P(E_8) =$ _____	.147; .343

d. The random variable y, the number of correct classifications for the set of three prints, takes the value $y = 1$ for sample point E_2. Similarly, we would assign the value $y =$ _____ to E_1. Assign a value of y to each sample point in the sample space.

0

Sample Points	Value of y
_____	0
E_2, E_3, E_5	1
	2
_____	3

E_1

E_4, E_6, E_7
E_8

e. The numerical event $y = 0$ contains only the sample point E_1. Summing the probabilities of the sample points in the event $y = 0$, we have

.027

$P[y = 0] = P(E_1) = $ _____ . Similarly, the numerical event $y = 1$ contains three sample points. Summing the probabilities of these sample points, we have $P[y = 1] = p(1) = $ _____ .

.189

f. The probability distribution, $p(y)$, presented in tabular form is

y	p(y)
0	.027
1	_____
2	_____
3	_____

.189
.441
.343

Calculate the probabilities $p(2)$ and $p(3)$ and complete the table.

g. Present $p(y)$ graphically in the form of a probability histogram.

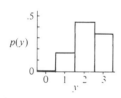

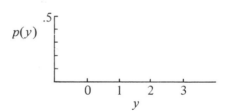

Self-Correcting Exercises 5A

1. An electronic system involves four components. If each component has a reliability of .99 and the components act independently, find the probability distribution for y, the number of components that have failed. Note that reliability is measured as the probability that an item will not fail.
   a. What is the reliability for the total system?
   b. What would the reliability of the system be if the requirement for successful operation was that at least three components in the system had not failed?

2. Five equally qualified applicants for a managerial position were ranked in order of preference by a personnel manager. If two of the applicants hold master's degrees in business administration, find the probability distribution for y, the number of applicants holding a master's in business administration ranked as the first or second applicant.

3. A car rental agency has three Fords and two Chevrolets left in its car pool.

If two cars are needed and the keys are randomly selected from the key-board, find the probability distribution for y, the number of Fords in the selection.

5.4 Continuous Random Variables and Their Probability Distributions (5.4)

1. A _____ random variable can assume a(n) (<u>countable</u>, un-countable) infinity of values corresponding to points on a line interval. Since the mathematical treatment of continuous random variables requires the use of calculus, we will do no mathematics here, but merely state some basic concepts.

   continuous; uncountable

2. The probability distribution for a continuous random variable can be thought of as the limiting relative frequency histogram for a very (small, <u>large</u>) set of measurements using the (<u>smallest</u>, largest) possible interval width. In such a case, the outline of the histogram would appear as a smooth curve.

   large; smallest

3. Let us illustrate what happens if we begin with a histogram and allow the interval width to get smaller and smaller while the number of measurements gets larger and larger.

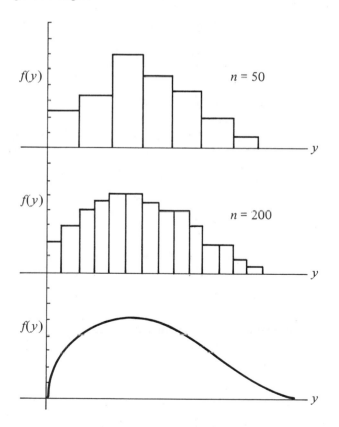

1

horizontal
probability

function
$f(y)$

probability density
model
histogram
area
probability

probability

4. The area under the smooth curve is adjusted to equal _____. The values that the random variable y may assume are shown graphically by the (horizontal, vertical) axis. The height of the curve above the horizontal axis represents the _____ of the values of y which lie below the curve.

5. The curve may be represented by a mathematical formula or _____ and be symbolized by _____.

6. The formula $f(y)$ is called the probability distribution function or the _____ _____ function for the random variable y.

7. The density function $f(y)$ provides a mathematical _____ for the actual population relative frequency _____.

8. The _____ under the curve $f(y)$ lying above a given interval on the horizontal axis equals the _____ that y will fall in that interval. Thus, the area under the curve between two points, say a and b, represents the _____ that the random variable y will fall into the interval from a to b.

9. When choosing a model to describe the population of measurements of interest, we must choose $f(y)$ appropriate to our data. Any inferences which we may make will only be as valid as the model we are using. It is therefore very important to know as much as possible about the phenomenon under study that will give rise to the measurements that we record.

approximate

experimentation

10. These mathematical models can only _____ reality. The goodness of these models and their associated approximations must be verified through _____.

5.5 Mathematical Expectation (5.5)

1. When we develop a probability distribution for a random variable, we are actually proposing a model that will describe the behavior of the random variable in repeated trials of an experiment. For example, when we propose the model for describing the distribution of y, the number of heads in the toss of 2 fair coins, given by

y	p(y)
0	¼
1	½
2	¼

we mean that if the two coins were tossed a large number of times, about one-fourth of the outcomes would result in the outcome "_____ heads," one-half would result in the outcome "_____ head" and the remaining fourth would result in "two heads."

zero

one

2. A probability distribution is not only a measure of belief that a specific outcome will occur on a single trial, but more important, it actually describes a population of observations on the random variable y. Consequently, the random variable must possess a _____, _____, standard deviation, and other measures that describe the probability distribution of the population.

mean

variance

3. The average value of a random variable defined over a theoretical population is called the _____ _____ of the random variable.

expected value

4. If y is a discrete random variable with probability distribution $p(y)$, then the expected value of y is given by the formula

$$\sum_{y} \underline{}$$

$yp(y)$

and is denoted by the symbol _____.

$E(y)$

5. If the probability distribution $p(y)$ accurately describes the relative frequencies of a real population, then the expected value of y equals the _____ of the population. That is, $E(y) =$ _____ and we can use the two symbols interchangeably.

mean; μ

6. *Example:*
The manager of an automobile parts supply store has recorded the daily demand for a certain part over a long period of time. From his records, he has developed the following probability distribution for y, the daily demand for the part.

y	p(y)
0	.30
1	.25
2	.20
3	.15
4	.08
5	.02

Find the expected daily demand.
Solution:
Before calculating the mean of y, we see that this (is, is not) a valid probability distribution since

is

1; 0; 1

$$\sum_y p(y) = \underline{\hspace{2cm}} \text{ and } \underline{\hspace{2cm}} \leqslant p(y) \leqslant \underline{\hspace{2cm}}$$

The expected daily demand, $E(y)$, is calculated as

$$\mu = E(y) = \sum_y y\, p(y)$$

.25; .20; .15
.08; .02

$$= 0(.30) + 1(\underline{\hspace{1.5cm}}) + 2(\underline{\hspace{1.5cm}}) + 3(\underline{\hspace{1.5cm}})$$
$$+ 4(\underline{\hspace{1.5cm}}) + 5(\underline{\hspace{1.5cm}})$$

1.52

$$= \underline{\hspace{1.5cm}}$$

7. Construct the probability histogram for the distribution of daily demand given in Example 6. Visually locate the mean and compare it with the computed value, $\mu = 1.52$.

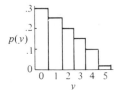

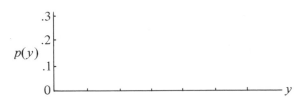

8. *Example:*
A corporation has four investment possibilities A, B and C with respective gains of 10, 20 and 50 million dollars and investment possibility D with a loss of 30 million dollars. If one investment will be made and the probabilities of choosing A, B, C or D are .1, .4, .2 and .3, respectively, find the expected gain for the corporation.
Solution:
The random variable is y, the corporation's gain, with possible values 10, 20, 50 and –30 million dollars. The probability distribution for y is given as

y (in millions)	p(y)
10	.1
20	.4
50	.2
-30	.3

10

The expected gain, $E(y) = \underline{\hspace{2cm}}$ million dollars.

9. *Example:*
A parcel post service which insures packages against loss up to $200 wishes to re-evaluate their insurance rates. If one in a thousand packages had been reported lost during the last several years, what rate should be charged on a package insured for $200 if the postal service's expected

gain is zero? Administrative costs will be added to this rate.

Solution:

Let y be the gain to the parcel post service and let r be the charge for insuring a package for $200.

a. In this example, the "experiment" has two possible outcomes:

   i. The parcel post service receives r dollars in insurance charges and pays out nothing in insurance claims. In this case, the value of y (the parcel post service's gain) is _____ .

                      r

   ii. It receives r dollars in insurance charges but must pay a $200 claim because a package has been reported lost. In this case the value of y is _____ .

                      $r - 200$

b. Complete the probability distribution for y.

y	$p(y)$
r	_____
$r - 200$	_____

                      .999

                      .001

c. If $E(y)$ is to be zero, we need to solve the equation

$$\sum_{y} y\, p(y) = 0$$

Hence, for our problem

$$r(.999) + (r - 200)(.001) = 0$$

$$r =$$

                      $ .20

5.6 The Variance of a Random Variable (5.6)

1. The expected value of a random variable gives no information on how the random variable is distributed about its expected value. In many situations, such as in using Tchebysheff's Theorem or the _____ _____ , for example, we also need a measure of the spread of the probability distribution $p(y)$ of the random variable y.

                      Empirical
                      Rule

2. It is natural to use the _____ and _____ _____ of y to measure the variability of $p(y)$.

                      variance; standard
                      deviation

3. We have seen in the previous section how the mean of a random variable can be thought of as an "expected value." The same is true for the variance of a random variable.

4. If y is a discrete random variable with probability distribution $p(y)$ and expected value $E(y) = \mu$, then the variance of the probability distribution $p(y)$ is $E($_____$)^2 = \sum_{y}$ _____ and is symbolized by _____ .

                      $y - \mu; (y - \mu)^2 p(y)$
                      σ^2

5. The standard deviation of a random variable y is equal to the _____

                      square

root; variance; σ

_____ of its _____, and is symbolized by _____.

6. Let us calculate the variance and standard deviation of the daily demand in the auto parts store example from Section 5.5. Recall that $\mu = 1.52$.

2 – 1.52
.20; 3 – 1.52; .15; 4 – 1.52
.08; 5 – 1.52; .02

$$\sigma^2 = (0 - 1.52)^2\,(.30) + (1 - 1.52)^2\,(.25) + (\underline{\hspace{1.5cm}})^2$$
$$(\underline{\hspace{1.5cm}}) + (\underline{\hspace{1.5cm}})^2\,(\underline{\hspace{1.5cm}}) + (\underline{\hspace{1.5cm}})^2$$
$$(\underline{\hspace{1.5cm}}) + (\underline{\hspace{1.5cm}})^2\,(\underline{\hspace{1.5cm}})$$

That is,

1.8696

$$\sigma^2 = \underline{\hspace{2cm}}$$

7. If y is a discrete random variable, it can be shown using summation theorems that in calculating the variance, r^2,

$$E(y - \mu)^2 = E(y^2) - \mu^2$$

This result is true in general, and

$$\sigma^2 = E(y^2) - \mu^2$$

is known as the shortcut formula for calculating the variance of the random variable y.

8. Use the shortcut formula $E(y - \mu^2) = E(y^2) - \mu^2$ to find the variance in the problem above. Since $E(y^2) = \sum\limits_y y^2\,p(y)$,

3
.15; 4; .08; 5
.02

$$\sigma^2 = [(0)^2\,(.30) + (1)^2\,(.25) + (2)^2\,(.20) + (\underline{\hspace{1.5cm}})^2$$
$$(\underline{\hspace{1.5cm}}) + (\underline{\hspace{1.5cm}})^2\,(\underline{\hspace{1.5cm}}) + (\underline{\hspace{1.5cm}})^2$$
$$(\underline{\hspace{1.5cm}})] - (1.52)^2$$

$$= 4.18 - 2.3104$$

1.8696

$$= \underline{\hspace{2cm}}$$

9. Therefore, the standard deviation of the daily demand for that particular auto part is _____.

1.37

10. Find the variance and standard deviation of y in Example 9 in the previous section when $r = \$\,.20$.

.001

$$\sigma^2 = (.20 - .20)^2\,(.999) + (.20 - 200 - .20)^2\,(\underline{\hspace{1.5cm}})$$

$$= 0 + (-200)^2\,(.001)$$

$40

$$= \underline{\hspace{2cm}}$$

The standard deviation is _____. $6.32

Self-Correcting Exercises 5B

1. A publishing company is considering the introduction of a monthly gardening magazine. Advance surveys show the initial market for the magazine will be approximated by the following distribution for y, the number of subscribers.

y	$p(y)$
5,000	.30
10,000	.35
15,000	.20
20,000	.10
25,000	.05

Find the expected number of subscribers and the standard deviation of the number of subscribers.
2. Refer to Exercise 1. Suppose the company expects to charge $10 for an annual subscription. Find the mean and standard deviation of the revenue the company can expect from the annual subscriptions of the initial subscribers.
3. Refer to Exercise 2. Production and distribution costs for the gardening magazine are expected to amount to slightly over $100,000. What is the probability that revenue from initial subscriptions will fail to cover these costs?
4. You are given the following information. An insurance company wants to insure a $30,000 home against fire. One in every hundred of such homes is likely to have a fire; 75% of the homes having fires suffered damages amounting to $15,000, while the remaining 25% suffered total loss. Ignoring all other partial losses, what premium should the company charge in order to break even?

5.7 Summary (5.7)

1. Random variables represent _____ events defined over a sample space.   numerical
2. Random variables may be classified as _____ or _____,   discrete; continuous
depending on whether the number of points in the sample space is or is not _____.   countable
3. The theoretical population frequency distribution for a discrete random variable is called a _____ _____.   probability distribution
4. The frequency distribution for a continuous random variable is a mathematical function called the probability _____ function.   density
5. The probability density function of a continuous random variable is chosen so that the total area under its curve is equal to _____. The   1

areas

expected value

probabilities associated with a continuous random variable are given as _____ under the curve $f(y)$.

6. The _____ _____ of a random variable is its average in the theoretical population as defined by its probability distribution.

Exercises

1. Suppose it is known that two out of four given stocks will show a rapid and profitable rise in price during the coming year. If a person holding shares of these four stocks randomly decides to sell two of the stocks, what is the probability distribution for y, the number of "profitable" stocks he still owns?

2. Graph $p(y)$ for Exercise 1.

3. Let two pennies and two nickels represent the two poor and two good stocks, respectively, for Exercise 1. Randomly draw two of the coins and record y, the number of good stocks in the selection. Repeat this experiment 50 times and construct a relative frequency histogram. Compare with $p(y)$ in Exercise 2. What would happen to the histogram if the number of repetitions of the experiment were allowed to become infinitely large?

4. Show that $p(y)$, Exercise 1, satisfies the two requirements for a probability distribution.

5. A manufacturing organization believes that the chances are 2/3 they will win each of three contracts on which they have submitted bids. Let y be the number (out of three) of contracts which they win. Find the probability distribution for y. Construct a probability histogram for $p(y)$.

6. Show that $p(y)$, Exercise 5, satisfies the two requirements for a probability distribution.

7. Suppose that a radio contains six transistors, two of which are defective. Three transistors are selected at random, removed from the radio, and inspected. Let y be the number of defective transistors observed. Find the probability distribution for y in tabular form with all calculations performed. That is, express each of the probabilities in decimal form correct to the nearest hundredth.

8. The probability of hitting oil in a single drilling operation is 1/4. If drillings represent independent events, find the probability distribution for y, the number of drillings until the first success ($y = 1, 2, 3, \ldots$). Proceed as follows:

   a. Find $p(1)$.

   b. Find $p(2)$.

   c. Find $p(3)$.

   d. Give a formula for $p(y)$.

   Note that y can become infinitely large.

e. Will $\sum\limits_{y=1}^{\infty} p(y) = 1$?

9. Given a random variable y with the probability distribution

y	$p(y)$
1	1/8
2	5/8
3	1/4

graph $p(y)$ and make a visual approximation to the mean and standard deviation. (Use your knowledge of Tchebysheff's Theorem to assist in approximating σ.)

10. Refer to Exercise 9 and find the expected value and standard deviation of y. Compare with the answers to Exercise 9.

11. Given the following probability distribution, find the expected value and variance of y.

y	$p(y)$
0	1/2
3	1/3
6	1/6

12. The following is the probability function for a discrete random variable, y.

$$p(y) = (.1)(y + 1) \qquad y = 0, 1, 2, 3$$

Find $E(y)$, the expected value of y.

13. In a marketing experiment, a subject can make one of three decisions with equal probability, 1/3. If three subjects perform the experiment, let y be the number that select decision number one. Find $p(y)$.

14. Refer to Exercise 13 and find the expected value and variance of y.

15. An investment can result in one of the three outcomes: a $10,000 gain, a $6,000 gain, or a $5,000 loss, with probabilities .3, .3, and .4, respectively. Find the expected gain for the investor.

16. History has shown that buildings of a certain type of construction suffer fire damage during a given year with probability .01. If a building suffers fire damage, it will result in either a 50% or a 100% loss with probabilities of .7 and .3, respectively. Find the premium required per $1,000 coverage in order that the expected gain for the insurance company will equal zero (break-even point).

17. Let y be a discrete random variable with probability distribution given by

y	$p(y)$
0	1/6
1	4/6
2	1/6

a. Construct a probability histogram for $p(y)$.

b. Use the histogram to obtain a visual approximation to the expected value and standard deviation of y.

18. Refer to Exercise 17. Find the expected value and standard deviation of y. Compare with the visual approximations obtained in Exercise 17.

19. A police car visits a given neighborhood a random number of times, y, per evening. If $p(y)$ is given by

y	$p(y)$
0	.1
1	.6
2	.2
3	.1

a. Find $E(y)$.

b. Find σ^2.

20. Refer to Exercise 19. What is the probability that the patrol will visit the neighborhood at least twice in a given evening?

21. Experience has shown that a rare disease will cause partial disability with probability .6, complete disability with probability .3 and no disability with probability .1. Only one in ten thousand will become afflicted with the disease in a given year. If an insurance policy pays $20,000 for partial disability and $50,000 for complete disability, what premium should be charged in order that the insurance company break even (i.e., in order that the expected loss to the insurance company will be zero)?

Chapter 6

THREE USEFUL DISCRETE PROBABILITY DISTRIBUTIONS

6.1 Introduction (6.1)

1. Random variables which are defined over a finite or countably infinite number of points are called _____ random variables.

   discrete

2. Three discrete probability distributions are good approximate descriptions, or _____, for a wide variety of business and economic phenomena. They are the _____, the _____, and the _____ probability distributions.

   models

   binomial; Poisson
   hypergeometric
   probability distribution

3. A _____ _____ is a formula or model that assigns a probability to each possible numerical outcome of an experiment.

4. Before choosing a particular probability distribution as the appropriate model for an economic or business process, one must consider the nature of the _____ and the numerical _____ of the experiment.

   experiment; outcomes

5. *Review: The Binomial Theorem*

   a. The following identity is proved in most high school algebra books.

   $$(a + b)^n = \sum_{y=0}^{n} \frac{n!}{y! \, (n - y)!} \, a^y \, b^{n-y}$$

   where a and b are any real numbers and n is a positive integer. This identity is known as the binomial theorem. The coefficients in the sum are known as binomial coefficients and we can write

   $$\frac{n!}{y! \, (n - y)!} = C_y^n$$

   to represent the coefficient of $a^y b^{n-y}$ in the expansion of $(a + b)^n$. Recall from Chapter 2 that $n! = n(n - 1)(n - 2) \ldots (3)(2)(1)$ and $0! = 1$.

b. For the special case when $n = 2$ we find

$$(a + b)^2 = \sum_{y=0}^{2} C_y^2 \, a^y b^{2-y}$$

$a^2 + 2ab + b^2$

$$= \underline{\hspace{3cm}}$$

When $n = 3$, we have

$$(a + b)^3 = \sum_{y=0}^{3} C_y^3 \, a^y b^{3-y}$$

$3ab^2 + b^3$

$$= a^3 + 3a^2 b + \underline{\hspace{3cm}}$$

c. If a is replaced by a probability, p, and b is replaced by the probability, $q = 1 - p$, then the binomial theorem implies that

$$\sum_{y=0}^{n} C_y^n \, p^y q^{n-y} = (p + q)^n$$

Note the following points about this binomial identity involving p and q when $0 < p < 1$.
  i. The terms $C_y^n p^y q^{n-y}$ are each positive.

1

  ii. The sum of the terms is $(p + q)^n = \underline{\hspace{2cm}}$.
  iii. Since the total can be no greater than any of its parts

0; 1

$$\underline{\hspace{2cm}} \leqslant C_y^n p^y q^{n-y} \leqslant \underline{\hspace{2cm}}$$

Thus the function

$$p(y) = C_y^n p^y q^{n-y}, \qquad y = 0, 1, 2, \ldots, n$$

satisfies the two requirements of a probability function for a discrete random variable, namely

0; 1

$$\underline{\hspace{2cm}} \leqslant p(y) \leqslant \underline{\hspace{2cm}}$$

and

1

$$\sum_y p(y) = \underline{\hspace{2cm}}.$$

6.2 The Binomial Experiment (6.2)

1. Many experiments in business and economics are analogous to a series of
   _____ _____ in which the outcome on each trial is
   either a head or a tail. Consider the following situations:

   a. The closing price of a stock will either rise (head) or not rise (tail) above
      the previous day's price.

   b. A consumer identifies either correctly (head) or incorrectly (tail) a given
      product by its advertising slogan.

   c. A voter cases his ballot either for candidate A (head) or against him
      (tail).

   d. An executive makes either a correct decision (head) or an incorrect one
      (tail).

   e. A house insured against fire either has a fire (head) or does not have a
      fire (tail) during the term of the policy.

   f. A licensed driver either has an accident (head) or does not have an acci-
      dent (tail) during the period his license is valid.

   g. An item from a production line is inspected and classified as either
      defective (head) or not defective (tail).

   Notice, however, that the analogy to a coin toss is not perfect, in that we
   tend to regard a head or a tail on a real coin as equiprobable. Such is not
   generally the case with the examples above.

2. If any of the above situations were repeated n times and we counted the
   number of *heads* that occurred in the n trials, the resulting random variable
   would behave approximately as a _____ random variable. Let
   us examine the characteristics that these experiments have in common. We
   shall call a head a success (S) and a tail a failure (F). Note well that the
   designation *success* does not necessarily denote a desirable outcome, but
   rather identifies the event of interest.

3. The five defining characteristics of a binomial experiment are:

   a. The experiment consists of _____ identical trials.

   b. Each trial results in one of _____ outcomes, success (S) or
      failure (F).

   c. The probability of success on a single trial is equal to _____ and
      remains constant from trial to trial. The probability of failure is equal
      to $q =$ _____ . Note that, in general, q is (equal, not equal) to p.

   d. The n trials are _____ .

   e. Attention is directed to the random variable y, the total number of
      _____ observed in n trials.

   Although very few real-life situations perfectly satisfy all five characteristics, this model can be used with fairly good results provided the viola-
   tions are moderate. The next several examples will illustrate binomial
   experiments.

4. *Example:*

   The "triangle test," a procedure often used to control the quality of
   name-brand food products, utilizes a panel of n "tasters." Each member of

---

coin tosses

binomial

n

two

p

$1 - p$; not equal
independent

successes

1/3

trials
1/3

binomial; n

.01

100; .70

binomial
10
p

the panel is presented three specimens, two of which are from batches of product known to possess the desired taste while the other is a specimen from the latest batch. Each panelist is asked to select the specimen which is different from the other two. If the latest batch does possess the desired taste, then the probability that a given taster will be "successful" in selecting the specimen from the latest batch is _____ . If there is no communication among the panelists their responses will comprise n independent _____ with probability of success on a given trial equal to _____ .

5. *Example:*

Almost all auditing of accounts is done on a sampling basis. Thus, an auditor might check a random sample of n items from a ledger or inventory list comprising a large number of items. If 1% of the items in the ledger are erroneous, then the number of erroneous items in the sample is essentially a _____ random variable with _____ (give number) trials and probability of "success" (finding an erroneous item) on a given trial equal to _____ .

6. *Example:*

No treatment has been known for a certain serious disease for which the mortality rate in the United States is 70%. If a random selection is made of 100 past victims of this disease in the United States, the number, y_1, of those in the sample who died of the disease is essentially a binomial random variable with $n =$ _____ and $p =$ _____ . More importantly, if observation is made of the next 100 persons in the United States who will in the future become victims of this disease, the number, y_2, of these who will die from the disease has a distribution approximately the same as that of y_1 if conditions affecting this disease remain essentially constant for the time period considered.

7. The continued operation (reliability) of a complex assembly often depends on the joint survival of all or nearly all of a number of similar components. Thus, a radio may give at least 100 hours of continuous service if no more than two of its ten transistors fail during the first 100 hours of operation. If the ten transistors in a given radio were selected at random from a large lot of transistors, then each of these (ten) transistors would have the same probability, p, of failing within 100 hours. The number of transistors in the radio which will fail within 100 hours is a _____ random variable for _____ trials with probability of "success" on each trial equal to _____ . ("Success" is a word that denotes one of the two outcomes of a single trial and does not necessarily represent a desired outcome.)

8. Three experiments are described below. In each case state whether or not the experiment is a binomial experiment. If the experiment is binomial, specify the number, n, of trials and the probability, p, of success on a given trial. If the experiment is not binomial, state which characteristics of a binomial experiment are not met.

a. A fair coin is tossed until a head appears. The number of tosses, y, is

observed. If binomial, $n =$ _____ and $p =$ _____.
If not binomial, list characteristic(s) (a, b, c, d, and e) violated.

_____

b. The probability that an applicant scores above the 90th percentile on a qualifying examination is .10. The examiner is interested in y, the number of applicants out of 25 taking the examination that score above the 90th percentile. If binomial, $n =$ _____ and $p =$ _____.
If not binomial, list characteristic(s) (a, b, c, d, and e) violated.

_____

c. A sample of five transistors will be selected at random from a box of twenty transistors of which ten are defective. The experimenter will observe the number, y, of defective transistors appearing in the sample.
If binomial, $n =$ _____ and $p =$ _____. If not binomial, list characteristic(s) (a, b, c, d, and e) violated. _____

	not binomial
	a, e
	25; .10
	none
	not binomial
	c, d

6.3 The Binomial Probability Distribution (6.3)

1. a. The binomial probability distribution gives the distribution of y, the number of _____ in _____ (give number) trials where _____ is the probability of a success on a given trial. As shown in the text and in Section 6.1 of this study guide, the probabilities $p(y)$ are terms of the expansion of (_____)^n, where $q =$ _____.
   b. The probability distribution for y is given by the formula

   $$p(y) = C_y^n \, p^y q^{n-y}$$

   where $C_y^n =$ _____ and $y = 0, 1, 2, \ldots, n$
   c. In the preceding notation, the symbol p is used in two different ways. It is important not to confuse them. By itself, p stands for the probability of a success in a single trial of a binomial experiment, such that $0 \leqslant p \leqslant 1$ and $p + q = 1$. But p is also used in the notation $p(y)$, where it stands for the probability of a particular value of the random variable y. The two uses of p must be kept separate and distinct. In the first case above, p is a (number, function), while in the second case, it is a _____.

	successes; n
	p
	$p + q$; $1 - p$
	$\dfrac{n!}{y!(n-y)!}$
	number
	function

2. *Example:*
   To help us in using the formula for the binomial distribution, consider the following example.
   Suppose that the probability that an electronic component fails before 1000 hours of use is .7. Four such components are put on test. Let y be the number of components out of the four on test that fail before 1000 hours of use. Then y is a binomial random variable with $p =$ _____ and $n =$ _____. There are 5 possible values for y, namely _____, _____, _____, _____ and _____.
   a. The probability that no component fails before 1000 hours is

	.7
	4; 0
	1; 2; 3; 4

$$p(0) = \frac{4!}{0! \, 4!} (.7)^0 (.3)^4$$

.0081

$$= (.3)^4 = \underline{\hspace{2cm}}$$

b. The probability that exactly three components fail before 1000 hours is

$$p(3) = \frac{4!}{3! \, 1!} (.7)^3 (.3)^1$$

.343

$$= 4 \, (\underline{\hspace{2cm}}) \, (.3)$$

.4116

$$= \underline{\hspace{2cm}}$$

c. The probability that at least three components fail before 1000 hours is

$$P[y \geqslant 3] = p(3) + p(4)$$

$$= p(3) + \frac{4!}{4! \, 0!} (.7)^4 (.3)^0$$

.2401

$$= .4116 + \underline{\hspace{2cm}}$$

.6517

$$= \underline{\hspace{2cm}}$$

d. To check that $p(y)$ is a properly defined probability distribution, complete the following table and find $\sum_{y} p(y)$.

y	$p(y)$
0	____
1	____
2	____
3	____
4	____

.0081
.0756
.2646
.4116
.2401

$$\sum_{y=0}^{4} p(y) = \underline{\hspace{2cm}}$$

1.0000

3. *Example:*
A marketing research survey shows that approximately 80% of the car owners surveyed indicated that their next car purchase would be either a compact or an economy car. If the 80% figure is taken to be correct, and five prospective buyers are interviewed,

a. find the probability that all five indicate that their next car purchase would be either a compact or an economy car.
b. find the probability that at most one indicates that his next purchase will be either a compact or an economy car.

Solution:

Let y be the number of car owners who indicate that their next purchase will be a compact or an economy car. Then $n =$ _____ and

$p =$ _____ and the distribution for y is given by

5

.8

$$p(y) = \frac{5!}{y!\,(5-y)!}\,(.8)^y\,(.2)^{5-y} \qquad y = 0, 1, 2, \ldots, 5 \quad .$$

a. The required probability is $p(5)$ which is given by

$$p(5) = \frac{5!}{5!\,0!}\,(.8)^5(.2)^0$$

$$= (.8)^5$$

$$= \underline{\hspace{2cm}}$$

.32768

b. The probability that at most one car owner indicates that his next purchase will be either a compact or an economy car will be

$$P[y \leqslant 1] = p(0) + p(1)$$

For $y = 0$,

$$p(0) = \frac{5!}{0!\,5!}\,(.8)^0(.2)^5$$

$$= (.2)^5$$

$$= \underline{\hspace{2cm}}$$

.00032

For $y = 1$,

$$p(1) = \frac{5!}{1!\,4!}\,(.8)^1(.2)^4$$

$$= 5(.8)(.0016)$$

$$= \underline{\hspace{2cm}}$$

.0064

Hence $P[y \leqslant 1] = .0064 + .00032$

.00672

$= \underline{\hspace{2cm}}$

4. As you might expect, the calculation of the binomial probabilities becomes quite tiresome as n, the number of trials, increases. Table 1 of binomial probabilities in the Appendix of your text, can be used to find binomial probabilities for values of $p = .01, .05, .10, .20, \ldots, .90, .95, .99$ when $n = 5, 10, 15, 20, 25$.

a. The tabled entries are not the individual terms for binomial probabilities, but rather cumulative sums of probabilities, beginning with $y = 0$ up to and including the value $y = a$. By formula, the entries for n, p, and a are

$$\sum_{y=0}^{y=a} p(y) = p(0) + p(1) + \ldots + p(a)$$

b. By using a tabled entry, which is $\sum_{y=0}^{a} p(y)$, these tables allow the user to find

i. left-tailed cumulative sums (so-called because they are sums of probabilities beginning with the left end or tail of the probability distribution),

$$P[y \leqslant a] = \sum_{y=0}^{a} p(y)$$

ii. right-tail cumulative sums,

$$P[y \geqslant a] = 1 - \sum_{y=0}^{a-1} p(y)$$

iii. or individual terms such as

$$P[y = a] = \sum_{y=0}^{a} p(y) - \sum_{y=0}^{a-1} p(y)$$

5. *Example:*
Refer to Example 3 in this section. Let us find the probabilities asked for by using Table 1.
Solution:
For this problem, we shall use the table $n = 5$ and $p = .8$.

a. To find the probability that $y = 5$ we proceed as follows.

$$p(5) = [p(0) + p(1) + p(2) + p(3) + p(4) + p(5)]$$

$$- [p(0) + p(1) + p(2) + p(3) + p(4)]$$

$$= \sum_{y=0}^{5} p(y) - \sum_{y=0}^{4} p(y)$$

$$= 1 - \underline{\hspace{3cm}}$$ .672

$$= \underline{\hspace{3cm}}$$ .328

b. To find the probability that $y \leqslant 1$, we need

$$P[y \leqslant 1] = p(0) + p(1)$$

$$= \sum_{y=0}^{1} p(y)$$

$$= \underline{\hspace{3cm}}$$ .007

c. Let us extend the problem and find the probabilities associated with the terms, $y = 2$ and $y = 3$.
For $y = 2$,

$$p(2) = \sum_{y=0}^{2} p(y) - \sum_{y=0}^{1} p(y)$$

$$= \underline{\hspace{3cm}} - .007$$ .058

$$= \underline{\hspace{3cm}}$$ .051

For $y = 3$,

$$p(3) - \sum_{y=0}^{3} p(y) \quad \sum_{y=0}^{2} p(y)$$

$$= \underline{\hspace{3cm}} - .058$$ .263

$$= \underline{\hspace{3cm}}$$ .205

d. Complete the following table.

y	$p(y)$
0	
1	_____
2	_____
3	_____
4	_____
5	_____

.000
.007
.051
.205
.409
.328

1

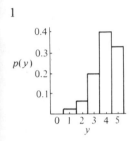

with $\displaystyle\sum_{y=0}^{5} p(y) =$ _____

e. Graph this distribution as a probability histogram.

6. *Example:*
Using Table 1, find the probability distribution for y if $n = 5$ and $p = \frac{1}{2}$, and graph the resulting probability histogram.
Solution:
a. To find the individual probabilities for $y = 0, 1, 2, \ldots, 5$, we need but subtract successive entries in the table for $n = 5, p = .5$.

.031

$$p(0) = \sum_{y=0}^{0} p(y) = \underline{\qquad}$$

.157

$$p(1) = \sum_{y=0}^{1} p(y) - \sum_{y=0}^{0} p(y) = .188 - .031 = \underline{\qquad}$$

.312

$$p(2) = \sum_{y=0}^{2} p(y) - \sum_{y=0}^{1} p(y) = .500 - .188 = \underline{\qquad}$$

.812; .312

$$p(3) = \underline{\qquad} - .500 = \underline{\qquad}$$

.969; .157

$$p(4) = \underline{\qquad} - .812 = \underline{\qquad}$$

.969; .031

$$p(5) = 1.000 - \underline{\qquad} = \underline{\qquad}$$

b. Using the results of part a we find the probability histogram to be symmetric about the value $y =$ _____.

2.5

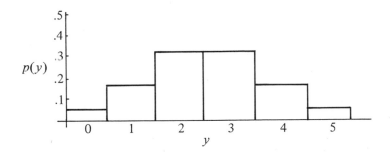

7. *Example:*

Find the probability distribution for y if $n = 5$ and $p = .3$, and graph the probability histogram in this case.

Solution:

a. Again, subtracting successive entries for $n = 5, p = .3$, we have

$p(0) =$ _____ .168

$p(1) = .528 - .168 =$ _____ .360

$p(2) = .837 - .528 =$ _____ .309

$p(3) = .969 - .837 =$ _____ .132

$p(4) = .998 - .969 =$ _____ .029

$p(5) = 1 - .998 =$ _____ .002

b. Graph the resulting histogram using these probabilities.

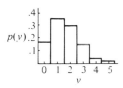

8. In comparing the histograms in Examples 5, 6, and 7, notice that when $p = \frac{1}{2}$, the histogram is _____. However, if $p = .8$, which is greater than $\frac{1}{2}$, the mass of the probability moves to the _____ with p; and for $p = .3$, which is less than $\frac{1}{2}$, the mass of the probability distribution moves to the _____ with p. Locating the center of the distribution by eye, we see that the mean of the binomial distribution varies directly as _____, the probability of success.

symmetric

right

left

p

Let us consider two more examples. You are now free either to calculate the probabilities by hand or to use the tables when appropriate.

9. *Example:*

To test two alloys for resistance to corrosion, 10 pairs each consisting of a strip of alloy 1 and a strip of alloy 2 were subjected to artificial weathering and wear. At the end of the test, each pair was examined and the member of each pair exhibiting the most corrosion was recorded. If the two alloys are actually equally resistant to corrosion, then the probability that alloy 1 exhibits more corrosion than alloy 2 can be taken to be $p = .5$. If the alloys are equally resistant,

a. what is the probability that alloy 1 exhibited more corrosion than alloy 2 in 8 or more of the ten pairs?
b. what is the probability that alloy 2 exhibited more corrosion than alloy 1 in 6 or more pairs?

Solution:

Let y be the number of times that alloy 1 exhibited more corrosion. If the alloys are equally resistant we can take $p = .5$. Then

$$p(y) = \frac{10!}{y! \, (10 - y)!} \, (.5)^y (.5)^{10-y}$$

for $y = 0, 1, 2, \ldots, 10$.

a. Using Table 1,

$$P[y \geqslant 8] = \sum_{y=8}^{10} p(y)$$

$$= 1 - \sum_{y=0}^{7} p(y)$$

.945

$$= 1 - \underline{\hspace{2cm}}$$

.055

$$= \underline{\hspace{2cm}}$$

b. If 6 or more pairs listed alloy 2 as more corroded, then 4 or less pairs listed alloy 1 as more corroded. Hence

.377

$$P[y \leqslant 4] = \sum_{y=0}^{4} p(y) = \underline{\hspace{2cm}}$$

10. *Example:*

Suppose that a trainee is taught to do a task in two different ways. Studies have shown that, when subjected to mental strain and asked to perform the task, the trainee most often reverts to the method first learned, regardless of whether it was more difficult or easier than the second. If the probability that a trainee returns to the first method learned is .8 and six trainees are tested, what is the probability that at least 5 of the trainees revert to their first learned method when asked to perform their task under mental strain?

Solution:

a. Letting y equal the number of trainees who revert to the first method, we have a binomial random variable with $n = 6$ and $p = .8$. There is no table of binomial probabilities for $n = 6$, so we must calculate $P[y \geqslant 5]$.

b. In this case

$$p(y) = \frac{6!}{y!(6-y)!}(.8)^y(.2)^{6-y} \qquad y = 0, 1, 2, \ldots, 6$$

Since

$$P[y \geqslant 5] = p(5) + p(6)$$

we need to calculate $p(5)$ and $p(6)$.

c. $\qquad p(5) = \dfrac{6!}{5!\,1!}(.8)^5(.2)^1$

$\qquad\qquad = (6)(.32768)(.2)$

$\qquad\qquad = \underline{\hspace{2cm}}$ .393216

d. $\qquad p(6) = \dfrac{6!}{6!\,0!}(.8)^6(.2)^0$

$\qquad\qquad = (.8)^6$

$\qquad\qquad = \underline{\hspace{2cm}}$ .262144

e. Collecting results we have

$$P[y \geqslant 5] = .393216 + .262144$$

$\qquad\qquad = \underline{\hspace{2cm}}$ .655360

Self-Correcting Exercises 6A

1. A city planner claims that 20% of all apartment dwellers move from their apartments within a year from the time they first moved in. In a particular

city, 7 apartment dwellers who had given notice of termination to their landlords are to be interviewed.
   a. If the city planner is correct, what is the probability that 2 of the 7 had lived in the apartment for less than one year?
   b. What is the probability that at least 6 had lived in their apartment for at least one year?
2. Suppose that 70% of the first class mail from New York to California is delivered within four days of being mailed. If twenty pieces of first class mail are mailed from New York to California,
   a. find the probability that at least 15 pieces of mail arrive within 4 days of the mailing date.
   b. find the probability that 10 or fewer pieces of mail arrive later than four days after the mailing date.
3. On the average, a contractor has been awarded three out of every five contracts for which he has submitted bids. If this contractor plans to submit five bids in the near future,
   a. what is the probability that he will be awarded all five contracts?
   b. what is the probability that he will be awarded at least three contracts?
4. A builder has found that 60% of the grade 2 lumber is satisfactory for a specific purpose. Ten pieces of grade 2 lumber are brought to a building site for use by a workman.
   a. What is the probability that at most three pieces will be satisfactory?
   b. What is the probability that at least eight pieces will be usable?
   c. If the workman needs seven usable pieces of lumber to complete the job, what is the probability that he gets the required number of satisfactory pieces of lumber?

6.4 The Mean and Variance for the Binomial Random Variable (6.4)

1. The calculation of $p(y)$ when y has a binomial distribution becomes very tedious for (small, large) values of n, the number of _____.

large; trials

2. Consequently, we use the fact that any probability distribution can be described by its _____ and _____ _____.

mean; standard deviation
center
dispersion

In particular, these two measures locate the _____ of the distribution and describe the _____ of the measurements about the mean.
3. The mean and variance (and hence the standard deviation) can be found using the expectation definitions of Chapter 5 together with

$$p(y) = \frac{n!}{y! \, (n-y)!} \, p^y \, q^{n-y} \qquad y = 0, 1, 2, \ldots, n$$

It can be shown by those willing to tackle the algebra (and can be *used* by those not so willing) that for a binomial experiment consisting of n trials with the probability of success equal to p,

a. $\mu = E(y) = $ _____ np

b. $\sigma^2 = E(y - \mu)^2 = $ _____ npq

c. $\sigma = $ _____ $\sqrt{npq}$

4. *Example:*

If studies have shown that about 10% of new small business enterprises close in less than six months, find the mean and standard deviation of the number of small business closures in a sample of 100 such enterprises.

Solution:

With $n = 100$ and $p = .1$,

a. $\mu = np = 100\,(.1) = $ _____   10

b. $\sigma^2 = npq = 100\,(.1)\,(.9) = $ _____ and   9

         $\sigma = \sqrt{npq} = \sqrt{\rule{2cm}{0pt}} = $ _____   9; 3

We would expect to see _____ closures with a standard deviation of   10

_____.   3

5. *Example:*

A random sample of sixty-four people were asked to state a preference for Brand A or Brand B. If there is no underlying preference for either brand, then the probability that an individual chooses Brand A will be $p = .5$. What is the expected number and standard deviation of preferences for Brand A?

Solution:

Let y be the number of people stating a preference for Brand A. If there really is no preference for either brand (i.e. the consumer considers them as being the same and picks one at random) then y has a binomial distribution with $n = $ _____ and $p = $ _____. Then   64; .5

a. $\mu = np = 64(.5) = $ _____   32

b. $\sigma^2 = npq = 64(.5)\,(.5) = $ _____ and   16

         $\sigma = \sqrt{npq} = \sqrt{\rule{2cm}{0pt}} = $ _____   16; 4

The average number of preferences for Brand A will be _____ with a   32

standard deviation of _____.   4

6. Tchebysheff's Theorem can be used in conjunction with the distribution of a binomial random variable since *at least* $(1 - 1/k^2)$ of *any* distribution lies within _____ standard deviations of the mean. However, when the number of trials, n, becomes large, the Empirical Rule can be used with fairly accurate results. The interval $np \pm 2\sqrt{npq}$ should contain approxi- k

95%
99.7% or all

10; 3

10; 3

4; 16

32; 4

24; 40

mately _____ of the distribution while the interval $np \pm 3 \sqrt{npq}$ should contain approximately _____ of the distribution.

7. *Example:*

Refer to Example 4 in this section. With 95% chance, within what limits would you expect to find the number of small business closures out of $n = 100$?

Solution:

a. We have found that $\mu = np =$ _____ and $\sigma = \sqrt{npq} =$ _____. Using two standard deviations, we find the interval $\mu \pm 2\sigma$ to be _____ $\pm 2 ($ _____ $)$ or 10 ± 6.

b. With a 95% chance of being correct, we would expect the number of closures to lie between _____ and _____ if, in fact, $p = .1$.

8. *Example:*

Refer to Example 5 in this section. If there is actually no preference for either brand, between what limits would you expect the number of stated preferences for Brand A to lie?

Solution:

a. In Example 5 we found $\mu =$ _____ and $\sigma =$ _____. Hence $\mu \pm 2\sigma$ is $32 \pm 2(4)$.

b. With a 95% chance of being correct, we would expect the number of preferences for Brand A to lie between _____ and _____ if, in fact, $p = \frac{1}{2}$.

Self-Correcting Exercises 6B

1. Assume that 30% of the voting stockholders of a company favor a proposal put forth by the board of directors. If 100 stockholders are randomly selected and interviewed, find the mean and standard deviation of the sample number of stockholders that agree with the proposal. Within what limits would you expect the number of agreements to lie with approximately 95% chance?

2. If 20% of the registered voters in a given city belong to a minority group and voter registration lists are used in selecting potential jurors, within what limits would you expect the number of minority members on a list of 80 potential jurors to lie if the 80 persons were randomly selected from the voter registration lists?

3. A television network claims that its Wednesday evening prime time program attracts 40% of the television audience. If a random sample of 400 television viewers was asked whether they had seen the previous show, within what limits would you expect the number of viewers who had seen the previous show to lie if the 40% figure is correct? What would you conclude if the interviews revealed that 96 of the 400 had actually seen the previous show?

6.5 The Poisson Distribution (6.5)

1. The Poisson probability distribution has two important applications:
   a. It serves as an approximation to the _____ probability distribution when the sample size is (small, large) and the probability of success is (small, large).
   b. It serves as a model for _____ (i.e., integer) data resulting from any experiment where the count y represents the number of _____ events observed in a given unit of time or space.

2. The probability distribution of a Poisson random variable y is given by the formula

$$p(y) = \underline{\hspace{2cm}}$$

where
   a. $y = 0, 1, 2, \ldots$
   b. μ is the _____ of the distribution.
   c. e is the base of the natural logarithms and is approximately equal to 2.71828.
      [In Table 2 of the Appendix in your text, $e^{-\mu}$ has been tabulated for values of μ from 0 through 10 in 0.1 increments.]

3. When the Poisson probability distribution is used to approximate the binomial distribution with n trials and probability of success p, the Poisson mean μ should be set equal to _____.

4. The Poisson distribution provides a good approximation to the binomial distribution when n is (small, large) and $\mu = np$ is _____, preferably with $\mu = np$ less than or equal to _____ (give number).

5. *Example:*
   Evidence shows that the probability that a driver will be involved in a serious automobile accident during a given year is .01. The Ajax Company employs 100 full-time traveling salesmen. Based upon the above evidence, what is the probability that exactly two Ajax salesmen will be involved in a serious automobile accident during the coming year?
   Solution:
   This is an example of a binomial experiment with $n =$ _____ trials and $p =$ _____. The exact probability distribution for the number of serious automobile accidents in $n = 100$ trials is

$$p(y) = \frac{100!}{y!\,(100-y)!}\,(.01)^y\,(.99)^{100-y} \quad y = 0, 1, 2, \ldots, 100$$

Since we do not have binomial tables for $n = 100$, we note that the binomial mean $\mu = np = 1$. The Poisson approximation to binomial probabilities can be used in this case with the Poisson mean taken to be $\mu =$ _____.
Therefore,

Answers (right margin):

binomial
large
small
count

rare

$\dfrac{\mu^y e^{-\mu}}{y!}$

mean

np

large; small
7

100
.01

1

$$p(2) \approx \frac{(1)^2 e^{-1}}{2!}$$

$$= \frac{.367879}{2}$$

.1839

$$=\underline{\hspace{2cm}}$$

6. *Example:*

Suppose that past records show that the probability of default on an FHA loan is about .01. If 25 homes in a given area are financed by FHA, use the Poisson approximation to binomial probabilities to find

a. the probability that there will be no defaults among these 25 loans.

b. the probability that there will be two or more defaults.

Compare the values found in parts a and b with the actual binomial probabilities found using Table 1, Appendix.

Solution:

Although a sample of size $n = 25$ is not usually considered to be large, the value of $p = .01$ is small and $\mu = np = .25$ is less than 7. We will in any case assess the accuracy of the Poisson approximation compared to the actual binomial probabilities. We shall use

$$p(y) = \frac{(.25)^y e^{-.25}}{y!}$$

with $e^{-.25} = .778801$. (This value is *not* given in Table 2.)

a. The probability of $y = 0$ defaults is approximated to be

$$p(0) \approx \frac{(.25)^0 e^{-.25}}{0!}$$

.778801

$$=\underline{\hspace{2cm}}$$

.778

The actual probability from Table 1 is _____.

b. The probability of two or more defaults can be found by using

$$P[y \geqslant 2] = 1 - P[y \leqslant 1]$$

0; 1

$$= 1 - [p(\underline{\hspace{2cm}}) + p(\underline{\hspace{2cm}})]$$

We need

$$p(1) \approx \frac{(.25)^1 e^{-.25}}{1!}$$

$= (.25)(\underline{\hspace{2cm}})$

.778801

$= \underline{\hspace{2cm}}$

.194700

Hence

$P[y \geqslant 2] \approx 1 - (.778801 + .194700)$

$= 1 - \underline{\hspace{2cm}}$

.973501

$= \underline{\hspace{2cm}}$

.026499

The actual value from Table 1 is

$P[y \geqslant 2] = 1 - \underline{\hspace{2cm}}$

.974

$= \underline{\hspace{2cm}}$

.026

Notice that for this problem there is fairly good agreement between the Poisson approximations and the actual binomial probabilities even though n is not large. This is due mainly to the small value of $\mu = np = \underline{\hspace{1cm}}$.

.25

7. The Poisson distribution provides an excellent model for the probability distribution of "rare" events such as the number of calls received at a telephone switchboard or the number of ships arriving in a harbor. In such applications, y represents the number of rare events during a period of time over which an \underline{\hspace{2cm}} of μ such events can be expected to occur.

average

8. In order to use the Poisson distribution, one must be able to assume that the rare events occur \underline{\hspace{2cm}} and \underline{\hspace{2cm}}.

randomly; independently

9. *Example:*

In a food processing and packaging plant, there are, on the average, two packaging machine breakdowns per week. Assuming the weekly machine breakdowns follow a Poisson distribution, what is
a. the probability that there are no machine breakdowns in a given week?
b. the probability that there are no more than two machine breakdowns in a given week?

Solution:

Machine breakdowns occur at the average rate of $\mu = \underline{\hspace{1cm}}$ breakdowns per week. If the number of breakdowns follows a Poisson distribution, then

2

$$p(y) = \frac{2^y e^{-2}}{y!} \quad \text{for } y = 0, 1, 2, \ldots$$

a. $P[y = 0] = p(0) = \dfrac{2^0 e^{-2}}{0!}$

$$= \frac{e^{-2}}{1}$$

.135335

$$=\underline{\hspace{2cm}}$$

b. The probability that no more than two machine breakdowns occur in a given week is

$$P[y \leqslant 2] = p(0) + p(1) + p(2)$$

.135335

From part a, we know that $p(0) = \underline{\hspace{2cm}}$. We need to evaluate $p(1)$ and $p(2)$.

.270670

$$p(1) = \frac{2^1 e^{-2}}{1!} = 2(.135335) = \underline{\hspace{2cm}}$$

.270670

$$p(2) = \frac{2^2 e^{-2}}{2!} = 2(.135335) = \underline{\hspace{2cm}}$$

Hence

.676675

$$P[y \leqslant 2] = \underline{\hspace{2cm}}$$

10. It is important to keep in mind that the Poisson distribution is fixed in time or space. In the last example, the mean number of breakdowns per week was two. The mean number of breakdowns in a three-week period would be 6. The parameter μ in a Poisson distribution is always equal to the *mean* number of rare events observed occurring in a *given unit* of time or space.

6.6 The Hypergeometric Probability Distribution (6.6)

binomial

1. One of the assumptions required for the application of the $\underline{\hspace{2cm}}$ probability distribution is that probability of a success remains constant from trial to trial.

replacement

2. The assumption is violated whenever the trials involving the selection of elements from a population are performed without $\underline{\hspace{2cm}}$.

3. This departure from the conditions required of the ideal binomial experiment is not important when the population is (small, large) relative to the $\underline{\hspace{2cm}}$ size. In such circumstances, the probability p of a success is approximately $\underline{\hspace{2cm}}$ for each trial or selection.

large
sample
constant

population
sample
dependent on

4. However, if the number of elements in the $\underline{\hspace{2cm}}$ is small in relation to the number of elements in the $\underline{\hspace{2cm}}$, the probability of a success for a given trial is (dependent on, independent of) the out-

comes of preceding trials. In this case, the number y of successes follows the _____ probability distribution.

hypergeometric

5. The probability distribution of a random variable y having the hypergeometric distribution is given by the formula

$$p(y) = \frac{C_y^k C_{n-y}^{N-k}}{C_n^N}$$

for $y = 0, 1, 2, \ldots ,$ _____ if $n < k$

n

$y = 0, 1, 2, \ldots ,$ _____ if $n \geq k$

k

where $C_y^k =$ _____ , etc.

$\dfrac{k!}{y!\,(k-y)!}$

and where

N = number of elements in the _____

population

k = number of elements in the _____ that (are, are not) successes

population; are

n = number of elements in the _____ which are selected from the population

sample

y = number of _____ in the _____

successes; sample

6. The hypergeometric probability distribution is applicable when one is selecting a sample of elements from a population without _____ and one records whether or not each element does or does not possess a certain characteristic.

replacement

7. *Example:*

An auditor is checking the records of an accountant who is responsible for ten clients. The accounts of two of the clients contain major errors, and the accountant will fail the inspection if the auditor finds even a single erroneous account. What is the probability that the accountant will fail the inspection if the auditor inspects the records of three clients chosen at random?

Solution:

Let y be the number of erroneous accounts found in the (population, sample). Then

sample

$N =$ _____

10

$k =$ _____

2

8

3

1; 2
1; 1; 2

$\dfrac{8!}{2!\,6!}$

$\dfrac{10!}{3!\,7!}$

.467

$\dfrac{2!}{2!\,0!}\,;\,\dfrac{8!}{1!\,7!}$

.067

.467; .067; .534

$$N - k = \underline{\hspace{2cm}}$$

$$n = \underline{\hspace{2cm}}$$

The accountant will fail the inspection if $y = \underline{\hspace{2cm}}$ or $\underline{\hspace{2cm}}$.
So $P(\text{accountant fails}) = P(y \geqslant \underline{\hspace{2cm}}) = p(\underline{\hspace{2cm}}) + p(\underline{\hspace{1cm}})$

$$P(y = 1) = \frac{\left(\frac{2!}{1!\,1!}\right)\left(\underline{\hspace{2cm}}\right)}{\left(\underline{\hspace{1cm}}\right)}$$

$$= \underline{\hspace{2cm}}$$

$$P(y = 2) = \frac{\left(\underline{\hspace{1.5cm}}\right)\left(\underline{\hspace{1.5cm}}\right)}{\left(\frac{10!}{3!\,7!}\right)}$$

$$= \underline{\hspace{2cm}}$$

Therefore, the probability that the accountant will fail the inspection
is $\underline{\hspace{1.5cm}} + \underline{\hspace{1.5cm}} = \underline{\hspace{1.5cm}}$.

Self-Correcting Exercises 6C

1. The probability of a serious fire during a given year to any one house in a particular city is believed to be .005. The Inferno Fire Insurance Company holds fire insurance policies on 1000 homes in this city.
   a. Find the probability that Inferno will not have any serious fire damage claims by the owners of these homes during the next year.
   b. Find the probability they will have no more than three claims.
2. In a certain manufacturing plant, wood-grain printed 4' × 8' wall board panels are mass produced and packaged in lots of 100. Past evidence indicates that the number of damaged or imperfect panels per bundle follows a Poisson distribution with mean $\mu = 2$.
   a. Find the probability that there are exactly three damaged or imperfect panels in a bundle of 100.
   b. Find the probability that there are at least two damaged or imperfect panels in a bundle of 100.
3. The Home Improvement Store has purchased two bundles (2 bundles of 100 each) of panels from the manufacturer described in Exercise 2. Find the probability his lot contains no more than four damaged or imperfect panels.

4. The board of directors of a company has voted to create an employee council for the purpose of handling employee complaints. The council will consist of the company president, the vice-president for personnel, and four employee representatives. The four employees will be randomly selected from a list of 15 volunteers. This list consists of nine men and six women.
   a. What is the probability that two or more men will be selected from the list of volunteers?
   b. What is the probability that exactly three women will be selected from the list of volunteers?
5. A bin of 50 parts contains three defective units. A sample of five units is drawn randomly from the bin. What is the probability that no defective units will be selected?

6.7 Making Decisions: Lot Acceptance Sampling (6.7)

1. Think of a manufacturing plant as a process that turns raw material into a finished product. In order to operate efficiently, the plant must (maximize, minimize) the number of defective material items received and _____ the number of acceptable finished items. To achieve these goals a method is needed for screening incoming and outgoing lots. Note that screening (rejecting bad lots) is an inferential procedure in which a decision must be made about the population of items contained in the lot. Rejection is equivalent to inferring that the fraction defective, p, is too large.

   minimize; maximize

2. These goals can be achieved in different ways. A manufacturer producing television sets would obviously test and adjust *each* set before it leaves the plant, but would probably not test each transistor in an incoming lot before accepting the whole shipment. He would probably accept or reject the shipment depending upon the number of defective transistors observed in a random sample drawn from that lot. Sometimes the act of testing an item is destructive, so that each item cannot be individually tested. Testing whether a flashbulb produces the required intensity of light obviously destroys the flashbulb.
3. The process of screening lots is an inferential procedure in which a decision about the proportion defective in a lot (population) is made. The sampling of items from incoming or outgoing lots or the sampling of items from a production line closely approximates the defining characteristics of a _____ experiment.

   binomial

4. However, lot acceptance sampling differs from the examples of ideal binomial experiments encountered thus far. First (and this is especially evident with destructive testing), lot acceptance sampling is usually done without _____. This means that the _____ probability distribution can be correctly applied only when the sample to be inspected is small relative to the size of the entire lot. When such is not the case, the _____ probability distribution should be used.

   replacement; binomial

   hypergeometric

is not

sample

lot

defectives

accepted

acceptance

rejected

sampling plan

high

low

operating characteristic

1

0

0

10

1

large

binomial

$C_1^{10}\,(.1)^1\,(.9)^9$

.736

5. The most important difference between the examples of ideal binomial experiments and lot acceptance sampling is that with the latter, the probability p of a defective in the population (is, is not) known. We must use the _____ to make an inference concerning the true value of p, so that a decision to accept or reject the lot can be made.

6. Thus, a sample of n items is selected from the _____ and inspected, and the number y of _____ is recorded. The lot is (accepted, rejected) if y, the number of defectives, is less than or equal to a preselected number a, called the _____ number. If y exceeds a, the lot is _____.

7. Every _____ _____ is defined by a sample size n and an acceptance number a.

8. How does one choose a sampling plan from among the many plans available? One acceptable criterion is that the probability of accepting a good lot shall be (high, low) and that the probability of accepting a bad lot shall be _____. Thus, we might select plan B (with the larger sample size) rather than plan A if good lots have a higher probability of acceptance and bad lots have a lower probability of acceptance when plan B is used. To obtain this comparison we construct the _____ _____ curve for each of these plans. The operating characteristic curve is a graph which shows the probability of acceptance for an incoming lot with fraction defective p. The curve will be shown for values of p ranging from 0 (perfect lot) to 1. If a lot contains no good items ($p =$ _____) then the probability that it will be accepted is _____. If a lot contains no defective items ($p =$ _____) it is certain to be accepted. For intermediate values of p the operating characteristic curves for two different plans will not in general coincide. In the next two paragraphs we obtain the operating characteristic curves for two sampling plans.

9. Given the plan $n = 10, a = 1$, we take a sample of size _____ and accept the lot if no more than _____ defective is found in the sample. We now assume that the lot is (large, small) enough to justify treating the number of defectives found in the sample as a _____ random variable. If a lot containing 10% defectives ($p = .1$) is submitted, the probability of lot acceptance is

$$p(0) + p(1) = C_0^{10}\,(.1)^0\,(.9)^{10} + \text{_____}$$

It is not necessary to complete this calculation since the result correct to the nearest thousandth may be read directly from Table 1 in the Appendix of your text. Thus,

$$C_0^{10}\,(.1)^0\,(.9)^{10} + C_1^{10}\,(.1)^1\,(.9)^9 = \text{_____}$$

By referring to Table 1, obtain the probabilities of acceptance which are omitted in the following table when $n = 10$ and $a = 1$.

Fraction Defective (p)	Probability of Lot Acceptance	
.01	.996	
.05	_____	.914
.10	.736	
.20	_____	.376
.30	_____	.149
.40	_____	.046
.50	.011	

A graph may now be constructed showing the probability of acceptance as a function of the fraction defective in the incoming lot. The curve so obtained is called the _____ _____ curve for the sampling plan.

operating characteristic

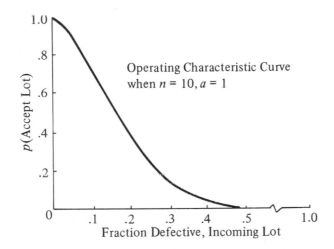

10. *Example:*
    Construct an *OC* curve for the plan $n = 20, a = 2$.
    Solution:
    The probability of accepting a lot under this plan is the probability of obtaining no more than _____ defective items in a random sample of size 20. Thus, the probability of accepting an incoming lot with fraction defective *p* is

2

$$P[y \leqslant 2] = \sum_{y=\underline{\quad}} C_y^{20} p^y (1-p)^{20-y}$$

$$\sum_{y=0}^{2}$$

(fill in the summation limits).
    Using Table 1 (text) complete the following table.

Fraction Defective (p)	Probability of Lot Acceptance
.05	_____
.10	_____
.20	_____
.30	_____

.925
.677
.206
.035

Complete the *OC* curve below by labeling and scaling the axes, plotting the points obtained from the above table, and joining the points with a smooth curve.

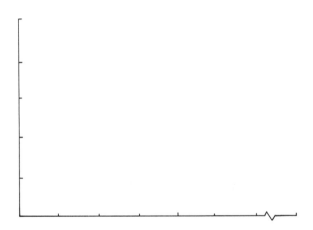

less

Since an *OC* curve falls as one moves to the right, the probability of accepting a lot containing a high fraction defective is (more, <u>less</u>) than the probability of accepting a good lot.

11. To aid in the comparison of plan *A* ($n = 10, a = 1$) and plan *B* ($n = 20$, $a = 2$), we shall show their operating characteristic curves on the same graph, using acceptance values recorded in the following table.

Fraction Defective (p)	Probability of Acceptance	
	Plan A	Plan B
.00	1.000	1.000
.05	.914	.925
.10	.736	.677
.20	.376	.206
.30	.149	.035
.40	.046	.004
.50	.011	.000

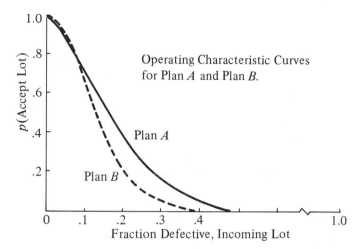

The two curves appear to cross at about $p = .06$. Thus, the probability of accepting a lot with fraction defective less than .06 is (higher, lower) with plan B than with plan A. The probability of accepting a lot with fraction defective more than .06 is _____ with plan B than with plan A. Thus plan B is more sensitive in discriminating between good and bad lots. The expense of inspecting a larger sample (as in plan B) may be justified by the greater sensitivity of plan B as compared with plan A.

higher

lower

Self-Correcting Exercises 6D

1. Large lots of portable radios are accepted in accordance with the sampling plan with sample size $n = 4$ and acceptance number $a = 1$.
   a. Complete the following table and construct the *OC* curve for this plan. The axes should be properly labeled and scaled.

Fraction Defective, p	0	.10	.30	.50	1
Probability of acceptance	_____	.95	_____	.31	_____

   b. State two essentially different ways in which one might modify the above sampling plan to increase the probability of accepting a lot with fraction defective $p = .10$.
2. To discover the effect on acceptance probabilities of varying the sample size we study the additional sampling plans ($n = 10$, $a = 1$) and ($n = 25$, $a = 1$).
   a. Use Table 1 in your text to complete the following table.

Fraction Defective, p		0	.10	.30	.50	1.0
Probability of acceptance	$n = 10$ $a = 1$	___	.74	___	.01	___
	$n = 25$ $a = 1$	___	___	.00	___	___

b. Construct the *OC* curves for the plan in Exercise 1 and the plans considered in part a on the same set of axes.

c. If the acceptance number is kept the same and the sample size increased, what is the effect on the probability of accepting a given lot?

3. To discover the effect on acceptance probabilities of varying the acceptance number we study the additional sampling plans ($n = 25, a = 3$) and ($n = 25, a = 5$).

a. Use Table 1 in your text to complete the following table.

Fraction Defective, p		0	.10	.30	.50	1.0
Probability of acceptance	$n = 25$ $a = 3$	___	___	.03	___	___
	$n = 25$ $a = 5$	___	.97	___	___	___

b. Construct the *OC* curves for the plans considered in part a together with the *OC* curve for the plan ($n = 25, a = 1$) (see Exercise 2) on the same set of axes.

c. If the sample size is kept the same and the acceptance number increased, what is the effect on the probability of accepting a given lot?

6.8 Making Decisions: A Test of an Hypothesis (6.8–6.10)

1. We have described binomial populations in the first sections of this chapter using the viewpoint that if we know the values of n and p, the population distribution can be found and the mean and variance of the population can be calculated. In short, we are able to calculate the probability of our sample outcome.

2. Let us now look at the same problem in a different light. Given that we have a sample of n measurements from a dichotomous population with y of these outcomes as "successes," what information about the value of p can be gleaned from the sample? As we have seen, the mass of the probability distribution shifts with the value of _____, the probability of success, so that certain values of y are highly probable for one value of p and highly improbable for other values of p.

3. Our approach will be to draw a random sample from a dichotomous population and decide whether we shall accept or reject an hypothesized value

p

for *p*. The decision will be made on the basis of whether the sample results are highly _____ and support the hypothesized value or are _____ and fail to support the hypothesized value. Our procedure is very similar to a court trial in which the accused is assumed innocent until proved guilty. In fact, our _____ acts as the evidence for or against the accused. What we do is to compare the hypothesized value with reality. Let us illustrate how a test of an hypothesis is conducted.

    probable
    improbable

    sample

4. In an initial experiment to assess the merits of using a newly developed filling material in bed pillows, 10 persons randomly selected from a group of volunteers agreed to test the new filling by actually using both the standard pillow and one made with the new filling in their homes. To avoid biases that might influence the volunteer's decision, both pillows were covered with the same material. One pillow carried the number one and the other the number two. Only the experimenter knew which number represented the standard and which represented the new material. After one week's use, each volunteer stated his preference for one of the two pillows.

5. If there is no underlying difference between the new and standard pillow, then the probability that a volunteer would prefer the new pillow to the standard would be *p* = _____. If, on the other hand, this is not true and the new pillow has more desirable properties than the standard, then *p*, the probability that a volunteer prefers the new pillow, would be greater than _____.

    ½

    ½

    Assuming that there is no difference between the pillows ($p = ½$), it would be extremely unlikely that in a sample of $n = 10$ trials we would observe 9 or more people preferring the new pillow. From the table of binomial probabilities this probability, $p(9) + p(10)$, is _____. Therefore more than 8 preferences for the new pillow would be sufficient evidence to reject the value $p = ½$.

    .011

    Since *y*, the number of preferences, is a binomial random variable with possible values 0, 1, 2, . . . , 10, the possible outcomes can be divided into those (9 and 10) for which we agree to _____ the null hypothesis, and those (0, 1, 2, . . . , 8) for which we _____ the null hypothesis:

    reject
    accept

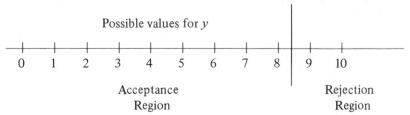

The decision to reject the null hypothesis will be made if the observed value of *y* lies in the rejection region.

hypothesis

alternative

test statistic

preferences
rejection region

null

H_a

6. A statistical test of a theory possesses four elements:
  a. There must be a theory to be tested, which we call the _____ _____, H_0. In our problem, H_0 declares that $p = \frac{1}{2}$. The objective of the test is to give the facts (data) a chance to refute H_0.
  b. There must be an _____ hypothesis, H_a. If H_0 is false, then some alternative hypothesis is true. H_a generally expresses the experimenter's intuitive feeling about the true state of nature. In our example, if the new filling is better than the standard, then H_a *would appropriately be H_a: $p > \frac{1}{2}$.*
  c. There must be a _____ _____, that is, a number that has been calculated from the information contained in the sample and that is used in making a decision concerning H_0. In the present example, the statistic that best reflects the true value of p is y, the number of _____ in 10 trials.
  d. There must be a _____ _____, that is, a set of predetermined values of the test statistic, the occurrence of which will cause us to reject the _____ hypothesis in favor of the alternative hypothesis. The rejection region consists of values of the test statistic that are more likely if (H_0, H_a) is true. In our example, the expected number of preferences would be 5 if H_0 is true. However, if H_a is true and $p = .8$, then the expected number of preferences would be $np = 10(.8) = 8$. Thus, when H_a : $p > \frac{1}{2}$ is true, we would expect to obtain larger values of y, and the rejection region $y = 9, 10$ would be appropriate for our alternative.

7. The rejection region given as $y = 9, 10$ is not the only possible choice available to the experimenter. Someone requiring stronger evidence before rejecting H_0 as false might prefer the following assignment.

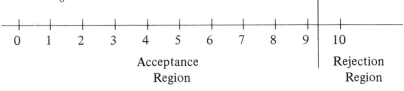

Another person might be particularly interested in protecting himself against accepting H_0 when in fact p is greater than $\frac{1}{2}$, and could argue for the following assignment.

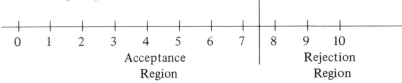

A sound choice among various reasonable rejection regions can be made after considering the possible errors that can be made in a test of an hypothesis.

null; true

8. Rejecting the _____ hypothesis when it is _____ is

called a Type I error for a statistical test. The probability of making a
Type I error is denoted by the symbol _____.

9. Accepting the _____ hypothesis when it is _____ is
called a Type II error for a statistical test. The probability of making a
Type II error when a specific alternative is true is denoted by the symbol

_____.

α

null; false

β

10. The following is called a decision table and looks at the two possible states
of nature (H_0 and H_a) and the two possible decisions in a test of an
hypothesis. Fill in the missing entries as either "correct" or "error":

	Decision	
Null Hypothesis	Reject H_0	Accept H_0
True	error	_____
False	correct	_____

correct
error

An error of Type I is made when one rejects H_0 when H_0 is (true, false).
An error of Type II is made when one fails to reject H_0 when H_a is (true,
false). In considering a statistical test of an hypothesis, it is essential to
know the probabilities of committing errors of Type I and Type II when
the test is used. We define

true

true

$$\alpha = P \text{ [Type I error]} = P \text{ [reject } H_0 \text{ when } H_0 \text{ true]}$$

$$\beta = P \text{ [Type II error]} = P \text{ [accept } H_0 \text{ when } H_a \text{ true]}$$

11. For our example, let us look at α and β for the three rejection regions discussed in Number 7, using the tables of binomial probabilities, Table 1,
Appendix.

a. For the rejection region given as $y = 9, 10$ for $n = 10$,

$$\alpha = P \text{ [reject } H_0 \text{ when } H_0 \text{ true]}$$

$$= P [y = 9 \text{ or } 10 \text{ when } p = \tfrac{1}{2}]$$

$$= 1 - P [y \leqslant 8 \text{ when } p = \tfrac{1}{2}]$$

$$= 1 - \underline{\hspace{2cm}}$$

.989

$$= \underline{\hspace{2cm}}$$

.011

If H_0 is false and if $p = .8$, then

$$\beta = P \text{ [accept } H_0 \text{ when } H_a \text{ true]}$$

$$= P [y \leqslant 8 \text{ when } p = .8]$$

$$= \underline{\hspace{2cm}}$$

.624

.999

.001

.893

.945

.055

.322

decreases

.05

b. For the second rejection region, $y = 10$,

$$\alpha = P\,[y = 10 \text{ when } p = \tfrac{1}{2}]$$

$$= 1 - P\,[y \leqslant 9 \text{ when } p = \tfrac{1}{2}]$$

$$= 1 - \underline{\qquad}$$

$$= \underline{\qquad}$$

while if H_0 is false and if $p = .8$,

$$\beta = P\,[y \leqslant 9 \text{ when } p = .8]$$

$$= \underline{\qquad}$$

c. For the third rejection region, $y = 8, 9, 10$,

$$\alpha = P\,[y \geqslant 8 \text{ when } p = \tfrac{1}{2}]$$

$$= 1 - P\,[y \leqslant 7 \text{ when } p = \tfrac{1}{2}]$$

$$= 1 - \underline{\qquad}$$

$$= \underline{\qquad}$$

If H_0 is false and if $p = .8$, then

$$\beta = P\,[y \leqslant 7 \text{ when } p = .8]$$

$$= \underline{\qquad}$$

12. Notice that both α and β depend upon the rejection region employed and that when the sample size n is fixed, α and β are inversely related: as one increases, the other _____. Increasing the sample size provides more information on which to make the decision and will reduce the Type II error probability. Since these two quantities measure the risk of making an incorrect decision, the experimenter chooses reasonable values for α and β and then chooses the rejection region and sample size accordingly.

Since experimenters have found that a 1-in-20 chance of a Type I error is usually tolerable, common practice is to choose $\alpha \leqslant$ _____ and a sample size n large enough to provide the desired control of Type II error.

13. *Example:*

Twenty office workers were tested for reaction time before and after lunch. Seventeen of the workers showed increased reaction time after lunch. Is this sufficient evidence to indicate that reaction times are increased after lunch?

Solution:

We begin by putting this problem into the context of a test of an hypothesis concerning p, the probability that reaction time has increased after lunch. The twenty office workers will be considered as $n = 20$ trials in a binomial experiment with $y = 17$. If eating lunch does not affect reaction time, then $p = $ _____ ; but if eating lunch causes reaction time to increase, then p _____ .

a. The *hypotheses* to be tested are

$$H_0 : p = \tfrac{1}{2} \qquad \text{versus}$$

$$H_a : p > \tfrac{1}{2}$$

b. The *test statistic* will be y, the number of office workers exhibiting increased reaction time after lunch.

c. To choose a *rejection region*, we note that if H_0 is true, $\mu = np = 20(\tfrac{1}{2})$ = _____ , while if H_a is true, and say $p = .7$, then $\mu = np = 20(.7)$ = _____ . If $p = .9$, $\mu = np = 20(.9) = $ _____ . If H_a is true, we should expect to obtain _____ values of y. Using your table of binomial probabilities with $n = 20$ and $p = \tfrac{1}{2}$, we need to find a cutoff number, a, such that

$$\alpha = P\,[y \geqslant a \text{ when } p = \tfrac{1}{2}] \leqslant .05$$

Complete the entries below:

a	$P\,[y \geqslant a \text{ when } p = \tfrac{1}{2}] = 1 - P\,[y \leqslant (a-1) \text{ when } p = \tfrac{1}{2}]$
20	.000
19	.000
18	.000
17	.001
16	_____
15	_____
14	_____
13	_____

The largest rejection region with $\alpha \leqslant .05$ would consist of the values $y = $ _____ , _____ , . . . , 20. (Note that an experimenter might be willing to include $y = 14$ in the rejection region and use $\alpha = .058$.)

d. Since the observed value of $y = 17$ lies in the rejection region, we reject the _____ _____ and conclude that eating lunch _____ significantly increase reaction time.

e. It is worthwhile to note that both types of errors cannot be made at the

---

Margin answers:

½
> ½

10
14; 18
larger

.006
.021
.058
.132

15; 16

null hypothesis
does

Type I
Type II

.021

same time. If we decide to reject H_0, the only error applicable is the
_____ error. If we decide to accept H_0, the only possible
error is _____. For this problem, we could then put a
measure of goodness on our inference by noting that we conclude that
eating lunch increases reaction time with probability _____ of
being incorrect.

Self-Correcting Exercises 6E

1. While ordering a new shipment of shirts, the owner of a men's shop was told that the demand for a new color was anticipated to comprise about 40% of sales during the next season. The owner ordered his shipment in line with this 40% figure. If a random inspection of 25 sales slips involving the sale of a shirt revealed that 6 of these sales involved shirts of the new color, could the owner conclude that the 40% figure was actually too high?

2. A manufacturer has claimed that the proportion of defective items in lots supplied by him is at most 5%. To verify his claim, a random sample of 20 items produced by this manufacturer were examined and 4 items found to be defective. Is this sufficient evidence to reject the manufacturer's claim at the 5% level of significance?

3. A comparison of the color quality of two brands of television sets, A and B, was of interest to manufacturer A, since B was his strongest competitor. Fifteen subjects, who had ample opportunity to view both brands of television, were asked to state a preference for Brand A or Brand B solely on the basis of the color of the television picture. If 12 of the 15 subjects stated a preference for Brand A, would this be sufficient evidence to conclude that the sets are not equally preferred when compared on the basis of picture color?

6.9 Summary (6.11)

1. The five defining characteristics of a binomial experiment are:

trials
success; failure
same

independent
number
trials

$C_y^n p^y q^{n-y}$

np; npq

  a. The experiment consists of n _____.
  b. Each trial results in either _____ or _____.
  c. The probability, p, of success on a given trial is the _____ from trial to trial.
  d. The trials are _____.
  e. The random variable observed, y, is the _____ of successes in the n _____.

2. The probability function for y is

$$p(y) = \underline{\hspace{2cm}} \qquad y = 0, 1, 2, \ldots, n$$

3. The expected value, μ, and the variance, σ^2, of y are

$$\mu = \underline{\hspace{2.5cm}} \qquad \text{and } \sigma^2 = \underline{\hspace{2.5cm}}$$

4. We considered the practical problem of making inferences about the binomial parameter, p. The first example was the problem of lot acceptance
sampling which requires a decision to be made about a production lot on
the basis of a sample of n items drawn at random from the lot. If a or
fewer defective items are found in the sample, the lot is (accepted,
rejected). If more than a defectives are found in the sample the lot is
_____. Thus if the lot is accepted we infer that p is small and
acceptable, and if rejected we infer that p is unacceptably large.

accepted
rejected

5. The second example of inference making described in this chapter is testing an hypothesis concerning the binomial parameter, _____. The
specification of a value for p is called the _____ hypothesis, H_0.
We use information contained in a sample to decide whether to reject H_0.
The information-bearing quantity (test statistic) in this chapter is the binomial random variable, y. The set of values of y for which we agree to
reject H_0 is called the _____ region.

p
null

rejection

    A decision regarding the null hypothesis can result in one of two types
of errors. A Type _____ error occurs when H_0 is rejected if H_0 is
(true, false). A Type _____ error occurs when H_0 is not rejected if
H_0 is _____.

I
true: II
false

    The goodness of a statistical test of an hypothesis is measured by the
probabilities of Type I and Type II errors. These probabilities are measures
of risk associated with this decision-making inferential process. The probabilities of committing Type I and Type II errors are denoted by the
symbols _____ and _____, respectively.

α; β

6. If count data represent the number of rare events occurring within a given
unit of time or space, the distribution of these counts can be described by
the Poisson distribution whose probability function is given by

$$p(y) = \frac{\mu^y e^{-\mu}}{y!}, \qquad y = 0, 1, 2, \ldots$$

where μ is the _____ number of _____ events in the
given unit of time or space. In other words, μ is the _____ of
the random variable y.

mean; rare
mean

7. Binomial probabilities can be approximated by the Poisson probability distribution if n is _____ and p or $q = 1 - p$ is _____, or
in general, if np is less than or equal to _____.

large; small
seven

8. The _____ probability distribution models give the probability
of drawing y elements of a particular type from a population when N, the
number of elements in the population, is small in relation to the sample
size, n. The _____ probability distribution is closely related to
the hypergeometric distribution and can be used to approximate the
hypergeometric probability distribution when N is large relative to n.

hypergeometric

binomial

Exercises

1. Give the five defining characteristics of a binomial experiment.
2. Let y denote a binomial random variable for n trials. Give the probability function for y and list its possible values.
3. Four experiments are described below. Identify which of these might reasonably be treated as a binomial experiment. If a given experiment is clearly not binomial, state what feature disqualifies it. If it is a binomial experiment, write down the probability function for y.
    a. Five percent of the stamps in a large collection are extremely valuable. The stamps are withdrawn one at a time until ten extremely valuable stamps are located. The observed random variable is y, the total number of stamps withdrawn.
    b. There are 15 students in Bill's economics class. The names of these students are written on tags placed in a box. Periodically, a tag is drawn at random from the box and the student with that name is asked to recite. The tag is returned to the box and the proceedings continued. Let y denote the number of times Bill will be called upon to recite when the teacher draws from the box five times.
    c. This example is conducted in the manner prescribed for part b except that a tag drawn from the box is not returned. Let y denote the number of times Bill will be called upon to recite when the teacher draws from the box five times.
    d. Sixty percent of the homes in a given county carry fire insurance. A sample of five homes is drawn at random from this county. Let y denote the number of insured homes among the five selected.
4. Let y denote the number of successes in a single trial given that the probability of success is p.
    a. Construct the probability distribution for y in tabular form.
    b. Use the definitions of mean and variance to determine the mean and variance of y.
5. A binomial experiment consists of four independent trials in which the probability of success on a given trial is $1/2$. Let y denote the number of successes in the four trials.
    a. Write down the probability function for y as a formula.
    b. Construct the probability distribution of y in tabular form.
    c. Use the table constructed in part b and the definition of $E(y)$ to find the expected value of y.
    d. Use the table constructed in part b and the definition of σ^2 to find the variance of y.
    e. Use the formula for the mean and variance of a binomial random variable to check the values determined in parts c and d.
6. If y is binomial for $n = 100$ trials and $p = .9$, find limits A and B such that $P[A < y < B] \geqslant 8/9$. Hint: Use Tchebysheff's Theorem.
7. If a TV program cannot attract about a third of the available viewers it is apt to be tabbed as unequal to competing programs in the same time slot.

Suppose a certain program is preferred in its time slot by 1/3 of the viewers. In a random sample of 450 viewers, within what limits would you expect to find the number preferring this program?

8. Harvard University has found that about 90% of its accepted applicants for enrollment in the freshman class will actually take a place in that class. In 1967, 1360 applicants to Harvard were accepted. Within what limits would you expect to find the size of the freshman class at Harvard in the fall of 1967?

9. In the past history of a certain serious disease it has been found that about 1/2 of its victims recover.
   a. Find the probability that exactly one of the next five patients suffering from this disease will recover.
   b. Find the probability that at least one of the next five patients afflicted with this disease will recover.

10. The length of life of a certain type of battery is at least 15 hours with probability $p = .80$. Suppose that five of these batteries are put into service.
    a. What is the probability that all five of these batteries will serve for at least 15 hours?
    b. What is the probability that at least three of these batteries will serve for at least 15 hours?

11. The probability of rain is 1/2 for each of the next five days. For the purpose of this problem, assume that the five days comprise independent trials.
    a. What is the probability of no rain at all during the next five days?
    b. What is the probability of rain on at least two of the next five days?

12. On a certain university campus a student is fined $1.00 for the first parking violation of the academic year. The fine is doubled for each subsequent offense, so that the second violation costs $2.00, the third $4.00, etc. The probability that a parking violation on a given day is detected is .10. Suppose that a certain student will park illegally on each of 20 days during a given academic year.
    a. What is the probability he will not be fined?
    b. What is the probability that his fines will total no more than $15.00?

13. A multiple-choice test offers four alternative answers to each of 100 questions. In every case there is but one correct answer. Bill responded correctly to each of the first 76 questions when he noted that just 20 seconds remained in the test period. He quickly checked an answer at random for each of the remaining 24 questions without reading them.
    a. What is Bill's expected number of correct answers?
    b. If the instructor assigns a grade by taking 1/3 of the wrong from the number marked correctly, what is Bill's expected grade?

14. Consider 10 management trainees in a firm's rotation program where three of the 10 are members of minority groups. If five of the trainees are randomly assigned to the marketing division, what is the probability that there will be three minority trainees in the group assigned to marketing?

15. Improperly wired control panels were mistakenly installed on two of eight large automated machine tools. It is uncertain which of the machine tools have the defective panels, and a sample of four tools is randomly chosen for inspection.
    a. What is the probability that the sample will include no defective panels? Both defective panels?
    b. Find the binomial approximations for part a.

16. Shipments of refrigerators are accepted in accordance with the sampling plan $n = 2, a = 0$.
    a. Find the probability of accepting a lot with fraction defective, $p = .01$.
    b. Find the probability of accepting a lot with fraction defective, $p = .20$.

17. Refer to Exercise 16.
    a. Find a sampling plan with sample size $n = 20$ which has approximately the same probability of accepting a lot with fraction defective, $p = .01$, as the plan $n = 2, a = 0$.
    b. What is the probability under the plan determined in part a of accepting a lot which has fraction defective, $p = .20$?
    c. If you were purchasing refrigerators by the lot, what advantage would there be in using the plan determined in part a rather than the plan $n = 2, a = 0$? What disadvantages can you cite for using the plan with sample size $n = 20$?

18. A coroner's null hypothesis is H_0: "This man is alive." If you were "this man" would you prefer a test with $\alpha = .05$ and $\beta = .001$ or a test with $\alpha = .001$ and $\beta = .05$? Explain your preference.

19. A new method of packaging Brand A candy has been proposed as a means of increasing sales. It is known that approximately 40% of the potential customers now purchase Brand A. If at least six of the next ten customers (each of whom is given a choice of Brand A in the new package or one of its competitors) select Brand A, we shall conclude that the new packaging method is effective in increasing sales.
    a. State H_0 in terms of p, the probability that a given customer will select Brand A.
    b. Find α for this experiment. (Use Table 1 in the text.)
    c. State H_a in terms of p.
    d. Find β for H_a: $p = .6$. (Use Table 1 in the text.)

20. It is thought that cottage cheese batches in two tanks (Tank A and Tank B) are equally desirable. Let p denote the probability that a given taster will express a preference for the cottage cheese in Tank A. To test the null hypothesis, H_0: $p = 1/2$, against the alternative, H_a: $p \neq 1/2$, each member of a panel of ten tasters is asked to judge which cottage cheese is the more desirable. Let y denote the number of tasters who will state a preference for the product in Tank A. Suppose that the rejection region consists of the values $y = 0, 1, 9$ and 10.
    a. Describe the Type I error in terms of the cheeses.
    b. Describe the Type II error in terms of the cheeses.
    c. Find α for the above test.

d. Find β if indeed $p = .60$.

e. Find β if indeed $p = .90$.

f. Find β if indeed $p = .99$.

g. From the answers recorded for parts d, e, and f state whether β is larger when p is close to the value specified in H_0 or when p is grossly different from the value specified in H_0.

21. A delicatessen has found that the weekly demand for caviar follows a Poisson distribution with a mean of four tins (each tin contains 8 ounces of caviar).

 a. Find the probability that no more than 4 tins are requested during a given week.

 b. As caviar spoils with time, it must be replenished weekly by the delicatessen's owner. How many tins should he buy if it is desired that the probability not exceed .10 that demand cannot be met during a given week?

22. A manufacturer of a small mini-computer has found that the average number of service calls per computer each year is 2.2. Assume the number of service calls follows a Poisson distribution.

 a. Find the probability that a particular mini-computer requires no service during a given year.

 b. The Ajax Company has purchased two mini-computers from the manufacturer. Find the probability that Ajax requires no service calls during a given year.

 c. Find the probability that Ajax requires exactly two service calls during a given year.

23. Refer to Exercise 22. Suppose service calls cost the computer manufacturer an average of $20 each.

 a. What is the expected cost per computer each year?

 b. If the manufacturer has sold 50 mini-computers in the Seattle area, what is the expected annual cost of service in this area?

24. Customers arrive at a certain gasoline filling station at the average rate of one every ten minutes. Assume the arrivals follow a Poisson distribution. The station has only one attendant and he takes an average of five minutes to service each arrival. What is the probability that two customers arrive while the attendant is servicing an earlier arrival?

25. A buyer and a seller agree to use sampling plan ($n = 25$, $a = 2$) or sampling plan ($n = 10$, $a = 1$). Under each of these plans, determine the probability that the buyer would accept the lot if the fraction defective of the lot is:

 a. $p = 0$ c. $p = .10$ e. $p = .50$

 b. $p = .05$ d. $p = .20$ f. $p = 1.0$

Chapter   7

THE NORMAL
PROBABILITY DISTRIBUTION

7.1 Introduction (7.1)

1. Random variables can be assigned to one of two categories: _____   discrete
   random variables and _____ random variables. Thus far, we   continuous
   have considered only discrete random variables, which can take on only a
   _____, or at most, a countably infinite number of values.   finite
2. On the other hand, continuous random variables are associated with
   sample spaces containing the infinitely many sample points found in a
   _____. That is, any random variable whose   line interval
   values are _____, as opposed to _____, is a con-   measurements; counts
   tinuous random variable.
3. The probabilistic model for the frequency distribution of a continuous
   random variable is represented by a _____ curve called the   smooth
   probability _____ function.   density
4. Many random variables encountered in practice have approximately a
   _____-shaped, or approximately a _____ probability   bell; normal
   distribution.
5. The probability density function for the normal random variable y is

$$f(y) = \frac{1}{\sigma \sqrt{2\pi}} \, e^{-1/2 \left(\frac{y - \mu}{\sigma} \right)^2} \quad \text{for } -\infty < y < \infty$$

and has the following _____-shaped graph: bell

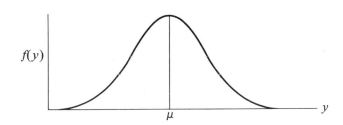

135

3.1416
2.7183
mean
standard deviation

6. The symbols used in the function $f(y)$ are defined as follows:
   a. π and e are irrational numbers whose approximate values are _____ and _____, respectively.
   b. μ and σ are constants which represent the population _____ and _____ _____, respectively.

7. Encountering a random variable whose values can be extremely small (a large negative value) or extremely large might at first be disconcerting to the student who has heard that heights, weights, response times and errors of measurements are approximately normally distributed. Surely we do not have heights, weights or times that are less than zero! Certainly not, but 99.7% of the distribution of a normally distributed random variable lies within the interval $\mu \pm 3\sigma$. In the case of heights or weights this interval almost always encompasses positive values.

8. Keep in mind this curve is merely a *model* that approximates an actual distribution of measurements. Its great utility lies in the fact that it *can* be used effectively as a model for so many types of measurements.

Central
Limit

9. The justification for using the normal probability distribution to approximate actual distributions of measurements, and indeed, to approximate the distributions of discrete random variables, is provided by the _____ _____ Theorem.

7.2   The Central Limit Theorem (7.2)

sums; means

repeated
need not

1. The Central Limit Theorem states that under rather general conditions, _____ and _____ of samples of measurements drawn from a population tend to possess, approximately, a bell-shaped distribution in _____ sampling. It is important to note explicitly that the measurements themselves (must, need not) have a bell-shaped distribution.

2. A second important contribution of the Central Limit Theorem is conveyed by the following example.

   Consider a meat processing center which as part of its output prepares one-pound packages of bacon. If the weights of the packaged bacon were carefully checked, some weights would be slightly heavier than 16 oz. while others would be slightly lighter than 16 oz. A frequency histogram of these weights would probably exhibit the mound-shaped distribution characteristic of a normally distributed random variable. Why should this be the case? One can think of the weight of each package as differing from 16 oz. due to an error in the weighing process, to a scale that needs adjustment, to the thickness of the slices of bacon so that the package contains either one more or less slice than it should, or perhaps some of the fat has melted, and so on. Hence any one weight would consist of an average weight (hopefully 16 oz.) modified by the addition of random errors that might be either positive or negative.

3. The Central Limit Theorem loosely stated says that sums or averages are approximately normally distributed with a mean and standard deviation

that depend upon the sampled population. If one considers the error in the weight of a one-pound package of bacon as a *sum* of various effects in which small errors are highly likely and large errors are highly improbable, then the Central Limit Theorem helps explain the apparent normality of the package weights.

4. Equally as important, the Central Limit Theorem assures us that sample means will be approximately normally distributed with a mean and variance that depend upon the population from which the sample has been drawn. This aspect of the Central Limit Theorem will be the focal point for making inferences about populations based upon random samples when the sample size is large.

5. *The Central Limit Theorem:*

    a. If random samples of n observations are drawn from a population with finite mean _____ and standard deviation _____ , then when n is large, the sample mean, $\bar{y}$, will be approximately _____ distributed with mean μ and standard deviation $\sigma/\sqrt{n}$.

    μ; σ
    normally

    b. The Central Limit Theorem could also be stated in terms of the sum of the measurements,

$$\sum_{i=1}^{n} y_i$$

rather than in terms of the sample mean, $\bar{y}$.

   If random samples of n observations are drawn from a population with finite _____ μ and _____ _____ σ, then when n is large,

mean; standard deviation

$$\sum_{i=1}^{n} y_i$$

will be approximately _____ distributed with mean _____ and standard deviation _____ . In both cases, the approximation becomes more and more accurate as n becomes _____ .

normally
$n\mu$; $\sigma\sqrt{n}$

large

6. The Central Limit Theorem is important for two reasons.

    a. It partially explains *why* certain measurements possess approximately a _____ distribution.

    normal

    b. Many of the _____ used in inference making are sums of means of sample measurements and thus possess approximately _____ distributions for large samples.

    estimators

    normal

7. The student should notice that the Central Limit Theorem (does, does not) specify that the sample measurements come from a normal population. The population (could, could not) have a frequency distribution that is flat or

does not

could

sample
mean

skewed or is non-normal in some other way. It is the _____
_____ that behaves as a random variable having an approximately normal distribution.

8. To clarify a point we note that the sample mean, $\bar{y}$, computed from a random sample of n observations drawn from any population with mean μ and standard deviation σ always has a mean equal to μ and a standard deviation equal to $\sigma/\sqrt{n}$. This result is not due to the Central Limit Theorem. The important contribution of the theorem lies in the fact that when n, the sample size, is _____, we may approximate the distribution of $\bar{y}$ with a _____ probability distribution.

large
normal

7.3   Random Samples (7.3)

1. Since it is the sample that provides the information that is used in inference making, we must be duly careful about the selection of the elements in the sample so that we do not systematically exclude or include certain elements of the population in our sampling plan. The sample should be representative of the _____ being sampled.

population
random

2. We call a sample that has been drawn without bias a _____ sample. This is a shorthand way of saying that the sample has been drawn in a random manner. A sample of size n is said to have been randomly drawn if each possible sample of size n has the _____ _____ of being selected.

same
chance

3. If a population consists of N elements and we wish to draw a sample of size n from this population, there are

$$C_n^N = \frac{N!}{n!\,(N-n)!}$$

samples to choose from. A random sample in this situation would be one drawn in such a manner that each sample of size n had the same chance of being drawn, namely _____.

$1/C_n^N$

4. Although perfect random sampling is difficult to achieve in practice, there are several methods available for selecting a sample that will satisfy the conditions of random sampling when N, the population size is not too large.

a. *Method A*. List all the possible samples and assign them numbers. Place each of these numbers on a chip or piece of paper and place them in a bowl. Drawing one number from the bowl will select the random sample to be used.

b. *Method B*. Number each of the N measurements in the population. Write each of these numbers on a chip or slip of paper and place them in a bowl. Now draw n numbers from the bowl and use the members of the population having these numbers as elements to be included in the sample.

c. *Method C*. A useful technique for selecting random samples is one in which a table of random numbers is used to replace the chance device of drawing chips from a bowl.

5. Why is it so important that the sample be randomly drawn? From the practical point of view, one would want to keep the experimenter's biases out of the selection, and at the same time keep the sample as representative of the _____ as possible. From the statistical point of view, we can assess the probability of observing a random sample and hence make valid _____ about the parent population. If the sample is nonrandom, its probability _____ in general be determined and hence no valid inferences can be made from it.

population

inferences
cannot

7.4 Tabulated Areas of the Normal Probability Distribution (7.4)

A. *The Standard Normal Probability Distribution*

1. Probability is the vehicle through which we are able to make inferences about a population in the form of either estimations or decisions. To make inferences about a normal population, we must be able to compute or otherwise find the probabilities associated with a normal random variable. However, since the probability distribution for a normal random variable y depends upon the population parameters, _____ and _____ , one would be required to calculate anew the probabilities associated with y each time a new value for μ or σ was encountered.

$\mu; \sigma$

2. Because of the symmetry of the normal curve about the mean, _____ of the area under the curve lies to the _____ of the mean, and half to the right.

half
left

3. Also because of the symmetry of the normal curve, the area under the curve and a specified number of standard deviations, say z, to the left of the curve is _____ to the area under the curve between the mean and a point z standard deviations to the right.

equal

4. We can simplify our tabulation of the areas under the normal curve by resorting to a standardization process in which we convert a normal random variable y to one that follows the _____ _____ distribution.

standardized normal

5. This standard normal random variable, symbolized by _____ , represents the distance of y from its mean μ, in units of its standard deviation σ.

z

6. To standardize a normal random variable y we use the following procedure.
   a. From y, subtract its mean, μ: This results in the signed distance of y from its mean, a negative sign indicating

   $$y - \mu$$

   y is to the _____ of μ and a positive sign indicating y is to the _____ of μ.

left
right

   b. Now divide by σ: Dividing by σ converts the distance in part a to the number of standard deviations y lies to the right or left of μ.

   $$\frac{(y - \mu)}{\sigma}$$

c. Define

$$z = \frac{y - \mu}{\sigma}$$

z is the standard normal variable having the standardized normal distribution with mean 0 and standard deviation 1.

7. There is a one-to-one correspondence between z and y, meaning that we can associate a unique value of z to each value of y, and vice versa. Note that $z =$ _____ when $y = \mu$.

0

8. The mean of z, the standard normal random variable, is _____, and its standard deviation equals _____.

0

1

9. Given the curve representing the distribution of a continuous random variable y the probability that $a \leqslant y \leqslant b$ is represented by the

area; a

b

_____ under the curve between the points _____ and _____. Hence in finding probabilities associated with a standardized normal variable z we could refer directly to the areas under the curve. These areas are tabulated for your convenience in Table 3 of the Appendix of your text.

symmetric

Since the standardized normal distribution is _____ about the mean zero, half of the area lies to the left of zero and half to the right of zero, and the areas to the left of the mean $z = 0$ can be calculated by using the corresponding and equal area to the right of $z = 0$. Hence Table 3 exhibits areas only for positive values of z correct to the nearest hundredth. Table 3 gives the area between $z = 0$ and a specified value of z, say z_0. A convenient notation used to designate the area between $z = 0$ and z_0 is $A(z_0)$.

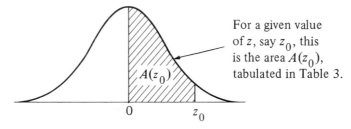

For a given value of z, say z_0, this is the area $A(z_0)$, tabulated in Table 3.

a. For $z = 1$, the area between $z = 0$ and $z = 1$ is $A(z = 1) = A(1) = .3413$.

.4772

b. For $z = 2$, $A(z = 2) = A(2) =$ _____.

.4452

c. For $z = 1.6$, $A(1.6) =$ _____.

.4918

d. For $z = 2.4$, $A(2.4) =$ _____.

Now try reading the table for values of z given to two decimal places.

.4951

e. For $z = 2.58$, $A(2.58) =$ _____.

.2734

f. For $z = 0.75$, $A(0.75) =$ _____.

.4545

g. For $z = 1.69$, $A(1.69) =$ _____.

.4979

h. For $z = 2.87$, $A(2.87) =$ _____.

10. We will now find probabilities associated with the standard normal random variable z, by use of Table 3.

11. *Example:*
Find the probability that z is greater than 1.86, that is, $P[z > 1.86]$.
Solution:
a. Illustrate the problem with a diagram as follows:

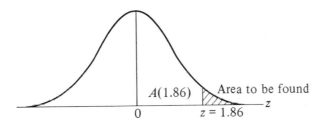

A(1.86) Area to be found

0 $z = 1.86$

b. The total area to the right of $z = 0$ is equal to .5000.
c. From Table 3, $A(1.86) =$ _____.   .4686
d. Therefore, the shaded area is found by subtracting $A(1.86)$ from

_____.   .5000

e. Hence

$$P[z > 1.86] = .5000 - A(1.86)$$

$$= .5000 - \underline{\hspace{1.5cm}}$$ .4686

$$= \underline{\hspace{1.5cm}}$$ .0314

12. *Example:*
Find $P[z < -2.22]$.
Solution:
a. Illustrate the problem with a diagram.

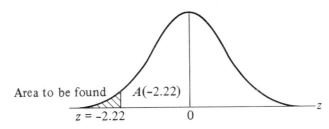

Area to be found A(-2.22)

$z = -2.22$ 0

b. Using the symmetry of the normal distribution, $A(-2.22) = A(2.22)$
= _____. The minus value of z indicates that you are to the   .4868
(left, right) of the mean, $z = 0$.   left
c. Hence

$$P[z < -2.22] = .5000 - \underline{\hspace{1.5cm}}$$ .4868

$$= \underline{\hspace{1.5cm}}$$ .0132

13. *Example:*
   Find $P[-1.21 < z < 2.43]$.
   Solution:
   a. Illustrate the problem with a diagram.

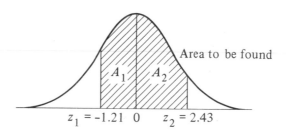

Area to be found

$z_1 = -1.21$ 0 $z_2 = 2.43$

   b. Now

$$P[-1.21 < z < 2.43] = P[-1.21 < z < 0] + P[0 < z < 2.43]$$

$$= A(-1.21) + A(2.43)$$

.3869; .4925

$$= \underline{\hspace{1.5cm}} + \underline{\hspace{1.5cm}}$$

.8794

$$= \underline{\hspace{1.5cm}}$$

14. A second type of problem that arises is that of finding a value of z, say z_0, such that a probability statement about z will be true. We explore this type of problem with examples.

15. *Example:*
   Find the value of z_0 such that

$$P[0 < z < z_0] = .3925$$

   Solution:
   a. Once again, illustrate the problem with a diagram and list pertinent information.

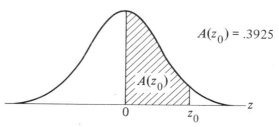

$A(z_0) = .3925$

$A(z_0)$

0   z_0 z

   b. Search Table 3 until the area .3925 is found. The value such that
1.24 $A(z_0) = .3925$ is $z_0 = \underline{\hspace{1.5cm}}$.

c. Therefore

$$P[0 < z < \underline{\hspace{2cm}}] = .3925$$

1.24

16. *Example:*
Find the value of z_0 such that

$$P[z > z_0] = .2643$$

Solution:
a. Illustrate the problem and list pertinent information.

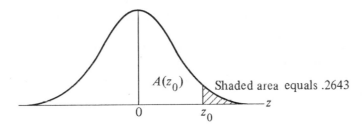

b. $A(z_0) = .5000 - .2643 = \underline{\hspace{2cm}}$.

.2357

c. The value of z_0 such that $A(z_0) = \underline{\hspace{2cm}}$ is $z_0 = \underline{\hspace{2cm}}$.

.2357; 0.63

d. Hence

$$P[z > \underline{\hspace{2cm}}] = .2643$$

0.63

Self-Correcting Exercises 7A

1. Find the following probabilities associated with the standard normal
random variable, z.

a. $P[z > 2.1]$

b. $P[z < -1.2]$

c. $P[.5 < z < 1.5]$

d. $P[-2.75 < z < -1.70]$

e. $P[-1.96 < z < 1.96]$

f. $P[z > 1.645]$

2. Find the value of z, say z_0, such that the following probability statements
are true.

a. $P[z > z_0] = .10$

b. $P[z < z_0] = .01$

c. $P[-z_0 < z < z_0] = .95$

d. $P[-z_0 < z < z_0] = .99$

3. An auditor has reviewed the financial records of a hardware store and has found that their billing errors follow a normal distribution with mean and standard deviation equal to $0 and $1 respectively.
   a. What proportion of the store's billings are in error by more than $1?
   b. What is the probability that a billing represents an overcharge of at least $1.50?
   c. What is the probability that a customer has been undercharged from $0.50 to $1.00?
   d. Within what range would 95% of the billing errors lie?
   e. Of the extreme undercharges, 5% would be at least what amount?

B. *The Normal Probability Distribution in General*

1. We can now proceed to find probabilities associated with any normal random variable y having mean μ and standard deviation σ. This is accomplished by converting the random variable y to the standard normal random variable z and then working the problem in terms of z.
2. Since probability statements are written in the form of inequalities, the reader is reminded of two facts. A statement of inequality is maintained if
   a. the same number is subtracted from each member of the inequality and/or
   b. each member of the inequality is divided by the same *positive* number. The following are equivalent statements about y.

3. a. $y < 24$

   b. $y - 20 < 24 - 20$ (by Number 2a)

   c. $\dfrac{y - 20}{2} < \dfrac{24 - 20}{2}$ (by Number 2b)

4. The following are equivalent statements about y.

   a. $70 < y < 95$

   b. $70 - 15 < y - 15 < 95 - 15$ (by Number 2a)

c. $\dfrac{70-15}{5} < \dfrac{y-15}{5} < \dfrac{95-15}{5}$ (by Number 2b)

5. *Example:*

   Let y be a normal random variable with mean $\mu = 100$ and standard deviation $\sigma = 4$. Find $P[92 < y < 104]$.

   Solution:

   Recalling that $z = (y - \mu)/\sigma$, we can apply Number 2a and 2b to convert the probability statement about y to one about the standard normal random variable z.

   a. $P[92 < y < 104]$ $= P[92 - 100 < y - 100 < 104 - 100]$

   $$= P\left[\dfrac{92-100}{4} < \dfrac{y-100}{4} < \dfrac{104-100}{4}\right]$$

   $$= P[-2 < z < 1]$$

   b. The problem now stated in terms of z is readily solved.

   $$P[92 < y < 104] \quad = P[-2 < z < 1]$$

   $$= A(-2) + A(1)$$

   $$= \underline{\hspace{2cm}} + \underline{\hspace{2cm}} \qquad\qquad .4772; .3413$$

   $$= \underline{\hspace{2cm}} \qquad\qquad\qquad .8185$$

6. *Example:*

   Let y be a normal random variable with mean 100 and standard deviation 4. Find

   $$P[93.5 < y < 105.2]$$

   Solution:

   Since $z = (y - \mu)/\sigma$, we can write

   $$P[93.5 < y < 105.2]$$

   $$= P\left[\dfrac{93.5-(\underline{\hspace{1cm}})}{(\underline{\hspace{1cm}})} < \dfrac{y-(\underline{\hspace{1cm}})}{(\underline{\hspace{1cm}})} < \dfrac{105.2-(\underline{\hspace{1cm}})}{(\underline{\hspace{1cm}})}\right] \qquad \begin{array}{l}100; 100; 100 \\ 1; 1; 1\end{array}$$

   $$= P[-1.63 < z < 1.30]$$

   $$= A(\underline{\hspace{1cm}}) + A(\underline{\hspace{1cm}}) \qquad\qquad -1.63; 1.30$$

.4484; .4032

.8516

0; 0
equal to

$$= \underline{\hspace{2cm}} + \underline{\hspace{2cm}}$$

$$= \underline{\hspace{2cm}}$$

7. It is important to note that, as with any continuous random variable, the probability that a normally distributed random variable y equals a specific number a is _____. That is, $P[y = a] = $ _____. Hence, $P[y < a]$ is (less than, equal to) $P[y \leqslant a]$.

8. We will have to recognize this fact when we use the normal distribution to approximate the probability distribution of a discrete random variable, as we will in the next section. This is because $P[y = a]$ is possibly nonzero when y is a discrete random variable and a is an integer.

Self-Correcting Exercises 7B

1. If y is normally distributed with mean 10 and variance 2.25, evaluate the following probabilities.

   a. $P[y > 8.5]$

   b. $P[y < 12]$

   c. $P[9.25 < y < 11.25]$

   d. $P[7.5 < y < 9.2]$

   e. $P[12.25 < y < 13.25]$

2. An industrial engineer has found that the standard household light bulbs produced by a certain manufacturer have a useful life which is normally distributed with a mean of 250 hours and a variance of 2500. What is the probability that a randomly selected bulb from this production process will have a useful life
   a. in excess of 300 hours?
   b. between 190 and 270 hours?
   c. not exceeding 260 hours?
   d. Ninety percent of the bulbs have a useful life in excess of how many hours?
   e. The probability is .95 that a bulb does not have a useful life in excess of how many hours?

3. Scores on a personnel evaluation form exhibit the characteristics of a normal distribution with mean and standard deviation of 50 and 5 respectively. What proportion of the scores on this evaluation form would be
   a. greater than 60,
   b. less than 45,

   c. between 35 and 65?

   d. If to be considered eligible for a given position, an applicant must score beyond the 95th percentile on this form, what score must an applicant have to be eligible?

7.5 The Normal Approximation to the Binomial Distribution (7.5)

1. For large values of n, the binomial probabilities, $p(y) = C_y^n p^y q^{n-y}$ are very tedious to compute. Is there an alternative to long computations? There is, as we shall see.

2. For a binomial experiment consisting of n trials, let

$$y_1 = \begin{cases} 1 & \text{if trial one is a success} \\ 0 & \text{if trial one is a failure} \end{cases}$$

$$y_2 = \begin{cases} 1 & \text{if trial two is a success} \\ 0 & \text{if trial two is a failure} \end{cases}$$

.
.
.

$$y_n = \begin{cases} 1 & \text{if trial } n \text{ is a success} \\ 0 & \text{if trial } n \text{ is a failure} \end{cases}$$

Then y, the number of successes in n trials, can be thought of as a sum of n independent random variables *each* with a mean equal to _____ and a variance equal to _____ . (See Chapter 6 in the text.)

                                                     p
                                                     pq

3. For

$$y = y_1 + y_2 + \ldots + y_n$$

the _____ _____ Theorem says this sum is _____ normally distributed with mean _____ and variance _____ . Hence when n is _____ , we can approximate the distribution of a binomial random variable with the distribution of a normal random variable whose mean and variance are identical to those for the binomial random variable.

                                                    Central Limit
                                                    approximately; np
                                                    npq; large

4. When can we reasonably apply the normal approximation? For small values of n and values of p close to zero or one, the binomial distribution will exhibit a "pile-up" around $y =$ _____ or $y =$ _____ . The data will not be _____ -shaped and the normal approximation will be poor.

                                                    $0; n$
                                                    bell

5. For a normal random variable, _____ % of the measurements will be

                                                    95

0; n

4

2

within the interval $\mu \pm 2\sigma$. For $\mu = np$ and $\sigma = \sqrt{npq}$, the interval $np \pm 2\sqrt{npq}$ should be within the bounds of the binomial random variable y, or within the interval _____ to _____ to obtain reasonably good approximations to the binomial probabilities.

6. To show how the normal approximation is used, let us consider a binomial random variable y with $n = 8$ and $p = 1/2$ and attempt to approximate some binomial probabilities with a normal random variable having the same mean, $\mu = np$, and variance, $\sigma^2 = npq$, as the binomial y. In this case

a. $\quad \mu = np = 8(1/2) = $ _____

b. $\quad \sigma^2 = npq = 8(1/2)(1/2) = $ _____

c. Note that the interval

$$\mu \pm 2\sigma = 4 \pm 2\sqrt{2} = (1.2, 6.8)$$

is contained within the interval $(0, 8)$; therefore our approximation should be adequate.

7. Consider the following diagrammatic representation of the approximation where $p(y)$ is the frequency distribution for the binomial random variable and $f(y)$ is the frequency distribution for the corresponding normal random variable y.

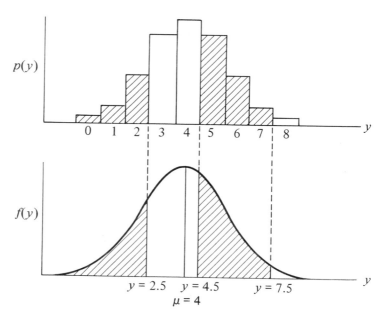

8. *Example:*

Find $P[y < 3]$ using the normal approximation.

Solution:

a. $P[y < 3]$ for the binomial random variable with mean $\mu = 4$ and $\sigma = \sqrt{2}$ corresponds to the shaded bars in the histogram over $y =$ _____, _____ and _____. The approximating probability corresponds to the shaded area in the normal distribution with mean 4 and standard deviation $\sqrt{2}$ to the left of $y =$ _____.

b. We proceed as follows.

$$P[y < 3] \approx P[y < 2.5]$$

$$= P\left[\frac{y - 4}{\sqrt{2}} < \frac{2.5 - 4}{\sqrt{2}}\right]$$

$$= P[z < \underline{\hspace{1.5cm}}]$$

$$= .5000 - A(\underline{\hspace{1.5cm}})$$

$$= .5000 - \underline{\hspace{1.5cm}}$$

$$= \underline{\hspace{1.5cm}}$$

9. *Example:*

Find $P[5 \leqslant y \leqslant 7]$.

Solution:

a. For the binomial random variable with mean 4 and standard deviation $\sqrt{2}$, $P[5 \leqslant y \leqslant 7]$ corresponds to the shaded bars over $y =$ _____, _____ and _____. This corresponds in turn to the shaded area for the approximating normal distribution with mean 4 and standard deviation $\sqrt{2}$ between $y = 4.5$ and $y = 7.5$.

b. Therefore

$$P[5 \leqslant y \leqslant 7] \approx P[4.5 < y < 7.5]$$

$$= P\left[\frac{4.5 - 4}{\sqrt{2}} < \frac{y - 4}{\sqrt{2}} < \frac{7.5 - 4}{\sqrt{2}}\right]$$

$$= P[\underline{\hspace{1.5cm}} < z < \underline{\hspace{1.5cm}}]$$

$$= A(\underline{\hspace{1.5cm}}) - A(\underline{\hspace{1.5cm}})$$

$$= \underline{\hspace{1.5cm}} - \underline{\hspace{1.5cm}}$$

$$= \underline{\hspace{1.5cm}}$$

10. Notice that we used $P[y < 2.5]$ to approximate the binomial probability

Answer column:

0
1; 2

2.5

−1.06

−1.06

.3554

.1446

5
6; 7

.35; 2.47

2.47; .35

.4932; .1368

.3564

continuous

$P[y < 3]$. In like manner we used $P[4.5 < y < 7.5]$ to approximate the binomial probability $P[5 \leq y \leq 7]$. The addition or subtraction of 0.5 is called *correction for continuity* since we are approximating a discrete probability distribution with a probability distribution that is _____.

11. A student may become confused as to whether 0.5 should be added or subtracted in the process of approximating binomial probabilities. A common sense rule that always works is to examine the binomial probability statement carefully, and determine which values of the binomial random variable are included in the statement. (Draw a picture if necessary.) The probabilities associated with these values correspond to the bars in the histogram centered over them. Locating the end points of the bars to be included determines the values needed for the approximating normal random variable.

12. *Example:*
Suppose y is a binomial random variable with $n = 400$ and $p = .1$. Use the normal approximation to binomial probabilities to find:

   a. $P[y > 45]$

   b. $P[y \leq 32]$

   c. $P[34 \leq y \leq 46]$

Solution:
If y is binomial, then its mean and variance are

40

$$\mu = np = 400\,(.1) = \text{_____}$$

36

$$\sigma^2 = npq = 400\,(.1)\,(.9) = \text{_____}$$

a. To find $P[y > 45]$ we need the probabilities associated with the values $46, 47, 48, \ldots, 400$. This corresponds to the bars in the binomial histogram beginning at _____. Hence

45.5

45.5

$$P[y > 45] \approx P[y > \text{_____}]$$

45.5

$$= P\left[z > \dfrac{\text{_____} - 40}{6}\right]$$

.92

$$= P[z > \text{_____}]$$

.1788

$$= \text{_____}$$

32

b. To find $P[y \leq 32]$ we need the probabilities associated with the values $0, 1, 2, \ldots,$ up to and including $y = $ _____. This corresponds to finding the area in the binomial histogram to the left of _____. Hence

32.5

$$P[y \leqslant 32] \approx P[y < \underline{\hspace{2cm}}]$$ 32.5

$$= P\left[z < \dfrac{\underline{\hspace{1cm}} - 40}{6}\right]$$ 32.5

$$= P[z < \underline{\hspace{2cm}}]$$ -1.25

$$= \underline{\hspace{2cm}}$$ .1056

c. In finding $P[34 \leqslant y \leqslant 46]$, we need the probabilities associated with the values beginning at 34 up to and including 46. This corresponds to finding the area in the histogram between _____ and _____.   33.5; 46.5
So that

$$P[34 \leqslant y \leqslant 46] \approx P[\underline{\hspace{1.5cm}} < y < \underline{\hspace{1cm}}]$$ 33.5; 46.5

$$= P\left[\dfrac{\underline{\hspace{1cm}} - 40}{6} < z < \dfrac{\underline{\hspace{1cm}} - 40}{6}\right]$$ 33.5; 46.5

$$= P[\underline{\hspace{1.5cm}} < z < \underline{\hspace{1cm}}]$$ -1.08; 1.08

$$= \underline{\hspace{2cm}}$$ .7198

Notice that the interval $\mu \pm 2\sigma$ or 40 ± 12 is well within the binomial range of 0 to 400, so that these approximate probabilities should be reasonably accurate.

Self-Correcting Exercises 7C

1. A company claims that at most 15% of the items it produces contain defects. Assuming the maximal value of .15 for p, the probability that an item is defective, what is the probability of observing 23 or more defectives in a random sample of 100 items chosen at random from this company's production? If the sample did contain 23 defectives, would you still be willing to accept the 15% figure as claimed?
2. If the median income in a certain area is claimed to be $12,000, what is the probability that 37 or fewer of 100 randomly chosen wage-earners from this area have incomes less than $12,000? Would the $12,000 figure seem reasonable if your sample actually contained 37 wage-earners whose income was less than $12,000?
3. If the failure rate of a given component is 10%, within what limits would the number of failures in a sample of 100 be expected to lie with probability .95?
4. If it is known that 25% of newly formed small business enterprises fail within a year, what is the probability that 30 or more such enterprises in a random sample of 100 are recorded as having failed within a year?

7.6 Summary (7.6–7.7)

bell
normal

Central Limit Theorem

normally; repeated

normally

standardization

mean; standard
deviation

normal
variance

continuity

Empirical

sketch; locate

rectangles
half

1. Many random variables observed in nature possess a _____-shaped probability distribution. For this reason we can use the _____ probability distribution to approximate these distributions.

2. The _____ _____ _____ gives a partial explanation of why normal random variables occur with such frequency in nature. It states that, under general conditions, the sum or mean of a random sample of n measurements drawn from a population is approximately _____ distributed in _____ sampling when n is large.

3. Since the binomial random variable can be interpreted as a sum of n independent random variables, when n is large, y will be approximately _____ distributed.

4. To efficiently solve probability problems concerning any normal random variable y with mean μ and standard deviation σ, we can use a _____ process whereby y is converted to the standard normal random variable z by subtracting its _____ and dividing by its _____ _____.

5. Under certain conditions we are able to approximate binomial probabilities by using corresponding areas in a _____ probability distribution having the same mean and _____ as the binomial random variable. In so doing we take into account the fact that we are approximating the probabilities associated with a discrete binomial random variable with the probabilities associated with a continuous normal random variable by using a correction for _____.

6. In addition to justifying the normal distribution as a model for many natural phenomena and as an approximation to the binomial distribution, the Central Limit Theorem provides justification for the _____ Rule.

7. When using the normal curve in problem solving, one should always _____ a normal curve and _____ the probability areas pertinent to the problem.

8. When using the normal curve to approximate a binomial distribution, always sketch in the binomial probability _____ as well as the normal curve, using a _____-unit correction to make the proper correspondence of areas between the binomial distribution and the normal curve.

Exercises

1. Consider the following situation: A man has an urn containing 20 white and 3 red balls. He asks a little boy to close his eyes and pick 3 balls from the urn. For each red ball selected by the youngster, the man promises him

a candy bar. Just as the boy is ready to pick the first ball, the doorbell rings. The man instructs the boy to continue and leaves the room to answer the door. Upon his return he finds the lad has picked 3 red balls. Would you consider this random sampling on the part of the boy?

2. Find the following probabilities for the standard normal variable z.

    a. $P[z < 1.9]$

    b. $P[1.21 < z < 2.25]$

    c. $P[z > -0.6]$

    d. $P[-2.8 < z < 1.93]$

    e. $P[-1.3 < z < 2.3]$

    f. $P[-1.62 < z < 0.37]$

3. Find the value of z, say z_0, such that the following probability statements are true:

    a. $P[z > z_0] = .2420$

    b. $P[z < z_0] = .0668$

    c. $P[z < z_0] = .9394$

    d. $P[z > z_0] = .8643$

4. Find a value of z, say z_0, such that the following probability statements are true:

    a. $P[-z_0 < z < z_0] = .9668$

    b. $P[-z_0 < z < z_0] = .90$

5. If y is distributed normally with mean 25 and standard deviation 4, find

    a. $P[y > 21]$

    b. $P[y < 30]$

    c. $P[15 < y < 35]$

    d. $P[y < 18]$

6. A sidewalk interviewer stopped three men who were walking together, asked their opinions on some topical subjects and found their answers quite similar. Would you consider the interviewer's selection to be random in this case? Is it surprising that similar answers were given by these three men?

7. The length of life of brand A television picture tubes is normally distributed with mean and standard deviation equal to 3.7 and 0.5 years, respectively. What is the probability that a tube
   a. lasts at least 4 years?
   b. lasts no longer than 4.5 years?

8. The test scores on a standardized examination are normally distributed with mean and standard deviation 75 and 9, respectively. What percentage of the scores
   a. will be greater than 90?
   b. will be less than 60?
   c. will fall between 70 and 85?

9. For a given type of cannon and a fixed range setting, the distance that a shell fired from this cannon will travel is normally distributed with a mean and standard deviation of 1.5 and 0.1 miles, respectively. What is the probability that a shell will travel
   a. farther than 1.72 miles?
   b. less than 1.35 miles?
   c. at least 1.45 miles but at most 1.62 miles?

10. For a binomial experiment with $n = 20$ and $p = .7$, calculate $P[10 \leqslant y \leqslant 16]$
    a. using the binomial tables.
    b. using the normal approximation.

11. Using the information given in Exercise 10, repeat parts a and b for $P[y \geqslant 14]$.

12. A pre-election poll taken in a given city indicated that 40% of the voting public favored candidate A, 40% favored candidate B and 20% were as yet undecided. If these percentages are true, in a random sample of 100 voters what is the probability that
    a. at most 50 voters in the sample prefer candidate A?
    b. at least 65 voters in the sample prefer candidate B?
    c. at least 25 but at most 45 voters in the sample prefer candidate B?

13. In introducing a new breakfast sausage to the marketing public, an advertising campaign claimed that 7 out of 10 shoppers would prefer these new sausages over other brands. If 100 people were randomly chosen, and the advertiser's claim is true, what is the probability that
    a. at most 65 people preferred the new sausages?
    b. at least 80 people preferred the new sausages?
    c. If only 60 people stated a preference for the new sausages, would this be sufficient evidence to indicate that the advertising claim is false and that in fact, less than 7 out of 10 people would prefer the new sausages?

14. Assuming that y is normally distributed with $\mu = 5$ and $\sigma^2 = 9$, find

a. $P[2 \leqslant y \leqslant 8]$

b. $P[-4 \leqslant y \leqslant 2]$

15. A manufacturer's process for producing steel rods can be regulated so as to produce rods with an average length of μ. If these lengths are normally distributed with a standard deviation of 0.2 inches, what should be the setting for μ if one wants at most 5% of the steel rods to have a length greater than 10.4 inches?

16. A manufacturing plant produces flashlight batteries that have a length of life which is normally distributed with mean and standard deviation equal to 300 and 25 hours, respectively. What percentage of the batteries produced will last at least 340 hours?

17. On a college campus, the student automobile registration revealed that the ratio of small to large cars (as measured by engine displacement) is 2 to 1 If 72 car owners are chosen at random from the student body, find the probability that this group includes at most 46 owners of small cars. (Use the normal approximation with the correction for continuity to find this probability.)

18. A psychological "introvert-extrovert" test produced scores which had a normal distribution with mean and standard deviation 75 and 12, respectively. If we wish to designate the *highest* 15% as extrovert, what would be the proper score to choose as the cut off point?

19. A large supermarket is located so as to service both in-town and out-of-town customers. If 60% of its customers are townspeople, use the normal approximation to find the probability that 380 or more of the 600 customers on a given day are townspeople.

20. An auto insurance company has found from past experience that it must pay approximately 20% of its customer claims. Recent indications suggest a drop in this percentage. To obtain statistical support that the percentage of customer claims requiring payment is now less than 20%, the company will examine the next 100 claims. Let p be the fraction of customer claims that must be paid. Let y be the number of claims in the sample of 100 claims that require payment.
    a. State H_0 and H_a in terms of p.
    b. If the null hypothesis is rejected when y is 15 or less, use the normal approximation (with the correction for continuity) to find α, the probability of rejecting H_0 when it is, in fact, true.
    c. Use the normal approximation to find β, the probability of falsely accepting H_0 if p is actually .10.

21. The ages of employees in a certain industry are normally distributed with mean and standard deviation 30 and 2.5 years, respectively.
    a. What is the probability that a worker chosen at random from this industry will be 34 years of age or older?
    b. If three employees are randomly selected from this industry, what is the probability that all three will be 34 years of age or older?

Chapter 8

LARGE-SAMPLE STATISTICAL INFERENCE

8.1 Introduction (8.1–8.2)

1. The objective of statistics is to make _____ about a _____ based on information contained in a _____. Since populations are described by numerical descriptive measures, called _____ of the population, one can make inferences about the population by making inferences about its parameters. For example, the test of the effectiveness of a new vaccine and lot acceptance sampling were inferences which resulted in decisions concerning the binomial parameter p.
   - inferences; population
   - sample
   - parameters

2. Some common examples of population parameters are the _____, the _____ _____, or the _____ under the probability distribution above, below, or between some value(s) of the random variable.
   - mean
   - standard deviation; area

3. There are two general methods for making inferences about parameters:
   a. Make _____ concerning the value of the parameter.
   b. _____ or predict the value of the parameter.
   - decisions
   - Estimate

4. There (are, are no) definite, formal rules about which method should be used in a particular situation. The method used usually (is, is not) a matter of personal preference.
   - are no
   - is

5. The quantities to be used in making inferences about population parameters will often be sums or averages of the measurements in a random sample and consequently will possess a frequency distribution in repeated sampling that is approximately _____ due to the _____ Theorem.
   - normal; Central
   - Limit

6. One of the most important concepts to grasp is that inference making is a two-step procedure. These steps are:
   a. Make the _____.
   b. Measure its _____.
   A measure of goodness for an inference is essential to enable the person using the inference to measure its reliability. For example, we would wonder whether the drug employed in a medical experiment was truly
   - inference
   - goodness

effective, or whether the drug was ineffective and favorable experimental response occurred due to chance.

8.2   Types of Estimators (8.3)

1. Using the measurements in a sample to predict the value of one or more _____ of the population is called estimation.

parameters

2. An estimator is a _____ that tells how to calculate an estimate of a parameter based on the information contained in a sample. There are often many different estimators that can be used for a particular population parameter, though some will have more desirable properties than others.

rule

3. An estimation rule is often expressed as a mathematical _____.

formula

4. Estimators are of two types:

   a. A _____ _____ of a population parameter is a rule which tells how to calculate a single number based on sample data. The resulting number is called a _____ _____ of the parameter.

point estimator

point estimate

   b. An _____ _____ of a population parameter is a rule for calculating two numbers based on sample data.

interval estimator

5. The pair of numbers obtained from an interval estimator is called an interval estimate or _____ _____ for the parameter. The larger number locates the _____ end of the interval and is called the _____ _____ _____. It is denoted by the symbol _____. The smaller number locates the _____ end of the interval and is called the _____ _____ _____. It is denoted by the symbol _____.

confidence interval
upper
upper confidence limit
UCL
lower; lower
confidence limit; LCL

6. _____ _____ are more commonly used in industrial experimentation, while _____ _____ arise more frequently in consumer preference surveys.

Confidence intervals
point estimates

7. An estimator is most often expressed in terms of a mathematical formula that gives the estimate as a function of the sample measurements. For example, $\bar{y}$ is an _____ of the population parameter, μ. If a sample of $n = 20$ pieces of aluminum cable is tested for strength and the mean of the sample is $\bar{y} = 100.7$, then 100.7 is an _____ of the population mean strength, μ. The estimator of a parameter is usually designated by placing a "hat" over the parameter to be estimated. Thus an estimator of μ would be $\hat{\mu} = \bar{y}$.

estimator

estimate

8.3   Evaluating the Goodness of Estimators (8.4–8.5)

1. Recall that an estimator is a rule for calculating an estimate of some population parameter from the data contained in a particular sample. We cannot, however, evaluate the goodness of a particular estimator from that single sample.

2. Instead, the goodness or _____ of an estimator is evaluated by observing its behavior in _____ _____.

   reliability
   repeated sampling

3. In general, we could investigate the characteristics of, for example, a point estimator if we knew what its relative frequency _____ looked like. Statisticians use the repeated sampling referred to in 8.3(2) above to generate the estimator's relative frequency distribution.

   distribution *or* histogram

4. The probability distribution for an estimator is called its _____ _____. The probability distribution is the conceptual result of calculating the estimator for an _____ number of samples.

   sampling
   distribution
   infinite

5. There are two properties that we especially seek in an estimator. First, we would like the _____ distribution of the estimator to _____ on the true value of the parameter being estimated. That is, we want the estimator to be _____.

   sampling
   center
   unbiased
   standard deviation

6. Second, we would like the _____ _____ of the estimator's sampling distribution to be small. That is, we would like the estimator to have minimum variance.

7. An estimator of a population parameter is said to be unbiased if the _____ of its sampling distribution is equal to the parameter estimated. Otherwise, the estimator is said to be _____.

   mean
   biased

8. For most estimators, the standard deviation of the sampling distribution is controllable by varying the _____ _____. For example, the standard deviation of $\bar{y}$, the estimator of the population mean, μ, has a standard deviation equal to _____. Thus, we can make the standard deviation of $\bar{y}$ as small as we wish by _____ n, the sample size.

   sample size

   $\sigma/\sqrt{n}$
   increasing

9. Suppose we are interested in estimating some parameter θ. The distributions obtained in repeated sampling are shown below for four different estimators of θ. Which estimator appears to possess the most desirable properties?_____
   Which estimator appears to be next most desirable (i.e., second best)?

   $\hat{\theta}_4$

   $\hat{\theta}_2$

   _____

(a)

$\hat{\theta}_1$ θ

(b)

$\hat{\theta}_2$ θ

(c)

$\hat{\theta}_3$ θ

(d)

$\hat{\theta}_4$ θ

error of estimation

75
Empirical Rule

confidence; narrow
enclosing
1

confidence coefficient

larger

mean; $\bar{y}$

unbiased
standard deviation
all

expected value
μ

$\sigma/\sqrt{n}$

population
$N; n$
1
$\sigma/\sqrt{n}$
normally
Central Limit Theorem

10. The distance between an estimate and the estimated parameter is called the _____ _____ _____. Tchebysheff's Inequality tells us that the error of estimation will be less than two standard deviations _____ percent of the time. According to the _____ _____ the same probability is .95.

11. Thus far, we have been talking mostly about point estimators. But it is also important to assess the goodness of interval estimators.

12. For interval estimators, we desire two properties:
   a. that the _____ interval be as _____ as possible;
   b. that the probability of the confidence interval _____ the estimated parameter be as close to _____ as possible.

13. The probability that a confidence interval will enclose the estimated parameter is called the _____ _____.

14. The width of the confidence interval can be decreased by obtaining _____ samples.

15. It is important to stress that true population parameters do not vary from sample to sample. Rather, it is the confidence limits that "bounce around" as they are calculated anew for each sample. The failure of a particular confidence interval to enclose the population parameter is *not* due to movement by the parameter. Rather, the confidence interval itself has moved "too far" away from the parameter. (See Figure 8.5 in the textbook.)

8.4 Estimation of a Population Mean (8.6–8.7)

1. Of the many estimators available for estimating the population mean μ, the sample _____, symbolized by _____, is usually superior. Regardless of the population from which the sample was drawn, the sample mean is _____, and for most populations, it has a minimum _____ _____.

2. For _____ populations, the probability distribution of $\bar{y}$ (obtained in repeated random sampling of n measurements from a population with mean μ and variance σ^2) has three important properties:
   a. The _____ _____ of $\bar{y}$ is equal to the population mean; i.e., $E(\bar{y}) =$ _____.
   b. The standard deviation of $\bar{y}$ is

$$\sigma_{\bar{y}} = \frac{}{} \sqrt{\frac{N-n}{N-1}}$$

where N is the number of measurements in the _____. We usually assume that _____ is large relative to _____, so that $\sqrt{(N-n)/(N-1)}$ is approximately equal to _____, and $\sigma_{\bar{y}} =$ _____.

   c. When n is large, $\bar{y}$ is approximately _____ distributed, according to the _____ _____ _____ (assuming that μ and σ are finite).

3. By property 2a., $\bar{y}$ is a(n) _____ estimator of _____ .   unbiased; μ
   By property 2b., the standard deviation of $\bar{y}$ _____ as σ in-   increases
   creases, and _____ as n increases.   decreases

4. A point estimate for the population mean μ is given by the formula $\sum\limits_{i=1}^{n} y_i/n$
   _____ .

5. The two-standard-deviation bound on the error of estimation of the
   population mean is given by

   $$2\sigma_{\bar{y}} = \underline{\hspace{2cm}}$$ $2\sigma/\sqrt{n}$

   The probability that the error of estimation is less than $2\sigma/\sqrt{n}$ is____ . .95

6. Often the value of _____ , the population standard deviation, is σ
   unknown. If n is greater than _____ , we may approximate σ with   30
   _____ , the _____ standard deviation. s; sample

7. *Example:*
   The mean length of stay for patients in a hospital must be known in order
   to estimate the number of beds required. The length of stay, recorded for a
   sample of 400 patients at a given hospital, produced a mean and standard
   deviation equal to 5.7 and 8.1 days, respectively. Give a point estimate for
   μ, the mean length of stay for patients entering the hospital and place a
   bound of error on this estimate.
   Solution:
   a. The point estimate for μ is $\bar{y}$ = _____ .   5.7
   b. Since σ is unknown the *approximate* bound on error is

   $$2\frac{s}{\sqrt{n}} = 2\left(\frac{8.1}{\sqrt{400}}\right) = \underline{\hspace{2cm}}$$ .81

8. Before considering the interval estimator of a population mean specifically,
   we will briefly review the interval estimation for any population parameter
   θ.

9. Let $\hat{\theta}$ be an *unbiased* point estimator of θ and suppose that $\hat{\theta}$ generates a
   normal distribution of estimates in repeated sampling. The mean of this
   distribution of estimates is _____ and the standard deviation is $\sigma_{\hat{\theta}}$. θ
   Then _____ % of the point estimates will lie within $1.96\sigma_{\hat{\theta}}$ of the   95
   parameter θ. Similarly, _____ % will lie in the interval $\theta \pm 1.645\sigma_{\hat{\theta}}$ 90
   (See below).

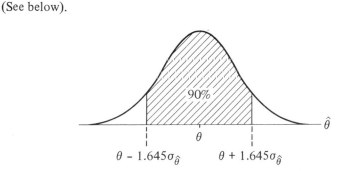

$\theta - 1.645\sigma_{\hat{\theta}}$ $\theta + 1.645\sigma_{\hat{\theta}}$

90

10. Suppose that one were to construct an interval estimate by measuring the distance $1.645\sigma_{\hat{\theta}}$ on either side of $\hat{\theta}$. *Intervals constructed in this manner will enclose θ _____ % of the time* (See below).

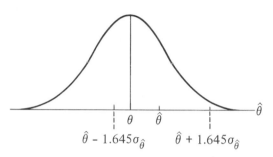

$$\hat{\theta} - 1.645\sigma_{\hat{\theta}} \qquad \hat{\theta} + 1.645\sigma_{\hat{\theta}}$$

Thus for a confidence interval with confidence coefficient $(1 - \alpha)$, we use

$$\hat{\theta} \pm z_{\alpha/2}\sigma_{\hat{\theta}}$$

to construct the interval estimate. The quantity $z_{\alpha/2}$ satisfies the relation $P[z > z_{\alpha/2}] = \alpha/2$ as indicated below:

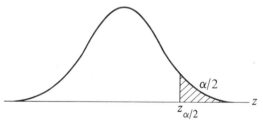

Not all good interval estimators are constructed by measuring $z_{\alpha/2}\sigma_{\hat{\theta}}$ on either side of the best point estimator, but this is true for the parameters $\mu, p, (\mu_1 - \mu_2)$, and $(p_1 - p_2)$. These confidence intervals are good for samples that are large enough to achieve approximate normality for the distribution of $\hat{\theta}$ and good approximation for unknown parameters appearing in $\sigma_{\hat{\theta}}$.

1.96

30

11. A 95% confidence interval for μ is $\bar{y} \pm$ _____ $\sigma/\sqrt{n}$. As a rule of thumb, the sample size, n, must be greater than or equal to _____ in order that s be a good approximation to σ.

12. Give the z values corresponding to the following confidence coefficients:

1.645
2.58

Confidence Coefficients	$z_{\alpha/2}$
.95	1.96
.90	_____
.99	_____

13. *Example:*

To construct a 95% confidence interval for the mean length of hospital stay, μ, based on the sample of $n = 400$ patients ($\bar{y} = 5.7$ and $s = 8.1$) we calculate

$$\bar{y} \pm z_{\alpha/2}\sigma/\sqrt{n}$$

Using $z_{.025} = 1.96$ and an estimate for σ given by $s = 8.1$, we obtain the interval estimate for the mean length of hospital stay

$5.7 \pm$ _____	.79

More properly, we estimate that _____ $< \mu <$ _____ with 95% confidence.   4.91; 6.49

14. Note that the width of a confidence interval _____ as the confidence coefficient increases, and _____ as the sample size increases.   increases / decreases

15. *Example:*

Suppose it is desired to estimate the average purchase volume for an individual credit customer of the Palace Department Store for the month of December. A sample of 40 credit customers' files were examined and the latest December purchase volume available was recorded for each customer in the sample. The mean volume was found to be $\bar{y} = \$22.40$ with a standard deviation, $s = \$0.95$. Give a 90% confidence interval for the mean purchase volume for December for all the credit customers of the Palace Department Store.

Solution:

The confidence coefficient, $1 - \alpha =$ _____. Therefore, $\alpha/2 =$ _____   .90; .05

and $z_{\alpha/2} =$ _____. To find the interval estimate, use   1.645

$$\bar{y} \pm \text{_____} \; s/\sqrt{n}$$ 1.645

Substituting,

$$\$22.40 \pm \text{_____} . 95/\sqrt{40}$$ 1.645

$$\$22.40 \pm \text{_____}$$ $.25

Hence, the 90% confidence interval for μ is

_____ to _____ $22.15; $22.65

8.5 Estimation from Large Samples (8.8)

1. The sample mean and other estimators still to be presented in this chapter possess sampling distributions that are approximately _____   normally

Central Limit

distributed as a consequence of the _____ _____ Theorem.

2. The four situations for which estimators are given in this chapter are:
   a. a single population mean μ;
   b. the difference between two population means;
   c. a single population proportion p;
   d. the difference between two population proportions.

3. Although the point estimators for these situations are all different, the Central Limit Theorem tells us that the sampling distributions of these estimators have similar properties, and we can make general statements about error bounds and confidence intervals which are applicable to all four situations.

2

point estimator

4. The bound on the error of estimation for a large-sample point estimator is equal to _____ standard deviations of the sampling distribution of the _____ _____.

5. Similarly, a $(1 - \alpha)$ 100% large-sample confidence interval is given by the formula

$$\hat{\theta} \pm z_{\alpha/2} \sigma_{\hat{\theta}}$$

where $z_{\alpha/2}$ is obtained from a table of normal curve areas, $\hat{\theta}$ the point estimator and $\sigma_{\hat{\theta}}$ its standard deviation.

Self-Correcting Exercises 8A

1. A random check of 50 savings accounts at the local city bank showed an average savings of $89.50 with a standard deviation of $25.10. Estimate the average savings in the accounts at this bank. Place a bound on the error of estimation. Calculate 95% confidence limits for the mean savings in the bank's accounts.

2. In an attempt to update rates in a specific area, a fire insurance company randomly selects 50 fire insurance claims involving damage to one-family wooden frame dwellings with approximately 1500 square feet of living area. The average claim was found to be $8,750 with a standard deviation of $3050. Estimate the true mean claim for structures of this type with a 95% confidence interval estimate.

8.6 Estimating $\mu_1 - \mu_2, p$ and $p_1 - p_2$ (8.9–8.11)

1. We now consider the problem of estimating the difference between two population means. That is, we consider two populations, the first with mean and variance μ_1 and σ_1^2, and the second with mean and variance μ_2 and σ_2^2. A random sample of n_1 measurements is drawn from the first population, and one of n_2 measurements from the second.

2. The point estimator of $(\mu_1 - \mu_2)$, the difference between the population means, is _____, the difference between the _____ _____.

$(\bar{y}_1 - \bar{y}_2)$; sample means

3. The standard deviation of the sampling distribution of $(\bar{y}_1 - \bar{y}_2)$ is

$$\sigma_{(\bar{y}_1 - \bar{y}_2)} = \underline{\hspace{3cm}}$$

$$\sqrt{\frac{\sigma_1^2}{n_1} + \frac{\sigma_2^2}{n_2}}$$

4. The bound on the error of the estimator is. _____.

$$2\sqrt{\frac{\sigma_1^2}{n_1} + \frac{\sigma_2^2}{n_2}}$$

5. If the population variances σ_1^2 and σ_2^2 are unknown, the _____ _____, denoted by _____ and _____, can be used as approximations, provided both n_1 and n_2 are _____ or greater.

sample variances; s_1^2; s_2^2
30

6. A $(1 - \alpha)$ 100% confidence interval for $(\mu_1 - \mu_2)$ is given by

$$\underline{\hspace{2cm}} \pm \underline{\hspace{2cm}} \sqrt{\frac{\sigma_1^2}{n_1} + \frac{\sigma_2^2}{n_2}}$$

$(\bar{y}_1 - \bar{y}_2)$; $z_{\alpha/2}$

7. *Example:*
   A company was interested in comparing the average daily sales made by two different salesmen. The daily sales of each salesman were recorded for 72 consecutive days. The mean and variance of the daily sales in hundreds of dollars for the two salesmen were found to be

$$\bar{y}_1 = 7.8, s_1^2 = .10, \bar{y}_2 = 8.4, \text{ and } s_2^2 = .06$$

   respectively. Find a 95% confidence interval for the difference in average daily sales for the two salesmen.
   Solution:
   We are interested in placing a confidence interval about the parameter _____. The confidence interval is

$$(\bar{y}_1 - \bar{y}_2) \pm z_{\alpha/2} (\underline{\hspace{2cm}})$$

$\mu_1 - \mu_2$

$$\sqrt{\frac{\sigma_1^2}{n_1} + \frac{\sigma_2^2}{n_2}}$$

   Using the sample approximations for σ_1^2 and σ_2^2 the interval estimate is

$$\underline{\hspace{2cm}} \pm \underline{\hspace{2cm}}$$

$-.6$; .092

   or

$$\underline{\hspace{2cm}} \text{ to } \underline{\hspace{2cm}}$$

$-.692; -.508$

8. Many surveys seek to estimate the proportion of people or objects in a large group which possess a particular characteristic. These surveys are examples of a _____ experiment, and require the estimation of the binomial parameter _____.

binomial
p

9. The best point estimator of the binomial parameter p, denoted by

$\hat{p}$; successes
trials

y/n

unbiased; smaller

Central Limit Theorem

$\sqrt{\dfrac{pq}{n}}$

$1 - p$

$\sqrt{\dfrac{pq}{n}}$

$\hat{p}; \dfrac{\hat{p}\hat{q}}{n}$

n
normal
0; 1; larger

$\hat{p} \pm 1.96 \sqrt{\dfrac{\hat{p}\hat{q}}{n}}$

_____, is calculated by dividing y, the total number of _____, by n, the total number of _____. Therefore,

$$\hat{p} = \underline{\qquad}$$

10. By "best" we mean that $\hat{p}$ is _____ and has a _____ variance than other possible estimators.

11. The estimator $\hat{p}$ has a sampling distribution that is normally distributed because of the _____ _____ _____.

12. The standard deviation of the estimator $\hat{p}$ is given by

$$\sigma_{\hat{p}} = \underline{\qquad}$$

where p is the unknown population proportion, $q = $ _____, and n is the sample size.

13. Therefore, the bound on the error of the estimator $\hat{p}$ is

$$2\sigma_{\hat{p}} = 2\underline{\qquad}$$

14. Correspondingly, a $(1 - \alpha)$ 100% confidence interval for p is given by

$$\underline{\qquad} \pm z_{\alpha/2}\sqrt{\underline{\qquad}}$$

15. The substitution of $\hat{p}$ and $\hat{q}$ for p and q in the formula for the confidence interval is justified provided _____ is large enough for the distribution of $\hat{p}$ to be approximately _____. In general, the closer p is to _____ or _____, the _____ n must be.

16. The formula for a 95% confidence interval for a binomial parameter, p, is

$$\underline{\qquad}$$

where $\hat{p}$ is used to approximate p in the formula for $\sigma_{\hat{p}}$ since its value is unknown.

17. *Example:*

An experimental rehabilitation technique employed on released convicts showed that 79 of a total of 121 men subjected to the technique pursued useful and crime-free lives for a three-year period following prison release. Find a 95% confidence interval for p, the probability that a convict subjected to the rehabilitation technique will follow a crime-free existence for at least three years after prison release.

Solution:

The sampling described above satisfies the requirements of a binomial experiment consisting of $n = 121$ trials. In estimating the parameter p with a 95% confidence interval we use the estimator

$$\hat{p} \pm 1.96 \sqrt{\frac{pq}{n}}$$

Since p is unknown, the sample value, p, will be used in the approximation of $\sqrt{pq/n}$. Collecting pertinent information, we have

a. $\quad \hat{p} = \dfrac{y}{n} = \dfrac{79}{121} = .65$

b. $\quad \sqrt{\dfrac{pq}{n}} = \sqrt{\dfrac{(.65)(.35)}{121}} = .04$

c. The interval estimate is given as

$$.65 \pm 1.96 \,(.04)$$

or $\quad .65 \pm .08$

d. We estimate that _____ $< p <$ _____ with 95% | .57; .73
     confidence.

18. We finally consider the case in which we wish to estimate the difference between the parameters of two binomial populations. We will assume that the two populations have binomial parameters p_1 and p_2, respectively, that independent random samples consisting of n_1 and n_2 trials are drawn, and that estimates $\hat{p}_1$ and $\hat{p}_2$ are calculated from the respective samples.

19. The estimates $\hat{p}_1$ and $\hat{p}_2$ are calculated from the following formulas:

a. $\quad \hat{p}_1 = $ _____ | y_1/n_1

b. $\quad \hat{p}_2 = $ _____ | y_2/n_2

20. Our estimator for the difference between the parameters of the two binomial populations is _____. | $(\hat{p}_1 - \hat{p}_2)$

21. Because $\hat{p} = y/n$ for any binomial population is approximately _____   normally
    distributed for large values of _____, the estimator $(\hat{p}_1 - \hat{p}_2)$ is n
    also approximately normally distributed for large values of _____ n_1
    and _____. n_2

22. The expected value of the estimator $(\hat{p}_1 - \hat{p}_2)$ is _____, so that $p_1 - p_2$
    the estimator $(\hat{p}_1 - \hat{p}_2)$ is _____.   unbiased

23. The standard deviation of the estimator $(\hat{p}_1 - \hat{p}_2)$ is

$$\sigma_{(\hat{p}_1 - \hat{p}_2)} = \sqrt{\underline{\hspace{3cm}}} \qquad\qquad \dfrac{p_1 q_1}{n_1} + \dfrac{p_2 q_2}{n_2}$$

$1 - p_1; 1 - p_2$

where $q_1 =$ _____ and $q_2 =$ _____.

24. Consequently, the bound on the error of the estimator $(\hat{p}_1 - \hat{p}_2)$ is

$2; \dfrac{\hat{p}_1\hat{q}_1}{n_1} + \dfrac{\hat{p}_2\hat{q}_2}{n_2}$

$$\underline{\hspace{2cm}} \sqrt{\underline{\hspace{2.5cm}}}$$

and a $(1 - \alpha)$ 100% confidence interval for $(\hat{p}_1 - \hat{p}_2)$ is given by

$(\hat{p}_1 - \hat{p}_2); z_{\alpha/2}$

$$\underline{\hspace{2cm}} \pm \underline{\hspace{1.5cm}} \sqrt{\dfrac{\hat{p}_1\hat{q}_1}{n_1} + \dfrac{\hat{p}_2\hat{q}_2}{n_2}}$$

when n_1 and n_2 are large.

25. In the formulas given above, notice that:
   a. The estimates $\hat{p}_1, \hat{p}_2, \hat{q}_1$ and $\hat{q}_2$ have been substituted into the formulas for the bound on error and confidence interval.
   b. The properties and formulas presented here are very similar to those discussed earlier for the difference between two means.

26. *Example:*
   To estimate the difference between the proportion of printed pages with misprints for two printing firms, a prospective printing contractor randomly chooses pages of works printed by each firm and has the number of pages containing errors tabulated. The results of the tabulation follow.

	Firm 1	Firm 2
Number of pages	200	200
Pages with errors	94	60

   Construct an interval that should contain the difference in proportion of misprinted pages, $p_1 - p_2$, with 98% confidence.
   Solution:
   From the data we calculate

.47; .30

$$\hat{p}_1 = 94/200 = \underline{\hspace{1.5cm}} \text{ and } \hat{p}_2 = 60/200 = \underline{\hspace{1.5cm}}$$

Using

2.58

$$(\hat{p}_1 - \hat{p}_2) \pm \underline{\hspace{1.5cm}} \sqrt{\dfrac{\hat{p}_1\hat{q}_1}{n_1} + \dfrac{\hat{p}_2\hat{q}_2}{n_2}}$$

to calculate the required confidence interval we have

$$(.47 - .30) \pm 2.58 \sqrt{\dfrac{(.47)(.53)}{200} + \dfrac{(.30)(.70)}{200}}$$

.17; .048

$$\underline{\hspace{2cm}} \pm 2.58 (\underline{\hspace{2cm}})$$

_____ ± _____

.17; .12

Hence the required confidence interval is _____ to _____ .

.05; .29

27. To provide a brief summary of the preceding sections, complete the following tables.

a. Give the best estimator for each of the following parameters:

Parameter	Estimator
μ	_____
p	_____
$(\mu_1 - \mu_2)$	_____
$(p_1 - p_2)$	_____

$\bar{y}$

$\hat{p}$

$\bar{y}_1 - \bar{y}_2$

$\hat{p}_1 - \hat{p}_2$

b. Give the standard deviations for the following estimators:

Estimator	Standard Deviation
$\bar{y}$	_____
$\hat{p}$	_____
$\bar{y}_1 - \bar{y}_2$	_____
$\hat{p}_1 - \hat{p}_2$	_____

$\sigma/\sqrt{n}$

$\sqrt{\dfrac{pq}{n}}$

$\sqrt{\dfrac{\sigma_1^2}{n_1} + \dfrac{\sigma_2^2}{n_2}}$

$\sqrt{\dfrac{p_1 q_1}{n_1} + \dfrac{p_2 q_2}{n_2}}$

c. The exact values for standard deviations of estimators cannot usually be found because they are functions of unknown population parameters. Indicate the best approximations of the standard deviations for use in confidence intervals:

Estimator	Best Approximation of Standard Deviation
$\bar{y}$	_____
$\hat{p}$	_____
$\bar{y}_1 - \bar{y}_2$	_____

$s/\sqrt{n}$

$\sqrt{\dfrac{\hat{p}\hat{q}}{n}}$

$\sqrt{\dfrac{s_1^2}{n_1} + \dfrac{s_2^2}{n_2}}$

$$\sqrt{\frac{\hat{p}_1\hat{q}_1}{n_1} + \frac{\hat{p}_2\hat{q}_2}{n_2}}$$

Estimator	Best Approximation of Standard Deviation
$\hat{p}_1 - \hat{p}_2$	————

Self-Correcting Exercises 8B

1. In investigating the potential market for a new product within a given area, a market researcher asked 100 randomly chosen people to rank the new product together with four standard brands. Twenty-five people ranked the new product either first or second in a possible ranking from one to five. If p is the proportion of the population which would rank the new product either first or second, use the sample data to estimate p and place a bound on the error of estimation.

2. In measuring the tensile strength of two alloys, strips of the alloys were subjected to tensile stress and the force (measured in pounds) at which the strip broke recorded for each strip. The data is summarized below.

	Alloy 1	Alloy 2
$\bar{y}$	150.5	160.2
s^2	23.72	36.37
n	35	35

Use these data to estimate the true mean difference in tensile strength by finding a point estimate for $\mu_1 - \mu_2$ and placing a bound on the error of estimation.

3. Using the following data, give a point estimate with bounds on error for the difference in mortality rates in breast cancers where radical or simple mastectomy was used as a treatment.

	Radical	Simple
Number died	31	41
Number treated	204	191

4. In studying the feasibility of expanding public television programming, an investigator found that 86 out of 200 randomly chosen families with television sets watch at least two hours of public television programming per week.
   a. Use this data to find a point estimate of the proportion of viewers that watch at least two hours of public T.V. programming per week and place a bound on the error of estimation.
   b. Find a 90% confidence interval for the proportion of viewers watching at least two hours of public T.V. programming.

5. Last year's records of auto accidents occurring on a given section of highway were classified according to whether the resulting damage was $200 or

more and to whether or not a physical injury resulted from the accident. The tabulation follows:

	Under $200	$200 or more
Number of accidents	32	41
Number involving injuries	10	23

a. Estimate the true proportion of accidents involving injuries and damage of $200 or more for similar sections of highway with a 95% confidence interval.

b. Estimate the true difference in proportion of accidents involving injuries for accidents involving less than $200 in damage and those involving $200 or more with a 95% confidence interval.

6. The yearly incomes of employees of two manufacturing plants producing equivalent items yielded the following tabulation.

	Plant 1	Plant 2
Number of employees	90	60
Average income	$10,520	$9,210
Standard deviation	$ 1,510	$ 950

a. If the employees of each plant are thought of as samples from two populations of employees in this industry, use these data to construct a 99% confidence interval for the difference in mean annual incomes.

b. Using the results of part a, would you be willing to conclude that these two plants belong to populations having the same mean annual income?

8.7 Choosing the Sample Size (8.12)

1. The amount of information in a sample depends on two factors:
   a. The quantity of information per _____, which depends on the sampling _____ (or experimental _____). *observation procedure; design*
   b. The number of measurements or observations taken, which in turn depends on the _____ _____. *sample size*
2. In this chapter, we will concentrate on choosing the sample size to obtain the amount of information desired.
3. One of the first steps in planning an experiment is deciding on the quantity of information that we wish to buy. At first glance it would seem difficult to specify a measure of the quantity of information in a sample relevant to a parameter of interest. However, such a practical measure is available in the _____ on the _____ of estimation; *bound; error* or, we could use the width of the confidence interval for the parameter.
4. The larger the sample size, the greater will be the amount of _____ *information* contained in the sample. This intuitively appealing fact is evident upon examination of the large-sample confidence intervals. The width of each of

sample size

.95

9

81

81

2.58

2.58

2.58

134.79

the four confidence intervals described in the preceding section is inversely proportional to the square root of the _____ _____.

5. Suppose that $\hat{\theta}$ is an estimator of θ and satisfies the conditions for the large-sample estimators previously discussed. Then, as shown below, the bound, B, on the error of estimation will be $2\sigma_{\hat{\theta}}$. This means that the error (in repeated sampling) will be less than $2\sigma_{\hat{\theta}}$ with probability _____.

6. If B represents the desired bound on the error, then for a *point* estimator, $\hat{\theta}$, the restriction is:

a. $\qquad 2\sigma_{\hat{\theta}} = B$

In an interval estimation problem with $(1 - \alpha)$ confidence coefficient, the restriction is:

b. $\qquad z_{\alpha/2}\sigma_{\hat{\theta}} = B$

For all practical purposes, parts a and b are equivalent for a confidence coefficient equal to .95.

7. *Example:*

Suppose it is known that $\sigma = 2.25$ and it is desired to estimate μ with a bound on the error of estimation less than or equal to 0.5 units with probability .95. How large a sample should be taken?

Solution:

The estimator for μ is $\bar{y}$ with standard deviation $\sigma/\sqrt{n}$; $1 - \alpha = .95$, $\alpha/2 = .025$, $z_{.025} = 1.96$, or approximately 2. Hence we solve

$$2(\sigma/\sqrt{n}) = B$$

or $\qquad 2(2.25/\sqrt{n}) = 0.5$

$$2(2.25/0.5) = \sqrt{n}$$

$$\underline{\qquad} = \sqrt{n}$$

$$\underline{\qquad} = n$$

The solution is to take a sample of size _____ or greater to insure that the bound is less than or equal to 0.5 units. Had we wished to have the same bound with probability .99, the value $z_{.005} =$ _____ would have been used, resulting in the following solution:

$$(\underline{\qquad})\,(2.25/\sqrt{n}) = 0.5$$

$$(\underline{\qquad})\,(2.25/0.5) = \sqrt{n}$$

$$\underline{\qquad} = n$$

Hence, a sample of size 135 or greater would be taken to insure estimation with $B = 0.5$ units.

8. *Example:*

If an experimenter wished to estimate the fraction of university students that daily read the college newspaper, *The Agitator,* correct to within .02 with probability .90, how large a sample of students should he take?

Solution:

To estimate binomial p with a 90% confidence interval we would use

$$\hat{p} \pm \underline{\hspace{2cm}} \sqrt{\frac{pq}{n}}$$

1.645

We wish to find a sample size n so that

$$1.645 \sqrt{\frac{pq}{n}} = \underline{\hspace{2cm}}$$

.02

Since neither p nor $\hat{p}$ are known, we can solve for n by assuming the worst possible variation, which occurs when $p = q = \underline{\hspace{1cm}}$. Hence we solve

0.5

$$1.645 \sqrt{\frac{(.5)(.5)}{n}} = .02$$

$$\frac{1.645 \, (.5)}{.02} = \sqrt{n}$$

or

$$\underline{\hspace{2cm}} = n$$

1691.27

Therefore we should take a sample of size $\underline{\hspace{2cm}}$ or greater to achieve the required bounds even if faced with the maximum variation possible.

1692

9. *Example:*

An experiment is to be conducted to compare two different sales techniques at a number of sales centers. Suppose that the range of sales for the sales centers is expected to be $4000. How many centers should be included for each of the sales techniques in order to estimate the difference in mean sales correct to within $500?

Solution:

We will assume that the two sample sizes are equal, that is, $n_1 = n_2 = n$, and that the desired coefficient is .95. Then,

$$\underline{\hspace{2cm}} = B$$

$$2\sqrt{\frac{\sigma_1^2}{n} + \frac{\sigma_2^2}{n}}$$

1000

$$\frac{2(1000)^2}{n}$$

32

32

The quantities σ_1^2 and σ_2^2 are unknown but we know that the range is expected to be $4000. Then we can use $R/4$ as an approximation for σ and take $\sigma_1 = \sigma_2 =$ _____ as the best available approximation. Then, substituting into the above equation,

$$2\sqrt{\underline{\hspace{2cm}}} = 500$$

or

$$n = \underline{\hspace{2cm}}$$

Thus $n =$ _____ sales centers would be required for each of the two sales techniques.

Self-Correcting Exercises 8C

1. A device is known to produce measurements whose errors in measurement are normally distributed with a standard deviation $\sigma = 8$ mm. If the average measurement is to be reported, how many repeated measurements should be used so that the error in measurement is no larger than 3 mm. with probability .95?

2. How many items from a production line should be sampled to estimate the true proportion of defectives for the line to within .01 with probability .95? The value of p is expected to be at most 0.1.

3. In investigating what appears to be an unusually large difference in overtime pay between the accounting records for two subsidiaries, the general manager has asked that all records be checked in each subsidiary to find the average number of overtime hours per week. If a sampling plan rather than a complete audit were to be used, how many weekly records should be checked to insure that the estimate is no further than 10 hours from the true mean difference with probability .95? You may assume that the overtime hours per week will range from 10 to 160 hours for each subsidiary.

4. How many individuals from each of two politically oriented groups should be included in a poll designed to estimate the true difference in proportions favoring a tuition increase at the state university correct to within .01 with probability .95? (In the absence of any prior information regarding the values of p_1 and p_2, solve the problem assuming maximum variation.)

8.8 A Statistical Test of an Hypothesis (8.13)

1. We now leave estimation and turn our attention to a decision making form of inference, hypothesis testing. In hypothesis testing, we formulate an

hypothesis about a population in terms of its _____ and then after observing a _____ drawn from this population, decide whether our sample value could have come from the hypothesized population. We then accept or reject the hypothesized value.

parameters
sample

2. A statistical test of an hypothesis consists of four parts:

   a. _____ _____: (H_0) This is the hypothesis to be tested and gives hypothesized values for one or more population parameters.

   Null hypothesis

   b. _____ _____: (H_a) This is the hypothesis against which H_0 is tested. We look for evidence in the sample that will cause us to reject H_0 in favor of H_a.

   Alternative hypothesis

   c. _____ _____: This function of the sample values extracts the information about the parameter contained in the sample. The observed value of the test statistic leads us to reject one hypothesis and accept the other.

   Test statistic

   d. _____ _____: Once the test statistic to be used is selected, the entire set of values that the statistic may assume is divided into two regions. The acceptance region consists of those values most likely to have arisen if _____ were true. The rejection region consists of those values most likely to have arisen if _____ is true. If the observed value of the test statistic falls in the rejection region, H_0 is _____; if it falls in the acceptance region, H_0 is _____. The alternative hypothesis (H_a) is sometimes referred to as the _____ hypothesis, since this is the hypothesis that the researcher wishes to prove true.

   Rejection region

   H_0
   H_a

   rejected; accepted

   research

3. A statistical test of an hypothesis may result in one of two types of error:

   a. Type I error: _____ H_0 when _____ is true.
   b. Type II error: _____ H_0 when _____ is true.

   rejecting; H_0
   accepting; H_a

4. Define:

   a. $\alpha = P[$_____$]$
   b. $\beta = P[$_____$]$

   The goodness of a statistical test of an hypothesis is measured by the size of _____ and _____.

   Type I error
   Type II error

   α; β

5. Complete the following two-way decision table, indicating either the type of error or that the decision is correct, and the probability of each outcome:

Decision	Null Hypothesis	
	True	False
Reject H_0	Type I error (α)	_____
Accept H_0	_____	_____

correct decision $(1 - \alpha)$
correct decision $(1 - \beta)$;
Type II error (β)

6. a. For a fixed sample size n,

   i. if the rejection region is enlarged, α will (increase, decrease), while β will (increase, decrease).

   increase
   decrease

decrease
increase
decrease

ii. if the rejection region is made smaller, α will (increase, decrease) while β will (increase, decrease).

b. When the sample size n is increased, β will (increase, decrease) because of the added information contained in the sample.

7. Let θ be the true value of the parameter in a particular test, and θ_0 and θ_a be the values of the parameter under the null and alternative hypotheses respectively. Then the probability of a Type II error, β, depends on the difference between _____ and _____.

$\theta_0 ; \theta_a$

operating characteristic
curve
unknown
should
null

8. The graph of the probability β of a Type II error as a function of the true value of the parameter is called the _____ _____ _____ of the test. Such curves were discussed in Chapter 6.

9. In practice, β is often _____. In such a case, when the test statistic falls in the acceptance region, one (should, should not) withhold judgment rather than accepting the _____ hypothesis.

8.9 A Large-Sample Statistical Test (8.14)

1. In this section we will refer to the parameter of interest as θ (θ might represent μ, p, etc.). If an *unbiased* point estimator, $\hat{\theta}$, exists for θ and $\hat{\theta}$ is normally distributed, we can employ $\hat{\theta}$ as a test statistic to test the hypothesis, $H_0: \theta = \theta_0$.

If H_a states that $\theta > \theta_0$, i.e., the value of the parameter is greater than that given by H_0, then the sample value for $\hat{\theta}$ should reflect this fact and

larger

be (larger, smaller) than a value of $\hat{\theta}$ when sampling from a population whose mean is θ_0. Hence we would reject H_0 for large values of $\hat{\theta}$. Large can be interpreted as too many standard deviations to the right of the mean, θ_0. The value of $\hat{\theta}$ selected to separate the acceptance and rejection

critical value

regions is called the _____ _____ of the test statistic. In the following diagram,

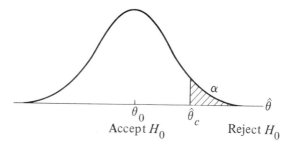

$$\theta_0 \qquad \hat{\theta}_c$$
Accept H_0 \qquad\qquad Reject H_0

$\hat{\theta}$
α; one

$\hat{\theta}_c$ represents the critical value of _____ and the shaded area to the right of $\hat{\theta}_c$ is equal to _____. This is a _____-tailed statistical test.

2. A similar picture could have been used with the critical value of $\hat{\theta}$ to the

<

left of the mean for testing $H_0: \theta = \theta_0$ against $H_a: \theta$ _____ θ_0. Then

we would reject H_0 for values of $\hat{\theta}$ lying too many standard deviations to the left of θ_0 (resulting in a _____ - _____ test in the left | one-tailed
tail) and would reject H_0 for small values of $\hat{\theta}$.
3. A third type of alternative hypothesis would be $H_a: \theta \neq \theta_0$ where we seek
departures either greater or less than θ_0. This results in a _____ - | two
tailed statistical test.

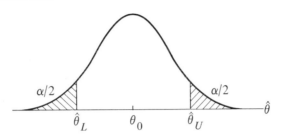

Then for a probability of a Type I error equal to α, we use a value of $\hat{\theta}$
with an area of $\alpha/2$ to its left and a second value of $\hat{\theta}$ with an area of $\alpha/2$
to its right, rejecting H_0 when $\hat{\theta} \leqslant \hat{\theta}_L$ or $\hat{\theta} \geqslant \hat{\theta}_U$. The quantities $\hat{\theta}_L$ and
$\hat{\theta}_U$ are the critical values for the test.
4. Since the estimator $\hat{\theta}$ is normally distributed, we can standardize the
normal variable, $\hat{\theta}$, by converting the distance that $\hat{\theta}$ departs from θ_0 to z
(the number of standard deviations to the left or right of the mean). Thus,
we will use z as the test statistic. The four elements of the test are:

a. $\quad H_0: \theta = \theta_0$

b. One of the three alternatives

  i. $\quad H_a: \theta > \theta_0 \quad$ (right-tailed)

  ii. $\quad H_a: \theta < \theta_0 \quad$ (left-tailed)

  iii. $\quad H_a: \theta \neq \theta_0 \quad$ (two-tailed)

c. Test statistic: z, where

$$z = \frac{\hat{\theta} - \theta_0}{\sigma_{\hat{\theta}}}$$

d. Rejection region:

  i. For $H_a: \theta > \theta_0$

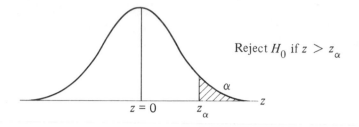

Reject H_0 if $z > z_\alpha$

ii. For $H_a: \theta < \theta_0$

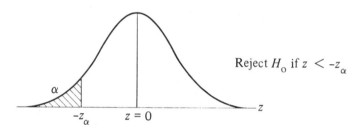

Reject H_0 if $z < -z_\alpha$

iii. For $H_a: \theta \neq \theta_0$

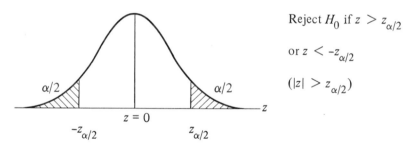

Reject H_0 if $z > z_{\alpha/2}$

or $z < -z_{\alpha/2}$

$(|z| > z_{\alpha/2})$

We now apply this test of an hypothesis.

5. *Example:*

Test of a population mean μ. Test the hypothesis at the $\alpha = .05$ level that a population mean $\mu = 10$ against the hypothesis that $\mu > 10$ if for a sample of 81 observations, $\bar{y} = 12$ and $s = 3.2$. Note that

a. $\theta = \mu$

b. $\theta_0 = \mu_0 = 10$

c. $\hat{\theta} = \bar{y}$

d. $\sigma_{\hat{\theta}} = \sigma/\sqrt{n}$

e. $\alpha = .05$

Solution:
Since σ is unknown, use s, the sample standard deviation, as its approximation. Then, the elements of the test are:

a. $H_0: \mu = 10$

b. $H_a: \mu > 10$

c. Test statistic:

$$z = \frac{\bar{y} - \mu_0}{\sigma/\sqrt{n}} \quad \text{(Using } s \text{ if } \sigma \text{ is unknown.)}$$

d. Rejection region:

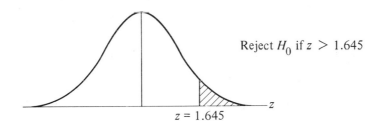

Reject H_0 if $z > 1.645$

$z = 1.645$

Having defined the test, calculate z.

$$z = \frac{\bar{y} - \mu_0}{s/\sqrt{n}} = \frac{12 - 10}{3.2/\sqrt{81}}$$

$$z = 2/.356 = 5.62$$

Since $z = 5.62 > 1.645$, the decision is "Reject H_0" with $\alpha = .05$.

6. *Example:*
   A machine shop is interested in determining a measure of the current year's sales revenue in order to compare it with known results from last year. From the 9682 sales invoices to date for the current year, the management randomly selected $n = 400$ invoices and from each recorded y, the sales revenue per invoice. Using the following data summary, test the hypothesis that the mean revenue per invoice is $3.35, the same as last year, versus the alternative hypothesis that the mean revenue per invoice is different than $3.35 with $\alpha = .05$.

Data Summary

$n = 400$

$$\sum_{i=1}^{400} y_i = \$1264.40$$

$$\sum_{i=1}^{400} y_i^2 = 4970.3282$$

Solution:

Using the values given in the data summary calculate $\bar{y}$, s^2 and s.

$3.16

$$\bar{y} = \frac{\displaystyle\sum_{i=1}^{400} y_i}{400} = \frac{\$1264.40}{400} = \underline{\hspace{2cm}}$$

4970.3282

$$s^2 = \frac{\displaystyle\sum_{i=1}^{400} y_i^2 - \frac{\left(\displaystyle\sum_{i=1}^{400} y_i\right)^2}{400}}{399} = \frac{\underline{\hspace{1cm}} - \frac{(1264.40)^2}{400}}{399}$$

2.4400

$$= \underline{\hspace{2cm}}$$

2.4400; 1.56

$$s = \sqrt{\underline{\hspace{2cm}}} = \underline{\hspace{2cm}}$$

The test proceeds as follows.

3.35

a. $H_0: \mu = \underline{\hspace{2cm}}$

$\neq 3.35$

b. $H_a: \mu \underline{\hspace{2cm}}$

c.   Test statistic:

$$z = \frac{\bar{y} - \mu_0}{\sigma/\sqrt{n}}$$

1.96

d.   Rejection region: reject H_0 if $|z| > \underline{\hspace{2cm}}$

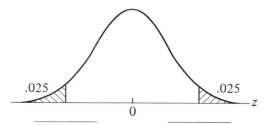

-1.96; 1.96

Calculate the observed value of z using μ_0 = $3.35 and σ approximated by the sample standard deviation s.

$$z = \frac{3.16 - 3.35}{1.56/\sqrt{\underline{}}} = \frac{-.19}{\underline{}} = \underline{}$$

400; .08; –2.38

Based upon the sample evidence we (reject, do not reject) H_0 and conclude that the mean income per invoice (is, is not) different from $3.35 with probability of error equal to .05.

reject

is

At this point the management would want to estimate the current year's mean income per invoice. A 95% confidence interval estimate would be

$$\bar{y} \pm \underline{} s/\sqrt{n}$$

1.96

or

$$\$3.16 \pm \underline{} (.08)$$

1.96

$$\$3.16 \pm \underline{}$$

.16

so that the mean income per invoice is estimated to lie between _____ and _____ with 95% confidence.

$3.00

$3.32

7. *Example:*

A test of a binomial p. Suppose it is hypothesized that $p = 0.1$. Test this hypothesis at the $\alpha = .01$ level against the alternative that $p < 0.1$ if the number of successes is $y = 8$ in a sample of $n = 100$. In this problem

a. $\theta = p$

b. $\theta_0 = p_0 = 0.1$

c. $\hat{\theta} - \hat{p} - y/n$

d. $\sigma_{\hat{\theta}} = \sqrt{p_0 q_0/n}$

e. $\alpha = .01$

Solution:

Note that p_0 and q_0 are used in $\sigma_{\hat{p}}$ to conform with $H_0: p = p_0$. The elements of the test are:

0.1

a. $H_0: p = $ _____

0.1

b. $H_a: p < $ _____

c. Test statistic:

$$z = \frac{\hat{p} - p_0}{\sqrt{p_0 q_0 / n}}$$

d. Rejection region:

–2.33

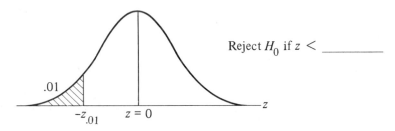

Reject H_0 if $z < $ _____

To calculate z, we need $\hat{p} = y/n$.

8; 100; .08

$$\hat{p} = (\underline{\hspace{1.5cm}}) / (\underline{\hspace{1.5cm}}) = \underline{\hspace{1.5cm}}$$

and

.08

.09

$$z = \frac{\hat{p} - 0.1}{\sqrt{\dfrac{(0.1)(0.9)}{100}}} = \frac{(\underline{\hspace{1.5cm}}) - 0.1}{\sqrt{\dfrac{(\underline{\hspace{1.5cm}})}{100}}}$$

$\dfrac{-.02}{.03}$; –.667

$$z = \frac{(\underline{\hspace{1.5cm}})}{(\underline{\hspace{1.5cm}})} = \underline{\hspace{1.5cm}}$$

does not

will not

Since the value of z (does, does not) fall in the rejection region, we (will, will not) reject H_0.

  Before deciding to accept H_0 as true, we may wish to evaluate the probability of a Type II error for meaningful values of p described by H_a. Until this is done, we shall state our decision as "Do not reject H_0."

8. *Example:*

Test of an hypothesis concerning $(\mu_1 - \mu_2)$. Before launching a full-scale training program, a company must decide which of two manager training programs it will use. Seventy participants were randomly divided into two groups of thirty-five. During a six-week trial period one group was trained according to program A while the other was trained according to program B. At the end of the trial period the programs were evaluated by means of a test given to each participant. Assuming the test to be a valid criterion in comparing the programs, test the hypothesis that there is no difference in mean scores for the two programs at the $\alpha = .05$ level of significance. Which program should the company decide to use? The data follow.

Program A	Program B
$\bar{y}_1 = 80.2$	$\bar{y}_2 = 72.8$
$s_1^2 = 49.3$	$s_2^2 = 64.5$
$n_1 = 31$	$n_2 = 34$

(Not all participants completed the six-week program.)

Solution:

This problem involves a test of $\mu_1 - \mu_2$. The unbiased estimator used in this test is _____ with standard deviation _____.

$\bar{y}_1 - \bar{y}_2; \sqrt{\dfrac{\sigma_1^2}{n_1} + \dfrac{\sigma_2^2}{n_2}}$

a.　　$H_0: \mu_1 - \mu_2 = $ _____

0

b.　　$H_a: \mu_1 - \mu_2 \neq $ _____

0

c. Test statistic:

$$z = \frac{(\bar{y}_1 - \bar{y}_2) - 0}{\sqrt{\dfrac{s_1^2}{n_1} + \dfrac{s_2^2}{n_2}}} \quad (\sigma_1 \text{ and } \sigma_2 \text{ are unknown})$$

d. Rejection region:
   This is a two-tailed test with $\alpha = .05$.

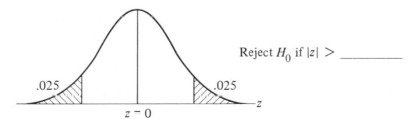

Reject H_0 if $|z| > $ _____

1.96

Computing the value of the test statistic,

80.2; 72.8

$$z = \frac{(\underline{\qquad} - \underline{\qquad}) - 0}{\sqrt{\dfrac{49.3}{31} + \dfrac{64.5}{34}}}$$

7.4

$$= \frac{\underline{\qquad}}{1.87}$$

3.96

$$= \underline{\qquad}$$

1.96
reject
A

Since the calculated value of $z = 3.96$ is greater than $z_{.025} = \underline{\qquad}$, we $\underline{\qquad}$ H_0 and conclude that there is a difference in the effectiveness of the programs. The data indicate that program $\underline{\qquad}$ should be the one adopted for full-scale use.

Self-Correcting Exercises 8D

1. The board of directors of the Mallon Company is considering the possible merger of their company with another. If 34 shareholders in a random sample of 65 shareholders stated that they were in favor of the merger, test the hypothesis that a majority of the stockholders favor merger (the proportion favoring merger is greater than .5) at the $\alpha = .05$ level of significance.

2. To compare the assembly times for two assembly techniques, 30 workers were randomly chosen to use Method 1 and 40 workers were randomly chosen to use Method 2. Using the data summary below, could you conclude that there is a significant difference in the mean assembly times for these two methods at the $\alpha = .01$ level of significance?

Method 1	Method 2
$n_1 = 30$	$n_2 = 40$
$\bar{y}_1 = 21.1$ min.	$\bar{y}_2 = 18.0$ min.
$s_1 = 3.5$ min.	$s_2 = 4.2$ min.

3. A market research organization found that 160 in a random sample of 400 households in City 1 had at least one color television set, while a random sample of 250 households in City 2 showed 90 with at least one color television set. Is there reason to believe that the proportion of households with color televisions differs between City 1 and City 2? Answer the question by testing the appropriate hypothesis at the $\alpha = .05$ level of significance.

4. In a manufacturing plant employing a double inspection procedure, the first inspector is expected to miss an average of 25 defective items per day with a standard deviation of 3 items. If the first inspector has missed an average of 29 defectives per day based upon the last 30 working days, is he

working up to company standards? Answer the question using a test of an hypothesis at the $\alpha = .01$ level of significance.

8.10   Summary (8.15–8.16)

1. The practical problem of interest to the experimenter (who is the "sampler") must be phrased in terms of numerical descriptive measures of a population. These measures are called _____ . Consequently, the statistician seeks to make inferences about these unknown parameters based on information contained in a sample.

      parameters

2. Inference making can be accomplished in one of two ways. We either _____ the unknown parameters or test _____ concerning their values.

      estimate; hypotheses

3. An estimator is a _____ that tells how to calculate a single _____ based on information contained in a sample. The goodness of an estimator is determined by examining the distribution of estimates that it generates in repeated sampling. Generally speaking, we like estimators to be _____ and to possess _____ variance.

      rule
      estimate

      unbiased; minimum

4. Estimation of parameters may be accomplished with either _____ or _____ estimators.

      point
      interval

5. An interval estimator called a _____ _____ is constructed so that it will enclose the parameter with a specified probability. This probability is called the _____ _____ .

      confidence interval

      confidence coefficient

6. All of the large-sample point estimators presented in Chapter 8 possess a normal probability distribution in repeated sampling because of the _____ _____ _____ . Each is unbiased with known standard deviation. When the populations satisfy certain requirements, these estimators are best in the sense that they possess minimum variances.

      Central Limit Theorem

7. The information in a sample relative to a given parameter can be measured by the width of the _____ _____ . The width of the confidence interval is inversely proportional to the square root of the _____ _____ for all of the estimators described in Chapter 8. This result holds for almost all estimators (but not all). Consequently, we can determine the sample size necessary to acquire a specified amount of information by equating the half-width of the confidence interval to a specified bound, B, and solving for n.

      confidence interval

      sample size

8. A statistical test contains four elements:
   a. _____ _____
   b. _____ _____
   c. _____ _____
   d. _____ _____

      null hypothesis
      alternative hypothesis
      test statistic
      rejection region

9. The goodness of a statistical test is expressed in terms of the risk associated with two types of error. A Type I error occurs when the null hypothesis is

rejected
false

$\alpha; \beta$
significance
level
95

large

Central Limit Theorem

_____ and it is true. Accepting the null hypothesis when it is _____ and some alternative is true is called a Type II error. The probabilities of making Type I and II errors are denoted by the symbols _____ and _____, respectively.

10. The probability of making a Type I error, α, is often called the _____ _____ of the test.

11. _____% of all estimates generated by the estimators in Chapter 8 should lie within two (1.96 to be exact) standard deviations of the parameter estimated. This result can be used to locate a rejection region for a statistical test. Large departures (measured in standard deviations of $\hat{\theta}$) from an hypothesized value of θ indicate disagreement with the hypothesis and provide evidence to support its rejection. This distance is indicated by the test statistic z.

12. Chapter 8 presents estimation and tests of hypotheses using _____- sample inference makers for purposes of illustration. Knowledge of the distributional properties of these inference makers is based on the _____ _____ _____ of Chapter 7.

Exercises

1. List the two essential elements of any inference-making procedure.
2. What are two desirable properties of a point estimator, $\hat{\theta}$?
3. A bank was interested in estimating the average size of its savings accounts for a particular class of customer. If a random sample of 400 such accounts showed an average amount of $61.23 and a standard deviation of $18.20, place 90% confidence limits on the actual average account size.
4. A company wished to estimate the percentage of defective items produced by its local plant. In a random sample of 50 items selected from the production of this factory, three defectives were observed. Estimate the true percentage of defectives with a 95% confidence interval.
5. An appliance dealer sells toasters of two different brands, brand A and brand B. Let p_1 denote the fraction of brand A toasters which are returned to him by customers as defective, and let p_2 represent the fraction of brand B toasters which are rejected by customers as defective. Suppose that of 200 brand A toasters sold, 14 were returned as defective, while of 450 brand B toasters sold, 18 were returned as defective. Provide a 90% confidence interval for $p_1 - p_2$.
6. If 36 measurements of the specific gravity of aluminum had a mean of 2.705 and a standard deviation of 0.028, construct a 98% confidence interval for the actual specific gravity of aluminum.
7. To compare the tensile strengths of two synthetic fibers, samples of 31 of each kind were selected and tested for breaking strength. The results are

summarized below. Find a 98% confidence interval for the difference between the true mean breaking strengths.

Fiber I	Fiber II
$\bar{y}_1 = 370$	$\bar{y}_2 = 332$
$s_1^2 = 1930$	$s_2^2 = 1670$

8. A sample of 39 cigarettes of a certain brand, tested for nicotine content, gave a mean of 22 and a standard deviation of 4 milligrams. Find a 90% confidence interval for μ.

9. A doctor wishes to estimate the average nicotine content in a certain brand of cigarettes correct to within 0.5 milligram. From previous experiments it is known that σ is in the neighborhood of 4 milligrams. How large a sample should the doctor take to be 95% confident of his estimate?

10. A manufacturer of dresses believes that approximately 20% of his product contains flaws. If he wishes to estimate the true percentage to within 8%, how large a sample should he take?

11. It is desired to estimate $\mu_1 - \mu_2$ from information contained in independent random samples from populations with variances $\sigma_1^2 = 9$ and $\sigma_2^2 = 16$. If the two sample sizes are to be equal ($n_1 = n_2 = n$), how large should n be in order to estimate $\mu_1 - \mu_2$ with an error less than 1.0 (with probability equal to .95)?

12. In order to bid competitively for the lumbering rights on a certain tract of land, a company needs to know the mean diameter of the trees on the tract to within 2.5 inches. If the company can assume $\sigma = 8$ inches, how large a sample of trees on this tract should be taken?

13. A marketing representative was assigned to observe the frequency of sales of his company's brand of canned ham at a supermarket. During a given day 25 canned hams were purchased from the supermarket. What is the probability that the percentage of those purchasing the company's brand exceeds 60%, if the true probability that any customer buying a canned ham buys the company's brand is .5?

14. What are the four essential elements of a statistical test of an hypothesis?

15. Assume that a certain set of "early returns" in an election is actually a random sample of size 400 from the voters in that election. If 225 of the voters in the sample voted for candidate A, could we assert with $\alpha = .01$ that candidate A has won?

16. A grocery store operator claims that the average waiting time at a checkout counter is 3.75 minutes. To test this claim, a random sample of 30 observations was taken. Test the operator's claim at the 5% level of significance using the sample data shown.

		Waiting Time in Minutes		
3	4	3	4	1
1	0	5	3	2
4	3	1	2	0
3	2	0	3	4
1	3	2	1	3
2	4	2	5	2

17. Random samples of 100 shoes manufactured by machine A and 50 shoes manufactured by machine B showed 16 and 6 defective shoes, respectively. Do these data present sufficient evidence to suggest a difference in the performance of the machines? Use $\alpha = .05$.

18. In order to test the effectiveness of a vaccine, 150 experimental animals were given the vaccine; 150 were not. All 300 were then infected with the disease. Among those vaccinated, ten died as a result of the disease. Among the control group (i.e., those not vaccinated), there were 30 deaths. Can we conclude that the vaccine is effective in reducing the mortality rate? Use a significance level of .025.

19. Two diets were to be compared. Seventy-five individuals were selected at random from a population of overweight people. Forty of this group were assigned diet A and the other thirty-five were placed on diet B. The weight losses in pounds over a period of one week were found and the following quantities recorded:

	Sample Size	Sample Mean (lbs)	Sample Variance
Diet A	40	10.3	7.00
Diet B	35	7.3	3.25

a. Do these data allow the conclusion that the expected weight loss under diet A (μ_A) is greater than the expected weight loss under diet B (μ_B)? Test at the .01 level. Draw the appropriate conclusion.

b. Construct a 90% confidence interval for $\mu_A - \mu_B$.

20. A random sample of 400 radio tubes is drawn from a certain population of radio tubes. Let p be the fraction defective in the population. Suppose we wish to test $H_0: p = .2$ at the .01 level of significance.

a. What statistic can be formed which has approximately the standard normal distribution when H_0 is true?

b. State the rejection region for z if the alternative hypothesis is H_a: $p > .2$.

c. State the rejection region for z if the alternative hypothesis is H_a: $p \neq .2$.

d. If indeed the number of defective tubes in the sample of 400 is 80, find a 90% confidence interval for p, the true fraction defective in the population of radio tubes.

21. A manufacturer of refrigerators suspects that about 10% of his product is

defective. How large a random sample should he select in order to estimate the true fraction defective to within 1% with probability .95?

22. Random samples of 200 bolts manufactured by machine A and 200 bolts manufactured by machine B showed 45 and 35 defective bolts, respectively. Do these data present sufficient evidence to suggest a difference in performances of the machines? Use $\alpha = .05$.

23. The following data pertain to breaking strengths of two types of rope, A and B.

	Type A	Type B
Number in sample	400	400
Mean breaking strength	168.2	149.1
Standard deviation	8.0	6.0

Determine 80% confidence limits for the difference in population mean breaking strengths.

24. A manufacturer had reason to believe that the percentage of younger people was greater than the percentage of older people who preferred his product. A sample of 800 persons under 40 years of age revealed that 200 preferred his product, while 120 of 800 persons over 40 years of age preferred his product. Does this provide sufficient evidence to support the manufacturer's claim?

25. To estimate the percentage of defective tubes produced by a certain machine, a sample of 100 tubes was taken and six were found to be defective. Find a 90% confidence interval for the true fraction defective produced by this machine.

26. In a sample of 400 seeds, 240 germinated. At the 2.5% level of significance is this reason enough to reject the claim that 64% or more will germinate?

27. Two different methods of manufacturing, die forging and casting, were used to make parts for an appliance. In service tests of 100 of each type, it was found that ten castings failed during the test, but only three forged parts failed. Place a 98% confidence interval on the true difference in the fractions of defectives produced by the two methods.

28. A manufacturer of cereal states that the average weight of cereal in his boxes is at least 20 ounces. A sample of 64 boxes of this cereal was examined and revealed a mean of 19 ounces and a standard deviation of three ounces. Does the sample provide enough evidence to reject the manufacturer's claim at the 5% significance level?

29. It is desired to test the hypothesis that the mean of a population is 145 against the alternative that the mean is less than 145. A sample of 100 measurements drawn from the population yields $\bar{y} - 140$ and $s - 20$. If α is chosen to be .05, calculate the probability of a Type II error, β, if the mean actually equals 137.

30. A market research organization has decided to introduce a special group of color television advertisements for a client in cities in which more than 40%

of the households have color television. If a random sample of 125 house-holds in a specific city showed that 55 of those households had at least one color television set, would this city be one in which the advertising campaign should be introduced? Test at the $\alpha = .05$ level of significance.

31. It is thought that about one-tenth of the individuals in a given population have a certain genetic defect. In order to determine the true fraction with a maximum error of .003 with probability .95, the sample size should be at least how large?

32. It is known from long experience that the variability in a certain method of determining the concentration of a chemical in solution is indicated by a standard deviation of .005 grams per cubic centimeter. Determine the number of measurements so that the error of the estimated concentration will be less than .0005 with probability .95.

Chapter 9

INFERENCES
FROM SMALL SAMPLES

9.1 Introduction (9.1)

1. Large-sample methods for making inferences about a population were
considered in the preceding chapter. When the sample size was large, the
_____ _____ Theorem assured the approximate
normality of the distributions of the estimators $\bar{y}, \hat{p}, (\bar{y}_1 - \bar{y}_2)$ and
$(\hat{p}_1 - \hat{p}_2)$.

2. However, time, cost or other limitations may prevent an investigator from
collecting enough data to feel confident in using large-sample techniques.
When the sample size is small, $n < 30$, the Central Limit Theorem may no
longer apply. This difficulty can be overcome if the investigator is reasonably sure that his measurements constitute a sample from a _____
population.

3. The results presented in this chapter are based upon the assumption that
the observations being analyzed have been _____ drawn from
a normal population. This assumption is not as restrictive as it sounds,
since the normal distribution can be used as a model in cases where the
underlying distribution is mound-shaped and fairly symmetrical.

9.2 Student's *t* Distribution (9.2)

1. When the sample size is large ($n \geqslant$ _____), the statistic

$$\underline{\hspace{2cm}} = \frac{\bar{y} - \mu}{\sigma/\sqrt{n}}$$

is approximately _____ distributed in _____ sampling.
What can be said about this statistic when the sample size is small and the
sample variance _____ is used to estimate σ^2?

Central Limit

normal

randomly

30

z

normally; repeated

s^2

normal

2. W. S. Gosset, who published his results under the pen name Student, drew repeated samples from a _____ population and tabulated the distribution of the statistic that he called t, where

$$t = \frac{\bar{y} - \mu}{s/\sqrt{n}}$$

3. The resulting distribution for t has the following properties:

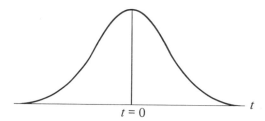

$$t = 0$$

mound

symmetrical

more

n

standard normal

normal

mound

random

a. The distribution is _____-shaped.

b. The distribution is _____ about the value $t = 0$.

c. The distribution has more flaring tails than z; hence t is (more, less) variable than the z-statistic.

d. The shape of the distribution changes as the value of _____, the sample size, changes.

e. As the sample size, n, becomes large, the t distribution becomes identical to the _____ _____ distribution.

These results are based on the following two assumptions:

a. The parent population has a _____ distribution. The t-statistic is, however, relatively stable for nonnormal, _____ shaped distributions.

b. The sample is a _____ sample. When the population is normal, this assures us that $\bar{y}$ and s^2 are independent.

4. For a fixed sample size, n, the statistic

$$z = \frac{\bar{y} - \mu}{\sigma/\sqrt{n}}$$

one

$\bar{y}$

contains exactly _____ random quantity, the sample mean, _____. However, the statistic

$$t = \frac{\bar{y} - \mu}{s/\sqrt{n}}$$

two; $\bar{y}$; s

more

contains _____ random quantities, _____ and _____.

5. This accounts for the fact that t is (more, less) variable than z. In fact $\bar{y}$ may be large while s is small, or $\bar{y}$ may be small while s is large. Hence it is

said that $\bar{y}$ and s are _____, which means that the value assumed by $\bar{y}$ in no way determines the value of s.

6. As the sample size changes, the corresponding *t* distribution changes so that each value of *n* determines a different probability distribution. This is due to the variability of _____ which appears in the denominator of *t*. Large-sample sizes produce (more, less) stable estimates of σ^2 than do small-sample sizes. These different probability curves are identified by the degrees of freedom associated with the estimator of σ^2.

7. The divisor $(n - 1)$ of the sum of squares of deviations that appears in the formula for s^2 is called the number of _____ of _____.

8. The term degrees of freedom can be explained in the following way. The sample estimate, s^2, uses the sum of squared deviations in its calculation. Recall that

$$\sum_{i=1}^{n} (y_i - \bar{y}) = \underline{\hspace{2cm}}$$

This means that if we know the values of $n - 1$ deviations, we can determine the last value uniquely since their sum must be zero. Therefore, the sum of squared deviations,

$$\sum_{i=1}^{n} (y_i - \bar{y})^2$$

contains only _____ independent deviations and not *n* independent deviations as one might expect. Degrees of freedom refer to the number of independent deviations that are available for estimating σ^2. When *n* observations are drawn from one population, we use

$$\hat{\sigma}^2 = s^2 = \frac{\sum_{i=1}^{n} (y_i - \bar{y})^2}{n - 1}$$

In this case, the degrees of freedom for estimating σ^2 is _____ and the resulting *t* distribution is indexed as having _____ degrees of freedom.

The Use of Tables for the t Distribution

9. We define t_α as that value of *t* having an area equal to α to its _____ and $-t_\alpha$ is that value of *t* having an area equal to α to its _____. See the following diagram.

---

independent

s^2
more

degrees; freedom

0

$n - 1$

$n - 1$
$n - 1$

right
left

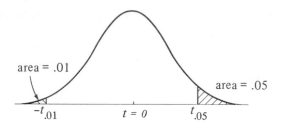

symmetrical

left

2.179

30

σ

2.920
3.169
1.313
2.583
2.086
5.841
1.771
1.397
2.131
2.819

10. The distribution of t is _____ about the value $t = 0$; hence, only the positive values of t need be tabulated. Problems involving left-tailed values of t can be solved in terms of right-tailed values, as was done with the z-statistic. A negative value of t simply indicates that you are working in the (left, right) tail of the distribution.

11. Table 4 of your text tabulates *commonly used* critical values, t_α, based on $1, 2, \ldots, 29, \infty$ degrees of freedom for $\alpha = .100, .050, .025, .010, .005$. Along the top margin of the table you will find columns labeled t_α for the various values of α, while along the left margin you will find a column marked degrees of freedom, d.f. By cross-indexing you can find the value t having an area equal to α to its right and having the proper degrees of freedom.

12. *Example:*
    To find the critical value of t for $\alpha = .05$ with five degrees of freedom, find five in the left margin. Now by reading across, you will find $t = 2.015$ in the $t_{.05}$ column. In the same manner, we find that for 12 degrees of freedom, $t_{.025} =$ _____ .

13. In using Table 4, a student should think of his problem in terms of α, the area to the right of the value of t, and the degrees of freedom used to estimate σ^2. The reader is asked to compare the different values of t based on an infinite number of degrees of freedom with those for a corresponding z. One can perhaps see the reason for choosing a sample size greater than _____ as the dividing point for using the z distribution when the standard deviation s is used as an estimate for _____ .

14. *Example:*
    Find the critical values for t when t_α is that value of t with an area of α to its right, based on the following degrees of freedom.

	α	d.f.	t
a.	.05	2	_____
b.	.005	10	_____
c.	.10	28	_____
d.	.01	16	_____
e.	.025	20	_____
f.	.005	3	_____
g.	.05	13	_____
h.	.10	8	_____
i.	.025	15	_____
j.	.005	22	_____

15. Students taking their first course in statistics usually ask the following questions at this point: "How will I know whether I should use z or t? Is sample size the only criterion I should apply?" No, sample size is not the only criterion to be used.

    When the sample size is *large*, both

$$T_1 = \frac{\bar{y} - \mu}{\sigma/\sqrt{n}} \quad \text{and} \quad T_2 = \frac{\bar{y} - \mu}{s/\sqrt{n}}$$

behave as a standard normal random variable _____, regardless of the distribution of the parent population. When the sample size is *small* and the sampled population is *not normal*, then in general neither T_1 nor T_2 behave as z or t. In the special case when the parent population is *normal*, then T_1 behaves as _____ and T_2 behaves as _____. $z; t$

16. Use this information to complete the following table when the sample is drawn from a *normal* distribution.

Statistic	Sample size	
	$n < 30$	$n \geqslant 30$
$\dfrac{y - \mu}{s/\sqrt{n}}$	_____	t or app. z
$\dfrac{\bar{y} - \mu}{\sigma/\sqrt{n}}$	_____	_____

   z

   t

   $z; z$

17. The estimators _____ and _____ must be independent (in a probabilistic sense) in order that the quantity $\bar{y}; s^2$

$$\frac{\bar{y} - \mu}{s/\sqrt{n}}$$

possess a _____ distribution in repeated sampling. This requirement is automatically satisfied when the sample is _____ drawn from a _____ population. t randomly normal

9.3 Small-Sample Inferences About a Population Mean (9.3)

A. Small-Sample Test Concerning a Population Mean, μ

1. A test of an hypothesis concerning the mean, μ, of a *normal* population when $n < 30$ and σ is unknown proceeds as follows.

   a. $H_0: \mu = \mu_0$

$$\frac{\bar{y} - \mu_0}{s/\sqrt{n}}$$

b. H_a: Appropriate one- or two-tailed alternative.

c. Test statistic:

$$t = \underline{\hspace{2cm}}$$

d. Rejection region with $\alpha = P$ [falsely rejecting H_0]:
   i. For $H_a: \mu > \mu_0$, reject H_0 if $t > t_\alpha$ based upon $n - 1$ degrees of freedom.
   ii. For $H_a: \mu < \mu_0$, reject H_0 if $t < -t_\alpha$ based upon $n - 1$ degrees of freedom.
   iii. For $H_a: \mu \neq \mu_0$, reject H_0 if $|t| > t_{\alpha/2}$ based upon $n - 1$ degrees of freedom.

2. *Example:*
A new electronic device that requires two hours per item to produce on a production line has been developed by Company A. While the new product is being run, profitable production time is used. Hence the manufacturer decides to produce only six new items for testing purposes. For each of the six items, the time to failure is measured, yielding the measurements 59.2, 68.3, 57.8, 56.5, 63.7, and 57.3 hours. Is there sufficient evidence to indicate that the new device has a mean life greater than 55 hours at the $\alpha = .05$ level?
Solution:
To calculate the sample mean and standard deviation we need

$$\Sigma y_i = 362.8 \text{ and } \Sigma y_i^2 = 22{,}043.60$$

Then

362.8/6; 60.47

$$\bar{y} = \frac{1}{n} \Sigma y_i = \frac{(\underline{\hspace{1.5cm}})}{(\underline{\hspace{1.5cm}})} = \underline{\hspace{1.5cm}}$$

and

$$s^2 = \frac{1}{n-1} \left[\Sigma y_i^2 - \frac{(\Sigma y_i)^2}{n} \right]$$

$$= \frac{1}{5} \left[22{,}043.60 - \frac{(362.8)^2}{6} \right]$$

$$= 21.2587$$

with $\quad s = \sqrt{21.2587} = 4.61$

The test proceeds as follows:

a. $H_0: \mu =$ _____   55

b. $H_a: \mu >$ _____   55

c. Test statistic:

$$t = \frac{\bar{y} - \underline{\quad\quad}}{s/\sqrt{n}}$$ 55

d. Rejection region:

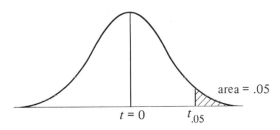

area = .05

$t = 0$ $t_{.05}$

Based on 5 degrees of freedom, reject H_0 if $t >$ _____ .   2.015

e. Now calculate the value of the test statistic.

$$t = \frac{\bar{y} - 55}{s/\sqrt{n}}$$

$$= \frac{\underline{\quad\quad} - 55}{4.61/\sqrt{6}}$$ 60.47

$$= \frac{\overline{\underline{\quad\quad}}}{1.88}$$ 5.47

$$= \underline{\quad\quad}$$ 2.91

f. Since the observed value (is, is not) larger than 2.015, we (reject, do   is
not reject) H_0. There (is, is not) sufficient evidence to indicate that the   reject; is
new device has a mean life greater than 55 hours at the 5% level of
significance.

B. *Confidence Interval for a Population Mean, μ*

3. In estimating a population mean, one can use either a point estimator with
   bounds on error or an interval estimator having the required level of confidence.

4. Small-sample estimation of the mean of a *normal* population with σ *unknown* involves the statistic

$$\frac{\bar{y} - \mu}{s/\sqrt{n}}$$

$t; n - 1$

which has a _____ distribution with (_____) degrees of freedom. The resulting $(1 - \alpha)$ confidence interval estimator is given as

$\bar{y} \pm t_{\alpha/2} \, s/\sqrt{n}$

_____

where $t_{\alpha/2}$ is that value of t based upon $n - 1$ degrees of freedom having an area of $\alpha/2$ to its right.

5. The lower confidence limit is _____ and the upper confidence

$\bar{y} - t_{\alpha/2} \, s/\sqrt{n}$
$\bar{y} + t_{\alpha/2} \, s/\sqrt{n} \, ; \bar{y}$

limit is _____. The point estimator of μ is _____ and the bound on the error of estimation can be taken to be $t_{\alpha/2} \, s/\sqrt{n}$.

6. A proper interpretation of a $(1 - \alpha)$ confidence interval for μ would be stated as follows: In repeated sampling, (_____) 100% of the

$1 - \alpha$
confidence intervals

_____ _____ so constructed would enclose the true value of the mean, μ.

7. *Example:*
Using the data from Example 2 of this section, find a 95% confidence interval estimate for μ, the mean life in hours for the new device.
Solution:
a. The pertinent information from Example 2 follows:

5

$\bar{y} = 60.47$ d.f. = _____

$s/\sqrt{n} = 1.88$ $\alpha/2 = .025$

2.571

$t_{.025} =$ _____

b. The confidence interval will be found by using

$$\bar{y} \pm t_{.025} \, s/\sqrt{n}$$

c. Substituting $\bar{y}$, $s/\sqrt{n}$, $t_{.025}$ we have

2.571

$60.47 \pm$ _____ (1.88)

4.83

$60.47 \pm$ _____

55.64; 65.30

or   (_____ , _____)

Thus, we can estimate with 95% confidence that the true mean life for the new device lies between 55.64 and 65.30 hours.

8. *Example:*

In a random sample of ten cans of corn from supplier B, the average weight per can of corn was $\bar{y} = 9.4$ oz. with standard deviation, $s = 1.8$ oz. Does this sample contain sufficient evidence to indicate the mean weight is less than 10 oz. at the $\alpha = .01$ level? Find a 98% confidence interval for μ.

Solution:

a. The following information is needed:

$n =$ _____   10

$\bar{y} =$ _____   9.4

$s =$ _____   1.8

$\alpha =$ _____   .01

b. Set up the test as follows:

$H_0 : \mu =$ _____   10

$H_a : \mu <$ _____   10

Test statistic:

$$t = \frac{\bar{y} - \mu}{s/\sqrt{n}}$$

Rejection region:

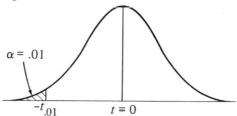

$\alpha = .01$

$-t_{.01}$ $t = 0$

Based on 9 degrees of freedom, reject H_0 if $t <$ _____   -2.821

Calculate:

$$t = \frac{\bar{y} - \mu}{s/\sqrt{n}}$$

$$= \frac{9.4 - (\underline{\hspace{2cm}})}{1.8/\sqrt{10}}$$ 10

-.6

$$= \frac{(\underline{\hspace{2cm}})}{.57}$$

-1.05

$$= \underline{\hspace{2cm}}$$

does not

do not

c. Since the calculated value of t (does, does not) fall in the rejection region we conclude that the data (do, do not) present sufficient evidence to indicate that the mean weight per can is less than 10 oz.

d. In finding a 98% confidence interval for μ, you need:

.02

$$\alpha = \underline{\hspace{2cm}}$$

9

$$\text{d.f.} = \underline{\hspace{2cm}}$$

2.821

$$t_{\alpha/2} = \underline{\hspace{2cm}}$$

Calculate:

$$\bar{y} \pm t_{\alpha/2}\, s/\sqrt{n}$$

9.4; .57

$$(\underline{\hspace{2cm}}) \pm 2.821\,(\underline{\hspace{2cm}})$$

9.4; 1.6

$$(\underline{\hspace{2cm}}) \pm (\underline{\hspace{2cm}})$$

7.8

11.0

Therefore the 98% confidence interval required is ($\underline{\hspace{2cm}}$, $\underline{\hspace{2cm}}$)

Self-Correcting Exercises 9A

1. In attempting to increase the number of miles traveled per gallon of gas, a designer has modified the fuel injection system on his company's V-8 engine. Seven modified engines were produced and installed into identical passenger cars. In road testing, the recorded miles per gallon for these seven vehicles were: 18.1, 19.7, 17.2, 18.9, 20.3, 18.5, 19.1.
   a. Find a 95% confidence interval for μ, the mean number of miles per gallon achieved with the modified engine.
   b. Has the modification significantly increased the average number of miles per gallon above the previous average of 17.5 mpg without the modification?

2. A pharmaceutical company must keep the amount of impurities in a certain product below .050 gram. The amount of impurities is monitored by analyzing 25 samples randomly drawn from the daily production and reporting the amount of impurities present per sample. Wednesday's sampling produced an average of .057 gram impurities with a standard deviation of .008 grams.

a. Use the framework of a test of a statistical hypothesis with $\alpha = .01$ in making a decision as to whether Wednesday's production has an excess amount of impurities present.

b. Find a 95% confidence interval for the mean amount of impurities present in Wednesday's production.

9.4   Small-Sample Inferences About the Difference Between Two Means (9.4)

1. Inferences concerning $\mu_1 - \mu_2$ based on small samples are founded upon the following assumptions:

   a. Each population sampled has a _____ distribution,

   b. The population _____ are equal; that is, _____ = _____.

   $\qquad$ normal

   $\qquad$ variances; σ_1^2

   $\qquad$ σ_2^2

   c. The samples are independently drawn.

2. An unbiased estimator for $\mu_1 - \mu_2$, regardless of sample size, is _____.
   The standard deviation of this estimator is

   $\qquad$ $\bar{y}_1 - \bar{y}_2$

   $$\sqrt{\frac{\sigma_1^2}{n_1} + \frac{\sigma_2^2}{n_2}}$$

   When $\sigma_1^2 = \sigma_2^2$, we can replace σ_1^2 and σ_2^2 by a common variance, σ^2. Then the standard deviation of $\bar{y}_1 - \bar{y}_2$ becomes

   $$\sqrt{\frac{\sigma^2}{n_1} + \frac{\sigma^2}{n_2}} = (\text{_____})\sqrt{\frac{1}{n_1} + \frac{1}{n_2}}$$

   $\qquad$ σ

3. If σ were known, then in testing an hypothesis concerning $\mu_1 - \mu_2$ we would use the statistic

   $$z = \frac{(\bar{y}_1 - \bar{y}_2) - D_0}{\sigma\sqrt{\dfrac{1}{n_1} + \dfrac{1}{n_2}}}$$

   where $D_0 = \mu_1 - \mu_2$.

4. For small samples with σ unknown, we would use

   $$t = \frac{(\bar{y}_1 - \bar{y}_2) - D_0}{\text{_____}\sqrt{\dfrac{1}{n_1} + \dfrac{1}{n_2}}}$$

   $\qquad$ s

   where s is the estimate of σ, calculated from the sample values. When the data are normally distributed, this statistic has a _____ _____ distribution with degrees of freedom the same as those available for estimating _____.

   $\qquad$ Student's t

   $\qquad$ σ^2

5. In selecting the best estimate (s^2) for σ^2, one has three immediate choices:

variance

    a. s_1^2, the sample _____ from population I,

variance

    b. s_2^2, the sample _____ from population II,

$s_1^2 ; s_2^2$

    c. a combination of _____ and _____.

c

    (a, b, c) is the best choice since it uses the information from both samples. A logical method of combining this information into one estimate, s^2, is

    d. $$s^2 = \frac{(n_1 - 1)s_1^2 + (n_2 - 1)s_2^2}{(n_1 - 1) + (n_2 - 1)}$$

    a weighted average of the sample variances using the degrees of freedom as weights.

6. The expression in Number 5d can be written in another form by replacing s_1^2 and s_2^2 by their defining formulas. Then

$\displaystyle\sum_{i=1}^{n_1}(y_i - \bar{y}_1)^2 ; \sum_{i=1}^{n_2}(y_i - \bar{y}_2)^2$

$$s^2 = \frac{\rule{2cm}{0.4pt} + \rule{2cm}{0.4pt}}{(n_1 - 1) + (n_2 - 1)}$$

$n_1 + n_2 - 2$

In this form we see that we have pooled or added the sums of squared deviations from each sample and divided by the pooled degrees of freedom, _____. Hence s^2 is a pooled estimate of the common variance σ^2 and is based on $n_1 + n_2 - 2$ degrees of freedom.

7. Since our samples were drawn from normal populations, the statistic

$$t = \frac{(\bar{y}_1 - \bar{y}_2) - (\mu_1 - \mu_2)}{s\sqrt{\dfrac{1}{n_1} + \dfrac{1}{n_2}}}$$

Student's $t; n_1 + n_2 - 2$

has a _____ distribution with _____ degrees of freedom.

8. *Example:*

A restaurant owner claims that the eight-ounce steaks served at his restaurant contain, on the average, less waste than the eight-ounce steaks sold by his competitor. Twelve eight-ounce steaks were randomly selected from the claimant's restaurant, twelve from his competitor's, and their waste-free weights were recorded. The measurements yielded the following information.

	Restaurant I (Claimant)	Restaurant II (Competitor)
	$\bar{y}_1$ = 6.8 oz.	$\bar{y}_2$ = 5.3 oz.
	s_1 = 1.5 oz.	s_2 = 0.9 oz.
	n_1 = 12	n_2 = 12

Do these data present sufficient evidence to indicate at the α = .05 level that the mean waste-free content of steaks from Restaurant I is greater than the waste-free content of steaks from Restaurant II? Find a 90% confidence interval for $\mu_1 - \mu_2$, the mean difference in waste-free content between the two restaurants.

Solution:

a. We shall take the waste-free contents to be normally distributed with equal variances and calculate a pooled estimate for σ^2.

$$s^2 = \frac{(n_1 - 1) s_1^2 + (n_2 - 1) s_2^2}{n_1 + n_2 - 2}$$

$$= \frac{11(1.5)^2 + 11(0.9)^2}{12 + 12 - 2}$$

$$= \frac{(\underline{\hspace{2cm}})}{22} \qquad\qquad 33.66$$

$$= \underline{\hspace{2cm}} \qquad\qquad 1.530$$

Then

$$s = \sqrt{\underline{\hspace{2cm}}} = 1.237 \qquad\qquad 1.530$$

b. The test is as follows:

$$H_0: \mu_1 - \mu_2 = \underline{\hspace{2cm}} \qquad\qquad 0$$

$$H_a: \mu_1 - \mu_2 > \underline{\hspace{2cm}} \qquad\qquad 0$$

Test statistic:

$$t = \frac{(\bar{y}_1 - \bar{y}_2) - D_0}{s\sqrt{\dfrac{1}{n_1} + \dfrac{1}{n_2}}}$$

Rejection region:

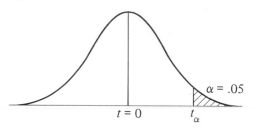

$\alpha = .05$

$t = 0$ t_α

22

1.717

With $n_1 + n_2 - 2 =$ _____ degrees of freedom, we would reject H_0 if $t >$ _____ . Calculate the test statistic.

$$t = \frac{(\bar{y}_1 - \bar{y}_2) - D_0}{s\sqrt{\dfrac{1}{n_1} + \dfrac{1}{n_2}}}$$

1.5; 0

$$= \frac{(\underline{\hspace{1.2cm}}) - (\underline{\hspace{1.2cm}})}{1.237\sqrt{.1667}}$$

1.5

$$= \frac{(\underline{\hspace{1.2cm}})}{.505}$$

2.97

$$= \underline{\hspace{1.5cm}}$$

reject H_0

Decision: _____ _____

1.717

c. To find a 90% confidence interval for $\mu_1 - \mu_2$, we need $t_{.05}$ based upon 22 degrees of freedom. $t_{.05} =$ _____ .
Hence we would use

$$(\bar{y}_1 - \bar{y}_2) \pm 1.717 \; s\sqrt{\frac{1}{n_1} + \frac{1}{n_2}}$$

1.5; .505

_____ $\pm 1.717 \;(\underline{\hspace{1.8cm}})$ from part b

1.5; .867

$(\underline{\hspace{1.5cm}}) \pm (\underline{\hspace{1.5cm}})$

Therefore a 90% confidence interval for $\mu_1 - \mu_2$ would be

.63; 2.37

$(\underline{\hspace{1.5cm}}, \underline{\hspace{1.5cm}})$

9. The testing procedure used to make decisions about the difference between two means requires the assumptions that each underlying population possesses

a _____ probability distribution, and that the population _____ are _____.

10. Departures from the normality assumption (are, are not) serious. However, the population variances must be _____ equal for the test to be valid.

Self-Correcting Exercises 9B

1. What are the assumptions required for the proper use of the statistic

$$t = \frac{(\bar{y}_1 - \bar{y}_2) - (\mu_1 - \mu_2)}{s\sqrt{\dfrac{1}{n_1} + \dfrac{1}{n_2}}}$$

2. In evaluating the efficiency of each of two teams of workers, a contractor records the length of time required for these teams to complete comparable assignments with the following results.

	Team 1	Team 2
Number of jobs	10	8
Mean completion time	6.3 hrs.	7.2 hrs.
Standard deviation	1.1 hrs.	2.2 hrs.

Test whether there is a significant difference in mean completion times for these two teams at the .05 level of significance.

3. In the evaluation of two possible advertising campaigns, a group of 30 volunteers were randomly divided into two groups of 15 people. Group number one was presented with advertising campaign one and the second presented with advertising campaign two. After the presentations, each person filled out an evaluation form prepared by the advertising agency. The information on each form was translated into a numerical score, resulting in the following summary.

	Campaigns	
	1	*2*
n	15	15
$\bar{y}$	80.3	68.7
s	6.2	9.3

a. Is there a significant difference in mean scores for the two presentations?
b. If the mean scores differ by 10 points or more, the campaign which scored 10 points higher than the other will proceed to the next stage of development. Estimate $\mu_1 - \mu_2$ with a 95% confidence interval. Based upon your estimate, would campaign number one be given approval to proceed to the next stage?

9.5 A Paired-Difference Test (9.5)

treatment

information

independent
random
reducing

1. In many situations an experiment is designed so that a comparison of the effects of two *treatments* is made on the same person, on twin offspring, two animals from the same litter, two pieces of fabric from the same loom, or two plants of the same species grown on adjacent plots. Such experiments are designed so that the pairs of experimental units (people, animals, fabrics, plants) are as much alike as possible. By taking measurements on the two treatments within the relatively homogeneous pairs of experimental units, we find the difference in the measurements for the two treatments in a pair will primarily reflect the difference between _____ means rather than the difference between experimental units. This experimental design reduces the error of comparison and increases the quantity of _____ in the experiment.

2. To analyze such an experiment using the techniques of the last section would be incorrect. In planning this type of experiment, we *intentionally violate* the assumption that the measurements are _____ and _____, and we hope that this violation will work to our advantage by _____ the variability of the differences of the paired observations. Consider the situation in which two products are to be compared by analyzing the sales in dollars over a one-week period for each of the products in each of three stores. Store number 1 is a department store, store number 2 is a specialty shop and store number 3 is a general merchandise store. At the end of the specified time the sales data are collected and presented for analysis.

| | Product | | |
Store	A	B	Difference
1	A_1	B_1	$A_1 - B_1$
2	A_2	B_2	$A_2 - B_2$
3	A_3	B_3	$A_3 - B_3$

large

small

Now A_1 and B_1 are not independent since both sales records were made during the same week in a department store. Although A_1 could be larger or smaller than B_1, if A_1 were a large amount, we would also expect B_1 to be a _____ amount. Since store 2 is a specialty store, it probably has less in total sales than a department store. Hence if A_2 were a small amount, then we would expect B_2 to be a _____ amount. Store 3 would probably produce sales for each product lying somewhere between that of store 1 and that of store 2.

3. By looking at the differences $(A_1 - B_1)$, $(A_2 - B_2)$, $(A_3 - B_3)$, we note that the volume of sales at the various stores will no longer be an issue, since these differences should represent the difference due to consumer choice between the two products.

4. In using a paired-difference design, we analyze the differences of the paired

measurements and, in so doing, attempt to *reduce* the *variability* that would be present in two *randomly* selected groups without pairing.

5. A test of the hypothesis that the difference in two population means, $\mu_1 - \mu_2$, is equal to a constant, D_0, is equivalent to a test of the hypothesis that the mean of the differences, μ_d, is equal to a constant, D_0. That is, $H_0: \mu_1 - \mu_2 = D_0$ is equivalent to $H_0: \mu_d = D_0$. Usually, we will be interested in the hypothesis that $D_0 = $ _____.

0

6. *Example:*

In order to evaluate a new training program for sales personnel, twelve new salesmen were selected and matched as closely as possible with respect to factors that could affect their potential sales ability, such as age, personality and past sales records. One member of each pair was randomly assigned to receive training under the standard program; the other member was trained according to the new program. At the end of their training periods, their progress was measured by their observed success in the market during a one-week period. Do the following data indicate that the new training program is better than the standard program? Use $\alpha = .05$.

	Sales Record		
Pair	Standard .	New	$d_i = N - S$
1	68	73	5
2	75	79	4
3	98	97	-1
4	81	83	2
5	72	78	6
6	109	109	0

Find a 95% confidence interval for the mean difference in sales records.
Solution:

a. We analyze the set of six differences as we would a single set of six measurements. The change in notation required is straightforward.

$$\sum_{i=1}^{6} d_i = 16 \qquad \sum_{i=1}^{6} d_i^2 = 82$$

The sample mean is

$$\bar{d} = \frac{1}{6} \sum_{i-1}^{6} d_i = \underline{\qquad\qquad}$$

2.67

The sample variance of the differences is

$$s_d^2 = \frac{\sum_{i=1}^{6} d_i^2 - \dfrac{\left(\sum_{i=1}^{6} d_i\right)^2}{6}}{5}$$

82; 16

$$= \frac{\underline{\qquad} - (\underline{\qquad})^2/6}{5}$$

$$= 7.8667$$

7.8667; 2.81

$$s_d = \sqrt{\underline{\qquad}} = \underline{\qquad}$$

b. The test is conducted as follows. Remember that $\mu_d = \mu_N - \mu_S$.

0

$$H_0: \mu_d = \underline{\qquad}$$

0

$$H_a: \mu_d > \underline{\qquad}$$

Test statistic:

$\dfrac{\bar{d} - 0}{s_d/\sqrt{n}}$

$$t = \underline{\qquad}$$

Rejection region: Based upon 5 degrees of freedom we will reject H_0 if the observed value of t is greater than $t_{.05} = \underline{\qquad}$. Note that this is a one-tailed test.

2.015

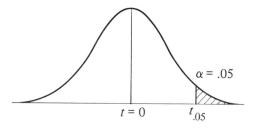

$\alpha = .05$

$t = 0$ $\quad t_{.05}$

The sample value of t is

$$t = \frac{\bar{d} - 0}{s_d/\sqrt{n}}$$

2.67

$$= \frac{\underline{\qquad} - 0}{2.81/\sqrt{6}}$$

$$= \frac{2.67}{1.15}$$

$$= 2.32$$

Since the value of the test statistic is greater than 2.015, we (reject, do not reject) H_0. — reject

c. This sample indicates that the new program appears to be superior to the standard program at the $\alpha = .05$ level, if we assume that the recorded sales are a valid criterion upon which to base our judgment.

d. A 95% confidence interval for μ_d is estimated by

$$\bar{d} \pm \underline{\hspace{2cm}}$$ — $t_{.025}\dfrac{s_d}{\sqrt{n}}$

Using our sample values and $t_{.025} = \underline{\hspace{2cm}}$, we have — 2.571

$$2.67 \pm \underline{\hspace{2cm}} (1.15)$$ — 2.571

$$2.67 \pm \underline{\hspace{2cm}}$$ — 2.96

With 95% confidence, we estimate that μ_d lies within the interval -0.29 to $\underline{\hspace{2cm}}$. — 5.63

7. Notice that in using a paired-difference analysis, the degrees of freedom for the critical value of t drop from $2n - 2$ for an unpaired design to $n - 1$ for the paired, a loss of $(2n - 2) - (n - 1) - \underline{\hspace{2cm}}$ degrees of freedom. — $n - 1$

This results in a (larger, smaller) critical value of t. Therefore a larger value — larger

of the test statistic is needed to reject H_0. Fortunately, *proper* pairing will reduce $\sigma_{\bar{d}}$. Hence the paired-difference experiment results in both a loss and a gain of information. However, the *loss* of $(n - 1)$ degrees of freedom is usually far overshadowed by the gain in information when $\sigma_{\bar{d}}$ is substantially reduced.

8. The statistical design of the paired-difference test is a simple example of a

$\underline{\hspace{3cm}}$ $\underline{\hspace{3cm}}$ design. In such a design, the $\underline{\hspace{2cm}}$ — randomized block; pairing

must occur when the experiment is planned and not after the data are collected.

9. Once one has used a $\underline{\hspace{3cm}}$ design for an experiment, one no — paired

longer has the choice of using the $\underline{\hspace{3cm}}$ design for testing the — unpaired

difference between means. This is because we have violated the assumptions needed for the unpaired design, namely, that the samples are $\underline{\hspace{2cm}}$ — randomly

and $\underline{\hspace{2cm}}$ drawn. — independently

Self Correcting Exercises 9C

1. The owner of a small manufacturing plant is considering a change in salary base by replacing an hourly wage structure with a per-unit rate. He hopes that such a change will increase the output per worker, but he has reserva-

tions about a possible decrease in quality under the per-unit plan. Before arriving at any decision, he formed 10 pairs of workers so that within each pair, the two workers had produced about the same number of items per day, and their work was of comparable quality. From each pair, one worker was randomly selected to be paid as usual and the other to be paid on a per-unit basis. In addition to the number of items produced, a cumulative quality score for the items produced was kept for each worker. The quality scores follow. (A high score is indicative of high quality.)

| | Rate | |
Pair	Per unit	Hourly
1	86	91
2	75	77
3	87	83
4	81	84
5	65	68
6	77	76
7	88	89
8	91	91
9	68	73
10	79	78

Do these data indicate that the average quality for the per-unit production is significantly lower than that based upon an hourly wage?

2. Refer to Number 1. The following data represent the average number of items produced per worker, based upon one week's production records.

| | Rate | |
Pair	Per unit	Hourly
1	35.8	31.2
2	29.4	27.6
3	31.2	32.2
4	28.6	26.4
5	30.0	29.0
6	32.6	31.4
7	36.8	34.2
8	34.4	31.6
9	29.6	27.6
10	32.8	29.8

a. Estimate the mean difference in average daily output for the two pay scales with a 95% confidence interval.

b. Test the hypothesis that a per-unit pay scale increases production at the .05 level of significance.

9.6 Inferences About a Population Variance (9.6)

1. In many cases, the measure of variability is more important than that of

central tendency. For example, an educational test consisting of 100 items has a mean score of 75 with standard deviation of 2.5. Although $\mu = 75$ may sound impressive, $\sigma = 2.5$ would imply that this test has very poor discriminating ability since approximately 95% of the scores would be between 70 and 80. In like manner a production line producing bearings with $\mu = .25$ inches and $\sigma = .5$ inches would produce many defective items; the fact that the bearings have a mean diameter of .25 inches would be of little value when the bearings are fitted together. *The precision of an instrument, whether it be an educational test or a machine, is measured by the standard deviation of the error of measurement.* Hence we proceed to a test of a population variance, σ^2.

2. The sample variance, s^2, is an _____ estimator for σ^2. To use s^2 unbiased
for inference making, we find that in repeated sampling, the distribution of s^2 has the following properties.

   a. $s^2 =$ _____ $\displaystyle\sum_{i=1}^{n} (y_i - \bar{y})^2 / (n-1)$

   b. $E(s^2) =$ _____ σ^2
   c. The distribution of s^2 is (symmetric, nonsymmetric).   nonsymmetric
   d. s^2 can assume any value greater than or equal to _____.   zero (0)
   e. The shape of the distribution changes for different values of

       _____ and _____. $n; \sigma^2$
   f. In sampling from a *normal* population, s^2 is independent of the population mean, _____, and the sample mean, _____. $\mu; \bar{y}$

3. As with the z-statistic, the distribution for s^2 when sampling from a normal population can be standardized by using

$$\frac{\underline{\hspace{2cm}}}{\sigma^2} = \frac{(n-1)s^2}{\sigma^2}$$

                                    χ^2

The chi-square random variable has the following properties in repeated sampling.
   a. $E(\chi^2) =$ _____. $n-1$
   b. The distribution of χ^2 is (symmetric, nonsymmetric).   nonsymmetric
   c. $\chi^2 \geqslant$ _____.   0
   d. The distribution of χ^2 depends upon the degrees of freedom, $n-1$.

4. Since χ^2 does not have a symmetric distribution, critical values of χ^2 have been tabulated for both the upper and lower tails of the distribution in Table 5 of your text. The degrees of freedom are listed along both the right and left margins of the table. Across the top margin are values, χ^2_α, indicating a value of χ^2 having an area equal to α to its right, that is,

$$P[\chi^2 > \chi^2_\alpha] = \alpha$$

5. *Examples:*
   Use Table 5 to find the following critical values of χ^2:

5.99147
2.55821
37.5662
18.4926
1.734926
27.4884
45.5585
10.0852

	α	d.f.	χ_α^2
a.	.05	2	
b.	.99	10	
c.	.01	20	
d.	.95	30	
e.	.995	9	
f.	.025	15	
g.	.005	24	
h.	.90	17	

6. The statistical test of an hypothesis concerning a population variance, σ^2, at the α level of significance is given as follows:
   a. H_0: $\sigma^2 = \sigma_0^2$
   b. H_a: Appropriate one- or two-tailed test
   c. Test statistic:

$$\chi^2 = \underline{\qquad}$$

$$\frac{(n-1)s^2}{\sigma_0^2}$$

   d. Rejection region:
      i. For H_a: $\sigma^2 > \sigma_0^2$, reject H_0 if $\chi^2 > \chi_\alpha^2$ based on $n-1$ degrees of freedom.
      ii. For H_a: $\sigma^2 < \sigma_0^2$, reject H_0 if $\chi^2 < \chi_{(1-\alpha)}^2$ based on $n-1$ degrees of freedom.
      iii. For H_a: $\sigma^2 \neq \sigma_0^2$, reject H_0 if $\chi^2 > \chi_{\alpha/2}^2$ or $\chi^2 < \chi_{(1-\alpha/2)}^2$ based on $n-1$ degrees of freedom.

7. *Example:*
   A producer of machine parts claimed that the diameters of the connector rods produced by his plant had a variance of at most .03 in.^{2} A random sample of 15 connector rods from his plant produced a sample mean and variance of 0.55 in. and 0.53 in.^{2}, respectively. Is there sufficient evidence to reject his claim at the $\alpha = .05$ level of significance?
   Solution:
   a. Collecting pertinent information:

$$s^2 = .053 \text{ in.}^2$$

$$\text{d.f.} = n - 1 = 14$$

$$\sigma_0^2 = .03 \text{ in.}^2$$

   b. The test of the hypothesis is given as:

$$H_0: \sigma^2 = .03$$

$> .03$

$$H_a: \sigma^2 \underline{\qquad}$$

Test statistic:

$$\chi^2 = \frac{(n-1)s^2}{\sigma_0^2}$$

Rejection region:

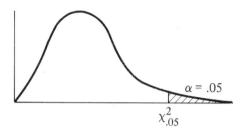

$\alpha = .05$

$\chi_{.05}^2$

For 14 degrees of freedom, we shall reject H_0 if

$\chi^2 \geqslant$ _____

23.6848

Calculate:

$$\chi^2 = \frac{(n-1)s^2}{\sigma_0^2}$$

$$= \frac{14\,(\underline{\qquad})}{(\underline{\qquad})}$$

.053

.03

$$= 24.733$$

Decision: _____ H_0 since

Reject

$$24.733 > \chi_{.05}^2 = 23.6848$$

The data produced sufficient evidence to reject H_0. Therefore we can conclude that the variance of the rod diameters is greater than .03 in.^{2}

8. The sample variance, s^2, is an unbiased point estimator for the population variance, σ^2. Utilizing the fact that $(n-1)s^2/\sigma^2$ has a chi-square distribution with $(n-1)$ degrees of freedom, we can show that a $(1-\alpha)\,100\%$ confidence interval for σ^2 is

$$\frac{(n-1)s^2}{\chi_U^2} < \sigma^2 < \frac{(n-1)s^2}{\chi_L^2}$$

where χ_U^2 is the tabulated value of the chi-square random variable based upon _____ degrees of freedom having an area equal to $\alpha/2$ to its _____, while χ_L^2 is the tabulated value from the same distribution having an area of $\alpha/2$ to its _____ or equivalently, an area of $1 - \alpha/2$ to its right.

$(n-1)$

right

left

9. *Example:*
Find a 95% confidence interval estimate for the variance of the rod diameters from Example 8.
Solution:
From Example 8 the estimate of σ^2 was $s^2 = .053$ with 14 degrees of freedom. For a confidence coefficient of .95 we need

5.62872

$$\chi_L^2 = \chi_{.975}^2 = \underline{\hspace{2cm}}$$

and

26.1190

$$\chi_U^2 = \chi_{.025}^2 = \underline{\hspace{2cm}}$$

a. Using the confidence interval estimator

$$\frac{(n-1)s^2}{\chi_U^2} < \sigma^2 < \frac{(n-1)s^2}{\chi_L^2}$$

we have

26.1190; 5.62872

$$\frac{14(.053)}{\underline{\hspace{1.5cm}}} < \sigma^2 < \frac{14(.053)}{\underline{\hspace{1.5cm}}}$$

or

.028; .132

$$\underline{\hspace{2cm}} < \sigma^2 < \underline{\hspace{2cm}}$$

b. By taking square roots of the upper and lower confidence limits, we have an equivalent confidence interval for the standard deviation, σ. For this problem

.167; .363

$$\underline{\hspace{2cm}} < \sigma < \underline{\hspace{2cm}}$$

10. *Comment:* Although the sample variance is an unbiased point estimator for σ^2, notice that the confidence interval estimator for σ^2 *is not symmetrically located about* $\hat{\sigma}^2$ as was the case with confidence intervals which were based upon the z or t distributions. This is because, unlike the z and t distributions, the

chi-square

distribution is not symmetric.

Self-Correcting Exercises 9D

1. A machine must be stopped and adjusted if the variability of the items it produces exceeds $\sigma = 1$ mm. Twenty randomly selected items from this machine's production produced a sample standard deviation of $s = 1.5$ mm. Is there sufficient reason to stop and adjust the machine?

2. An educational testing service, in developing a standardized test, would like the test to have a standard deviation of at least 10. The present form of the test has produced a standard deviation of $s = 8.9$ based upon $n = 30$ test scores. Should the present form of the test be revised based upon these sample data?

3. A faster technique for determining the concentration of an industrial solution has been proposed to replace the present technique which takes much longer. When a solution is tested for its concentration, 30 determinations using the new technique produced a standard deviation of $s = 7.3$ parts per million.

   a. Does it appear that the new technique is less sensitive (has larger variability) than the present technique whose standard deviation is $\sigma = 5$ ppm?

   b. Estimate the true standard deviation for the new technique with a 95% confidence interval.

9.7 Comparing Two Population Variances (9.7)

1. An experimenter may wish to compare the variability of two testing procedures or compare the precision of one manufacturing process with another. One may also wish to compare two population variances prior to using a t-test.

2. To test the hypothesis of equality of two population variances,

$$H_0: \sigma_1^2 = \sigma_2^2$$

we need the following assumptions.

   a. Each population sampled has a _____ distribution.

   b. The samples are _____ .

normal

independent

3. The statistic, s_1^2/s_2^2, is used to test

$$H_0: \sigma_1^2 = \sigma_2^2$$

A _____ value of this statistic implies that $\sigma_1^2 > \sigma_2^2$; a _____ value of this statistic implies that $\sigma_1^2 < \sigma_2^2$; while a value of the statistic close to one (1) implies that $\sigma_1^2 = \sigma_2^2$. In repeated sampling this statistic has an _____ distribution when $\sigma_1^2 = \sigma_2^2$ with the following properties:

large

small

F

nonsymmetric

$s_1^2 ; s_2^2$

zero

a. The distribution of F is (symmetric, nonsymmetric).

b. The shape of the distribution depends upon the degrees of freedom associated with _____ and _____ .

c. F is always greater than or equal to _____ .

4. The tabulation of critical values of F is complicated by the fact that the distribution is nonsymmetric and must be indexed according to the values of v_1 and v_2, the degrees of freedom associated with the numerator and denominator of the F-statistic. As we shall see, however, it will be sufficient to have only right-tailed critical values of F for the various combinations of v_1 and v_2.

5. Tables 6 and 7 of the text have tabulated right-tailed critical values, F_α, for the F-statistic where F_α is that value of F having an area equal to α to its right, based on v_1 and v_2, the degrees of freedom associated with the *numerator* and *denominator* of F, respectively. F_α satisfies the relationship

$$P[F > F_\alpha] = \alpha$$

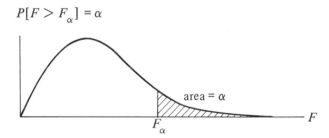

Table 6 has values of F_α for $\alpha = .05$, and various values of v_1 and v_2 between 1 and ∞, while Table 7 has the same information for $\alpha = .01$.

6. *Example:*

Find the value of F based upon $v_1 = 5$ and $v_2 = 7$ degrees of freedom such that

$$P[F > F_{.05}] = .05$$

Solution:

a. We wish to find a critical value of F with an area $\alpha = .05$ to its _____ based on $v_1 = 5$, $v_2 = 7$ degrees of freedom. Therefore, we will use Table 6.

b. Values of v_1 are found along the *top* margin of the table while values of v_2 appear on both the right *and* left margins of the table. Find the value of $v_1 = 5$ along the top margin and cross-index this value with $v_2 = 7$ along the left margin to find $F_{.05} = 3.97$.

7. *Example:*

Find the critical right-tailed values of F for the following:

right

	ν_1	ν_2	α	F_α
a.	5	2	.05	_____ 19.30
b.	7	15	.05	_____ 2.71
c.	20	10	.01	_____ 4.41
d.	30	40	.05	_____ 1.74
e.	17	13	.01	_____ 3.76

8. We can always avoid using left-tailed critical values of the F distribution by using the following approach. In testing H_0: $\sigma_1^2 = \sigma_2^2$ against the alternative H_a: $\sigma_1^2 > \sigma_2^2$, we would reject H_0 only if s_1^2/s_2^2 is too *large* (larger than a right-tailed critical value of F). In testing H_0: $\sigma_1^2 = \sigma_2^2$ against H_a: $\sigma_1^2 < \sigma_2^2$, we would reject H_0 only if s_2^2/s_1^2 *were too large.* In testing H_0: $\sigma_1^2 = \sigma_2^2$ against the two-tailed alternative, H_a: $\sigma_1^2 \neq \sigma_2^2$, we shall agree to *designate the population which produced the larger sample variance as population I and the larger sample variance as s_1^2.* We then agree to reject H_0 if s_1^2/s_2^2 is *too large.*

9. When we agree to designate the population with the larger sample variance as population I, the test of H_0: $\sigma_1^2 = \sigma_2^2$ versus H_a: $\sigma_1^2 \neq \sigma_2^2$ using s_1^2/s_2^2 will be right-tailed. However in so doing, we must remember that the tabulated tail area must be _____ to get the actual significance | doubled
level of the test. For example, if the critical right-tailed value of F has been found from Table 6, the actual significance level of the test will be
$\alpha = 2(.05) =$ _____ . If the critical value comes from Table 7, the | .10
actual level will be $\alpha = 2(.01) =$ _____ . | .02

10. *Example:*

A comparison of the precisions of two machines developed for extracting juice from oranges is to be made using the following data:

Machine A	Machine B
$s^2 = 3.1$ oz.^{2}	$s^2 = 1.4$ oz.^{2}
$n = 25$	$n = 25$

Is there sufficient evidence to indicate that $\sigma_A^2 > \sigma_B^2$ at the $\alpha = .05$ level?
Solution:
Let population I be the population of measurements on Machine A. The test would proceed as follows:

$$H_0: \sigma_1^2 = \sigma_2^2$$

$$H_a: \sigma_1^2 \underline{\quad\quad} \sigma_2^2$$ | $>$

Test statistic:

$$F = \underline{\quad\quad\quad}$$ | s_1^2/s_2^2

24

1.98

Rejection region:

Based upon $v_1 = v_2 =$ _____ degrees of freedom, we shall reject H_0 if $F > F_{.05}$ with $F_{.05} =$ _____ .

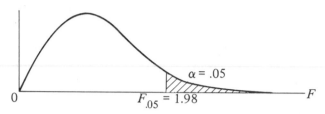

$\alpha = .05$

$F_{.05} = 1.98$

F

0

The value of the statistic is

2.21

$$F = \frac{s_1^2}{s_2^2} = \frac{3.1}{1.4} = \underline{\hspace{2cm}}$$

is

Decision: We reject H_0 and conclude that the variability of Machine A (is, is not) greater than that of Machine B.

11. *Example:*

An investor is studying the performance of two security portfolios. Performance of each portfolio is measured by its market closing price at the end of each market day. Use the following data to determine whether or not there is a significant difference in variability of closing prices for these two portfolios at the $\alpha = .02$ level of significance.

	Portfolio I	*Portfolio II*
	$s = 2.3$	$s = 5.8$
	$n = 10$	$n = 10$

Solution:

This problem involves a test of the equality of two population variances. Let population I be the population of market prices for portfolio II.

a. $\quad H_0: \sigma_1^2 = \sigma_2^2$

b. $\quad H_a: \sigma_1^2 \neq \sigma_2^2$

c. Test statistic:

$$F = s_1^2 / s_2^2$$

d. Rejection region: with $v_1 = v_2 = 9$ degrees of freedom, reject H_0 if

5.35

$\quad F > F_{.01} =$ _____ .

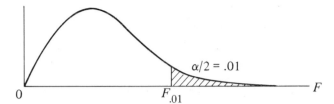

$$\alpha/2 = .01$$

e. Calculate the test statistic.

$$F = s_1^2/s_2^2$$

$$= (5.8)^2/(2.3)^2$$

$$= (\underline{\hspace{1cm}})/(\underline{\hspace{1cm}})$$ 33.64; 5.29

$$= \underline{\hspace{1cm}}$$ 6.36

f. Decision: Since F is (greater, less) than $F_{.01} = 5.35, H_0: \sigma_1^2 = \sigma_2^2$ greater
   (is, is not) rejected. is
g. If the population variances were judged to be not different, the
   investor's next step would be to look at the difference in mean closing
   price for the portfolios and choose the one with the _____ larger
   mean closing price. In the absence of equality of variances, the investor
   would ideally choose that portfolio with the _____ mean larger
   and the _____ variability. smaller

Self-Correcting Exercises 9E

1. Refer to Self-Correcting Exercises 9B, problem 3. In using the t-statistic in
   testing an hypothesis concerning $\mu_1 - \mu_2$, one assumes that $\sigma_1^2 = \sigma_2^2$. Based
   upon the sample information, could you conclude that this assumption had
   been met for this problem?
2. In following the daily fluctuations in prices for two commodities, an
   investor found the variability of the price for one commodity to be
   $s_1 = \$1.59$ while that of a second was $s_2 = \$2.49$. If 10 daily prices were
   involved in the calculation of each standard deviation, does it appear that
   both commodities are exhibiting the same basic variation?

9.8 Summary (9.8)

1. In this chapter we have discussed the distributions of the t, χ^2, and F-
   statistics used in making _____ about a _____ from inferences; population
   _____ contained in a _____. information; sample
2. The distribution of these statistics rests upon the assumption that the
   sampled population(s) have a _____ distribution. However, a normal

t

small; s^2

paired difference

reduce; blocking

variances

inferences

slight departure from this assumption will not introduce serious errors in your results.

3. The _____-statistic is used in testing hypotheses about population means when the sample size is _____ and _____ must be used to estimate σ^2.

4. An elementary but important design of experiment was introduced in the _____-_____ test of two means. This design attempts to _____ variability by pairing or _____ the measurements and represents the simplest form of a block design.

5. The χ^2 and F-statistics are used to make inferences about population _____.

6. In the construction of a statistical test of an hypothesis or the construction of a confidence interval, one should note the similarity of approaches and techniques associated with the t, χ^2, F, and z-statistics. This similarity should help unify and clarify the methods used in making _____ about the characteristics of a population, regardless of the statistic used.

Exercises

1. Why can we say that the test statistics employed in Chapter 8 are approximately normally distributed?

2. What assumptions are made when Student's t-statistic is used to test an hypothesis concerning a population mean, μ?

3. How does one determine the degrees of freedom associated with a t-statistic?

4. Let t_α be that value of t with the proper degrees of freedom, such that

$$P[t > t_\alpha] = \alpha$$

Complete the following table.

	α	d.f.	t_α
a.	.025	7	_____
b.	.005	15	_____
c.	.05	2	_____
d.	.10	26	_____
e.	.05	11	_____

5. Ten butterfat determinations for brand G milk were carried out yielding $\bar{y} = 3.7\%$ and $s = 1.7\%$. Do these results produce sufficient evidence to indicate that brand G milk contains on the average less than 4.0% butterfat? (Use $\alpha = .05$.)

6. Refer to Exercise 5. Estimate the mean percent of butterfat for brand G milk with a 95% confidence interval.

7. A new method of producing a long-lasting headache remedy consists of varying the type of coatings used on the pill, so as to produce a continuous

discharge of the drug into a person's system. If the mean time for the pill to dissolve is greater than 12 hours, the new method will be further investigated. From a sample of size $n = 16$ people, $\bar{y}$ and s were computed to be 13.2 hours and 1.5 hours, respectively. Based on this sample, would you conclude that this new pill should be further investigated?

8. Refer to Exercise 7. Estimate the mean time until dissolution with an 80% confidence interval.

9. Due to a cost factor, only ten experimental electronic devices were constructed. For each device, the time until failure was recorded. If $\bar{y} = 354.0$ hours and $s = 23.9$ hours, would you conclude that the mean time until failure was less than 370 hours?

10. During the course of one month, a truck whose capacity was given as five tons, was weighed at a weighing station five times. The fare weights on these five occasions were: 5.1, 5.2, 4.8, 5.1 and 5.2 tons. Does it appear that this truck is overloaded on the average?

11. What assumptions are made for an unpaired test of an hypothesis concerning $\mu_1 - \mu_2$ using Student's t-statistic?

12. In comparing the weights of one-pound loaves of bread from two different bakeries the following data summary was presented.

	Bakery 1	Bakery 2
Number of loaves	16	10
Mean weight	17.4 oz.	15.8 oz.
Standard deviation	3.0 oz.	4.0 oz.

Based on these data, could you conclude that there was a significant difference in the average weight of one-pound loaves of bread for these two bakeries?

13. Find a 90% confidence interval estimate for $\mu_1 - \mu_2$ using the data in Exercise 12.

14. In investigating which of two presentations of subject matter to use in a marketing management course, an experimenter randomly chose two groups of 18 students each, and assigned one group to receive presentation I and the second to receive presentation II. A short quiz on the presentation was given to each group and their grades recorded. Do the following data indicate that a difference in the mean quiz scores (hence, a difference in effectiveness of presentation) exists for the two methods?

	$\bar{y}$	s^2
Presentation I	81.7	23.2
Presentation II	77.2	19.8

15. To test the comparative brightness of two red dyes, nine samples of cloth were taken from a production line and each sample was divided into two pieces. One of the two pieces in each sample was randomly chosen and red dye 1 applied; red dye 2 was applied to the remaining piece. The following data represent a "brightness score" for each piece. Is there sufficient

evidence to indicate a difference in mean brightness scores for the two dyes?

Sample	Dye 1	Dye 2
1	10	8
2	12	11
3	9	10
4	8	6
5	15	12
6	12	13
7	9	9
8	10	8
9	15	13

16. Before contracting to have stereo music piped into each of his suites of offices, an executive had his office manager randomly select seven offices to have the system installed. The average time spent outside these offices per excursion among the employees involved was recorded before and after the music system was installed with the following results.

	Time in minutes	
Office number	No music	Music
1	8	5
2	9	6
3	5	7
4	6	5
5	5	6
6	10	7
7	7	8

Would you suggest that the executive proceed with the installation?

17. Find the following critical values of χ^2:

	α	d.f.	χ^2_α
a.	.10	17	
b.	.90	18	
c.	.005	7	
d.	.975	29	
e.	.025	29	

18. A manufacturer of odometers claimed that mileage measurements indicated on his instruments had a variance of at most .53 miles per ten miles traveled. An experiment, consisting of eight runs over a measured ten-mile stretch, was performed in order to check the manufacturer's claim. The variance obtained for the eight runs was 0.62. Does this provide sufficient evidence to indicate that $\sigma^2 > .53$? (Use $\alpha = .05$.)

19. Construct a 99% confidence interval estimate for σ^2 in Exercise 18.

20. In an attempt to assess the variability in the time until a pain reliever became effective for one of his patients, a doctor, on five different occa-

sions, prescribed a controlled dosage of the drug for this patient. The five measurements recorded for the time until effective relief were: 20.2, 15.7, 19.8, 19.2, 22.7 minutes. Would these measurements indicate that the standard deviation of the time until effective relief was less than three minutes (i.e., $\sigma^2 < 9$)?

21. Construct a 95% confidence interval estimate for σ^2 in Exercise 20.

22. If F_α is that value of F based on v_1 and v_2 degrees of freedom, respectively, such that $P[F > F_\alpha] = \alpha$, find the following critical values of F_α.

	α	v_1	v_2	F_α
a.	.05	15	19	_____
b.	.05	9	22	_____
c.	.01	24	14	_____
d.	.01	5	8	_____

23. In a test of heat resistance involving two types of metal paint, two groups of ten metal strips were randomly selected. Group one was painted with type I paint, while group two was painted with type II paint. The metal strips were placed in an oven in random order, heated, and the temperature at which the paint began to crack and peel recorded for each strip. Do the following data indicate that the variability in the critical temperatures differs for the two types of paint?

	$\bar{y}$	s^2	n
Type I	280.1°F	93.2	10
Type II	269.9°F	51.9	10

24. Refer to Exercise 23. Can you comfortably apply Student's t-statistic in a test of $\mu_1 - \mu_2$ in this situation? Why? If you decide that you can, test the hypothesis that the mean difference in critical temperatures is zero at the $\alpha = .01$ level.

25. In an attempt to reduce the variability of machine parts produced by process A, a manufacturer has introduced process B (a modification of A). Do the following data based on two samples of 25 items indicate that the manufacturer has achieved his goal?

	n	s^2
Process A	25	6.57
Process B	25	3.19

Chapter   10

DECISION ANALYSIS

10.1 Introduction (10.1)

classical
inferences; population
sample

distribution
sampling

confidence interval; hypothesis
decision analysis

uncertainty
logical; quantitative

errors
Type I
Type II; arbitrarily

prior
sample
expected

decision
maximizes
are not
formality

1. The objective of the _____ or empirical approach to statistics is to make _____ about certain characteristics of a _____ based on information contained in a _____ drawn from the population.
2. With this approach, certain assumptions are made about the _____ of the population. Given these assumptions, we can determine a _____ distribution for our statistic of interest and thus construct an appropriate _____ _____ or test of an _____.
3. In contrast, _____ _____ enables the decision maker to formally integrate his personal preferences and perceptions regarding _____ and value into the decision framework.
4. Decision analysis can be defined as the _____ and _____ analysis of all of the factors that influence a decision.
5. Classical statistical inference and decision analysis differ in the way they treat _____ that may result from the use of each procedure. In classical inference, the levels of α and β, the levels of _____ and _____ errors, respectively, are often chosen _____ , without regard to the losses associated with the errors they define, and without regard to any _____ information that is not formally contained in the _____.
6. Decision analysis uses _____ loss or gain as the criterion for comparing testing or decision-making procedures.
7. Decision analysis uses the concept of gain or loss associated with every possible _____ available and selects the decision that (maximizes, minimizes) the expected gain.
8. Classical statistical inference and decision analysis (are, are not) in fundamental conflict. They instead differ mostly in the degree of _____ used in the decision-making procedures.

10.2 Certainty, Uncertainty, and the Analysis of the Decision Problem (10.2, 10.3)

1. Associated with every decision-making situation are:
   a. A mutually exclusive and collectively exhaustive set of _____ available to the decision maker, one of which must be _____. These actions or alternatives are generally symbolized by _____, $i = 1, 2, \ldots, n$.

   alternatives
chosen
a_i

   b. A mutually exclusive and collectively exhaustive set of events called _____ of _____, over which the decision maker (has, has no) control. These are denoted by _____, $j = 1, 2, \ldots, k$.

   states; nature
has no; s_j

   c. The _____ probabilities representing the chances of occurrence of the identifiable _____ of _____ before gathering any _____ information.

   prior
states; nature
sample

   d. A list of _____ representing the value consequences to the decision maker if he takes a specific _____, assuming that each of the states of nature occurs.

   payoffs
alternative or action

2. Alternatives (states of nature) are _____ _____ if no two can be in effect at the same time. Alternatives (states of nature) are _____ _____ if all possible alternatives (states) are included within the analysis.

   mutually exclusive

collectively exhaustive

3. The exact alternatives and states of nature associated with a decision-making problem (are, are not) unique to that problem. Ingenuity and perceptiveness are needed to identify the available _____, their associated _____, and the states of nature affecting the outcome.

   are not
alternatives
payoffs

4. When the state of nature that actually occurs (or will occur) is unknown, the decision maker is operating under _____. If the state of nature is known, or if unknown, has no influence on the outcome of the _____, the decision is being made under _____.

   uncertainty

alternatives; certainty

5. Decision making under _____ is usually simpler, while decision making under _____ is always complicated, requiring probability theory, mathematical _____, and the decision maker's intuition and knowledge.

   certainty
uncertainty
expectation

6. A _____ _____ is a listing in tabular form of the value consequences associated with all possible actions under every state of nature in a decision problem.

   payoff table

7. If there are n alternatives and k states of nature, the payoff table will usually be a grid with _____ rows, _____ columns, and _____ cells.

   $n; k; nk$

8. A rational decision maker attempts to choose the alternative that best satisfies his _____. Hence, the payoffs should be measured in units _____ with his objectives.

   objectives
consistent

9. Before a decision maker can evaluate alternative actions, he must clearly _____ his goals and objectives. He must then define a payoff measure that can _____ the outcomes according to the amount by which they satisfy his goals and objectives.

   identify
rank

profit; opportunity loss

objectives
optimal

states
of nature
decision
alternatives
14 cents

9 cents

states
of nature
prior probability

levels of
demand
alternatives

a_i; s_j

maximum

a_i

zero
four

10. We shall restrict out attention to monetary payoffs measurable by the _____ or _____ _____ associated with each outcome.

11. The decision which best satisfies the decision maker's _____ is called the _____ decision.

12. *Example:*

The operator of a newsstand buys copies of the Evening News at a cost of 7 cents and sells them for 10 cents each. The possible levels of demand for the Evening News from the newsstand constitute the _____ _____ _____. The number of copies of the Evening News purchased by the operator constitutes his _____ which is one of many possible _____ available to him. His opportunity loss for buying two more newspapers than he can sell is _____; his opportunity loss for buying 22 newspapers if he has the opportunity to sell 25 newspapers is _____.

13. *Example:*

An oil wildcatter holds a lease on a plot of land and must decide whether to drill for oil on that land or to abandon his lease. Should he decide to drill, the outcomes "oil" or "no oil" represent the _____ _____ _____. The likelihood of striking oil assumed by the wildcatter is referred to as a _____ _____.

14. *Example:*

A production manager must decide which of two machines, machine A or machine B, to buy to manufacture a novelty item. Machine A is quite expensive to operate if few items are produced but economical for large lots; the opposite is true for machine B. The _____ _____ _____ for the novelty item represent the states of nature, while the _____ are to select machine A or select machine B.

15. A profit table is a listing, in tabular form, of the profit P_{ij} for selecting action _____ given that the state of nature _____ is in effect. An opportunity loss table is a tabulation of the opportunity losses, L_{ij}, associated with a decision problem where L_{ij} is the opportunity loss for selecting action a_i given that state of nature s_j is in effect. More precisely, L_{ij} is the difference between the _____ profit which could be realized if state of nature s_j occurs and the profit realized by selecting action _____.

16. *Example:*

A building contractor must decide how many speculative mountain cabins to build in a resort area. He builds each cabin at a cost of $6500 and sells each for $9000. All cabins unsold after six months will be sold to a local investor for $5000 so that costs can be recovered. The contractor estimates that it would be impossible to sell more than four cabins. Construct the profit table and the opportunity loss table for this decision problem.

Solution:

The alternatives available to the contractor are to build from _____ to _____ cabins. The states of nature would be represented by the

possible levels of demand, 0 through 4. The profit per cabin sold is
_____ as the contractor's costs per cabin are $6500 and the selling
price is _____. Since unsold cabins are sold at a loss of $1500 each,
the contractor's profit for building 3 cabins and selling 2 is $5000 - $1500
= _____. Similarly, his profit for building 4 cabins and selling 1 is
$2500 - $4500 = _____. Fill in the missing entries below.

$2500
$9000

$3500
-$2000

Profit Table

Number of cabins built	Number of cabins demanded				
	0	1	2	3	4
0	0	0	0	0	0
1	_____	2500	2500	2500	2500
2	-3000	_____	_____	5000	5000
3	-4500	_____	3500	_____	7500
4	-6000	-2000	2000	_____	_____

-1500
1000; 5000
-500; 7500
6000; 10,000

The opportunity loss table is computed by noting the largest payoff in
each column (under each state of nature) of the profit table and then subtracting each entry in the column from this maximum value. Fill in the
missing entries in the opportunity loss table which follows.

Opportunity Loss Table

Number of cabins built	Number of cabins demanded				
	0	1	2	3	4
0	_____	2500	5000	7500	10,000
1	1500	0	_____	_____	7500
2	_____	_____	0	2500	5000
3	4500	_____	1500	0	_____
4	6000	_____	3000	1500	0

0
2500; 5000
3000; 1500
3000; 2500
4500

17. *Example:*

A store owner must decide whether to stock one, two, or three units of a
perishable commodity each morning. It is assumed that demand will
always exist for at least one unit but will never exceed three units per day.
The units are purchased at a cost of $4.00 each and are sold for $6.00
each. Construct the store owner's profit table and opportunity loss table.
Solution:
The store owner's available alternatives are to stock 1, 2, or 3 units per day
while the states of nature are represented by the possible levels of demand,
1, 2, and 3 units. Complete the profit table below.

Profit Table

Stock level	Demand level		
	1	2	3
1	2	2	2
2	_____	_____	4
3	-6	_____	_____

-2; 4
0; 6

Fill in the missing entries in the opportunity loss table shown below.

	Opportunity Loss Table		
	Demand level		
Stock level	1	2	3
1	0	_____	_____
2	4	0	2
3	_____	_____	0

2; 4

8; 4

Self-Correcting Exercises 10A

1. A delivery service must decide how many new delivery vehicles it will purchase in a planned expansion of service routes. At least one, but not more than three new vehicles will be required. For each truck purchased, the delivery service will be required to pay $250 per month to cover installment payments, insurance, and other expenses. Each truck in service for a given month will earn about $1250, cost $150 for gas and service expenses, and require $500 in salary for the driver. Let us assume that one driver will be hired for each new service vehicle purchased and that each driver hired must be paid whether or not his vehicle is in service for a given month. Using these figures as monthly averages, construct a monthly profit table and the corresponding opportunity loss table for this decision problem.

2. A contractor must decide whether to submit one, two or three bids for three independent contracts, each for $100,000. The research and preparation of a $100,000 bid amounts to $5000. The cost of labor and materials per contract is expected to be about $80,000. If more than one contract is awarded to this contractor, he can save $5000 in the cost of materials by buying the materials for two jobs in bulk, and he can save $15,000 by buying the materials for three jobs in bulk. Construct a profit table and an opportunity loss table for this decision problem.

10.3 Expected Monetary Value Decisions (10.4, 10.5)

1. An expected monetary value decision is a decision to select an available alternative based on the expected _____ _____ or expected profit of the alternative.

opportunity loss

2. The _____ decision is a decision by the decision maker to select the alternative which best satisfies his objective. Expected opportunity loss decisions and expected profit decisions are _____ associated with the same optimal decision.

optimal

always

3. The _____ _____ associated with the states of nature are used as weights or multipliers on the opportunity losses or profits associated with each possible alternative in an expected monetary value decision.

prior probabilities

4. The expected opportunity loss for a given alternative a_i is found by computing

$$E(L_i) = \sum_{\text{all } j} \underline{\hspace{3cm}} \quad \text{where}$$

$L_{i,j}P(s_j)$

$L_{i,j}$ is the opportunity loss for selecting alternative i when state of nature j is in effect and $p(s_j)$ is the prior probability assigned to state of nature j. The decision which _____ the decision maker's expected opportunity loss is then to select the _____ associated with the smallest expected opportunity loss, $E(L_i)$.

minimizes
alternative

5. If the decision maker's objective is to maximize his expected profits, his optimal decision is to select the alternative associated with the _____ expected gain, $E(G_i)$, where

largest

$$E(G_i) = \sum_{\text{all } j} \underline{\hspace{3cm}}$$

$G_{i,j}P(s_j)$

and $G_{i,j}$ is the profit associated with the selection of alternative i under state of nature j.

6. The difference between the expected opportunity losses from any two actions is _____ in magnitude to, but _____ in sign from, the difference between their expected _____.

equal; opposite
profits

7. *Example:*
Return to the problem of the building contractor, Section 10.2(16). Suppose that after a careful analysis of the demand for mountain cabins in the resort area, the contractor decides the following distribution best represents his likelihood of selling from 0 through 4 cabins.

Number	0	1	2	3	4
Probability	.1	.2	.4	.2	.1

How many cabins should the contractor build if he wishes to minimize his expected opportunity loss?
Solution:
The opportunity loss table for the contractor's problem was given in 10.2 (16). To find the optimal decision, we must compute the _____ _____ for each alternative, 0, 1, 2, 3, or 4 cabins. The expected opportunity loss for building 0 cabins and 1 cabin are, respectively

expected
opportunity loss

$$E(L \text{ ``build 0''}) = \$0(.1) + \$2500(.2) + \$5000(.4)$$
$$+ \$7500(.2) + \$10,000(.1) = \$5000$$

$$E(L\ \text{"build 1"}) = \$1500(.1) + \$0(.2) + \$2500(.4)$$
$$+ \$5000(.2) + \$7500(.1) = \$2900$$

Compute the expected opportunity losses for the remaining alternatives.

$1600

$$E(L\ \text{"build 2"}) = \underline{\hspace{3cm}}$$

$1900

$$E(L\ \text{"build 3"}) = \underline{\hspace{3cm}}$$

$3000

$$E(L\ \text{"build 4"}) = \underline{\hspace{3cm}}$$

$1600

2

His minimum expected opportunity loss is _____ which is associated with the alternative of building _____ cabins. Thus, the decision which minimizes the contractor's expected opportunity loss is the decision

2

to build _____ cabins.

8. *Example:*

The portfolio manager for a firm must choose between either portfolio **A** or portfolio **B**. After a careful examination of the securities within each portfolio, the manager listed the following information:

| | | *Annual Return per $100 Invested* | |
| | | *Portfolio* | |
State of the Economy	*Probability*	*A*	*B*
Depression	.2	$ 40	$ 80
Stable	.5	105	95
Inflation	.3	190	110

Which portfolio should the manager select if he wishes to maximize his expected annual return?

Solution:

The expected return for each portfolio is the weighted average return, found

returns

by weighting the _____ under each portfolio by the

prior probabilities

_____ _____ of occurrence of the states of the economy associated with each return. Thus,

$$E(\text{Return "portfolio A"}) = \$40(.2) + \$105(.5)$$
$$+ \$190(.3) = \$117.50$$

$96.50

$$E(\text{Return "portfolio B"}) = \underline{\hspace{3cm}}$$

The portfolio manager's optimal decision is then to choose portfolio

A

_____.

9. An expected monetary analysis provides a model which combines both real economic data with qualitative or subjective information available to the decision maker related to the outcome of the economic data.

10. An expected monetary value analysis makes the decision maker more than just an impartial observer by forcing him to construct meaningful _____ to associate with the states of nature.

prior probabilities

11. Expected monetary value decisions, since they employ the prior probabilities in the decision analysis, assume that the priors assigned to the states of nature are the _____ priors for that problem. The optimal expected monetary value decision is meaningful only in terms of its associated _____.

true

priors

12. *Example:*
Suppose the portfolio manager from Example 8 is approached by an economist who states, "I have a much different impression about the state of the economy a year from now than you do. I believe the likelihoods of depression, a stable economy, and inflation are represented by the probabilities .5, .3, and .2, respectively." Find the expected monetary value decision based upon the economist's set of prior probabilities.
Solution:

$$E(\text{Return "portfolio A"}) = \$40(.5) + \$105(.3)$$
$$+ \$190(.2) = \$89.40$$

and

$$E(\text{Return "portfolio B"}) = \underline{\hspace{2cm}}$$

$90.50

Hence, using the economist's prior probabilities, the decision which maximizes the expected portfolio return is to select portfolio _____.

B

13. Under one set of priors, portfolio A is best, while under another, portfolio B is best. The portfolio manager, or any expected monetary value decision maker, must carefully assess all available information before selecting _____ _____ to represent the _____ of occurrence associated with the various states of nature. Once a set of priors has been selected, it should be assumed as _____ and should be used with confidence in an expected monetary value analysis.

prior probabilities;
likelihoods
fixed

10.4 The Economic Impact of Uncertainty (10.6)

1. When decisions must be made under uncertainty, the expected gains cannot be as great as the gains one would expect if the true state of nature were known with _____.

certainty

2. The expected opportunity loss associated with the optimal decision under uncertainty is called the _____ of _____, and is sometimes referred to as the _____ value of _____ _____ (EVPI).

cost; uncertainty
expected; perfect
information

3. The cost of uncertainty is the _____ amount the decision maker would _____ to know which state of nature will be in effect.

maximum
pay

profits
losses; uncertainty

perfect
less

true *or* correct
reliability

$1600
$1600

B
A
A

190

$117.50
A
$8.00

reduce

4. The cost of uncertainty (or EVPI) is the amount of _____ fore-gone or the additional _____ incurred due to _____ about the conditions affecting the outcome of a decision problem.

5. Since _____ information is hardly ever available, a decision maker usually would be only willing to pay an amount (more, less) than the EVPI. The difference between the amount the decision maker would pay for information concerning the _____ state of nature and the EVPI is a function of the _____ of the information.

6. Refer to Example 10.3(7). The cost of uncertainty associated with this example is _____ . Thus, the building contractor would be willing to pay up to _____ to know exactly how many cabins he is able to sell on the open market.

7. The cost of uncertainty can also be determined when the payoff table does not list the opportunity costs associated with the decision problem. Consider Example 10.3(8). If the portfolio manager knows the future state of the economy with certainty, he would make the following decisions. If the state of the economy is
   a. Depressed, he selects portfolio _____ ,
   b. Stable, he selects portfolio _____ ,
   c. Inflated, he selects portfolio _____ .
   Under certainty, his expected return is then

$$(80)\,(.2) + (105)\,(.5) + (\text{_____})\,(.3) = \$125.50$$

   Under uncertainty, the best that he can expect is a return of _____ by selecting portfolio _____ . The portfolio manager's cost of uncertainty is then _____ , the difference between his expected return under *certainty* and his expected return under *uncertainty*.

8. Perfect information is rarely, if ever, available at any price. The best that can be expected is that auxiliary information may _____ the uncertainty associated with the decision problem.

Self-Correcting Exercises 10B

1. Refer to Self-Correcting Exercises 10A, problem 1. Suppose that further study of this situation assessed the probability that 1, 2 or 3 trucks would be required in a given month to be .3, .6 and .1 respectively.
   a. How many trucks should be purchased in order to minimize the expected opportunity loss?
   b. What is the cost of uncertainty for this problem?

2. A farmer, under contract to sell his entire crop to a dealer, has the option of planting one of three crops the next season. From past experience he estimates that the yields in units per acre for the three crops under dry, average rain or excess rain weather conditions to be those given below. The contracted price per unit is also listed.

Weather	Crop		
	1	*2*	*3*
Dry	15	15	35
Average rain	30	25	30
Excess rain	35	15	20
Price/unit	$15	$20	$10

a. Assuming that the cost to the farmer per acre to be $60 for each of the three crops, construct a profit table and an opportunity loss table per acre by using the prices given above.

b. If the following represents a set of prior probabilities of the weather conditions for the coming season, what crop should be planted to minimize the farmer's expected opportunity loss?

Weather	Probability
Dry	.2
Average rain	.7
Excess rain	.1

c. What is the cost of uncertainty associated with this problem?

10.5 Decision Making That Involves Sample Information (10.7)

1. Occasionally a decision maker has the opportunity to reduce the _____ in a decision-making problem by obtaining additional information. Ordinarily such information is in the form of _____ data and is intended and used to update the values of the prior probabilities. In some cases, the auxiliary information consists of an expert opinion, or the result of a scientific or a behavioral experiment. In any case, it is of interest to find the value of the auxiliary information measured in terms of the amount by which the auxiliary information has _____ the *uncertainty* in the decision problem.

uncertainty
sample

reduced

2. Prior probabilities which have been revised to incorporate auxiliary information are called _____ probabilities. Posterior probabilities are computed by employing _____ Law.

posterior
Bayes'

3. The posterior probability $p(s_k|x)$ represents the chance of occurrence of the state of nature, s_k, given the experimental information, x. This probability is computed from Bayes' Law by

$$p(s_k|x) - $$

_____

$$\frac{p(x|s_k)p(s_k)}{\sum_{\text{all } j} p(x|s_j)p(s_j)}$$

The probabilities $p(x|s_j)$ are the conditional probabilities of observing the posterior

prior; experimental

posterior

prior

observational information x under the state of nature s_j and the probabilities $p(s_j)$ are the priors.

4. The _____ probabilities which have been computed as a function of the _____ probabilities and the _____ information are then used as the weights in an expected monetary value analysis. Expected opportunity losses or expected profits are computed for all alternatives as was done earlier except that _____ probabilities are now used where _____ probabilities were employed earlier.

5. *Example:*

A labor union is considering publishing a monthly journal for its 2000 members. The union leader believes the following probabilities adequately represents the likelihood that a given percentage of union members will subscribe to the journal.

Percentage, p	.20	.30	.40	.50
Probability, $P(p)$	.1	.3	.4	.2

Fixed costs of printing (rental of a printing press) will amount to $320 per month with a variable cost (materials, labor) of $.50 per journal. If the union publishes only as many journals as demand requires, each journal is to sell for $1.00 per copy:

a. What is the decision which minimizes the union's expected opportunity loss?

b. What is the union's cost of uncertainty?

Solution:

The profits which would be incurred for publishing or not publishing are as listed below.

$80

$180

	Decision	
p	Publish	Do not publish
.20	−$120	$0
.30	−20	0
.40	_____	0
.50	_____	0

maximum profit

The opportunity losses can be found by noting the difference between the _____ _____ at each level of p and the profit associated with each possible decision under level of p. For example, under $p = .20$, the maximum possible profit is $0. Thus, the opportunity loss for publishing when $p = .20$ is equal to $0 − (−$120) = $120 while the opportunity loss for not publishing is $0 − $0 = $0. Fill in the missing opportunity losses.

p	Publish	Do not publish	
.20	$120	$0	
.30	_____	_____	$20; $0
.40	_____	_____	$0; $80
.50	_____	_____	$0; $180

a. The expected opportunity loss associated with each possible decision is

$$E(\text{opportunity loss "publish"}) = \$120(.1) + \$20(.3)$$
$$+ \$0(.4) + \$0(.2)$$

$$= \underline{\hspace{1.5cm}}$$

$18

$$E(\text{opportunity loss "do not publish"}) = \underline{\hspace{1.5cm}}$$

$68

Thus, the optimal decision is for the labor union to publish the journal.

b. The cost of uncertainty is the expected opportunity loss associated with the _____ decision. Thus, the cost of uncertainty for the   optimal
union is _____ which is the _____ amount the union $18; maximum
would pay to know the exact percentage of members who will subscribe.

6. *Example:*
Refer to Example 5. Suppose that 20 union members are randomly selected from the membership and that three indicate they would subscribe to the journal.
a. What is the decision which minimizes the union's expected opportunity loss in light of this sample information?
b. What is the value of the sample information to the union?
Solution:
a. Employing Bayes' Law, we first want to find the likelihoods of occurrence of each level of p in light of the sample information that 3 of 20 respondents indicated they would subscribe to the journal. The use of Bayes' Law is most clearly illustrated by using the columnar approach. In column (1) are listed the states of nature and in column (2) their associated prior probabilities.

(1) s_j	(2) $p(s_j)$	(3) $p(x \vert s_j)$	(4) $p(s_j)p(x \vert s_j)$	(5) $p(s_j \vert x)$	
.20	.10	.205	.0205	_____	.435
.30	.30	.072	.0216	_____	.459
.40	.40	_____	.0048	_____	.012; .102
.50	.20	_____	.0002	_____	.001; .004
			.0471		

In column (3) we find the probability of occurrence of the sample information under each state of nature. In this case, since the states of nature are proportions, the experimental probabilities are binomial probabilities, and we can use Table 1 of the Appendix to compute the respective probabilities. Let n equal the sample size, y the number within the sample who indicate they would subscribe, and p the state of nature.

When $p = .20$, the probability that y is equal to three is found to be

$$P(y = 3, n = 20 \mid p = .20) = \sum_{y=0}^{3} p(y) - \sum_{y=0}^{2} p(y)$$

$$= .411 - .206$$

$$= .205$$

In like manner we find that

$$P(y = 3, n = 20 \mid p = .30) = .072$$

.012

$$P(y = 3, n = 20 \mid p = .40) = \underline{\hspace{2cm}}$$

.001

$$P(y = 3, n = 20 \mid p = .50) = \underline{\hspace{2cm}}$$

These values comprise the entries within column (3). In column (4), corresponding entries within columns (2) and (3) are multiplied together. Column (5) then lists the *posterior* probabilities computed by dividing each entry from column (4) by the *total* of the column (4) entries. Using the posterior probabilities as weights, we find the expected opportunity loss associated with the union's possible decisions.

$$E(\text{opportunity loss "publish"}) = \$120(.435) + \$20(.459)$$

.102; .004

$$+ \$0(\underline{\hspace{2cm}}) + \$0(\underline{\hspace{2cm}})$$

$61.38

$$= \underline{\hspace{2cm}}$$

$8.88

$$E(\text{opportunity loss "do not publish"}) = \underline{\hspace{2cm}}$$

Therefore, in light of the sample information, the optimal decision is for

abandon

the union to (abandon, proceed with) plans to publish the journal.

b. The union's optimal decision is now associated with an expected

$8.88

opportunity loss equal to _____. The sample information has, therefore, reduced the union's cost of uncertainty from $18 to $8.88, implying that the value of the sample information to the union is

$9.12

_____.

10.6 Other Topics in Decision Analysis (10.8)

A. *Decisions Ignoring Prior Information*

1. Some decision makers choose to ignore prior information regarding the likelihood of occurrence of the states of nature. The most common decision maker of this type is called a _____ decision maker. His objective is to _____ his _____ opportunity loss; hence the name, minimax. The minimax decision maker is characterized by an individual with a small bankroll who is concerned that the occurrence of a large loss may cause him severe financial harm. The minimax decision maker uses prior information only to identify the possible outcomes and focuses his entire attention on the magnitudes of the _____ _____ associated with these outcomes.

minimax
minimize; maximum

opportunity
losses

2. *Example:*
Refer to the building contractor's decision problem Example 10.2(16). Find the contractor's minimax decision.
Solution:
From the opportunity loss table constructed for Example 10.2(16), we can find the maximum opportunity loss associated with each possible alternative. List these maximum opportunity losses below.

	Number of cabins built				
Alternative	0	1	2	3	4
Maximum opportunity loss	10,000	7500	_____	_____	_____

5000; 4500; 6000

Thus, the minimax decision is for the building contractor to build _____ cabins.

three

3. Only by chance are the minimax decision and the expected monetary value decision the same. The minimax procedure offers a more _____ approach toward decision making than does the expected monetary value procedure.

conservative

4. *Example.*
Suppose the portfolio manager from Example 10.3(8) seeks to select the portfolio which will minimize his maximum opportunity loss. What is his minimax decision?
Solution:
The opportunity loss table associated with the two portfolios is as follows:

	A	B	
Depression	40	_____	0
Stable	0	_____	10
Inflation	_____	80	0

Since the maximum possible losses associated with the two portfolios are

40

80

portfolio A: _____

portfolio B: _____

A
maximax
maximizing
minimum
ignore
states
nature
are not

the minimax decision is for the manager to select portfolio _____.

5. Similarly, the _____ criterion selects the action that maximizes the maximum possible profit, while maximin criterion entails _____ the _____ profit.

6. Minimax, maximax, or maximin decision criteria _____ prior information regarding the probability distribution of the _____ of _____. They are generally used for one-shot or one-time-only decisions and, in practice, (are, are not) good criteria for repeated decision making.

B. *Decision Trees*

decision tree

multistage
time
squares

control; circles
base

chronological

terminal; payoffs
probabilities

1. A _____ _____ is a diagram used to illustrate a multi-stage decision analysis problem.

2. Decision trees are most useful for _____ decision problems, especially decision problems sequenced over _____.

3. In a tree diagram, decision points are represented by _____ while chance points (points over which the decision maker has no _____) are represented by _____.

4. The available first-stage alternatives are shown at the _____ of the tree.

5. From each alternative, the decision tree constructs the _____ path through chance points and other decision points to each assumed _____ outcome. A decision tree also shows the _____ associated with each path and the _____ of the chance events.

6. *Example*

Consider the data in Example 10.3 (8). A decision tree diagram could be constructed for that problem as follows:

Think of the decision problem as proceeding in two steps:

a. At the first stage, the portfolio manager must choose between portfolios A and B. That choice will be represented in the tree diagram as a _____ point between _____ A and B.

decision; alternatives

chance

b. At the second stage, the portfolio manager discovers the true state of the economy: depression, stability, or inflation. This _____ point will be represented by a circle.

C. *The Utility for Money*

1. The theory of utility allows for the outcomes of a decision problem to be scaled according to their relative _____ to the decision maker. The scalar units are then used in place of the _____ values associated with each outcome, such that maximization of utility insures maximization of _____ in terms of the way the decision maker perceives value.

   value
   monetary
   value

2. Utility measures are necessary *unless* we can assume that:
   a. The value of a dollar (does, does not) differ from one person to the next.
   b. The value of D dollars is (equal, not equal) to D times the value of a single dollar.

   does not
   equal

3. *Example:*
   Reconsider the problem of the building contractor given in Example 10.2 (16). After constructing his profit table, the contractor noticed that it is possible for him to lose as much as $6000 on the mountain cabin venture. As the contractor was very concerned with his liquidity and was interested in avoiding alternatives likely to lose him a significant amount of money, he sought to place all the possible dollar-valued outcomes in their proper perspective. In so doing, he constructed the utility curve, which follows, over the range of possible outcomes. He believes this curve to properly scale the outcomes according to their relative value to him. How many cabins should the contractor build in order to maximize his expected utility?

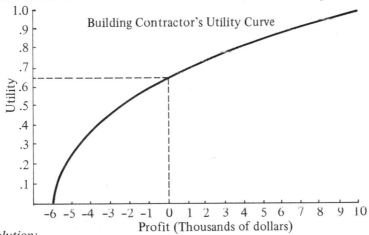

Building Contractor's Utility Curve

Utility

Profit (Thousands of dollars)

Solution:
The building contractor's profit table appears below.

	Profit Table				
Number of cabins built	*Number of cabins demanded*				
	0	*1*	*2*	*3*	*4*
0	0	0	0	0	0
1	−1500	2500	2500	2500	2500
2	−3000	1000	5000	5000	5000
3	−4500	−500	3500	7500	7500
4	−6000	−2000	2000	6000	10,000

.75

.45; .85
.31; .61
0; .74; 1.00

alternative

.730

.776

.748

2

outcomes
jeopardy

probability

We now must find utility units from the utility curve associated with each profit value. For instance, the utility of $0 is found by noting the point on the utility curve at profit equal to $0, and reading the corresponding point on the utility axis. We can see the utility of $0 is .64. Similarly, we find the utility of –$1500 is .55, and the utility of $2500 is _____. Fill in the missing entries in the following table.

	Utility Table				
Number of		Number of cabins demanded			
cabins built	0	1	2	3	4
0	.64	.64	.64	.64	.64
1	.55	.75	.75	.75	.75
2	_____	.68	_____	.85	.85
3	_____	_____	.79	.93	.93
4	_____	.52	_____	.88	_____

The decision which maximizes the contractor's expected utility can then be found by computing the expected utility for each _____.

$$E(\text{utility "build 0"}) = .64(.1) + .64(.2) + .64(.4) + .64(.2)$$

$$+ .64(.1) = .640$$

$$E(\text{utility "build 1"}) = .55(.1) + .75(.2) + .75(.4) + .75(.2)$$

$$+ .75(.1) = \underline{\hspace{2cm}}$$

Compute the expected utility for the remaining alternatives.

$$E(\text{utility "build 2"}) = \underline{\hspace{2cm}}$$

$$E(\text{utility "build 3"}) = \underline{\hspace{2cm}}$$

$$E(\text{utility "build 4"}) = .676$$

Therefore, the decision which maximizes the contractor's expected utility is to build _____ cabins.

4. Utility measures are needed when the decision problem contains some possible _____ that, should they occur, might place the decision maker in personal or financial _____. However, unlike a minimax decision, an expected utility decision allows the use of information concerning the _____ distribution of uncertain events.

Self-Correcting Exercises 10C

1. An equipment rental agency must decide whether to continue to keep one, two or three large pieces of equipment for rental purposes. These large

pieces of equipment are usually leased to contractors for a period of a week or more. If the required equipment is not available, a contractor, because of time limitations and schedules, will take his business elsewhere. Let us assume that the rental fee for one of these pieces of equipment is $500 per week. Repair, fuel, storage, insurance and other overhead costs to the agency are $50 a week for each piece of equipment.

a. Construct a weekly profit table for this problem by considering either 1, 2, or 3 available pieces of equipment, together with the possibility of either 0, 1, 2 or, 3 weekly rental requests.

b. Find the rental agency's minimax decision.

2. Refer to Self-Correcting Exercises 10A, problem 1. Find the delivery service's minimax decision.

3. Refer to Self-Correcting Exercises 10B, problem 2. Find the farmer's minimax decision.

4. Refer to problem 1 of Self-Correcting Exercises 10A and 10B. Suppose that the company has replaced the dollar valued outcomes with the following utility values.

Profits	-1150	-400	-50	350	700	1050
Utility	0	.05	.05	.30	.60	1.00

How many bids should the contractor submit to maximize his expected utility?

5. Refer to problem 1 of Self-Correcting Exercises 10A and 10B. Construct a decision tree diagram for this decision problem.

10.7 Summary (10.9)

1. Decision analysis is a tool of a decision maker who must select from among many _____, some of which have _____ outcomes, the one which best satisfies his _____.

2. When the decision analysis involves an expected _____ value decision, the following steps must be performed:

a. List all possible _____ and _____ of _____.

b. List the _____ associated with each alternative under every state of nature.

c. Assign _____ probabilities to the states of nature.

d. Compute the expected _____ or expected _____ _____ for each alternative.

e. Select the alternative with the _____ expected profit or the _____ expected opportunity loss. Either criterion will lead to the _____ decision.

3. If auxiliary information is available, _____ _____ can be used to update the _____ probabilities. The resulting

Right margin answers:

alternatives; uncertain
objective
monetary

alternatives; states; nature
payoff

prior
profit; opportunity
loss
maximum
minimum
same
Bayes' Law
prior

posterior
subjective; experimental

minimax
minimizes
maximum

_____ probabilities then contain all available information, both
_____ and _____.

4. The most common decision-making procedure which ignores information
regarding the likelihoods of occurrence of the states of nature is called the
_____ procedure. This procedure specifies that the optimal
decision is to select the alternative which _____ the
_____ opportunity loss.

Exercises

1. Consider yourself the decision maker associated with each of the following
decision-making situations. List what you would consider your available
alternatives in each situation and the states of nature which might result to
affect your economic payoff.
   a. Investment of a company's pension fund in either a mutual fund, corporate bonds, mortgages, government bonds, or a combination of the four.
   b. Investment of a personal windfall profit of $10,000 in either a savings
   account or a mutual fund.
   c. An opportunity to bid on a construction job when your competitor may
   submit a bid on the job.
   d. Whether or not to market a new product after observing the results of
   sales for the product in a trial area.
   e. Whether to keep an old assembly machine or buy a new one when the
   new machine can be expected to produce items at a lower cost per unit
   than the old machine.
   f. Whether the promoter of an outdoor sporting event should buy an
   insurance policy to cover possible losses should unfavorable weather
   occur on the day of the sporting event.

2. A grocer must stock a certain number of units of a perishable commodity
each morning. He sells the item for $0.50 each and pays $0.30 each for
them. His knowledge of the business as well as past sales records tell the
grocer that daily demand for the product is described by the following
probability distribution:

Demand (d)	27	28	29	30
Probability $P(d)$	.3	.4	.2	.1

   a. Construct the grocer's profit table.
   b. Construct the grocer's opportunity loss table.
   c. Find the grocer's minimax inventory level.
   d. Find the inventory level which minimizes the grocer's expected daily
   opportunity loss.

3. An investor must decide whether to finance an oil-drilling venture proposed
by an oil wildcatter or to invest in a savings account. The amount of
$2000 either will be supplied to the oil wildcatter or will be invested in

the savings account at an annual rate of 6% interest. If the wildcatter strikes oil, he will pay the investor $10,000 at the end of one year, but if he finds no oil, the investor will lose his investment. If the probability of the wild-catter's striking oil is .2, what is the investor's best decision if he wishes to maximize his expected annual return?

4. Refer to Exercise 3. How great must be the probability of the oil wild-catter's striking oil before the investor rejects the savings alternative and decides to support the oil-drilling venture?

5. The promoter of an outdoor sporting event must decide whether or not to purchase an insurance policy costing $2000 to cover possible losses should it rain on the day of the event. The promoter figures to earn $20,000 if there is no rain but will lose $5000 in event of rain. According to the insurance policy, the promoter will receive $5000 to cover his losses if it rains but will receive nothing if no rain falls. Suppose the chance of rain on the day of the sporting event is .25.
   a. Construct the promoter's profit table.
   b. If the decision maker's (promoter's) objective is to maximize his ex-pected profit, should he purchase the insurance policy?

6. Refer to Exercise 5. Find the maximum amount the promoter would have been willing to pay for the insurance policy.

7. The representative of a publishing company must decide whether or not to publish a certain book. The following profits and losses are associated with the actions the publishing company might take.

	Unfavorable market	Favorable market
Publish	−$5000	$20,000
Do not publish	0	− 10,000

   a. Suppose the representative calculates the expected profits for each alternative, and discovers that either decision is equally profitable. What value must he be assuming for the probability of a favorable mar-ket? Hint: Let p = probability of a favorable market, and $(1 - p)$ = probability of an unfavorable market.
   b. Suppose the representative actually assumes a probability of .20 for the existence of a favorable market. What is the company's expected profit for publishing?

8. A businessman is trying to decide which of two contracts he should accept. He will accept either contract A, contract B, or neither, but he will not accept both. He has computed his profits for accepting either contract under three states of the economy as follows:

	Depressed economy	Stable economy	Inflated economy
Contract A	$ 1,000	$12,000	$30,000
Contract B	−10,000	20,000	50,000

The businessman assigns the probabilities .4, .5, and .1 to the events "Depressed economy," "Stable economy,," and "Inflated economy," respectively.

a. If the businessman seeks to minimize his maximum opportunity loss, what is his optimum decision?

b. What is his optimum decision if he wishes to maximize his expected profits?

9. A baker believes that the daily demand for a large specialty cake is as follows:

Demand	0	1	2	3	4
Probability of demand	.10	.20	.40	.25	.05

The cakes are baked in the morning and sold on demand for $4.00 each during the day. Each cake costs $2.00 to bake and unsold cakes at the day's end are worthless.

a. Construct the opportunity loss for the baker's problem.

b. What is the minimax decision to the baker's problem?

c. How many cakes should the baker prepare if his objective is to minimize his expected opportunity loss?

d. What is the practical meaning to the baker of the expected opportunity value associated with the optimal inventory level found in part c?

10. A toy manufacturer must decide whether or not to manufacture and market a new novelty toy for the Christmas season. An affirmative decision would require that he purchase *either* special stamping tools at a cost of $1000 *or* a special machine at a cost of $2000 to manufacture the toys. Each toy will be sold for $2.00, and the variable cost of manufacturing will be $1.00 per unit if the stamping tools are used or $0.50 per unit if the machine is used. Neither the stamping tools nor the machine will have any value after the season. The manufacturer's probability distribution for sales volume for the toy is shown below.

Sales volume	Probability
1000	.4
2000	.4
5000	.2

a. Construct the manufacturer's profit table remembering that there are three possible alternatives.

b. What is the manufacturer's minimax decision?

c. What is the optimum decision if the manufacturer wishes to maximize his expected profits.

11. A heavy equipment salesman can contact either one or two customers per day with probability 1/5 and 4/5, respectively. Each contact will result in either no sale or a $50,000 sale with probability 9/10 and 1/10, respectively.

a. What is the salesman's expected daily sales volume?

b. Knowing that the salesman transacted $50,000 worth of business during a given day, what is the probability that he contacted only one customer? (Hint: Use Bayes' Law.)

c. What is his probability of transacting $9000 worth of business during a given day?

12. A manufacturer wishes to accept all incoming lots of widgets with fewer than 8% defectives. Based on historical observation, he believes that a certain supplier of widgets supplies lots described by the following information:

Proportion of Lot Defective (p_D)	Probability $P(p_D)$	Manufacturer's Loss	
		Accepting	Rejecting
.01	.6	$ 0	$13
.05	.2	0	7
.10	.1	15	0
.20	.1	25	0

a. If the manufacturer wishes to minimize his expected losses, using only the above information should he accept or reject lots of widgets from this supplier?

b. Suppose the manufacturer randomly selects 25 items from a lot of widgets furnished by the supplier and observes 3 defectives. Should he accept or reject the lot? (Use Table 1, Appendix II of the text.)

c. Suppose the manufacturer selects 10 and observes 2 defectives. Should he accept or reject? (Use Table 1, Appendix II.)

d. What is the value to the manufacturer of the sample information supplied in part b?

e. What is the value to the manufacturer of the sample information supplied in part c?

13. The owner of a camera shop must decide whether to buy a shipment of 10,000 flash bulbs from a domestic or a foreign supplier. He knows from past experience that the domestic bulbs are usually about 98% operable (2% defective per shipment). He is doubtful about the defective rate of the foreign flash bulbs and subjectively assigns the following probability distribution to the fraction defective of lots supplied by the foreign manufacturer.

Fraction defective	Probability
.01	.4
.05	.4
.10	.2

The cost of replacing defective flash bulbs is estimated to amount to $0.50. and the foreign flash bulbs cost the shop owner one cent per unit less than the domestic bulbs.

a. Based on only his subjective information, should the shop owner buy the foreign flash bulbs?

b. Suppose the owner randomly selects 25 flash bulbs from a shipment supplied by the foreign distributor and notes one defective bulb. Should he buy the foreign or domestic bulbs? (Use Table 1. Appendix II.)

14. Return to Exercise 8. In an attempt to rescale the possible outcomes of each contract according to his risk preferences, the businessman has defined the following utility values associated with the dollar valued outcomes accompanying each contract.

Utility	0	.60	.75	.80	.90	1.0
Dollar valued outcome	-$10,000	1,000	12,000	20,000	30,000	50,000

Which contract should the businessman accept if he wishes to maximize his expected utility?

Chapter 11

LINEAR REGRESSION AND CORRELATION

11.1 Introduction (11.1)

1. We have investigated the problem of making inferences about population parameters—especially population means—based on both large and small random _____.

   samples

2. We now consider the case in which the mean value of y is related to another variable, say x. That is, there is a _____ relationship between y and x.

   functional

3. In the present chapter, we assume that the functional relationship between $E(y)$ and x is _____. Since the values of $E(y)$ depend upon the values assumed by x, $E(y)$ is called the _____ variable and x is called the _____ variable.

   linear
   dependent
   independent

4. If we are interested in _____ or predicting values of y, we should make simultaneous observations on _____ and _____, use the information to estimate the particular linear relationship between y and x, and then predict particular values of y for predetermined values of x.

   forecasting
   y; x

The Algebraic Representation of a Straight Line

5. To understand the development of the following linear models, you must be familiar with the algebraic representation of the straight line and its properties.

6. The mathematical equation for a straight line is

   $$y = \beta_0 + \beta_1 x$$

   where
   a. _____ is the independent variable, x
   b. _____ is the dependent variable, y
   c. β_0 and β_1 are fixed constants.

7. When values of x are substituted into this equation, pairs of numbers, (x_i, y_i), are generated which, when plotted or graphed on a rectangular coordinate system, form a _____ _____ .

straight line

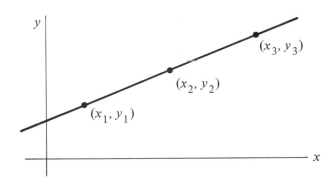

Consider the graph of a linear equation, $y = \beta_0 + \beta_1 x$, shown below.

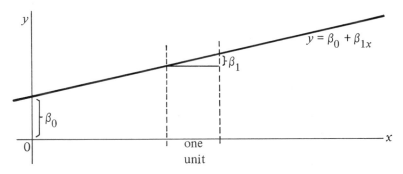

a. By setting $x = 0$, we have $y = \beta_0 + \beta_1(0) = \beta_0$. Because the line intercepts or cuts the y-axis at the value $y = \beta_0$, β_0 is called the y-_____ .

intercept

b. The constant, β_1, represents the increase in y for a one-unit increase in x and is called the _____ of the line.

slope

8. *Example:*

Plot the equation $y = 1 + 0.5x$ on a rectangular coordinate system.

Solution:

Two points are needed to uniquely determine a straight line and therefore a minimum of two points must be found. A third point is usually found as a check on calculations.

a. Using 0, 2 and 4 as values of x, find the corresponding values of y.

1

When $x = 0$, $y = 1 + 0.5(0) =$ _____ .

2

When $x = 2$, $y = 1 + 0.5(2) =$ _____ .

3

When $x = 4$, $y = 1 + 0.5(4) =$ _____ .

b. Plot these points on a rectangular coordinate system and join them by using a straightedge.

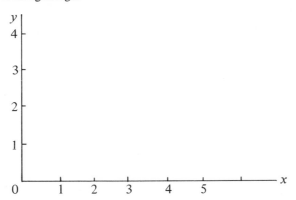

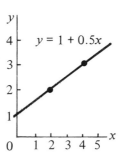

9. Practice plotting the following linear equations on a rectangular coordinate system.

a. $y = -1 + 3x$

b. $y = 2 - x$

c. $y = -0.5 - 0.5x$

d. $y = x$

e. $y = 0.5 + 2x$

11.2   A Simple Linear Probabilistic Model (11.2)

1. Suppose one is given a set consisting of n pairs of values for x and y, each pair representing the value of a response, y, for a given value of x. Plotting these points might result in the following _____ diagram.   scatter

2. Someone might say that these points appear to lie on a straight line. This person would be hypothesizing that a *model* for the relationship between x and y is of the form

$$y_i = \beta_0 + \beta_1 x_i \qquad i = 1, 2, \dots, n$$

deterministic

According to this model, for a given value of x, the value of y is *uniquely determined*. Therefore this is called a _____ model.

do not

3. However, a deterministic model is not especially applicable in the present case because the data (do, do not) lie precisely on a straight line. Our use of the deterministic model $y = \beta_0 + \beta_1 x$ to predict y would, in general,

error; deterministic

result in a(n) _____. A _____ model does not permit an evaluation of the error of prediction. That is, we cannot say anything

reliability

about the _____ of our estimates of β_0 and β_1 and of our prediction of y.

probabilistic
expected *or* mean
straight

4. So, instead, we postulate a _____ model in which we say that the _____ value of y for a given value of x, $E(y|x)$, has a graph that is a _____ line. That is,

$\beta_0 + \beta_1 x$

$$E(y|x) = \text{_____}$$

randomly

5. But for any given value of x, say x_0, the values of y will vary _____ about the point $E(y|x_0)$.

6. Hence, in the probabilistic model, the equation for y—as distinguished from $E(y|x)$—is

ϵ

$$y = \beta_0 + \beta_1 x + \text{_____}$$

ϵ; observed
expected

where _____ is a random error, the difference between the _____ value of y and the _____ value of y for a given value of x.

probability distribution

7. Thus we assume that, for a given value of x, the observed value of y possesses a _____ _____ with mean value $E(y|x)$.

independent

8. Suppose that we were to make many observations on y at each of the values x_1, x_2, and x_3 of the _____ variable x. We might then observe the illustrated probability distribution of y at each of the values

mean
expected
straight

of x. According to our probabilistic model, the _____ or _____ value of each probability distribution will lie on the same _____ line. The equation of that line is

$E(y|x) = \beta_0 + \beta_1 x$

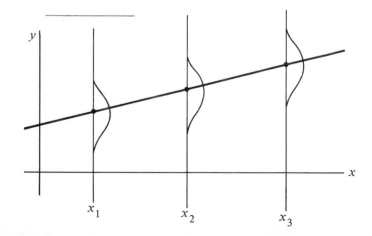

9. We make the following assumptions about the probability distribution of y for every value of x:

   For any given value of x, y possesses a _____ distribution, with mean value given by

   normal

$$E(y|x) = \underline{\hspace{2cm}}$$

   $\beta_0 + \beta_1 x$

   and with a _____ variance, denoted by _____. We also assume that, for a given value of x, any value of y is _____ of every other value of y.

   constant; σ^2
   independent

10. We need these assumptions in order to be able to construct _____ of hypotheses and _____ _____ for β_0, β_1 and $E(y|x)$.

    tests
    confidence intervals

11. Having selected the probabilistic model as the one best describing the data, we now proceed to find an estimate for this prediction equation, or _____ line,

    regression

$$\hat{y} = \hat{\beta}_0 + \hat{\beta}_1 x$$

11.3 The Method of Least Squares (11.3)

1. The criterion used for estimating β_0 and β_1 in the model

$$y_i = \beta_0 + \beta_1 x_i + \epsilon_i$$

   is to find an estimated line _____ that in some sense minimizes the deviations of the observed values of y from the fitted line. If the deviation of the ith observed value from the fitted value is $(y_i - \hat{y}_i)$, we define the "best" estimated line as one that minimizes the _____ _____ _____ of the deviations of the observed values of y from the fitted values of y. The quantity

   $\hat{y} = \hat{\beta}_0 + \hat{\beta}_1 x$

   sum
   of squares

$$\sum_{i=1}^{n} (y_i - \hat{y}_i)^2$$

   represents the sum of squares of deviations of the observed values of y from the fitted values and is called the _____ of _____ for _____ (*SSE*). Then

   sum; squares
   error

$$SSE = \sum_{i=1}^{n} (y_i - \hat{y}_i)^2 = \sum_{i=1}^{n} [y_i - (\hat{\beta}_0 + \hat{\beta}_1 x_i)]^2$$

   The values of $\hat{\beta}_0$ and $\hat{\beta}_1$ are determined mathematically so that *SSE* will be minimum.

least
squares

$\bar{y} - \hat{\beta}_1 \bar{x}$
SS_{xy}/SS_x

$\Sigma(x_i - \bar{x})^2$

$\Sigma(x_i - \bar{x})(y_i - \bar{y})$

prediction
$\hat{y} = \hat{\beta}_0 + \hat{\beta}_1 x$

5

5.2

26; 25

168; 26

32.8

170; 26; 25

40

2. This process of minimization is called the method of _____
_____ and results in the following estimates of β_0 and β_1.
(Note: For the remainder of this discussion all summations will be with
respect to i as the variable of summation, the sum taken as $i = 1, 2, \ldots, n$.)
a. $\hat{\beta}_0 = $ _____
b. $\hat{\beta}_1 = $ _____
where

$$SS_x = \underline{\hspace{3cm}} = \Sigma x_i^2 - \frac{(\Sigma x_i)^2}{n}$$

and

$$SS_{xy} = \underline{\hspace{3cm}} = \Sigma x_i y_i - \frac{(\Sigma x_i)(\Sigma y_i)}{n}$$

3. When $\hat{\beta}_0$ and $\hat{\beta}_1$ have been calculated, their values are substituted into the
equation of a straight line to obtain the least squares _____
equation _____

4. *Example:*
In this chapter we will use the following example to illustrate each type of
problem encountered. Be ready to refer to the information tabulated on
this page. For the following data, find the best fitting line, $\hat{y} = \hat{\beta}_0 + \hat{\beta}_1 x$.

x_i	y_i	x_i^2	y_i^2	$x_i y_i$
2	1	4	1	2
3	3	9	9	9
5	4	25	16	20
7	7	49	49	49
9	10	81	100	90
Σ ___	Σ ___	168	175	170

$\bar{y} = $ _____

$\bar{x} = $ _____

Solution:
a. First find all the sums needed in the computations.

$$SS_x = \Sigma x_i^2 - \frac{(\Sigma x_i)^2}{n} = \underline{\hspace{2cm}} - \frac{(\underline{\hspace{1cm}})^2}{5}$$

$$= \underline{\hspace{2cm}}$$

$$SS_{xy} = \Sigma x_i y_i - \frac{(\Sigma x_i)(\Sigma y_i)}{n} = \underline{\hspace{2cm}} - \frac{(\underline{\hspace{1cm}})(\underline{\hspace{1cm}})}{n}$$

$$= \underline{\hspace{2cm}}$$

b. To find $\hat{\beta}_1$, use

$$\hat{\beta}_1 = \frac{SS_{xy}}{SS_x} = \frac{\underline{\hspace{2cm}}}{32.8} = \underline{\hspace{2cm}}$$

40; 1.22

c. To find $\hat{\beta}_0$, use

$$\hat{\beta}_0 = \bar{y} - \hat{\beta}_1 \bar{x}$$

$$= (\underline{\hspace{2cm}}) - 1.22(\underline{\hspace{2cm}})$$

5; 5.2

$$= (\underline{\hspace{2cm}}) - (\underline{\hspace{2cm}})$$

5; 6.34

$$= -1.34$$

d. Therefore the best fitting line is

$$\hat{y} = \underline{\hspace{3cm}}$$

$-1.34 + 1.22x$

5. We can now use the equation $\hat{y} = -1.34 + 1.22x$ to predict values of
_____ for values of x in the interval $2 \leqslant x \leqslant 9$. However, we also
need to place _____ of _____ on this prediction. To
do this we need σ^2, or its estimator, s^2.

y

bounds; error

Self-Correcting Exercises 11A

(1) The registrar at a small university noted that the pre-enrollment figures and
the actual enrollment figures for the past 6 years (in hundreds of students)
were

x: pre-enrollment	30	35	42	48	50	51
y: actual enrollment	33	41	46	52	59	55

a. Plot these data. Does it appear that a linear relationship exists between
x and y?
b. Find the least-squares line, $\hat{y} = \hat{\beta}_0 + \hat{\beta}_1 x$.
c. Using the least-squares line, predict the actual number of students
enrolled if the pre-enrollment figure is 5000 students.
2. An agricultural economist, interested in predicting cotton harvest using the
number of cotton bolls per quadrate counted during the middle of the
growing season, collected the following data, where y is the yield in bales
of cotton per field quadrate and x is hundreds of cotton bolls per quadrate
counted during mid-season.

y	21	17	20	19	15	23	20
x		5.5	2.8	4.7	4.3	3.7	6.1	4.5

a. Fit the least-squares line $\hat{y} = \hat{\beta}_0 + \hat{\beta}_1 x$ using these data.

b. Plot the least-squares line and the actual data on the same graph. Comment on the adequacy of the least-squares predictor to describe these data.

3. Refer to problem 2. The same economist also had available a measure of the number of damaging insects present per quadrate during a critical time in the development of the cotton plants. The data follow.

y: yield	21	17	20	19	15	23	20
x: insects	11	20	13	12	18	10	12

a. Fit the least-squares line to these data.

b. Plot the least-squares line and the actual data points on the same graph. Does it appear that the predictor line adequately describes the relationship between yield (y) and the number of insects present (x)?

11.4 Calculating s^2, an Estimator of σ^2 (11.4)

$\sigma^2; y$

1. Before we can proceed with evaluations of the estimates $\hat{\beta}_0$ and $\hat{\beta}_1$, or assess the reliability of any forecast of y based on the estimated regression line, we must first estimate _____, the variance of _____ for a given value of x.

$n - 2$

2. To estimate σ^2, we use SSE, the sum of squares of deviations about the line, $\hat{y} = \hat{\beta}_0 + \hat{\beta}_1 x$. The n pairs of data points provide n degrees of freedom for estimation. Having estimated β_0 and β_1, we now have _____ remaining degrees of freedom to estimate σ^2.

Therefore the estimate of σ^2 is

$\dfrac{SSE}{n - 2}$

$$s^2 = \underline{\hspace{3cm}}$$

3. A computationally efficient formula for calculating SSE is given by

$SS_y ; SS_{xy}$

$$SSE = \underline{\hspace{3cm}} - \hat{\beta}_1 \underline{\hspace{3cm}}$$

where

$\Sigma(y_i - \bar{y})^2$

$$SS_y = \underline{\hspace{3cm}} = \Sigma y_i^2 - \frac{(\Sigma y_i)^2}{n}$$

and

$\Sigma(x_i - \bar{x})(y_i - \bar{y})$

$$SS_{xy} = \underline{\hspace{3cm}} = \Sigma x_i y_i - \frac{(\Sigma x_i)(\Sigma y_i)}{n}$$

(Note that SS_{xy} has already been found, in the course of calculating $\hat{\beta}_1$.)

4. *Example:*
Calculate s^2 for our data.
Solution:
a. First, calculate SS_y.

$$SS_y = \Sigma y_i^2 - \frac{(\Sigma y_i)^2}{n} = \underline{\hspace{2cm}} - \frac{(\underline{\hspace{2cm}})^2}{5}$$

175; 25

$$= \underline{\hspace{2cm}}$$

50

b. Then, using SS_{xy} from our calculations for $\hat{\beta}_1$, use the computational formula for *SSE*.

$$SSE = SS_y - \hat{\beta}_1 SS_{xy}$$

$$= \underline{\hspace{2cm}} - (\underline{\hspace{2cm}})(\underline{\hspace{2cm}})$$

50; 1.22; 40

$$= \underline{\hspace{2cm}}$$

1.2

c. Finally, calculate s^2, using the formula

$$s^2 = \frac{SSE}{n-2} = \frac{1.2}{(\underline{\hspace{1.5cm}})} = \underline{\hspace{2cm}}$$

3; 0.4

11.5 Inferences Concerning the Slope β_1 of a Line (11.5)

1. The slope, β_1, is the average increase in \underline{\hspace{2cm}} for a one-unit increase in \underline{\hspace{2cm}}. The question of the existence of a linear relationship between x and y must be phrased in terms of the slope β_1. If no linear relationship exists between x and y, then β_1 = \underline{\hspace{2cm}}. Hence a test of the existence of a *linear* relationship between x and y is given as $H_0: \beta_1$ = \underline{\hspace{2cm}} versus $H_a: \beta_1 \neq$ \underline{\hspace{2cm}}.

y

x

0

0; 0

2. When the random error, ϵ, is *normally* distributed, the estimator, $\hat{\beta}_1$, has the following properties:
a. $\hat{\beta}_1$ has a \underline{\hspace{2cm}} distribution.
b. $\hat{\beta}_1$ is an unbiased estimator for \underline{\hspace{2cm}} so that $E(\hat{\beta}_1)$ = \underline{\hspace{2cm}}
c. The variance of $\hat{\beta}_1$ is

normal

$\beta_1; \beta_1$

$$\sigma_{\hat{\beta}_1}^2 - \underline{\hspace{2cm}}$$

$$\frac{\sigma^2}{SS_x}$$

where

$$SS_x = \underline{\hspace{2cm}} = \Sigma x_i^2 - \frac{(\Sigma x_i)^2}{n}$$

$$\Sigma(x_i - \bar{x})^2$$

3. The following test statistics can be constructed using the fact that $\hat{\beta}_1$ is a *normally* distributed, *unbiased* estimator of β_1.

known

a. $$z = \frac{\hat{\beta}_1 - \beta_1}{\sigma/\sqrt{SS_x}} \quad \text{if } \sigma^2 \text{ is (known, unknown).}$$

σ^2

b. $$t = \frac{\hat{\beta}_1 - \beta_1}{s/\sqrt{SS_x}} \quad \text{if } s^2 \text{ is used to estimate _____.}$$

4. Since σ^2 is rarely known, we can test the hypothesis for linearity at the α significance level using the statistic given in part 3b, which has a Student's

$n-2$

t distribution with _____ degrees of freedom. A test of the hypothesis $H_0 : \beta_1 = 0$ versus $H_a : \beta_1 \neq 0$ is given as:

a. $H_0 : \beta_1 = 0$

b. $H_a : \beta_1 \neq 0$

c. Test statistic:

0

$$t = \frac{\hat{\beta}_1 - _____}{s/\sqrt{SS_x}}$$

d. Rejection region: Reject H_0 if $|t| > t_{\alpha/2}$ based on $n-2$ degrees of freedom.

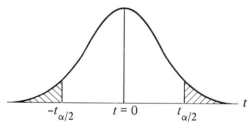

5. *Example:*

For our data test the hypothesis that there is no linear relationship between x and y at the $\alpha = .05$ level.

Solution:

0

a. $H_0 : \beta_1 = $ _____

0

b. $H_a : \beta_1 \neq $ _____

c. Test statistic:

$\dfrac{\hat{\beta}_1}{s} \cdot \sqrt{SS_x}$

$$t = _____$$

3.182

d. Rejection region: With 3 degrees of freedom, we shall reject H_0 if $|t| > t_{.025} = $ _____.

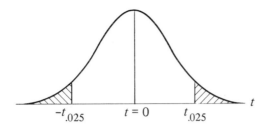

e. To calculate the test statistic, we first draw upon earlier calculations for the value of s and SS_x.

$$s = \sqrt{s^2} = \sqrt{\underline{\hspace{2cm}}} = \underline{\hspace{2cm}}$$

0.4; .632

and

$$SS_x = \underline{\hspace{2cm}}$$

32.8

So our test statistic is

$$t = \frac{\hat{\beta}_1}{s} \cdot \sqrt{SS_x}$$

$$= \frac{(\underline{\hspace{1cm}})}{.632} \cdot \sqrt{\underline{\hspace{1cm}}}$$

1.22; 32.8

$$= \underline{\hspace{2cm}}$$

11.06

f. Decision: Since $|11.06| > 3.182$, we (accept, reject) H_0.

reject

g. Since the hypothesis that no linear relationship exists was rejected, we can conclude that there is evidence to indicate the existence of a linear relationship between x and y.

6. *Confidence Interval for* β_1.
   If x increases one unit, what is the predicted change in y? Since $\hat{\beta}_1$ is an unbiased estimator for β_1 and has a normal distribution, the t-statistic, based on $n - 2$ degrees of freedom, can be used to derive the confidence interval estimator for the slope, β_1:

   $$\hat{\beta}_1 \pm \underline{\hspace{2cm}}$$

   $$t_{\alpha/2} \frac{s}{\sqrt{SS_x}}$$

7. *Example:*
   Find a 95% confidence interval for the average change in y for an increase of one unit in x.

Solution:

.05; .025

a. $1 - \alpha = .95$; $\alpha =$ _____; $\alpha/2 =$ _____;

3; 3.182

$n - 2 =$ _____; $t_{.025} =$ _____.

b. Then we can use

$$\hat{\beta}_1 \pm t_{.025} \frac{s}{\sqrt{SS_x}}$$

3.182

$$1.22 \pm (\underline{\hspace{2cm}}) \frac{.632}{\sqrt{32.8}}$$

0.351

$$1.22 \pm (\underline{\hspace{2cm}})$$

0.869; 1.571

c. a 95% confidence interval for β_1 is ($\underline{\hspace{1.5cm}}$, $\underline{\hspace{1.5cm}}$).

σ^2/SS_x

8. Since the variance of the estimator $\hat{\beta}_1$ is given by $\sigma_{\hat{\beta}_1}^2 =$ _____, and

$\Sigma(x_i - \bar{x})^2$; smaller

since $SS_x =$ _____, the larger is $\Sigma(x_i - \bar{x})^2$, the (larger, smaller) will

large

be $\sigma_{\hat{\beta}_1}^2$, and the more accurate will be our estimate $\hat{\beta}_1$ of β_1. The quantity $SS_x = \Sigma(x_i - \bar{x})^2$ can be made (large, small) by including widely dispersed values of x in the sample.

Points Concerning Interpretation of Results

does not

9. If the test $H_0: \beta_1 = 0$ is performed and H_0 is *not rejected,* this (does, does not) mean that x and y are *not related,* since

II

a. a Type _____ error may have been committed or

linearly

b. x and y may be related, but not _____. For example, the true relationship may be of the form $y = \beta_0 + \beta_1 x + \beta_2 x^2$.

If the test $H_0: \beta_1 = 0$ is performed and H_0 *is rejected,*

cannot

a. we (can, cannot) say that x and y are solely linearly related, since there may be other terms (x^2 or x^3) that have not been included in our model;

causal

b. we should not conclude that a _____ relationship exists between x and y, since the related changes we observe in x and y may actually be *caused* by an unmeasured _____ variable, say z.

third

10. Consider the problem where the true relationship between x and y is a "curve" rather than a straight line. Suppose we fitted a straight line to the data for values of x between a and b.

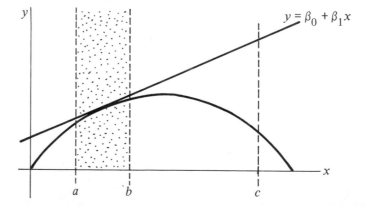

11. Using $\hat{y} = \hat{\beta}_0 + \hat{\beta}_1 x$ to predict values of y for $a \leqslant x \leqslant b$ would result in quite an accurate prediction. However, if the prediction line were used to predict y for the value $x = c$, the prediction would be highly _____.   inaccurate
Although the line adequately describes the indicated trend in the region $a \leqslant x \leqslant b$, there is no justification for assuming that the line would fit equally well for values of x outside the region $a \leqslant x \leqslant b$. The process of predicting outside the region of experimentation is called _____.   extrapolation
As our example shows, an experimenter should *not* extrapolate unless he is willing to assume the consequences of *gross errors*.

Self-Correcting Exercises 11B

1. Refer to Self-Correcting Exercises 11A, problem 1. Calculate SSE, s^2 and s for these data.
   a. Test the hypothesis that there is no linear relationship between actual and pre-enrollment figures at the $\alpha = .05$ level of significance.
   b. Estimate the average increase in actual enrollment for an increase of 100 in pre-enrolled students with a 95% confidence interval.
2. Refer to Self-Correcting Exercises 11A, problem 2. Calculate SSE, s^2 and s for these data and test for a significant linear relationship between yield and number of bolls at the $\alpha = .05$ level of significance.
3. Refer to Self-Correcting Exercises 11A, problem 3. Test for a significant linear relationship between yield and the number of insects present at the $\alpha = .05$ level of significance.

11.6 Estimating the Expected Value of _y_ for a Given Value of _x_ (11.6)

1. Assume that x and y are related according to the model

$$y = \beta_0 + \beta_1 x + \epsilon$$

We have found an estimator for this line which is

$$\hat{y} = \underline{\qquad\qquad}$$ $\hat{\beta}_0 + \hat{\beta}_1 x$

Suppose we are interested in estimating $E(y|x)$ for a given value of x, say x_p.

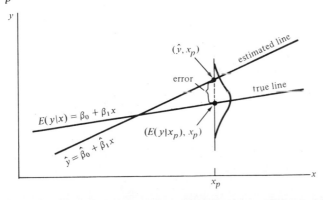

In repeated sampling, the predicted values of y will generate a distribution of estimates, $\hat{y}$, for the value of $x = x_p$, as shown in the diagram. The mean of these estimates is the true value

$$E(y|x = x_p) = \beta_0 + \beta_1 x_p$$

Therefore, we will use $\hat{y}$ to estimate the expected or average value of y for $x = x_p$, using as our estimator

$\beta_0 + \beta_1 x_p$

$$\hat{y} = \underline{\hspace{3cm}}$$

2. The estimator $\hat{y} = \hat{\beta}_0 + \hat{\beta}_1 x_p$ has the following properties:

y

unbiased

a. $E(\hat{y}|x_p) = E(\underline{\hspace{2cm}}|x_p)$
  This says that for a fixed value of x, $\hat{y}$ is an $\underline{\hspace{2cm}}$ estimator for the average value of y,

$\beta_0 + \beta_1 x_p$

$$E(y|x_p) = \underline{\hspace{3cm}}$$

$\dfrac{1}{n} + \dfrac{(x_p - \bar{x})^2}{SS_x}$

b. The variance, $\sigma_{\hat{y}}^2$, of the estimator $\hat{y}|x_p$ is given by

$$\sigma_{\hat{y}}^2 = \sigma^2 \left[\underline{\hspace{3cm}} \right]$$

normally

c. When the dependent variable, y, has the properties listed in 11.2(9), the estimator $\hat{y}|x$ is $\underline{\hspace{2cm}}$ distributed.

3. By using these results we can construct a z- or t-statistic to test an hypothesis concerning the expected value of y for a given $x = x_p$. Since σ^2 is rarely known, its sample estimate, s^2, is used, resulting in a $\underline{\hspace{2cm}}$ statistic with $\underline{\hspace{2cm}}$ degrees of freedom.

t-

$n - 2$

4. *Test of an hypothesis concerning $E(y|x_p)$.*

   a. $\quad H_0 : E(y|x_p) = E_0$

   b. $\quad H_a$: Appropriate one- or two-tailed test.

   c. Test statistic:

$\dfrac{\hat{y} - E_0}{\hat{\sigma}_{\hat{y}}}$

$$t = \underline{\hspace{3cm}}$$

$$= \frac{\hat{y} - E_0}{s\sqrt{\dfrac{1}{n} + \dfrac{(x_p - \bar{x})^2}{SS_x}}}$$

   d. Rejection region: Appropriate one- or two-tailed rejection region based on H_a.

5. *Example:*
   For our problem in Example 11.3(4) test the hypothesis that $\beta_0 = -1$ versus $\beta_0 < -1$ at the $\alpha = .05$ level.

Remark: By letting $x_p = 0$, $E(y|x_p = 0) = \beta_0 + \beta_1(0) = \beta_0$. Therefore, the test described above can be used to test an hypothesis about the

_____, β_0.

intercept

Solution:

a. $H_0: E(y|x = 0) = \beta_0 = -1$

b. $H_a: \beta_0 < -1$

c. Test statistic:

$$t = \frac{\hat{\beta}_0 - (-1)}{s\sqrt{\dfrac{1}{n} + \dfrac{(0 - \bar{x})^2}{SS_x}}}$$

$$= \frac{-1.34 - (-1)}{.632\sqrt{\dfrac{1}{5} + \dfrac{(0 - 5.2)^2}{32.8}}}$$

$$= \frac{(\underline{\hspace{2cm}})}{.64} = \underline{\hspace{2cm}}$$

$-.34; -.53$

d. Rejection region: With _____ degrees of freedom, we shall reject H_0 if $t <$ _____.

3

-2.353

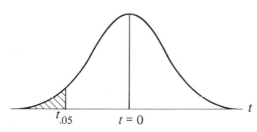

$t_{.05}$ $t = 0$

e. Decision: _____

Do not reject H_0

f. Hence, the data do not present sufficient evidence to indicate that $\beta_0 < -1$.

6. *Confidence Interval for $E(y|x_p)$.*
    A 100 $(1 - \alpha)\%$ confidence interval for $E(y|x_p)$ is

$$(\hat{y}|x_p) \pm \underline{\hspace{3cm}}$$

$$t_{\alpha/2}\, s\sqrt{\frac{1}{n} + \frac{(x_p - \bar{x})^2}{SS_x}}$$

where $(\hat{y}|x_p)$ is the value of the estimate for $x = x_p$, found using

$$\hat{y} = \hat{\beta}_0 + \hat{\beta}_1 x_p$$

7. *Example:*

Find a 95% confidence interval for $E(y|x = 6)$ for our previous problem.

Solution:

a. $(\hat{y}|x = 6) = -1.34 + 1.22(6)$

7.32

$= -1.34 +$ _____

5.98

$=$ _____

3.182

b. $t_{.025} =$ _____

.63

c. $\hat{\sigma}_{\hat{y}} = ($_____$)\sqrt{\dfrac{1}{5} + \dfrac{(6 - 5.2)^2}{32.8}}$

.2952

$=$ _____

d. Therefore a 95% confidence interval is constructed as follows:

$$(\hat{y}|x = 6) \pm 3.182\,\hat{\sigma}_{\hat{y}}$$

5.98; .2952

(_____) $\pm$ 3.182 (_____)

5.98; .94

(_____) $\pm$ (_____)

8. In order to obtain reasonably accurate results when predicting $E(y)$ at a particular x_p, it is desirable that x_p lie within the _____ of the

range

observed

_____ values of x.

11.7 Predicting a Particular Value of y for a Given Value of x (11.7)

1. In the last section, we were interested in estimating $E(y|x)$ when $x = x_p$.

true

That is, we estimated a point on the _____ regression line at the value of $x = x_p$. Now we consider the problem of predicting the actual single value of y that occurs (or will occur) when $x = x_p$, rather than the

expected *or* average

_____ value of all the y_i that would occur at $x = x_p$ in

repeated

_____ sampling.

2. We have as a predictor for this actual value of y, the quantity

$\hat{\beta}_0 + \hat{\beta}_1 x_p$

$\hat{y} =$ _____

3. By looking at the following graph, we can see that our error in predicting the actual value of y when $x = x_p$ will come from two sources:

a. The difference between the predicted value of y, $\hat{y}$, and the expected

II

value of y, $E(y|x_p)$. This difference is labeled _____ in the diagram and is the source of the variance of $\hat{y}$ as a predictor of $E(y|x_p)$ that was discussed in the last section.

b. The difference between the actual value of y and the expected value of y, $E(y|x_p)$. This difference is labeled _____ in the diagram, and is identical to _____, the _____ _____ term in the probabilistic model.

I

ϵ; random error

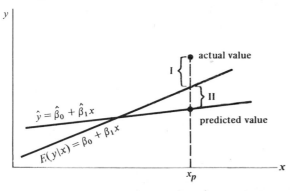

4. Thus the error associated with using $\hat{y} = \hat{\beta}_0 + \hat{\beta}_1 x_p$ as our prediction for the actual value of y which will occur when $x = x_p$, consists of the two components, I and II.

a. The variance associated with component I (the difference between the actual and expected values of y) is, by assumption, _____.

σ^2

b. The variance associated with component II (the difference between the true and estimated regression lines) is, as shown in the last section,

_____

$\sigma^2\left[\dfrac{1}{n} + \dfrac{(x_p - \bar{x})^2}{SS_x}\right]$

5. Not surprisingly, the variance of the error $(y - \hat{y})$ in predicting a particular value of y with $\hat{y}$ can be shown to be the sum of the variances of the components of that error

$$\sigma^2_{error} = \sigma^2 + \sigma^2\left[\dfrac{1}{n} + \dfrac{(x_p - \bar{x})^2}{SS_x}\right]$$

or more simply,

$$\sigma^2_{error} = \sigma^2 \left[\underline{\hspace{3cm}}\right]$$

$1 + \dfrac{1}{n} + \dfrac{(x_p - \bar{x})^2}{SS_x}$

6. Notice that this variance is (smaller, larger) than the variance of the error associated with using $\hat{y}$ to predict the expected or average value of y, $E(y|x_p)$, for a given value of $x = x_p$. This is a consequence of the fact the mean of a population of measurements on a random variable has a (smaller, larger) variance than does any individual measurement on the random variable.

larger

smaller

t

$$t_{\alpha/2}s\sqrt{1 + \frac{1}{n} + \frac{(x_p - \bar{x})^2}{SS_x}}$$

7. When s^2 is used to estimate σ^2, a prediction interval for the actual value of y when $x = x_p$ can be constructed based on the _____ - statistic, which has an associated confidence coefficient of $(1 - \alpha)$:

$$(\hat{y}|x_p) \pm \underline{\hspace{2cm}}$$

wider

8. Because the variance of the error in predicting the actual value of y when $x = x_p$ is larger than the variance of the error in estimating $E(y|x_p)$, the resulting confidence or prediction interval will be (wider, narrower) when predicting the actual value of y, for a given level of α.

9. *Example:*
Continuing the example from previous sections, predict the particular value of y when $x = 6$, with 95% confidence.
Solution:

a. $\hat{y} = -1.34 + 1.22(6)$

5.98

$= \underline{\hspace{2cm}}$

3.182

b. With 3 degrees of freedom, $t_{.025} = \underline{\hspace{2cm}}$.
c. The 95% prediction interval would be

3.182; .632

$$5.98 \pm (\underline{\hspace{1.5cm}})(\underline{\hspace{1.5cm}})\sqrt{1 + \frac{1}{5} + \frac{(6 - 5.2)^2}{32.8}}$$

2.21

$$5.98 \pm (\underline{\hspace{1.5cm}})$$

wider

d. Recall that the 95% confidence interval for our estimate of $E(y|x = 6)$ was $5.98 \pm .94$. Consequently, the prediction interval is _____ for the actual value of y at $x = 6$.

Self-Correcting Exercises 11C

1. Refer to Self-Correcting Exercises 11A, problem 1. Test the hypothesis that the expected enrollment is zero if there are no students pre-enrolled at the $\alpha = .05$ level. Does the line of means pass through the origin? Would you expect it to pass through the origin?

2. For Self-Correcting Exercises 11A, problem 2, predict the expected yield in cotton when the mid-season boll count is 450 with a 90% confidence interval. Could you use the prediction line to predict the cotton yield if the mid-season boll count was 250?

3. Refer to Self-Correcting Exercises 11A, problem 3. Using the least-squares prediction line for these data, predict the expected cotton yield if the insect count is 12 with a 90% confidence interval. Compare this interval with that found in problem 2 and comment on these two predictors of cotton yield.

4. Use the least-squares line from problem 1, Self-Correcting Exercises 11A to predict the enrollment with 95% confidence if the pre-enrollment figure is 4000 students.

11.8   A Coefficient of Correlation (11.8)

1. A common measure of the strength of the _____ relationship between two variables is the Pearson product-moment _____ _____ _____, symbolized by _____. This correlation coefficient is (dependent on, <u>independent of</u>) the scales of measurement of the two variables.

linear
coefficient
of correlation; r
independent of

2. The Pearson product-moment coefficient of correlation is given by

$$r = \underline{\hspace{3cm}}$$

where SS_x, SS_y and SS_{xy} are as defined earlier in this chapter, and where

$$\underline{\hspace{2cm}} \leqslant r \leqslant \underline{\hspace{2cm}}$$

$$\dfrac{SS_{xy}}{\sqrt{SS_x SS_y}}$$

$-1; 1$

3. Examine the formula for r above, and notice the following:
   a. The denominator of r is the square root of the product of two positive quantities and will always be _____.

   positive

   b. The numerator of r is identical to the numerator used to calculate _____, whose denominator is also always positive.

   $\hat{\beta}_1$

   c. Hence _____ and r will always have the same algebraic sign. When

   $\hat{\beta}_1$

   i. $\hat{\beta}_1 > 0$, then r _____.

   > 0

   ii. $\hat{\beta}_1 = 0$, then r _____.

   $= 0$

   iii. $\hat{\beta}_1 < 0$, then r _____.

   < 0

4. When $r > 0$, there is a _____ linear correlation; when $r < 0$, there is a _____ linear correlation; when $r = 0$, there is _____ linear correlation. See the following examples:

   positive
   negative
   no

r _____ 0

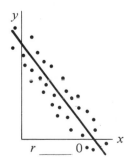
r _____ 0

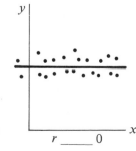
r _____ 0

$>$; $<$; $=$

5. *Example:*

Find the coefficient of correlation for our data.

Solution:

Drawing upon our earlier calculations of SS_x, SS_y and SS_{xy}, we have

$$r = \frac{SS_{xy}}{\sqrt{SS_x SS_y}} = \frac{40}{\sqrt{(\underline{\hspace{2cm}})(\underline{\hspace{2cm}})}}$$

32.8; 50

$$= \underline{\hspace{2cm}}$$

.988

6. The coefficient r, which is calculated from sample data, is actually an esti-

population   mator of the _____ coefficient of correlation, symbolized by

ρ; -1; 1 _____, where _____ $\leqslant \rho \leqslant$ _____.

β_1 7. Since ρ and _____ both measure the linear relationship between x
and y, the test of $H_0 : \beta_1 = 0$ is equivalent to testing $H_0 : \rho = 0$. Therefore,
no separate test of the hypothesis concerning the coefficient of correlation,
ρ, will be presented. (See Section 11.8 in the text.)

8. It should be noted that a dependent random variable, y, usually depends

several   on _____ predictor variables, rather than just one. Consequently,
the correlation between y and a single predictor variable is of doubtful
value.

9. It is even more important to bear in mind that r measures only the

linear   _____ relationship between two variables, say x and y. So even

nonlinear   when $r = 0$, x and y could be *perfectly* related by a _____
function.

10. Suppose that we want to predict the value of y for a given value of x. Consider these two estimators for y:

   a. $\hat{y} = \bar{y}$

   b. $\hat{y} = \hat{\beta}_0 + \hat{\beta}_1 x$

$\qquad = \bar{y} + \hat{\beta}_1 (x - \bar{x})$

a   Estimator (a, b) uses no information about the value of x in arriving at a
prediction for y. These estimators are shown in the following diagram:

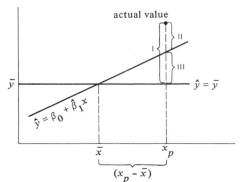

11. a. Distance I is equal to $y - \bar{y}$ and represents the error associated with using _____ as a predictor of y. When this error is squared and then summed over all observations, we have

$$\Sigma(y_i - \bar{y})^2 = \underline{\hspace{2cm}}$$

| $\bar{y}$ |

| SS_y |

which is the total variation in y.

b. Distance II is equal to $y_i - \hat{y}$ and represents the error associated with using _____ as a predictor of y. When this error is squared and summed over all observations, we have

$$\Sigma(y_i - \hat{y}_i)^2 = \underline{\hspace{2cm}}$$

| $\hat{y}$ |

| SSE |

which is the variation remaining after information about x is used to help predict y.

c. Distance III is equal to $\hat{y}_i - \bar{y}$, the reduction in prediction error realized by using $\hat{y}_i$ rather than _____ as a predictor of y_i. From Number 10(b), it is seen that $\hat{y}_i - \bar{y} = \hat{\beta}_1(x_i - \bar{x})$. When this quantity is squared and summed over all observations, we have

| $\bar{y}$ |

$$\Sigma(\hat{y}_i - \bar{y})^2 = \hat{\beta}_1^2 \Sigma(x_i - \bar{x})^2$$

$$= \hat{\beta}_1^2 \, SS_x$$

$$= \frac{SS_{xy}^2}{SS_x}$$

which is the portion of the total variation in y that is explained by the estimator $\hat{y}$ which utilizes information about x. $\Sigma(\hat{y}_i - \bar{y})^2$ is called the sum of squares due to regression, SSR.

12. We have the relationship

$$SS_y = SSE + \underline{\hspace{2cm}}$$

| SSR |

where $SSR = SS_{xy}^2/SS_x$. This can be written as

$$SSR = SS_y - \underline{\hspace{2cm}}$$

| SSE |

which upon division by SS_y becomes

$$\frac{SS_{xy}^2}{SS_x SS_y} = \frac{SS_y - SSE}{SS_y}$$

However, $SS_{xy}^2/SS_x SS_y = \underline{\hspace{2cm}}$, the Pearson product-moment coefficient of correlation. Therefore,

| r^2 |

$$r^2 = \frac{SS_y - SSE}{SS_y}$$

determination
reduction

0; 1
1

linear
$\bar{y}$; more

r

.976
97.6

13. The quantity r^2 is called the coefficient of _____ and is equal to the ratio of the _____ in the sum of squares of deviations obtained by using $\hat{y}$ as a predictor, to the sum of squares of deviations which would result if $\bar{y}$ were used as a predictor, ignoring x.

14. r^2 lies in the interval _____ $\leqslant r^2 \leqslant$ _____ and equals _____ only when all the values of y fall exactly on the fitted line.

15. Since r^2 gives the percentage reduction in the sum of squares for error achieved by using the _____ model as a predictor for y in preference to _____ as a predictor, r^2 gives a (more, less) meaningful interpretation of the strength of the relationship between x and y than does _____ itself

16. *Example:*
For our problem, the value of r was found to be $r = .988$; therefore, $r^2 =$ _____. This means that we have reduced the sum of squares for error approximately _____% by using the predictor $\hat{y} = -1.34 + 1.22x$ rather than $\bar{y} = 5$.

11.9 The Additivity of Sums of Squares (11.9)

1. In a regression analysis the values of x are recorded in an effort to help explain the variation observed in y, the response of interest. The variation in y is measured by the sum of squared deviations given as

$$\sum_{i=1}^{n} (y_i - \bar{y})^2$$

x
regression

SSE

and is referred to as the total variation or the total sum of squares. The difference between the total sum of squares and *SSE* measures the effectiveness of the regression of y on _____ and is called the sum of squares due to _____, *SSR*. Therefore the total sum of squares can be partitioned into two parts:

$$\text{Total } SS = SSR + \underline{\hspace{2cm}}$$

where

$$SSR = \sum_{i=1}^{n} (\hat{y}_i - \bar{y})^2$$

and

$$SSE = \sum_{i=1}^{n} \underline{\hspace{4cm}}$$

$(y_i - \hat{y}_i)^2$

Since Total $SS =$ _____ , neither SSR nor SSE can be larger than Total SS.

$SSR + SSE$

2. Notice that SSR measures the difference between the simple predictor $\bar{y}$ and the linear predictor $\hat{y}_i = \bar{y} + \hat{\beta}_1 (x_i - \bar{x})$. Therefore a large value of SSR indicates that the values of x are contributing (little, much) to the estimation of the values of y. SSR is said to be the amount of the total variation _____ by the auxiliary variable x.

much

explained

3. SSE measures the difference between the observed values y_i and the values predicted using $\hat{y}_i = \bar{y} + \hat{\beta}_1 (x_i - \bar{x})$. A (small, large) value of SSE indicates that the linear predictor is effectively reproducing the observed values $y_1, y_2, \ldots, y_n$. SSE is said to be the amount of the total variation that is _____ by the auxiliary variable x.

small

unexplained

4. The additivity of the sums of squares is important for several reasons.
   a. Only two of the quantities need to be calculated (Total SS and SSR) since the third (SSE) can be obtained by _____ .

subtraction

   b. SSR can be used to measure the contribution of the auxiliary variable x, since

$$r^2 = \frac{\text{Total } SS - SSE}{\text{Total } SS}$$

$$= \frac{\underline{\hspace{3cm}}}{\text{Total } SS}$$

SSR

In this form it is easily seen that r^2 represents the proportion of the total variation explained by the auxiliary variable _____ .

x

   c. When more than one auxiliary variable is included in the linear model, the additivity property still holds, and the ratio

$$R^2 = \frac{SSR}{\text{Total } SS}$$

now measures the joint contribution of the auxiliary variables in explaining the variation in y. R, the positive square root of R^2 is called the multiple correlation coefficient and is the multivariate counterpart of r.

Self-Correcting Exercises 11D

1. Refer to Self-Correcting Exercises 11A, problem 2.
   a. Use the additivity of the sums of squares to find the sum of squares due to regression.
   b. From part a find r^2 and explain its significance in using the number of cotton bolls to predict yield of cotton.
   c. Find the correlation between the number of bolls and the yield of cotton. (Remember that $\hat{\beta}_1$ and r *always* have the same algebraic sign.)
2. Refer to Self-Correcting Exercises 11A, problem 3.
   a. Find the value of r^2 and r for these data and explain the value of using the number of damaging insects present to predict cotton yield.
   b. Compare the values of r^2 using these two predictors of cotton yield. Which predictor would you prefer?
3. The data in problems 2 and 3, Self-Correcting Exercises 11A are related in that for each field quadrate, the yield, the number of bolls and the number of damaging insects were simultaneously recorded. Using this fact, calculate the correlation between the number of cotton bolls and the number of insects present for the 7 field quadrates. Does this value of r explain in any way the similarity of results using the predictors found for problems 2 and 3, Self-Correcting Exercises 11A?

11.10 Summary (11.10)

1. Until the present chapter, we were interested in predicting the value of a random variable y_i solely on the basis of the _____ values of y.

sample

2. We used the sample information in order to make _____ about the _____ of the probability distribution of the _____ from which the sample was drawn.

inferences
parameters; population

3. This chapter was concerned with the problem of predicting y when _____ information on another variable related to y is available.

auxiliary

4. We have discussed two-variable regression techniques, which permit us to estimate a _____ relationship between y and the auxiliary variable x.

linear

Exercises

1. For the following equations (1) give the y-intercept, (2) give the slope, and (3) graph the line corresponding to the equation.

   a. $y = 3x - 2$

   b. $2y = 4x$

   c. $-y = 0.5 + x$

d. $3x + 2y = 5$

e. $y = 2$

(2.) a. Find the least-squares line for the following data:

x	-3	-2	-1	0	1	2	3
y	-1	-1	0	1	2	2	3

b. As a check on your calculations, plot the data points and graph the least-squares line.

c. Calculate SSE and s^2. Under what conditions could $SSE = 0$?

d. Do the data present sufficient evidence to indicate that x and y are linearly related at the $\alpha = .05$ level of significance?

e. Estimate the average change in y for a one-unit change in x with a 95% confidence interval.

f. Calculate the coefficient of linear correlation for the data and interpret your results.

g. Calculate r^2 and state in words the significance of its magnitude.

h. Construct a 90% confidence interval estimate for a particular value of y when $x = 1$.

i. Test the hypothesis that $E(y|x = 0) = 0$ at the $\alpha = .05$ level of significance. (This is actually a test of $H_0: \beta_0 = 0$.)

3. For the following data,

x	0	2	4	6	8	10
y	9	7	3	1	-2	-3

a. Fit the least-squares line, $\hat{y} = \hat{\beta}_0 + \hat{\beta}_1 x$.

b. Plot the points, and graph the line to check your calculations.

c. Calculate SSE, s^2, and s.

d. Is there a linear relationship between x and y at the $\alpha = .05$ level of significance?

e. Calculate r^2, and explain its significance in predicting the response, y.

f. Predict the particular value of y when $x = 5$ with 80% confidence.

g. Predict the expected value of y when $x = 5$ with 80% confidence.

4. What happens if the coefficient of linear correlation, r, assumes the value one? The value -1?

5. The following data were obtained in an experiment relating the dependent variable, y (texture of strawberries), with x (coded storage temperature).

x	-2	-2	0	2	2
y	4.0	3.5	2.0	0.5	0.0

a. Find the least-squares line for the data.

b. Plot the data points and graph the least-squares line as a check on your calculations.

c. Calculate SSE, s^2, and s.

d. Do the data indicate that texture and storage temperature are linearly related? ($\alpha = .05$)

e. Predict the expected strawberry texture for a coded storage temperature of $x = -1$ with a 90% confidence interval.

f. Of what value is the *linear* model in increasing the accuracy of prediction as compared to the predictor, $\bar{y}$?

g. Estimate the particular value of y when $x = 1$ with a 98% confidence interval.

h. At what value of x will the width of the confidence interval for a particular value of y be a minimum, assuming n remains fixed?

6. In addition to increasingly large bounds on error, why should an experimenter refrain from predicting y for values of x outside the experimental region?

7. If the experimenter stays within the experimental region, when will the error in predicting a particular value of y be maximum?

8. An agricultural experimenter, investigating the effect of the amount of nitrogen (x) applied in 100 pounds per acre on the yield of oats (y) measured in bushels per acre, collected the following data:

x	1	2	3	4
y	22	38	57	68
	19	41	54	65

a. Fit a least-squares line to the data.

b. Calculate SSE and s^2.

c. Is there sufficient evidence to indicate that the yield of oats is linearly related to the amount of nitrogen applied? ($\alpha = .05$)

d. Predict the expected yield of oats with 95% confidence if 250 pounds of nitrogen per acre are applied.

e. Predict the average increase in yield for an increase of 100 pounds of nitrogen with 90% confidence.

f. Calculate r^2 and explain its significance in terms of predicting y, the yield of oats.

9. In an industrial process, the yield, y, is thought to be linearly related to temperature, x. The following coded data is available:

Temperature	0	0.5	1.5	2.0	2.5
Yield	7.2	8.1	9.8	11.3	12.9
	6.9	8.4	10.1	11.7	13.2

a. Find the least-squares line for this data.

b. Plot the points and graph the line. Is your calculated line reasonable?

c. Calculate SSE and s^2.

d. Do the data indicate a linear relationship between yield and temperature at the $\alpha = .01$ level of significance?

e. Calculate r, the coefficient of linear correlation and interpret your results.

f. Calculate r^2, and interpret its significance in predicting the yield, y.

g. Test the hypothesis that $E(y|x = 1,75) = 10.8$ at the $\alpha = .05$ level of significance.

h. Predict the particular value of y for a coded temperature $x = 1$ with 90% confidence.

10. A food technologist employed by a large supermarket chain devised a scale to measure the freshness of packaged meats that were frozen and displayed for varying periods of time before sale. In the following table, y represents the freshness measurement and x represents the length of time in days the meat is frozen and on display.

x	5	10	15	20	25
y	15.3	13.6	9.8	5.5	1.8
	16.8	13.8	8.7	4.7	1.0

a. Fit a least-squares line to these data.

b. Calculate SSE and s^2 for the data.

c. Is there sufficient evidence to indicate that a linear relationship exists between freshness and display time? ($\alpha = .05$)

d. Estimate the mean rate of change in freshness for a one-day increase in display time with a 98% confidence interval.

e. Predict the expected freshness measurement for a display time of 14 days with 95% confidence.

f. Of what value is the linear model in preference to $\bar{y}$ in predicting freshness?

Chapter   12

MULTIPLE REGRESSION

12.1 Introduction (12.1)

1. We have examined estimation, testing, and prediction techniques for the situation in which y, the response of interest, was linearly related to an independent variable x in the following way.

$$y = \beta_0 + \beta_1 x + \epsilon$$

2. In this chapter, we extend these techniques to the more general situation in which the response y is linearly related to one or more independent variables. These extended techniques can be used when the response is linearly related to several different independent variables, or when the response is a polynomial function of just one variable. Modeling, testing, and prediction in these cases belong to an area of statistics called multiple regression analysis.

12.2 Linear Statistical Models (12.2)

1. The general results in the remainder of this chapter produce standard solutions when the response, y, is a _____ function of the unknown regression coefficients. Although we normally think of the response, y, as being a linear function of one or more independent variables, our methodology requires that the unknown _____ in the model occur in a linear fashion.

linear

parameters

2. The following are statistical linear models.

a. $$y = \beta_0 + \beta_1 t + \beta_2 \sin\left(\frac{2\pi t}{n}\right) + \epsilon$$

b. $$y = \beta_0 + \beta_1 x + \beta_2 x^2 + \epsilon$$

c. $y = \beta_0 + \beta_1 x_1 + \beta_2 x_2 + \beta_3 x_1 x_2 + \epsilon$

Although the model given in part a involves the sine function, no unknown parameters occur within the function itself. By letting $x_1 = t$ and $x_2 = \sin(2\pi t/n)$, this model could be written as

$$y = \beta_0 + \beta_1 x_1 + \beta_2 x_2 + \epsilon$$

β_1

β_2

$x; x^2$

$x_1 x_2.$

which is a linear function of the unknown regression parameters β_0, _____, and _____. In a similar fashion the model given in part b can be rewritten by letting $x_1 =$ _____ and $x_2 =$ _____. In the third model, we can achieve the same result by letting $x_1 = x_1, x_2 = x_2$, and $x_3 =$ _____.

3. The next three models are examples of nonlinear statistical models.

a. $y = \beta_0 e^{\beta_1 x} + \epsilon$

b. $y = \beta_0 + \beta_1 \sin\left(\dfrac{2\pi t}{n} + \beta_2\right) + \epsilon$

c. $y = \beta_0 + \beta_1 x^{\beta_2} + \epsilon$

Notice that models a and c involve an unknown parameter as a power, while model b involves an unknown parameter, β_2, within the sine function itself.

4. Determine whether the following models are linear (L) or nonlinear (NL) models.

L

a. $y = \beta_0 + \beta_1 x_1^2 + \beta_2 x_2^2 + \beta_3 x_1 x_2 + \epsilon$ (L, NL)

NL

b. $y = \beta_0 + \beta_1 \cos\left(\dfrac{2\pi x}{5}\right) + \beta_2 x^{\beta_3} + \epsilon$ (L, NL)

L

c. $y = \beta_0 e^{-5x} + \epsilon$ (L, NL)

may

5. A linear statistical model (may, may not) involve nonlinear terms provided all unknown parameters occur in a linear fashion within the model.

12.3 The Least Squares Equations for a Multivariate Prediction Model (12.3, 12.4, 12.9)

1. In generalizing the results of simple linear regression to multiple linear regression, we consider the model

$$y = \beta_0 + \beta_1 x_1 + \beta_2 x_2 + \ldots + \beta_k x_k + \epsilon$$

where ϵ is a normally distributed random error component with a mean of zero and a variance σ^2. In addition, the error terms for any two values of y are taken to be _____. The parameters $\beta_1, \beta_2, \ldots, \beta_k$ are the partial slopes associated with the nonrandom quantities $x_1, x_2, \ldots, x_k$. The slope, β_i, represents the expected increase in the response y corresponding to a one-unit increase in x_i when the values of all other x's are held constant.

independent

2. Estimates of the unknown parameters in the model are found by using the method of least squares. Using this method, the estimates $\hat\beta_0, \hat\beta_1, \ldots, \hat\beta_k$ are chosen so as to _____ _____ the quantity

minimize

$$SSE = \sum_{i=1}^{n} (y_i - \hat{y}_i)^2$$

This minimization technique leads to a set of equations called the _____ _____ with $\hat\beta_0, \hat\beta_1, \ldots, \hat\beta_k$ as the unknown quantities.

**normal
equations**

3. In fitting the model

$$y = \beta_0 + \beta_1 x_1 + \beta_2 x_2 + \epsilon$$

involving two independent variables, x_1 and x_2, the normal equations are

$$\hat\beta_0 n + \hat\beta_1 \Sigma x_1 + \hat\beta_2 \Sigma x_2 = \Sigma y$$

$$\hat\beta_0 \Sigma x_1 + \hat\beta_1 \Sigma x_1^2 + \hat\beta_2 \Sigma x_1 x_2 = \Sigma x_1 y$$

$$\hat\beta_0 \Sigma x_2 + \hat\beta_1 \Sigma x_1 x_2 + \hat\beta_2 \Sigma x_2^2 = \Sigma x_2 y$$

where all summations extend over the observations, $i = 1, 2, \ldots, n$. These three equations are solved simultaneously to obtain values for $\hat\beta_0$, $\hat\beta_1$, and $\hat\beta_2$. The systematic pattern displayed by these equations is easily expanded to include more independent variables by adding the proper rows and columns to the display.

4. For example, if a third variable, x_3, were to be included in the model, the left-hand side of the three equations would include the terms $\hat\beta_3 \Sigma x_3$, $\hat\beta_3 \Sigma x_1 x_3, \hat\beta_3 \Sigma x_2 x_3$, respectively, and a fourth equation,

$$\hat\beta_0 \Sigma x_3 + \hat\beta_1 \Sigma x_1 x_3 + \hat\beta_2 \Sigma x_2 x_3 + \hat\beta_3 \Sigma x_3^2 = \Sigma x_3 y$$

would be added to the set to produce _____ equations in _____ unknowns. By the same token, one or more independent variables may be deleted from consideration by deleting the corresponding rows and columns from the set of equations.

**four
four**

5. *Example:*
   Write down the normal equations corresponding to the model

$$y = \beta_0 + \beta_1 x + \epsilon$$

Solution:
a. This is the simple linear regression model considered in Chapter 11, and the estimates $\hat{\beta}_0$ and $\hat{\beta}_1$ given there are obtained by solving the normal equations that we will develop.
b. By considering the model and the normal equations given in 12.3(3), we see that we need to delete the variable _____ from that model. In each of the normal equations we delete the term corresponding to $\hat{\beta}_2$, and we delete the equation involving $\Sigma x_2 y$. Hence, the normal equations are

$$\hat{\beta}_0 n + \hat{\beta}_1 \Sigma x_1 = \Sigma y$$

$$\hat{\beta}_0 \Sigma x_1 + \hat{\beta}_1 \Sigma x_1^2 = \Sigma x_1 y$$

with x_1 representing the one independent variable, x, in the model.
c. Solving the first equation for $\hat{\beta}_0$, we have

$$\hat{\beta}_0 n = \Sigma y - \hat{\beta}_1 \Sigma x$$

which, upon dividing both sides of the equation by n, becomes

$$\hat{\beta}_0 = \underline{\hspace{2cm}} - \underline{\hspace{2cm}}$$

the solution given in Chapter 11. Using the second equation together with the solution for $\hat{\beta}_0$ just found, we can show that

$$\hat{\beta}_1 = SS_{xy}/SS_x$$

where SS_{xy} and SS_x are defined in Chapter 11.
6. The general linear model given in 12.3(1) can be used to fit a polynomial regression model by proper definition of the independent variables x_1, $x_2, \ldots, x_k$. For example, if one wished to fit the quadratic model

$$y = \beta_0 + \beta_1 x + \beta_2 x^2 + \epsilon$$

one needs only to define $x_1 = \underline{\hspace{2cm}}$ and $x_2 = \underline{\hspace{2cm}}$. The model is now identical to that given in 12.3(3), and the estimators $\hat{\beta}_0$, $\hat{\beta}_1$, and $\hat{\beta}_2$ are the solutions to the equations given there.
7. *Example:*
   An agricultural economist interested in California cotton production gathered the following data concerning the mean number of cotton bolls

x_2

$\bar{y}; \hat{\beta}_1 \bar{x}$

$x; x^2$

per plant within a specified field area as measured at various times during the growing season in the San Joaquin Valley of California. Here y is the mean number of bolls per plant and x is the time measured in weeks.

x	1	4	7	9	12	15
y	110	470	1040	1100	1000	820

Fit a second degree polynomial model to these data using the method of least squares and find *SSE, SSR* and R^2.

Solution:

a. A second degree polynomial model would be

$$y = \beta_0 + \beta_1 x + \beta_2 x^2 + \epsilon$$

so that $x_1 = $ _____ and $x_2 = $ _____ . The following sums and sums of products are required.

$x; x^2$

$$\sum_{i=1}^{6} y_i = \underline{\hspace{1.5cm}} \qquad\qquad \sum_{i=1}^{6} x_i = \underline{\hspace{1.5cm}}$$

4540; 48

$$\sum_{i=1}^{6} x_i y_i = 43470 \qquad\qquad \sum_{i=1}^{6} x_i^2 = 516$$

$$\sum_{i=1}^{6} x_i^2 y_i = 476190 \qquad\qquad \sum_{i=1}^{6} x_i^3 = 6240$$

$$n = \underline{\hspace{1.5cm}} \qquad\qquad \sum_{i=1}^{6} x_i^4 = 80580$$

6

b. The normal equations to be solved are

$$6\hat{\beta}_0 + 48\hat{\beta}_1 + 516\hat{\beta}_2 = \underline{\hspace{1.5cm}}$$

4540

$$48\hat{\beta}_0 + 516\hat{\beta}_1 + 6240\hat{\beta}_2 = \underline{\hspace{1.5cm}}$$

43470

$$516\hat{\beta}_0 + 6240\hat{\beta}_1 + 80580\hat{\beta}_2 = \underline{\hspace{1.5cm}}$$

476190

(Notice the symmetry of the left-hand side of the three normal equations.)

c. By successive elimination (as in your text) or by other mathematical means solve the normal equations to find

-175.55

244.22

-11.88

$\hat{\beta}_0 =$ _____

$\hat{\beta}_1 =$ _____

$\hat{\beta}_2 =$ _____

d. The equation for predicting the mean number of bolls per plant is given as

$$\hat{y} = -175.55 + 244.22x - 11.88x^2$$

where x is the time measured in weeks.

e. Plot the observed values of x and y together with the graph of the prediction equation as a visual check on your calculations.

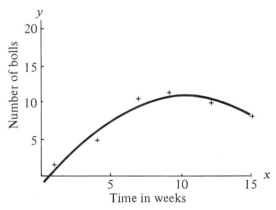

f. To find *SSE* we need the sum of the squared distances between the observed and the predicted values.

			Time			
	1	*4*	*7*	*9*	*12*	*15*
y_i	110	470	1040	1100	1000	820
$\hat{y}_i$	56.79		951.87	1060.15	1044.37	
$y_i - \hat{y}_i$		-141.25		39.85	-44.37	5.25

611.25; 814.75

53.21; 88.13

Note that *within rounding errors,*

0

$$\sum_{i=1}^{6} (y_i - \hat{y}_i) = \underline{\hspace{2cm}}.$$

The sum of squares for error is

$$SSE = \Sigma(y_i - \hat{y}_i)^2 = 34,134.0454$$

The method of least squares guarantees that no other estimates of the parameters β_0, β_1, and β_2 will produce a sum of squared deviations (smaller, larger) than 34,134.0454.

smaller

8. When the number of independent variables in the model exceeds two, the labor involved in solving the normal equations and subsequent calculations required for further analysis becomes excessive and tedious. However, there are several standard regression analysis programs available at most computer facilities that require only that the user provide the proper commands to activate the program and then submit the data to be analyzed. In order that the user be able to interpret the computer output resulting from the use of such programs, we will present a computer solution to the following problem.

9. *Example:*
In order to study the relationship of advertising and capital investment on corporate profits, the following data, recorded in units of $100,000, was collected for ten medium-sized firms within the same year. The variable y represents profit for the year, x_1 represents capital investment, and x_2 represents advertising expenditures.

y	x_1	x_2
15	25	4
16	1	5
2	6	3
3	30	1
12	29	2
1	20	0
16	12	4
18	15	5
13	6	4
2	16	2

Using the model

$$y = \beta_0 + \beta_1 x_1 + \beta_2 x_2 + \epsilon$$

find the least-squares prediction equation for these data.
Solution:

a. Using a computer program to perform a regression analysis eliminates the need to solve the least-squares equations by hand. If we wanted to verify the computer solution, we would need the following information.

$n = 10$ $\Sigma x_1 = 160$ $\Sigma x_2 = 30$ $\Sigma y = 98$

$\Sigma x_1^2 = 3464$ $\Sigma x_1 x_2 = 390$ $\Sigma x_1 y = 1433$

$\Sigma x_2^2 = 116$ $\Sigma x_2 y = 383$

The resulting normal equations would be

30

$$10\hat{\beta}_0 + 160\hat{\beta}_1 + ________\hat{\beta}_2 = 98$$

3464; 1433

$$160\hat{\beta}_0 + ________\hat{\beta}_1 + 390\hat{\beta}_2 = ________$$

30; 116

$$________\hat{\beta}_0 + 390\hat{\beta}_1 + ________\hat{\beta}_2 = 383$$

with solutions $\hat{\beta}_0 = -8.1770$, $\hat{\beta}_1 = .2921$, and $\hat{\beta}_2 = 4.4343$. Therefore the least-squares prediction equation is

.2921; 4.4343

$$\hat{y} = -8.1770 + ________x_1 + ________x_2$$

b. A standard multiple regression analysis program produced the following computer output for these data.

MULTIPLE R	.9072
R SQUARE	.8230
STD. ERROR OF EST.	3.3033

ANALYSIS OF VARIANCE

	DF	SUM OF SQUARES	MEAN SQUARE	F RATIO
REGRESSION	2	355.2151	177.6076	16.2762
RESIDUAL	7	76.3849	10.9121	

INDIVIDUAL ANALYSIS OF VARIABLES

VARIABLE	COEFFICIENT	STD. ERROR	F VALUE
(CONSTANT	-8.1770)		
CAPITAL	.2921	.1357	4.6335
ADVERTISING	4.4343	.8002	30.7048

At this point we are interested in that portion of the printout labeled INDIVIDUAL ANALYSIS OF VARIABLES. The first column identifies the estimated coefficients and the second column their values. Thus, the intercept, or CONSTANT, is estimated to be $\hat{\beta}_0 = -8.1770$, the partial regression coefficient corresponding to the variable CAPITAL (x_1) is $\hat{\beta}_1 = .2921$ and the partial regression coefficient corresponding to ADVERTISING (x_2) is $\hat{\beta}_2 = 4.4343$.

c. The least-squares prediction equation is

-8.1770

$$\hat{y} = ________ + .2921x_1 + 4.3434x_2$$

estimate
predict

10. The fitted prediction equation can be used to ________ the mean value of y for given values of $x_1, x_2, \ldots, x_k$ or to ________ speci-

fic values of y for given values of $x_1, x_2, \ldots, x_k$. Estimates and predictions are obtained by substituting the required values of $x_1, x_2, \ldots, x_k$ into the prediction equation.

11. *Example:*

Use the prediction equation derived in 12.3(9) to estimate yearly corporate profits for a medium sized firm whose capital investment was $2,200,000 and whose advertising expenditure was $400,000.

Solution:

The prediction equation is given as

$$\hat{y} = -8.1770 + .2921x_1 + 4.4343x_2$$

Since x_1, capital investment, and x_2, advertising expenditure, were given in units of $100,000, the values to be entered into the prediction equation are $x_1 = $ _____ and $x_2 = $ _____. Therefore   22; 4

$$\hat{y} = -8.1770 + .2921(\underline{\hspace{2cm}}) + 4.4343(\underline{\hspace{2cm}})$$ 22; 4

$$= -8.1770 + \underline{\hspace{2cm}} + \underline{\hspace{2cm}}$$ 6.4262; 17.7372

$$= \underline{\hspace{2cm}}$$ 15.9864

To find the actual profit, multiply 15.9864 by _____ to find that $100,000

when capital investment is $2,200,000 and advertising expenditure is $400,000, profit is estimated to be _____. $1,598,640

12. The point estimate found in 12.3(11) is the best estimate of either $E(y)$, the average value of y, or a particular value of y. We can construct confidence interval estimates for $E(y)$ or y using a procedure similar to that for the simple linear regression model presented in Chapter 11. However, the computational aspects of this problem are best handled by a computer. Some, but not all, regression analysis programs have options that allow the user to include confidence interval estimates for $E(y)$ and y in the computer output. In both cases, the point estimate for $E(y)$ and y remain the same; it is the width of the confidence interval that differs. The confidence interval for $E(y)$ is (narrower, wider) than the confidence interval for a   narrower
particular value of y.

12.4 Confidence Intervals and Tests of Simple Hypotheses Concerning the Partial Regression Coefficients (12.5)

1. In addition to the least-squares estimates of the regression coefficients, the INDIVIDUAL ANALYSIS OF VARIABLES portion of the computer printout provides the estimated standard deviation of the regression coefficients as well as the value of an F- or t-statistic used in testing.

2. Refer to the INDIVIDUAL ANALYSIS OF VARIABLES portion of the compu-

standard errors

$(k + 1)$

.8002

3
3; 7
2.365

.8002

1.8925

$254,180; $632,680

ter printout in 12.3(9). The estimated standard deviations of $\hat{\beta}_1$ and $\hat{\beta}_2$ are often referred to as _____ _____ . These standard errors, $s_{\hat{\beta}_1}$ and $s_{\hat{\beta}_2}$, are found in the column labeled STD. ERROR. These quantities can be used for producing confidence intervals for the parameters β_1 and β_2, or in testing an hypothesis concerning their values. A $100(1 - \alpha)\%$ confidence interval for β_i is given as

$$\hat{\beta}_i \pm t_{\alpha/2} s_{\hat{\beta}_i}$$

The table's value of $t_{\alpha/2}$ is based upon $n - (k + 1)$ degrees of freedom when the model contains k regression coefficients in addition to the intercept, or _____ β's in all.

3. *Example:*
Find a 95% confidence interval for the average increase in profit, β_2, for an increase of $100,000 in advertising expenditure.
Solution:
a. From the computer printout we find $\hat{\beta}_2 = 4.4343$ with $s_{\hat{\beta}_2} = $ _____ . The number of data points is $n = 10$, and the number of estimated parameters in the model is _____ . Therefore the tabulated value of t based upon $10 - $ _____ $=$ _____ degrees of freedom is $t_{.025} = $ _____ .

b. The resulting 95% confidence interval for β_2 is

$$\hat{\beta}_2 \pm t_{.025} s_{\hat{\beta}_2}$$

$$4.4343 \pm 2.3065(\underline{\hspace{2cm}})$$

or

$$4.4343 \pm \underline{\hspace{2cm}}$$

With 95% confidence we estimate that on the average, profit will increase $443,430 \pm 189,250$ or between _____ and _____ for an increase of $100,000 in advertising expenditure.

4. This same information can be utilized in testing an hypothesis concerning β_1 or β_2. For example, the test of the hypothesis $H_0: \beta_1 = 0$ versus $H_a: \beta_1 \neq 0$, is based upon the statistic

$$t = \frac{\hat{\beta}_1 - 0}{s_{\hat{\beta}_1}}$$

with $n - (k + 1)$ degrees of freedom. It can be shown that the square of a t-statistic with ν degrees of freedom has an F distribution with one numerator degree of freedom and ν denominator degrees of freedom. Therefore a two-tailed t-test is equivalent to a one-tailed F-test and the user may choose to use one test or the other.

5. *Example:*

Refer to 12.3(9). Test the hypothesis $H_0: \beta_1 = 0$ against the alternative $H_a: \beta_1 \neq 0$ at the 5% level of significance.

Solution:

Collecting pertinent information we have

$$\hat{\beta}_1 = \underline{\hspace{2cm}} \qquad\qquad s_{\hat{\beta}_1} = \underline{\hspace{2cm}}$$

.2921; .1357

Using a t-statistic with 7 degrees of freedom, we would reject H_0 if $|t| > t_{.025} = \underline{\hspace{2cm}}$. For our problem,

2.365

$$t = \frac{\hat{\beta}_1 - 0}{s_{\hat{\beta}_1}} = \frac{(\underline{\hspace{1.5cm}})}{(\underline{\hspace{1.5cm}})} = \underline{\hspace{1.5cm}}$$

.2921; 2.1525
.1357

Hence there (is, is not) sufficient evidence to reject H_0.

is not

6. Had we used the F-statistic for testing in the previous example, the value of the F-statistic from the computer printout, given under the column headed F VALUE, is \underline{\hspace{2cm}}. This value is compared with a critical value of F with one numerator and 7 denominator degrees of freedom given as $F_{.05} = 5.59$. Again, we (would, would not) reject H_0. Notice that

4.6335

would not

$$t^2 = (2.1525)^2 = 4.6332 = F$$

and

$$t^2_{.025} = (2.365)^2 = 5.5932 = F_{.05}$$

within rounding errors. Hence when testing the hypothesis $H_0: \beta_i = 0$ against the two-tailed alternative $H_a: \beta_i \neq 0$, the F-test rejects H_0 whenever the t-test rejects H_0.

7. In testing $H_0: \beta_i = 0$ against the one-tailed alternative $H_a: \beta_i > 0$ (or $H_a: \beta_i < 0$), the t-statistic is easier to use than the F-statistic. In testing $H_0: \beta_i = 0$ against $H_a: \beta_i > 0$ at the α-level of significance, H_0 is rejected if $t > t_\alpha$. For the alternative $H_a: \beta_i < 0$, we reject H_0 if $t < -t_\alpha$.

12.5 The Problem of Correlated Estimates: Multicollinearity (12.6)

1. In a multiple regression problem, the regression coefficients are called *partial* regression coefficients, since they are determined in conjunction with other variables in the model and only partially determine the value

would not

straight line

larger

of y. Further, the values of these partial regression coefficients (would, would not) in general be the same as those found by using several simple linear regression models, each with one independent variable. Estimates of the partial regression coefficients are correlated with each other to the extent that the underlying independent variables share the same predictive information.

2. When two or more of the independent variables are highly correlated with each other, we are confronted with the problem of multicollinearity. Multicollinearity is the technical way of saying, for example, that if one is given pairs of values for two independent variables that are highly correlated with each other, the pairs of values will exhibit a strong linear relationship when plotted on graph paper. When the correlation is very high, the points will almost plot as a _____ _____. Hence we say that these variables are collinear, and, for all practical purposes, one is working with one independent variable. When this situation is repeated for several pairs of independent variables, we refer to the problem as one of multicollinearity.

3. When the independent variables included in a regression analysis are correlated among themselves, the values of the estimated β's in the model take into account the amount of shared and independent information available in the x's for estimating the response y. In this situation, individual tests of the regression coefficients are of little value. More information concerning the utility of the independent variables $x_1, x_2, \ldots, x_k$ in predicting y can be obtained by testing the hypothesis

$$H_0: \beta_1 = \beta_2 = \ldots = \beta_k = 0$$

A test of this hypothesis is given in Section 12.7.

4. Many investigators prefer to use a stepwise regression program which at each step adds an independent variable to the regression model only if its inclusion significantly reduces SSE below the value achieved without the variable included. In this way, the investigator can look at the stepwise decrease in SSE and assess the additional contribution of the independent variable just added, above and beyond the contribution of those variables already in the model.

5. Another problem sometimes results when a multiple regression problem involves time series data. When one or more important variables have been omitted from the model, the residuals $(y_i - \hat{y}_i)$ will not be independent. In fact, if these residuals are plotted over time, the plot will exhibit some systematic pattern. When this happens, the residuals are said to be autocorrelated or serially correlated. Serial correlation may cause serious underestimation of the true error variation, which in turn causes observed values of t- or F-statistics to be (smaller, larger) than they should be.

6. The potential problems of multicollinearity and serial correlation require that we exercise caution when interpreting the results of tests involving individual parameters appearing in the model.

Self-Correcting Exercises 12A

1. A chemical company interested in maximizing the output of a chemical process by selection of the reaction temperature recorded the following data where y is the yield in kilograms and x is the coded temperature.

y	7.5	8.8	12.5	11.1	9.5
x	-2	-1	0	1	2

It is necessary to fit the least-squares model

$$y = \beta_0 + \beta_1 x + \beta_2 x^2 + \epsilon$$

to this data.
a. Write down the normal equations for the data.
b. Solve the equations simultaneously to find the least-squares estimates for $\beta_0, \beta_1, \beta_2$.
c. Predict the yield, y, of the chemical process when the coded temperature is $x = 1$.
2. Refer to Exercise 1. The following computer output resulted when the data in Exercise 1 was processed using a multiple regression analysis computer program.

MULTIPLE R   .9014
R SQUARE   .8126
STD. ERROR OF EST.   1.1985

ANALYSIS OF VARIANCE

	DF	SUM OF SQUARES	MEAN SQUARE	F RATIO
REGRESSION	2	12.4554	6.2277	4.3360
RESIDUAL	2	2.8726	1.4363	

INDIVIDUAL ANALYSIS OF VARIABLES

VARIABLE	COEFFICIENT	STD. ERROR	F VALUE
(CONSTANT	11.4371)		
LINEAR	.6300	.3790	2.7633
QUADRATIC	-.7786	.3203	5.9086

a. Is the quadratic regression coefficient significant at the 5% level of significance?
b. Find a 95% confidence interval for β_1, the linear regression coefficient.
c. Find a 95% confidence interval for β_2, the quadratic regression coefficient.
3. Refer to problems 2 and 3 of Self-Correcting Exercises 11A. Consider the

problem of using both the number of cotton bolls (x_1) and the number of damaging insects (x_2) to predict the cotton yield. The collected data are

y	x_1	x_2
21	5.5	11
17	2.8	20
20	4.7	13
19	4.3	12
15	3.7	18
23	6.1	10
20	4.5	12

a. Using the model

$$y_i = \beta_0 + \beta_1(x_{1i} - \bar{x}_1) + \beta_2(x_{2i} - \bar{x}_2) + \epsilon_i$$

find the least-squares predictor line by solving the necessary normal equations.

b. Using the least-squares prediction equation, predict the cotton yield when 16 damaging insects are found and the number of cotton bolls is 4.4.

4. Refer to Exercise 3. The following computer output resulted when the data in Exercise 3 was processed using a multiple regression analysis computer program.

MULTIPLE R   .9009
R SQUARE   .8115
STD. ERROR OF EST.   1.3972

ANALYSIS OF VARIANCE

	DF	SUM OF SQUARES	MEAN SQUARE	F RATIO
REGRESSION	2	33.6201	16.8101	8.6112
RESIDUAL	4	7.8084	1.9521	

INDIVIDUAL ANALYSIS OF VARIABLES

VARIABLE	COEFFICIENT	STD. ERROR	F VALUE
(CONSTANT	18.7934)		
BOLLS	1.0948	1.2729	.7411
INSECTS	-.3245	.3687	.7746

a. Test for a significant partial regression of y on x_1. That is, test H_0: $\beta_1 = 0$, in the presence of the second variable, x_2.
b. Test for a significant partial regression of y on x_2.
c. Find a 90% confidence interval for β_1.

12.6 Measuring the Goodness of Fit of the Model (12.7)

1. In the case of simple linear regression, we showed that the total sum of squares given by

$$\text{Total } SS = \sum_{i=1}^{n} (y_i - \bar{y})^2$$

could be partitioned into two parts, referred to as SSR and SSE. The sum of squares due to regression is given by

$$SSR = \sum_{i=1}^{n} (\hat{y}_i - \bar{y})^2$$

while the sum of squares for error is given by

$$SSE = \sum_{i=1}^{n} (y_i - \hat{y}_i)^2$$

Therefore

Total SS = _____ + _____ SSR; SSE

2. Notice that SSR measures the difference between the regression predictor $\hat{y}_i$ which uses the information contained in the independent variables $x_1, x_2, \ldots, x_k$ and the simple predictor $\bar{y}$ which uses none of the information from the independent variables. Large values of SSR indicate that the independent variables (are, are not) contributing strongly to the estimation of y. SSR is said to be that part of the total variation explained by the auxiliary variables $x_1, x_2, \ldots, x_k$.   are

3. The quantity SSE measures the discrepancy between observed and _____ values of y using the linear predictor $\hat{y}_i$. A (small, large) value of SSE indicates that the predictor is accurately reproducing the observed values of y.   predicted / small

4. The additivity property of the sums of squares is important for two reasons.
   a. Only two of the quantities need to be calculated since the third can be obtained by _____.   subtraction
   b. SSR can be used to measure the joint contribution of the independent variables $x_1, x_2, \ldots, x_k$ in the prediction of y.
   The quantity R^2 defined as

$$R^2 = \frac{SSR}{\text{Total } SS}$$

determination

is called the coefficient of _____. R^2, which measures the proportion of the variation in y explained by the independent variables, takes values in the interval

0; 1

$$\underline{\hspace{2cm}} \leqslant R^2 \leqslant \underline{\hspace{2cm}}$$

r

R, the positive square root of R^2, called the multiple correlation coefficient, is the multivariate counterpart of the simple correlation coefficient, _____. R measures the correlation between the response y and that portion of the model involving the predictor variables $x_1, x_2, \ldots, x_k$.

5. Refer to 12.3(9) concerning corporate profits, capital investments, and advertising expenditures. The first three lines of the computer printout of the multiple regression program using profit as the response of interest are produced below.

MULTIPLE R	.9072
R SQUARE	.8230
STD. ERROR OF EST.	3.3033

.9072; strong

6. The first line of output gives the value of the multiple correlation coefficient, R. For this example, the multiple correlation between corporate profits and the variables capital investments and advertising expenditures is _____, indicating the existence of a fairly (weak, strong) correlation (since the maximum value of R is one).

82.3

random variation

7. The second line in the printout gives the value of the coefficient of determination, R^2. In this example, $R^2 = .8230$, indicating that (_____)% of the total variation in y can be explained by the model. The remaining 19.7% of the variation is due to _____ _____ as well as the omission of other possible predictor variables that could have been included in the model.

8. The third line gives the value of s, the estimate of σ. The value of s is the positive square root of s^2 where

$$s^2 = \frac{SSE}{n - (k + 1)}$$

3.3033

and $(k + 1)$ is the number of parameters in the model. For this example, $s = $ _____. The value of s is utilized in two important ways.

a. The quantity s (or s^2) may be required for use in calculating a test statistic or confidence interval other than those given in the printout.

b. The quantity s can be used to detect errors in computation or unusual observations called outliers. When the deviations between the observed and predicted values of y have been calculated, approximately 95% of these deviations should be within the interval $(-2s, 2s)$ and almost all should lie within the interval (_____, _____). Values lying outside these limits are suspect, and indicate that all corresponding input values could be checked, or minimally, that the suspect observations should be checked for validity.

$-3s; 3s$

12.7 Testing the Utility of the Regression Model (12.8)

1. The partitioning of the total sum of squares into component parts is called an _____ _____ _____. In regression analysis,

analysis of variance

$$\text{Total } SS = \underline{\hspace{1cm}} + \underline{\hspace{1cm}}$$

$SSR; SSE$

where SSR represents the variation of the linear predictor $\hat{y}_i$ from the simple predictor $\bar{y}$, while SSE represents the variation between the observed and the predicted values of y. These sums of squares divided by their appropriate degrees of freedom can be used to test the effectiveness of the regression model in predicting y.

2. In testing the hypothesis $H_0: \beta_1 = \beta_2 = \ldots = \beta_k = 0$, that the predictor variables contribute no information in the prediction of y, the quantities

$$MSR = \frac{SSR}{k}$$

and

$$MSE = \frac{SSE}{n - (k + 1)}$$

are independent estimates of σ^2 when H_0 is true. When H_0 is false, and one or more of the predictor variables do contribute information in predicting y, MSR will in general be significantly (smaller, larger) than MSE. Therefore, the hypothesis $H_0: \beta_1 = \beta_2 = \ldots = \beta_k = 0$ is tested using the statistic

larger

$$F = \frac{MSR}{MSE}$$

which has an F distribution with $\nu_1 = $ _____ and $\nu_2 = $ _____ degrees of freedom, respectively, when H_0 is true. The null hypothesis is rejected at the α-level of significance only if the observed value of F exceeds F_α, a right-tailed critical value of F with $\nu_1 = k$ and $\nu_2 = n - (k + 1)$ degrees of freedom.

$k; n - (k + 1)$

3. The results of the test for a significant regression appear in the section

of the computer printout labeled ANALYSIS OF VARIANCE. For the data in 12.3(9) relating profits to capital investment and advertising expenditures, this portion of the printout appears as follows.

ANALYSIS OF VARIANCE

	DF	SUM OF SQUARES	MEAN SQUARE	F RATIO
REGRESSION	2	355.2151	177.6076	16.2762
RESIDUAL	7	76.3849	10.9121	

4. The entries in the third column give the quantities SSR and SSE where SSE corresponds to the entry in the line labeled RESIDUAL. The entries in the MEAN SQUARE column are found by dividing the SUM OF SQUARES entry by its respective degrees of freedom in the DF column. For this example, $SSR = 355.2151$, $SSE = 76.3849$, and

2; 177.6076

$$MSR = 355.2151/\underline{\hspace{2cm}} = \underline{\hspace{2cm}}$$

7; 10.9121

$$MSE = 76.3849/\underline{\hspace{2cm}} = \underline{\hspace{2cm}}$$

In testing for significant regression,

177.6076

$$F = \frac{MSR}{MSE} = \frac{(\underline{\hspace{1.5cm}})}{10.9121} = 16.2762$$

2; 7

4.74
reject

with $\nu_1 = \underline{\hspace{2cm}}$ and $\nu_2 = \underline{\hspace{2cm}}$ degrees of freedom. This calculated value appears in the column labeled F RATIO. The .05 critical value of F based upon $\nu_1 = 2$ and $\nu_2 = 7$ degrees of freedom is $F_{.05} = \underline{\hspace{2cm}}$. Since the observed value of F exceeds 4.74, we (reject, do not reject) the null hypothesis

$$H_0: \beta_1 = \beta_2 = 0$$

and conclude that at least one predictor variable contributes significant information for the prediction of y.

Self-Correcting Exercises 12B

1. Refer to Exercises 1 and 2, Self-Correcting Exercises 12A.
   a. Test the hypothesis $H_0: \beta_1 = \beta_2 = 0$ at the $\alpha = .05$ level of significance. Is there a significant regression of y on x_1 and x_2?
   b. What percentage of the variation in y is accounted for by the auxiliary variables x and x^2?
2. Refer to Exercises 3 and 4, Self-Correcting Exercises 12A.
   a. What percentage of the variation in y is accounted for by the auxiliary variables x_1 and x_2?

b. Test the hypothesis $H_0: \beta_1 = \beta_2 = 0$ at the $\alpha = .05$ level of significance. Is there a significant regression of y on x_1 and x_2?

c. Refer to Exercise 1, Self-Correcting Exercises 11D. What additional percentage of the variation in y is accounted for by adding x_2, the number of damaging insects present, to the model using x_1, the average number of bolls per quadrate?

d. Can you explain the results of part b, as well as parts a and b, Exercise 4, Self-Correcting Exercises 12A, in the light of the results of part c?

12.8 Some Comments on Formulating a Model (12.10)

1. Predictor variables are classified as being either quantitative or _____. A _____ independent variable is a variable that can take values corresponding to the points on the real line. If a variable is not quantitative, it is said to be _____.

   qualitative
   quantitative

   qualitative

2. Variables such as advertising expenditure, number or age of employees, per unit production cost, and number of delivery trucks are examples of _____ independent variables while geographic region, plant site, and kind of stock are examples of _____ independent variables.

   quantitative
   qualitative

3. The intensity setting of an independent variable is called a _____. The levels of a quantitative independent variable correspond to the values that the variable may assume. For example, if an experimenter interested in maximizing the output of a chemical process observed the process when the temperature was set at $100°F$, $200°F$ and $300°F$, respectively, the independent variable "temperature" was observed at _____ levels. The levels of a qualitative independent variable are defined by describing them. For example, the independent variable "occupational groups" might be described as white-collar workers, blue-collar workers, service workers, and farm workers. If all four groups were included in an investigation, the qualitative variable "occupational groups" would be taken to have _____ levels. Similarly, if an investigation were to be conducted in three regions, the qualitative variable "regions" would have _____ levels.

   level

   three

   four

   three

4. It is necessary to differentiate between quantitative and qualitative variables to be included in a regression analysis because these variables are entered into a regression model in different ways. Quantitative variables, in general, are entered directly into a regression equation, while qualitative variables are entered through the use of dummy variables which in effect produce different response curves at each setting of the qualitative independent variable.

5. When two or more quantitative independent variables appear in a regression model, the resulting response function produces a graph called a _____ _____ in three or higher dimensions. These graphs become difficult to produce when three or more independent variables are included

   response
   surface

in the model. Graphs of some simple response surfaces involving two in-dependent variables are given in Chapter 12 of your text.

6. A model involving quantitative variables is said to be a first-order linear model if each independent variable appears in the model with power _____. The model

one

$$y = \beta_0 + \beta_1 x_1 + \beta_2 x_2 + \ldots + \beta_k x_k + \epsilon$$

where ϵ is a random error term is a first-order model involving k indepen-dent variables, since the model is linear in each x. The graph of a first-order model is a response plane, which means that the surface is "flat," but has some directional tilt with respect to its axes.

7. Second-order linear models in k quantitative predictor variables include all the terms in a first-order model, all crossproduct terms, $x_1 x_2, x_1 x_3, \ldots,$ $x_{k-1} x_k$ and all pure quadratic terms $x_1^2, x_2^2, \ldots, x_k^2$. A second-order model involving two independent predictor variables is given as

$$y = \beta_0 + \beta_1 x_1 + \beta_2 x_2 + \beta_3 x_1^2 + \beta_4 x_1 x_2 + \beta_5 x_2^2 + \epsilon$$

where ϵ is a random error term. The quadratic terms involving x_1^2 and

curvature

x_2^2 allow for _____ while the crossproduct or interaction term $x_1 x_2$ allows for warping or twisting of the response surface.

8. Qualitative variables are entered into a regression model using dummy variables. For each independent qualitative variable in the model, the number of dummy variables required is one less than the number of levels associated with that qualitative variable. The following example will dem-onstrate how this technique is implemented.

9. *Example:*

An investigator is interested in predicting the strength of particle board (y) as a function of the size of the particles (x_1) and two types of bonding compounds. If the basic response is expected to be a quadratic function of particle size, write a linear model that incorporates the qualitative variable "bonding compound" into the predictor equation.

Solution:

The basic response equation for a specific type of bonding compound would be

$$y = \beta_0 + \beta_1 x_1 + \beta_2 x_1^2 + \epsilon$$

Since the qualitative variable "bonding compound" is at two levels, one dummy variable is needed to incorporate this variable into the model. Define the dummy variable x_2 as follows:

$$x_2 = 1 \text{ if bonding compound 2}$$

0

$$x_2 = \underline{\hspace{2cm}} \text{ if not}$$

The expanded model would now be written as

$$y = \beta_0 + \beta_1 x_1 + \beta_2 x_1^2 + \beta_3 x_2 + \beta_4 x_1 x_2 + \beta_5 x_1^2 x_2 + \epsilon$$

a. When $x_2 = 0$, the response has been measured using bonding compound 1 and the resulting equation is

$$y = \beta_0 + \beta_1 \underline{\hspace{2cm}} + \beta_2 \underline{\hspace{2cm}} + \epsilon \qquad\qquad x_1 ; x_1^2$$

b. When $x_2 = 1$, the response has been measured using bonding compound 2 and the resulting equation is

$$y = (\beta_0 + \beta_3) + (\underline{\hspace{2cm}}) x_1 + (\beta_2 + \beta_5) x_1^2 + \epsilon \qquad\qquad \beta_1 + \beta_4$$

c. The use of the dummy variable x_2 has allowed us to simultaneously describe two quadratic response curves for each of the two bonding compounds. Notice that β_3, β_4, and β_5 measure the differences between the intercepts, the linear components, and the quadratic components, respectively, for the two bonding compounds.

d. Had another bonding compound been included in the investigation, x_3, a second dummy variable, would be defined as

$$x_3 = \underline{\hspace{2cm}} \text{ if bonding compound 3} \qquad\qquad 1$$

$$x_3 = \underline{\hspace{2cm}} \text{ if not} \qquad\qquad 0$$

and the model would be expanded to include the terms $x_3, x_1 x_3$, and $\underline{\hspace{2cm}}$ to produce in effect a third quadratic response curve for compound 3. $\qquad\qquad x_1^2 x_3$

10. The formulation of the model is perhaps the most important aspect of a regression analysis since the fit of the model will depend not only upon the independent variables included in the model, but also upon the way in which the variables are introduced into the model. If, for example, the response increases with some variable x, achieves a maximum, and then begins to decrease, both linear and quadratic terms in x should be included in the model. Failure to include a term in x^2 may cause the model to fit poorly and/or to fail in predicting the response y for all values of x. Accurate formulation of a model requires experience and a knowledge of the mechanism underlying the response of interest. The latter is sometimes achieved by running several exploratory investigations, and combining this information within a more elaborate model.

Self-Correcting Exercises 12C

1. Graph the following polynomials in x:

a. $E(y) = 1 + x + x^2$

b. $E(y) = 1 - x + x^2$

c. $E(y) = 2 + 3x^2$

d. $E(y) = 2 - 3x^2$

2. Consider a situation in which the output (y) of an industrial plant is related to the number of individuals employed (x_1) and the area in which the plant is located. Define the following dummy variable:

$$x_2 = 1 \text{ if area } 2$$

$$x_2 = 0 \text{ if not}$$

Write a linear model relating output to x_1 and x_2 if we assume that the relationship between y and x_1 is linear for both areas.

3. Refer to problem 2. Suppose that three areas were involved in the experiment. Define the second dummy variable:

$$x_3 = 1 \text{ if area } 3$$

$$x_3 = 0 \text{ if not}$$

Write a linear model relating output to x_1, x_2, and x_3 if we assume again that the relationship between y and x_1 is linear for all areas.

4. Suppose, in problem 3, that an experiment is conducted and the following least-squares predictor equation is obtained (data are ficticious):

$$\hat{y} = 2 + x_1 + x_2 + 3x_1x_2 + 2x_3 + x_1x_3$$

Graph the three least-squares lines for the three areas, 1, 2, and 3.

12.9 Model Building: Testing Portions of a Model (12.11)

1. In previous sections we have presented procedures for testing the contribution of individual independent variables in predicting a response y, and the joint contribution of _____ the independent variables in the model in predicting y. Interpretation of the results of tests concerning individual parameters in the model was difficult because of the possible presence in the model of other independent variables contributing similar or perhaps identical information in the prediction of the response y.

2. In this section a more general version of the procedure for testing the joint contribution of a set of independent variables in predicting y is given.

all

The rationale in implementing this procedure is quite simple. A regression model utilizing all the independent variables of interest is fitted. To test the contribution of any group of these independent variables, a second model with these variables deleted is fitted and the _____ in the two sums of squares for error is found. This difference is used to assess the additional contribution of the deleted variables above and beyond the information contained in the variables that (were, were not) deleted from the model.

                                                difference

                                                were not

3. This procedure is formalized in the following way. Suppose we have k predictor variables, $x_1, x_2, \ldots, x_g, x_{g+1}, \ldots, x_k$ available for predicting the response y. For the *complete* or full model,

$$E(y) = \beta_0 + \beta_1 x_1 + \ldots + \beta_g x_g + \beta_{g+1} x_{g+1} + \ldots + \beta_k x_k$$

Testing whether the variables $x_{g+1}, x_{g+2}, \ldots, x_k$ contribute additional significant information in predicting y is equivalent to testing the hypothesis

$$H_0 : \beta_{g+1} = \beta_{g+2} = \ldots = \beta_k = \underline{\hspace{2cm}}$$

                                                0

When H_0 is true, the reduced model is

$$E(y) = \beta_0 + \beta_1 x_1 + \ldots + \beta_g x_g$$

Whenever terms are added to the model, SSE is _____. Hence, if SSE_1 is the sum of squares for error with the *reduced* model involving g predictor variables and SSE_2 is the sum of squares for error with the *complete* model, then SSE_1 will be (smaller, larger) than SSE_2. If the difference $(SSE_1 - SSE_2)$ is significantly large, we conclude that at least one of the variables $x_{g+1}, x_{g+2}, \ldots, x_k$ contributes significant information beyond that contained in the variables $x_1, x_2, \ldots, x_g$.

                                                reduced

                                                larger

4. In testing the hypothesis $H_0 : \beta_{g+1} = \beta_{g+2} = \ldots = \beta_k = 0$ we use the test statistic given as

$$F = \frac{MS(\text{Drop})}{MSE_2}$$

where $MS(\text{Drop}) = (SSE_1 - SSE_2)/(k - g)$ and $MSE_2 = SSE_2/(\underline{\hspace{1cm}})$. When the random errors are normally and independently distributed with mean zero and variance σ^2, this statistic has an F distribution with $v_1 = (\underline{\hspace{1cm}})$ and $v_2 = (\underline{\hspace{1cm}})$ degrees of freedom. If H_0 is false and one or more of the variables tested contribute significant additional information in predicting y, then $MS(\text{Drop})$ would tend to be significantly larger than MSE_2. Therefore the test is one-tailed, and H_0 is rejected if the observed value of F exceeds a (left, right)-tailed critical value of F.

                                                $n - k - 1$

                                                $k - g; n - k - 1$

                                                right

5. *Example:*

Refer to 12.3(9) in which the complete model was given as

$$y = \beta_0 + \beta_1 x_1 + \beta_2 x_2 + \epsilon$$

Test the hypothesis $H_0: \beta_2 = 0$ versus $H_a: \beta_2 \neq 0$ using the testing procedure presented in this section.

Solution:

a. If H_0 is true, the reduced model is

$$y = \beta_0 + \beta_1 x_1 + \epsilon$$

the simple linear regression model discussed in Chapter 11. The computer printout of the regression analysis using this model appears below.

MULTIPLE R   .2161
R SQUARE   .0467
STD. ERROR OF EST.   7.1715

ANALYSIS OF VARIANCE

	DF	SUM OF SQUARES	MEAN SQUARE	F RATIO
REGRESSION	1	20.1604	20.1604	.3920
RESIDUAL	8	411.4396	51.4300	

INDIVIDUAL ANALYSIS OF VARIABLES

VARIABLE	COEFFICIENT	STD. ERROR	F VALUE
(CONSTANT	12.1894)		
CAPITAL	-.1493	.2385	.3920

In the ANALYSIS OF VARIANCE portion of the printout, we find that the sum of squares for error in the reduced model is $SSE_1 =$ _____ with _____ degrees of freedom.

b. From the regression analysis printout using the complete model, we find $SSE_2 =$ _____ and $MSE_2 =$ _____ with 7 degrees of freedom. Then

$$SS(\text{Drop}) = SSE_1 - SSE_2$$

$$= 411.4396 - 76.3849$$

$$= \underline{\hspace{2cm}}$$

411.4396
8

76.3849; 10.9121

335.0547

with 8 – 7 = 1 degree of freedom. In this case $MS(\text{Drop})$ is the same as $SS(\text{Drop})$.

c. To test $H_0: \beta_2 = 0$ versus $H_a: \beta_2 \neq 0$, calculate

$$F = \frac{MS(\text{Drop})}{MSE_2}$$

$$= \frac{335.0547}{10.9121}$$

$$= \underline{\hspace{2cm}}$$ 30.7048

With $\alpha = .05$, the critical value of F based with $\nu_1 = 1$ and $\nu_2 = 7$ degrees of freedom is $F_{.05} = \underline{\hspace{2cm}}$. Hence, we reject H_0 and conclude   5.59

that the variable advertising expenditure (<u>does</u>, <u>does not</u>) contribute   does

significant information in predicting y.

d. In comparing this result with the F VALUE for this same test in the INDIVIDUAL ANALYSIS OF VARIABLES portion of the computer print-out for the complete model, we find the value $F = \underline{\hspace{2cm}}$ which,   30.7081

within rounding errors, is the same as the value we have just computed.

6. The general testing procedure just described is more appropriately applied when we are interested in assessing the joint contribution of several vari-ables in predicting a response y. It is worth pointing out, however, that in applying this procedure to one predictor variable as we have done, we produced results identical to those obtained directly from the computer printout for the complete model. This should help clarify and unify the test procedure which produces the F VALUE in the INDIVIDUAL ANALYSIS OF VARIABLES portion of the computer printout.

Self-Correcting Exercise 12D

1. A particular savings and loan corporation is interested in determining how well the amount of money in family savings accounts can be predicted using the three independent variables, annual income, number in the family unit, and area in which the family lives. Suppose that there are two specific areas of interest to the corporation. The following data were collected, where

y = amount in all savings accounts

x_1 = annual income

x_2 = number in family unit

x_3 = 0 if area 1; 1 if not

y	x_1	x_2	x_3
0.5	19.2	3	0
0.3	23.8	6	0
1.3	28.6	5	0
0.2	15.4	4	0
5.4	30.5	3	1
1.3	20.3	2	1
12.8	34.7	2	1
1.5	25.2	4	1
0.5	18.6	3	1
15.2	45.8	2	1

The following computer printout resulted when the data was processed using a multiple regression computer program.

MULTIPLE R	.8715
R SQUARE	.7595
STD. ERROR OF EST.	3.3394

ANALYSIS OF VARIANCE

	DF	SUM OF SQUARES	MEAN SQUARE	F RATIO
REGRESSION	3	211.2888	70.4296	6.3155
RESIDUAL	6	66.9112	11.1519	

INDIVIDUAL ANALYSIS OF VARIABLES

VARIABLE	COEFFICIENT	STD. ERROR	F VALUE
(CONSTANT	.1239)		
X1	.4325	.1381	9.8129
X2	-1.9902	1.1578	2.9547
X3	-0.6013	3.1509	.0364

a. Test the hypothesis $H_0: \beta_1 = \beta_2 = \beta_3 = 0$ at the $\alpha = .05$ level of significance. Is there a significant regression of y on x_1, x_2 and x_3?

b. Suppose that we are interested in testing the hypothesis that the variables x_2 and x_3 contribute no information for the prediction of y. To do so, we fit the reduced model, $y = \beta_0 + \beta_1 x_1 + \epsilon$ and obtain $SSE = 120.2263$. Test the above hypothesis in terms of the regression coefficients at the $\alpha = .05$ level of significance.

c. Refer to part b. Suppose instead that we hypothesize that the variable x_1 contributes no information. The reduced model $y = \beta_0 + \beta_2 x_2 + \beta_3 x_3 + \epsilon$ and $SSE = 176.3438$. Test the hypothesis $H_0: \beta_1 = 0$ at the $\alpha = .05$ level. Does the value of the test statistic appear in the computer printout?

d. Interpret the results of part b and part c in terms of their practical significance.

12.10 Summary (12.14)

1. Multiple regression analysis is an extension of _____ linear regression analysis to accommodate situations in which the response y is a function of a number of independent variables $x_1, x_2, \ldots, x_k$. The procedures given in Chapter 11 for the simple linear model have analogies in the multiple regression model. Hence, any simple linear regression problem (can, cannot) be analyzed using multiple regression techniques.	simple can
2. Although identical in concept, simple and multiple regression analysis differ in two important aspects. Simple linear regression analysis can be done (with, without) the use of a computer; for multiple regression analysis, this is generally not the case. However, multiple regression analysis programs are available at most computing facilities. Secondly, very few real life situations (can, cannot) be adequately described by a simple linear regression model. Multiple regression analysis provides greater utility and latitude in data analysis by allowing the inclusion of k independent variables, $x_1, x_2, \ldots, x_k$ in the regression model.	without can

Exercises

1. A manufacturer, concerned about the number of defective items being produced within his plant, recorded the number of defective items produced on a given day (y) by each of 10 machine operators, recording also the average output per hour (x_1) for each operator and the time from the last machine servicing (x_2) in weeks. The data were

y	x_1	x_2
13	20	3
1	15	2
11	23	1.5
2	10	4
20	30	1
15	21	3.5
27	38	0
5	18	2
26	24	5
1	16	1.5

a. Find the least-squares prediction equation using the model

$$y_i = \beta_0 + \beta_1 x_{1i} + \beta_2 x_{2i} + \epsilon_i$$

b. If $SSE = 2.1054$, complete the analysis of variance as indicated in the computer printout in 12.7(3). Is there a significant regression of y on x_1 and x_2?

c. Calculate the value of R^2 and comment upon the usefulness of x_1 and x_2 in predicting y.

2. In an experiment to investigate the relationship between y, the amount of

metal corrosion and x, the length of time the metal is exposed to the action of soil acids, the following data were collected.

x (weeks)	1	2	3	4	5	6	7	8
y (%)	.1	.3	.5	.8	1.2	1.8	2.5	3.4

a. Plot these data points in an effort to identify the relationship between x and y.
b. Fit the polynomial model

$$y_i = \beta_0 + \beta_1 x + \beta_2 x^2 + \epsilon$$

to these data using the normal equations.

3. The following computer output resulted when the second-degree polynomial model was fitted to the data in Exercise 2.

MULTIPLE R	.9992
R SQUARE	.9985
STD. ERROR OF EST.	.0530

ANALYSIS OF VARIANCE

	DF	SUM OF SQUARES	MEAN SQUARE	F RATIO
REGRESSION	2	9.4210	4.7105	1682.3214
RESIDUAL	5	.0140	.0028	

INDIVIDUAL ANALYSIS OF VARIABLES

VARIABLE	COEFFICIENT	STD. ERROR	F VALUE
(CONSTANT	.1964)		
X	-.1000	.0377	7.0359
X SQ.	.0619	.0041	227.9363

a. What percent of the total variation is explained by the quadratic regression of y on x and x^2?
b. Is the regression of y on x and x^2 significant at the $\alpha = .05$ level?
c. Is the linear regression coefficient significant at the 5% level of significance?
d. Is the quadratic regression coefficient significant at the 5% level of significance?
e. When the model $y_i = \beta_0 + \beta_1 x_i^2 + \epsilon_i$ (linear term omitted) was fitted to the data, $R^2 = .9964$ and $SSR = 9.4012$. What could you say about the contribution of the linear term in x to explaining the total variation? Should the linear term be deleted from the prediction model?

4. In a study to examine the relationship between the time required to complete a construction project and several pertinent independent variables, an analyst compiled a list of four variables that might be useful in predicting the time to completion. These four variables were size of the contract (in \$1000 units) (x_1), number of workdays adversely affected by the weather (x_2), number of subcontractors involved in the project (x_4), and a variable (x_3) that measured the presence or absence of a workers' strike during the construction. In particular,

$$x_3 = 0 \text{ if no strike}$$

$$x_3 = 1 \text{ if strike}$$

Fifteen contruction projects were randomly chosen, and each of the four variables as well as the time to completion were measured. The results are given below.

y	x_1	x_2	x_3	x_4
29	60	7	0	7
15	80	10	0	8
60	100	8	1	10
10	50	14	0	5
70	200	12	1	11
15	50	4	0	3
75	500	15	1	12
30	75	5	0	6
45	750	10	0	10
90	1200	20	1	12
7	70	5	0	3
21	80	3	0	6
28	300	8	0	8
50	2600	14	1	13
30	110	7	0	4

a. Write a linear model appropriate for using the independent variables x_1, x_2, x_3 and x_4 for predicting y.
b. Using a multiple regression computer program, find the least-squares estimates of the regression coefficients, β_i.
c. Use the prediction equation to predict the number of days to completion for a \$55,000 contract involving 7 subcontractors. Assume that there will be 6 workdays adversely affected by weather and that there will be no workers' strike.
5. Refer to problem 4. A multiple regression computer program was run to fit the model

$$y = \beta_0 + \beta_1 x_1 + \beta_2 x_2 + \beta_3 x_3 + \beta_4 x_4 + \epsilon$$

and the following output resulted.

MULTIPLE R   .9204
R SQUARE   .8471
STD. ERROR OF EST.   11.8450

ANALYSIS OF VARIANCE

	DF	SUM OF SQUARES	MEAN SQUARE	F RATIO
REGRESSION	4	7770.2972	1942.5743	13.8455
RESIDUAL	10	1403.0362	140.3036	

INDIVIDUAL ANALYSIS OF VARIABLES

VARIABLE	COEFFICIENT	STD. ERROR	F VALUE
(CONSTANT	-1.5887)		
X1	- .00784	.00623	1.5846
X2	.67533	.99978	.4563
X3	28.01342	11.37143	6.0688
X4	3.4889	1.93516	3.2504

Give a complete analysis of the printout and interpret your results.

6. Refer to problems 4 and 5. For the fifteen contruction projects used in the analysis, calculate the predicted values, $\hat{y}_i$, and the residuals, $(y_i - \hat{y}_i)$. Use the information given in the computer printout to verify that each of these residuals lies within the interval $(-2s, 2s)$.

7. Refer to problems 4 and 5. The analyst suspects that the variables x_1 and x_2 are not contributing significantly to the prediction. Test the null hypothesis $H_0: \beta_1 = \beta_2 = 0$, at the $\alpha = .05$ level. Note that when the reduced model is fitted, $SSE = 1656.6729$.

8. Refer to problems 4 and 5. Test the null hypothesis $H_0: \beta_3 = \beta_4 = 0$ at the $\alpha = .05$ level. When the reduced model is fitted $SSE = 4697.117$. Interpret the results of problems 7 and 8 in terms of the variables necessary to predict time to completion.

Chapter 13

THE ANALYSIS OF VARIANCE

13.1 Introduction (13.1)

1. Many investigations are directed toward establishing the effect of one or more variables upon a response of interest. The measurements that we record can be considered dependent variables while their modifiers, be they treatments, classifications, or other factors, can be considered to be _____ variables.

   independent

2. A dependent variable, or response, is assumed to be a function of one or more independent variables which are varied and controlled by the experimenter during the investigation. These independent variables may be either qualitative or _____.

   quantitative

3. In an investigation to determine how the amount of money invested in advertising affects the total sales, the _____ variable would be total sales and the independent variable would be _____ _____. In this case, the response is _____ and the independent variable is _____.

   dependent
   advertising
   expenditures; quantitative
   quantitative

4. In the investigation of the relative merits of three sales training programs aimed at increasing the actual value of sales made, the _____ or response variable would be value of sales and the _____ variable would be training programs. In this study, the independent variable is (quantitative, qualitative).

   dependent
   independent

   qualitative

5. In this chapter we will use an analysis of variation as a statistical technique for evaluating the relationship between one or more independent variables and a response, y.

13.2 The Analysis of Variance (13.2)

1. To perform an analysis of variance is to _____ the total variation in a set of measurements given by

   partition

$$\sum_{i=1}^{n} \text{\underline{\hspace{2cm}}}$$

   $(y_i - \bar{y})^2$

305

into portions associated with each independent variable in the experiment as well as a remainder attributable to random error.

2. The objective of the analysis of variance is to locate important _____ variables in a study and to determine how they interact and affect the _____, or _____ variable.

3. The total variation in a set of measurements,

$$\sum_{i=1}^{n} (y_i - \bar{y})^2$$

that is to be partitioned in an analysis of variance is called the total _____ of _____ of _____, and is symbolized by Total _____.

4. The total sum of squares of deviations can be partitioned into the sum of squares for _____, denoted _____, and the sum of squares for error, denoted _____.

5. When the sum of squares for treatments is divided by its degrees of freedom, the resulting quotient is called the _____ _____ for treatments, symbolized by _____. Similarly, the division of the sum of squares for error by its degrees of freedom is called the _____ square for _____, symbolized by _____.

6. When there is no difference in the dependent or response variable at different settings of the independent or treatment variable, both _____ and _____ estimate the same quantity, _____, the variance of the _____ error.

7. This suggests that we use the ratio _____, which follows the _____ distribution, to test the null hypothesis that the different settings of the _____ variable have the _____ effect on the dependent variable. If the null hypothesis is false, _____ will tend to be larger than _____.

8. *Example:*

The impurities in parts per million were recorded for five batches of chemicals supplied by two different suppliers.

	Supplier 1	*Supplier 2*
	25	32
	33	43
	42	38
	27	47
	36	30
Sum	163	190
	$\bar{y}_1 =$ _____	$\bar{y}_2 =$ _____

It will save confusion if we use two subscripts to identify each observation rather than just one. Let y_{ij} designate the *j*th observation recorded in the

Margin answers (left column):

independent

response; dependent

sum; squares; deviations
SS

treatments; *SST*
SSE

mean square
MST
mean
error; *MSE*

MSE
MST; σ^2
experimental
MST/MSE; *F*

independent; same
MST
MSE

32.6; 38

*i*th sample. When *i* is either 1 or 2, *j* can take the values 1, 2, 3, 4, or 5. We could then write:

Supplier 1	Supplier 2
$y_{11} = 25$	$y_{21} = 32$
$y_{12} = 33$	$y_{22} = 43$
$y_{13} = 42$	$y_{23} = 38$
$y_{14} = 27$	$y_{24} = 47$
$y_{15} = 36$	$y_{25} = 30$

a. *Total Variation:* Let us consider all measurements as one large sample of size 10. Then the total of the 10 measurements is

$$\sum_{i=1}^{2} \sum_{j=1}^{5} y_{ij} = \underline{\qquad}$$

353

and the grand mean is

$$\bar{y} = \frac{353}{10} = \underline{\qquad}$$

35.3

The total variation then is given by

$$\text{total } SS = \sum_i \sum_j (y_{ij} - \bar{y})^2$$

$$= \sum_i \sum_j y_{ij}^2 - \frac{\left(\sum_i \sum_j y_{ij}\right)^2}{10}$$

$$= 12929 - \frac{(353)^2}{10}$$

$$= 12929 - 12460.9$$

$$= \underline{\qquad}$$

468.1

This total sum of squares will be partitioned into two sources of variation: treatments and error.

b. *Treatment Variation:* Recall that the variance of a sample mean is _____, where *n* is the sample size and σ^2 is the variance in the population sampled. Suppose we had 2 samples of size *n* from the same population. Then, if $\bar{y}$ is the grand mean, the sample variance of the means,

σ^2/n

$$s_{\bar{y}}^2 = \frac{\sum\limits_{i=1}^{2} (\bar{y}_i - \bar{y})^2}{2 - 1}$$

estimates σ^2/n with $2 - 1 = 1$ degrees of freedom. If we multiply the sum of squares,

$$\sum\limits_{i=1}^{2} (\bar{y}_i - \bar{y})^2$$

by n, we return this sum of squares to a "per measurement" basis. Then, the sum of squares due to variation of the treatment means will be

$$n \sum\limits_{i=1}^{2} (\bar{y}_i - \bar{y})^2$$

If the sample sizes are not equal, then the sum of squares for treatments is

$$SST = \sum\limits_{i=1}^{2} n_i(\bar{y}_i - \bar{y})^2$$

As the difference between the sample means increases, this sum of

increases

squares _____. For the problem at hand,

$$\bar{y}_1 = 32.6, \bar{y}_2 = 38, \bar{y} = 35.3$$

$$n_1 = n_2 = 5$$

Therefore the treatment sum of squares is

$$SST = n_1(\bar{y}_1 - \bar{y})^2 + n_2(\bar{y}_2 - \bar{y})^2$$

32.6; 35.3; 38; 35.3

$$= 5(\underline{\quad} - \underline{\quad})^2 + 5(\underline{\quad} - \underline{\quad})^2$$

$$= 5(-2.7)^2 + 5(2.7)^2$$

$$= 5(7.29) + 5(7.29)$$

$$= 2(36.45)$$

72.9

$$= \underline{\quad}$$

c. *Error Variation:* If the two samples have come from the same population, we can use a pooled estimate of error given by

$$SSE = \sum_{j=1}^{5} (y_{1j} - \bar{y}_1)^2 + \sum_{j=1}^{5} (y_{2j} - \bar{y}_2)^2$$

For sample 1,

$$\sum_{j=1}^{5} (y_{1j} - \bar{y}_1)^2 = \sum_{j=1}^{5} y_{1j}^2 - \frac{(\Sigma y_{1j})^2}{5}$$

$$= 5503 - \frac{(\underline{\hspace{1cm}})^2}{5} \qquad\qquad 163$$

$$= 5503 - 5313.8$$

$$= \underline{\hspace{2cm}} \qquad\qquad 189.2$$

For sample 2,

$$\sum_{j=1}^{5} (y_{2j} - \bar{y}_2)^2 = \sum_{j=1}^{5} y_{2j}^2 - \frac{(\Sigma y_{2j})^2}{5}$$

$$= 7426 - \frac{(\underline{\hspace{1cm}})^2}{5} \qquad\qquad 190$$

$$= 7426 - 7220$$

$$= \underline{\hspace{2cm}} \qquad\qquad 206$$

It follows that

$$SSE = \underline{\hspace{2cm}} + \underline{\hspace{2cm}} \qquad\qquad 189.2;\ 206$$

$$= \underline{\hspace{2cm}} \qquad\qquad 395.2$$

d. Therefore we see directly that

$$SST = 72.9$$

$$SSE = 395.2$$

Total $SS = 468.1$

and that

$$\text{Total } SS = SST + SSE$$

e. Since simpler calculational forms will be given presently, we defer further calculations until then.

The F-Test and the Analysis of Variance

9. For the two-sample problem discussed in Example 8, the t-statistic is readily available for testing the hypothesis

$$H_0: \mu_1 = \mu_2$$

versus

$$H_a: \mu_1 \neq \mu_2$$

The two-sample unpaired t-test requires that both samples can be drawn randomly and independently from two normal populations with the same (equal) variances. With these assumptions we can construct an F-statistic, which is the ratio of two variances, to test these same hypotheses. The advantage to using the F-statistic is that the procedure can be easily extended for testing the equality of several population means.

σ^2

10. If $H_0: \mu_1 = \mu_2$ is true, then the partitioning of the total sum of squares provides us with two estimators of the common variance, _____.

SSE

a. $\quad MSE = \dfrac{\overline{}}{n_1 + n_2 - 2}$

where

$$SSE = \sum_{j=1}^{n_1} (y_{1j} - \bar{y}_1)^2 + \sum_{j=1}^{n_2} (y_{2j} - \bar{y}_2)^2$$

with $n_1 + n_2 - 2$ degrees of freedom.

SST

b. $\quad MST = \dfrac{\overline{}}{2 - 1}$

where

$$SST = n_1 (\bar{y}_1 - \bar{y})^2 + n_2 (\bar{y}_2 - \bar{y})^2$$

with $2 - 1$ degrees of freedom.
Therefore, when H_0 is true,

$$F = \underline{\hspace{2cm}}$$

MST/MSE

has an F distribution with $v_1 = \underline{\hspace{1.5cm}}$ and $v_2 = \underline{\hspace{1.5cm}}$ degrees of freedom.

$1; n_1 + n_2 - 2$

If H_0 is false and $H_a: \mu_1 \neq \mu_2$ is true, this fact should be reflected in *MST*, and *MST* should in probability be larger than $\underline{\hspace{1.5cm}}$. This implies that if H_0 is false, the F-ratio,

MSE

$$F = \frac{MST}{MSE}$$

will be too large. Hence, the rejection region for this test will consist of all values of F satisfying

$$F \underline{\hspace{1.5cm}} F_\alpha$$

$>$

where F_α is the right-tailed critical value of F having an area of α to its right based upon $v_1 = 1$ and $v_2 = n_1 + n_2 - 2$ degrees of freedom.

11. *Example:*

For the data in Example 8, test the null hypothesis $H_0: \mu_1 = \mu_2$ versus $H_a: \mu_1 \neq \mu_2$ at the $\alpha = .05$ level of significance.

Solution:

Let us first gather the information that we have compiled so far.

$$SST = \underline{\hspace{1.5cm}} \qquad MST = \frac{72.9}{1} = \underline{\hspace{1.5cm}}$$

$72.9; 72.9$

$$SSE = \underline{\hspace{1.5cm}} \qquad MSE = \frac{395.2}{8} = \underline{\hspace{1.5cm}}$$

$395.2; 49.4$

a. $H_0: \mu_1 = \mu_2$ versus $H_a: \mu_1 \neq \mu_2$

b. The test statistic will be

$$F = \frac{MST}{MSE}$$

with $v_1 = \underline{\hspace{1.5cm}}$ and $v_2 = \underline{\hspace{1.5cm}}$ degrees of freedom.

$1; 8$

c. Rejection region: For $\alpha = .05$, a right-tailed value of F with $v_1 = 1$ and $v_2 = 8$ degrees of freedom is $F_{.05} = \underline{\hspace{1.5cm}}$. Therefore, we shall reject H_0 if $F > \underline{\hspace{1.5cm}}$.

5.32
5.32

d. Using the sample values,

$$F = \frac{72.9}{49.4} = \underline{\hspace{1.5cm}}$$

1.48

less; do not reject

$$\frac{(\bar{y}_1 - \bar{y}_2) - 0}{\sqrt{s^2 \left(\frac{1}{n_1} + \frac{1}{n_2} \right)}}$$

-1.215

2.306

F

$F_{.05}$

1

Since this value is (<u>less</u>, greater) than 5.32, we (reject, <u>do not reject</u>) the null hypothesis. There is not sufficient evidence to indicate that $\mu_1 \neq \mu_2$.

Had we tested using the t-statistic,

$$t = \underline{\hspace{2cm}}$$

with $n_1 + n_2 - 2 = 8$ degrees of freedom, the calculated value would have been

$$t = \frac{32.6 - 38.0}{\sqrt{49.4 \left(\frac{1}{5} + \frac{1}{5} \right)}}$$

$$= \frac{-5.4}{\sqrt{19.76}}$$

$$= \frac{-5.4}{4.445} = \underline{\hspace{2cm}}$$

The rejection region would have consisted of values of t such that $|t| > t_{.025} = \underline{\hspace{2cm}}$. Hence, we would not have rejected $H_0 : \mu_1 = \mu_2$ even had we used the t-statistic. Noting that

$$t^2 = (-1.215)^2 = 1.48 = \underline{\hspace{2cm}}$$

and

$$(t_{.025})^2 = (2.306)^2 = 5.32 = \underline{\hspace{2cm}}$$

the results should be identical. This verifies the fact that an F with $\nu_1 = 1$ and ν_2 degrees of freedom is the same as t^2 with ν_2 degrees of freedom; further, $F_\alpha = t^2_{\alpha/2}$ *only if* $\nu_1 = \underline{\hspace{2cm}}$.

13.3 A Comparison of More Than Two Means (13.3)

1. In extending the problem of testing for a significant difference between two population means to one of testing for significant differences among several population means, let us consider an experiment run in a completely randomized design. A completely randomized design involves the selection of randomly drawn independent samples from each of p populations.

2. Consider an experiment designed to compare the quality of the resulting color when identical pieces of material are dyed in one of three chemical formulations for red dye. Fifteen pieces of identical material have been randomly divided into three groups of five pieces of cloth, and each group randomly assigned to be dyed using one of the three dye formulations. Since each piece of cloth is dyed or 'treated' by using one of the formulations, the dyes in statistical terminology are called _____. This type of randomization procedure is called a _____ _____ design.

treatments
completely
randomized

3. The completely randomized design involves one independent variable, treatments. In this design, the total sum of squares of deviations of the measurements about their overall mean can be partitioned into two parts.

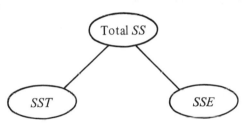

4. In generalizing the two-sample problem, we will now assume that *the p samples have been randomly and independently drawn from p normal populations with means* $\mu_1, \mu_2, \ldots, \mu_p$ *respectively, and with common variance,* σ^2.

5. Let T_i and $\bar{T}_i$ be the sum and the mean of the n_i observations in the sample from the *i*th population, with $n = n_1 + n_2 + \ldots + n_p$ being the total number of observations. Then

a. $$\text{Total } SS = \sum_{i=1}^{p} \sum_{j=1}^{n_i} \underline{\hspace{2cm}}$$

               $(y_{ij} - \bar{y})^2$

with _____ degrees of freedom.

               $n - 1$

b. $$SST = \sum_{i=1}^{p} \underline{\hspace{1.5cm}}$$

               $n_i(\bar{T}_i - \bar{y})^2$

with _____ degrees of freedom.

               $p - 1$

c. $$SSE = \sum_{i=1}^{p} \sum_{j=1}^{n_i} \underline{\hspace{2cm}}$$

               $(y_{ij} - \bar{T}_i)^2$

$n - p$

$SST; SSE$

$n - 1$

correction; mean

y_{ij}

SST

observations

Total SS

degrees of freedom

with $\displaystyle\sum_{i=1}^{p} (n_i - 1) = n_1 + n_2 + \ldots + n_p - p =$ _____ degrees of freedom. Not only does

$$\text{Total } SS = \text{_____} + \text{_____}$$

but the same relationship holds for the degrees of freedom associated with each sum of squares.

$$\text{d.f.}_{\text{Total}} = \text{d.f.}_{\text{Treatments}} + \text{d.f.}_{\text{Error}}$$

since

$$(p - 1) + (n - p) = \text{_____}$$

6. The formulas actually used for computing these sums of squares are given below. Let CM, the _____ for the _____, be given by

$$CM = \frac{\left(\displaystyle\sum_{i=1}^{p} \sum_{j=1}^{n_i} \text{\_\_\_\_}\right)^2}{n} = \frac{(\text{Grand Total})^2}{n}$$

Then

a. Total $SS = \displaystyle\sum_{i=1}^{p} \sum_{j=1}^{n_i} y_{ij}^2 - CM.$

b. $SST = \displaystyle\sum_{i=1}^{p} \frac{T_i^2}{n_i} - CM.$

c. $SSE = \text{Total } SS - \text{_____}$

Notice that in SST, the square of each treatment total is divided by the number of _____ in that total. Although SSE can be computed directly as a pooled sum of squared deviations within each sample, it is computationally easier to use the additivity property, $SST + SSE$ = _____.

7. The mean squares for treatments and error are calculated by dividing each sum of squares by its _____ _____ _____.

Therefore

$$s^2 = MSE = \frac{SSE}{\underline{\hspace{2cm}}}$$

$n - p$

and

$$MST = \frac{SST}{\underline{\hspace{2cm}}}$$

$p - 1$

If all samples are from the same normal population, then MST and MSE are each _____ of the population variance, σ^2. In this case, the statistic

estimators

$$F = \frac{MST}{MSE}$$

has an _____ distribution with $\nu_1 = p - 1$ and $\nu_2 = n - p$ degrees of freedom.

F

8. Consider testing the hypothesis $H_0: \mu_1 = \mu_2 = \ldots = \mu_p$ against the alternative that at least one mean is different from at least one other. *If H_0 is true, then all samples have come from the same normal population* and the statistic

$$F = \frac{MST}{MSE}$$

has the F distribution specified in Number 7 above. However, if H_a is true (at least one of the equalities does not hold), then

$$MST = \frac{1}{p-1} [n_1(\bar{T}_1 - \bar{y})^2 + n_2(\bar{T}_2 - \bar{y})^2 + \ldots + n_p(\bar{T}_p - \bar{y})^2]$$

will in probability be _____ than MSE and F will tend to be _____ than expected. Hence, H_0 will be rejected for _____ values of F; that is, we shall reject H_0 if

larger
larger
large

$$F > F_\alpha$$

with $\nu_1 = p - 1$ and $\nu_2 = n - p$ degrees of freedom.

9. *Example:*
Do the following data provide sufficient evidence to indicate a difference in the means of the three underlying treatment populations?

	Treatment		
	1	*2*	*3*
	3	7	5
	4	9	4
	2	8	5
		7	
9; 31; 14 T_i	______	______	______ Total = 54
n_i	3	4	3 $n = 10$
$\bar{T}_i$	3	7.75	4.67

Solution:

A. We must first partition the total variation into *SST* and *SSE*.

54; 291.6

$$CM = \frac{(______)^2}{10} = \frac{2916}{10} = ______$$

1. Total $SS = 3^2 + 4^2 + 2^2 + \ldots + 5^2 + 4^2 + 5^2 - 291.6$

338 $= ______ - 291.6$

46.4 $= ______$

9; 31; 14

2. $$SST = \frac{(______)^2}{3} + \frac{(______)^2}{4} + \frac{(______)^2}{3} - 291.6$$

$$= \frac{81}{3} + \frac{961}{4} + \frac{196}{3} - 291.6$$

$$= 27 + 240.25 + 65.33 - 291.6$$

332.58 $= ______ - 291.6$

40.98 $= ______$

46.4; 40.98

3. $SSE = ______ - ______$

5.42 $= ______$

4. To compute the degrees of freedom we need the values $n = 10$, $p = 3$.
2 Hence, *SST* has $p - 1 =$ ______ degrees of freedom while *SSE* has
7 $n - p =$ ______ degrees of freedom. The resulting mean squares are

$$MST = \frac{40.98}{2} = \underline{\hspace{2cm}}$$

20.49

$$MSE = \frac{5.42}{7} = \underline{\hspace{2cm}}$$

0.77

B. We are now in a position to test $H_0: \mu_1 = \mu_2 = \mu_3$ versus H_a: at least _____ equality does not hold.

one

   1. The test statistic is

$$F = \frac{MST}{MSE}$$

     with $\nu_1 = $ _____ and $\nu_2 = $ _____ degrees of freedom.

2; 7

   2. The rejection region: Using $\alpha = .05$, we shall reject H_0 if $F > F_{.05}$ = _____.

4.74

   3. For our example,

$$F = \frac{20.49}{0.77} = \underline{\hspace{2cm}}$$

26.61

     which is (greater, less) than $F_{.05} = 4.74$. Hence we _____ H_0 and conclude that there is evidence to indicate a difference in means for the three treatment populations at the $\alpha = .05$ level of significance.

greater; reject

10. *Example:*

In the investigation of a citizens committee's complaint about the availability of fire protection within the county, the distance in miles to the nearest fire station was measured for each of 5 randomly selected residences in each of four areas.

		Areas		
	1	*2*	*3*	*4*
	7	1	7	4
	5	4	9	6
	5	3	8	3
	6	4	7	7
	8	5	8	5
T_i	_____	_____	_____	_____ Total = 112
n_i	5	5	5	5 $n = 20$
$\bar{T}_i$	6.2	3.4	7.8	5.0

31; 17; 39; 25

Do these data provide sufficient evidence to indicate a difference in mean distance for the four areas at the $\alpha = .01$ level of significance?

Solution:

A. We first partition the total sum of squares into SST and SSE to find MST and MSE.

112; 627.2

$$CM = \frac{(\underline{\hspace{2cm}})^2}{20} = \frac{12544}{20} = \underline{\hspace{2cm}}$$

1. Total $SS = 7^2 + 5^2 + \ldots + 7^2 + 5^2 - CM$

708

$$= \underline{\hspace{2cm}} - 627.2$$

80.80

$$= \underline{\hspace{2cm}}$$

5

3396

2. $$SST = \frac{31^2 + 17^2 + 39^2 + 25^2}{\underline{\hspace{1.5cm}}} - CM$$

$$= \frac{\overline{\hspace{2cm}}}{5} - CM$$

679.2

$$= \underline{\hspace{2cm}} - 627.2$$

52.00

$$= \underline{\hspace{2cm}}$$

80.80; 52.00

3. $$SSE = \underline{\hspace{2cm}} - \underline{\hspace{2cm}}$$

28.80

$$= \underline{\hspace{2cm}}$$

4. With $n = 20$ and $p = 4$,

17.33

$$MST = \frac{SST}{p-1} = \frac{52.00}{3} = \underline{\hspace{2cm}}$$

1.80

$$MSE = \frac{SSE}{n-p} = \frac{28.80}{16} = \underline{\hspace{2cm}}$$

B. Test of the null hypothesis.

$\mu_1 = \mu_2 = \mu_3 = \mu_4$

1. $$H_0: \underline{\hspace{3cm}}$$

H_a: At least one equality does not hold.

2. Test statistic:

MST/MSE

$$F = \underline{\hspace{2cm}}$$

3; 16

with $\nu_1 = \underline{\hspace{2cm}}$ and $\nu_2 = \underline{\hspace{2cm}}$ degrees of freedom.

3. Rejection region: Reject H_0 if $F > F_{.01} =$ _____ .

                                                                         5.29

4. For these data,

$$F = \frac{17.33}{1.80} = \underline{\hspace{2cm}}$$

                                                                         9.63

Hence, we _____ H_0 and conclude that there is sufficient evidence to indicate a difference in mean distance for the four areas.

                                                                         reject

13.4 An Analysis of Variance Table for a Completely Randomized Design (13.4)

1. The results of an analysis of variance are usually displayed in an analysis of variance (*ANOVA* or *AOV*) summary table. The table displays the sources of variation together with the degrees of freedom, sums of squares, and mean squares for each source listed in the table. The results of the *F*-test appear as a final entry in the table.

    For a completely randomized design, the *ANOVA* table is as follows:

ANOVA				
Source	*d.f.*	*SS*	*MS*	*F*
Treatments	$p-1$	*SST*	*MST*	_____
Error	$n-p$	*SSE*	*MSE*	
Total	_____	_____		

                                    MST/MSE

                                    $n-1$; Total *SS*

This display gives all the pertinent information leading to the *F* test and further emphasizes the fact that the degrees of freedom and the sums of squares are both additive.

2. *Example:*
Display the results of the analysis of the data in Example 13.3(9).
Solution:
We need but collect the results that we have for this example.

ANOVA				
Source	*d.f.*	*SS*	*MS*	*F*
Treatments	_____	40.98	20.49	_____
Error	_____	5.42	_____	
Total	_____	_____		

                                    2; 26.61

                                    7; 0.77

                                    9; 46.40

3. *Example:*
Display the results of the analysis of the data in Example 13.3(10).
Solution:
Since the term "treatments" is a general way of describing the differences in the sampled populations, we can replace the term "treatments" in this problem by the more descriptive word "areas."

ANOVA				
Source	d.f.	SS	MS	F
Areas	3	52.00	_____	_____
Error	16	28.80	_____	
Total	_____	_____		

17.33; 9.63
1.80

19; 80.80

13.5 Estimation for the Completely Randomized Design (13.5)

1. In using the analysis of variance F-test to test for significant differences among a group of population means, an experimenter can conclude that either (a) there is no difference among the _____ or (b) at least one mean is _____ _____ at least one other. In the second case, (b), an experimenter may wish to proceed with estimating the value of a treatment mean or with estimating the difference between two treatment means.

means
different from

2. Since the analysis of variance requires that all samples be drawn from _____ populations with a _____ variance, confidence intervals can be constructed using the t-statistic based upon $n - p$ degrees of freedom. Hence for estimating the ith treatment mean with a $(1 - \alpha)$ 100% confidence interval, use

normal; common

$$\bar{T}_i \pm t_{\alpha/2} \sqrt{\frac{MSE}{n_i}}$$

where $\bar{T}_i$ is the ith sample mean, n_i the number of observations in the ith sample, and MSE the pooled estimate of σ^2 from the analysis of variance with _____ degrees of freedom. Note that this formula is equivalent to

$n - p$

$$\bar{T}_i \pm t_{\alpha/2} \frac{s}{\sqrt{n_i}}$$

$\sqrt{MSE}$

since $s =$ _____

3. To estimate the difference between two population means with a $(1 - \alpha)$ 100% confidence interval, use

$$(\bar{T}_i - \bar{T}_j) \pm t_{\alpha/2} \sqrt{MSE \left(\frac{1}{n_i} + \frac{1}{n_j} \right)}$$

which is equivalent to

$$(\bar{T}_i - \bar{T}_j) \pm \underline{\hspace{2cm}}$$

$$t_{\alpha/2} s \sqrt{\frac{1}{n_i} + \frac{1}{n_j}}$$

4. *Example:*
   Refer to 13.3, Example 10. Estimate the mean distance to the nearest fire station for those residents in Area 1 with a 95% confidence interval.
   Solution:
   a. The required information can be obtained from Example 10, and 13.4, Example 3.

   $\bar{T}_1 = 6.2$ d.f. = _____   16

   $n_1 = 5$

   $MSE = $ _____ $t_{.025} = $ _____   1.80; 2.120

   b. Therefore the estimate is given by

   $$\underline{\hspace{2cm}} \pm \underline{\hspace{2cm}} \sqrt{\frac{1.80}{5}}$$ 6.2; 2.120

   $6.2 \pm 2.120 (\underline{\hspace{2cm}})$ .6

   $6.2 \pm$ _____ miles   1.27

   or

   $$\underline{\hspace{2cm}} < \mu_1 < \underline{\hspace{2cm}}$$ 4.93; 7.47

5. *Example:*
   Refer to 13.3, Example 10. Construct a 95% confidence interval for $\mu_1 - \mu_3$.
   Solution:
   a. Collecting pertinent information,

   $\bar{T}_1 = $ _____ $\bar{T}_3 = $ _____ $MSE = 1.80$ 6.2; 7.8

   $n_1 = 5$ $n_3 = 5$ d.f. = 16

   With 16 degrees of freedom, $t_{.025} = 2.120$.
   b. The confidence interval estimate is found using

   $$(\bar{T}_1 - \bar{T}_3) \pm t_{.025} \sqrt{MSE \left(\frac{1}{n_1} + \frac{1}{n_3} \right)}$$

which when evaluated becomes

$$(6.2 - 7.8) \pm 2.120 \sqrt{1.80\left(\frac{1}{5} + \frac{1}{5}\right)}$$

.849

1.8

$$- 1.6 \pm 2.120 \; (\underline{\hspace{2cm}})$$

$$- 1.6 \pm \underline{\hspace{2cm}}$$

-3.4; 0.2

c. Hence with 95% confidence, we estimate that $\mu_1 - \mu_3$ lies between
   _____ and _____ miles. Notice that even though
   we found that at least one area differed from at least one other area in
   average distance to the nearest firehouse using the analysis of variance
   F-test, we would conclude that there appears to be no difference between areas 1 and 3.

Self-Correcting Exercises 13A

1. In the evaluation of three rations fed to chickens grown for market, the
   dressed weights of five chickens fed from birth on one of the three rations
   were recorded.

	Rations		
	1	*2*	*3*
	7.1	4.9	6.7
	6.2	6.6	6.0
	7.0	6.8	7.3
	5.6	4.6	6.2
	6.4	5.3	7.1
Total	32.3	28.2	33.3
Averages	6.46	5.64	6.66

   a. Do the data present sufficient evidence to indicate a difference in the
      mean growth for the three rations as measured by the dressed weights?
   b. Estimate the difference in mean weight for rations 2 and 3 with a 95%
      confidence interval.
2. The length of time required for new employees to assemble a device was
   compared for four training periods of different lengths. Four employees
   were randomly assigned to each training group, but two were eliminated
   during the experiment due to sickness. The length of time to assemble the
   device was recorded for each employee in the experiment.

	Training Periods (in hours)			
	0.5	*1.0*	*1.5*	*2.0*
	8	9	4	4
	14	7	6	7
	9	5	7	5
	12		8	
Total	43	21	25	16
Mean	10.75	7.00	6.25	5.33

a. Do the data present sufficient evidence to indicate a difference in mean time to assemble the device for the four different lengths of instructional time?

b. Estimate the difference in mean time to assemble the device for training periods of 1 hour and 2 hours with 95% confidence.

c. Estimate the difference in mean time to assemble the device for training periods of 1 and 1.5 hours, with 95% confidence.

13.6 A Randomized Block Design (13.6)

1. The randomized block design is a natural extension of the _____ _____ experiment. Its purpose is to increase the _____ in the design by making comparisons between treatments within relatively homogeneous blocks of experimental material.

   paired difference; information

2. The randomized block design for p treatments and b blocks assumes blocks of relatively homogeneous material with each block containing _____ experimental units. Each treatment is applied to one experimental unit in each block. Consequently, the number of observations for a given treatment for the entire experiment will equal _____. Thus, for the randomized block design, $n_1 = n_2 = \ldots = n_p = b$. A randomized block design for $p = 3$ treatments and $b = 4$ blocks is shown below. Denote the treatments as T_1, T_2, and T_3.

   p

   b

Blocks

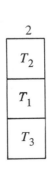
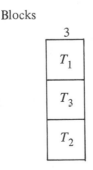

1 2 3 4

T_3	T_2	T_1	T_3
T_1	T_1	T_3	T_2
T_2	T_3	T_2	T_1

bp

treatments

blocks; treatments

The total number of observations for a randomized block design with *b* blocks and *p* treatments is *n* = _____.

3. The word "randomized" means that the _____ are randomly distributed over the experimental units within each block.

4. The randomized block design involves two independent variables: _____ and _____. For an experiment run in a randomized block design, the total variation can now be partitioned into three sources of variation; blocks (*B*), treatments (*T*), and error (*E*).

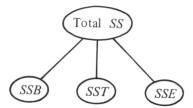

5. Randomized block designs prove to be very useful in business and economics. Many investigations involve human subjects which exhibit a large subject-to-subject variability.

block

a. By using a subject as a "_____" and having each subject receive all the treatments in a random order, treatment comparisons made within subjects would exhibit less variation than treatment comparisons made between subjects.

b. Since every subject receives each treatment in some random order, a _____ number of subjects would be required in a randomized block design than in a completely randomized design.

smaller

13.7 The Analysis of Variance for a Randomized Block Design (13.7)

1. In partitioning the sums of squares for an experiment run in a randomized block design with *b* blocks and *p* treatments, the calculational formulas for Total *SS* and *SST* remain the same except that now every treatment total will contain exactly *b* measurements and the total number of observations will be *n* = *pb*. Hence,

$$CM = \frac{\left(\sum\limits_{i=1}^{p}\sum\limits_{j=1}^{b} y_{ij}\right)^2}{pb} = \frac{(\text{Grand Total})^2}{pb}$$

$$\text{Total } SS = \sum_{i=1}^{p}\sum_{j=1}^{b} y_{ij}^2 - CM$$

$b - 1$

$(b - 1)(p - 1)$

When H_0 is true, this statistic has an F distribution with $v_1 =$ _____ and $v_2 =$ _____ degrees of freedom. H_0 is rejected if $F > F_\alpha$, where F_α is an α-level critical value of F with $(b - 1)$ and $(b - 1)(p - 1)$ degrees of freedom.

A significant test of block means provides a method of assessing the efficiency of the experimenter's blocking procedure, since if

MSB

$$F = \frac{(\underline{\hspace{2cm}})}{MSE}$$

increased

is significant, the experimenter has _____ the available information in the experiment by blocking, and would certainly use this same technique in subsequent experiments. In business and economics where subjects are often used as blocks, a nonsignificant test of block means should not be taken as a license to discontinue blocking in subsequent experiments involving different subjects, since the next group of subjects selected for participation could exhibit strong subject-to-subject variability and provide a highly significant test of blocks.

4. *Example:*

The readability of four different styles of textbook types was compared using a speed-reading test. The amount of reading material was identical for all four type styles. The sample material for each of the four type styles was read in random order by each of five readers in order to eliminate the natural variation in reading speed between readers. The length of time to completion of reading was needed. Thus, each reader corresponds to a

block

_____ and comparisons of the four styles were made within readers. Do the data present evidence of a difference in mean reading times for the four type styles?

| Type Style | Readers | | | | | Totals | Means |
	1	2	3	4	5		
1	15	18	13	21	15	82	16.40
2	19	19	16	22	15	91	18.20
3	13	20	14	21	16	84	16.80
4	11	18	12	17	12	70	14.00
Totals	58	75	55	81	58	327	
Means	14.50	18.75	13.75	20.25	14.50		

Solution:

Before analyzing these data, it should be pointed out that the order in which the type style was presented was randomized for each reader. The data layout presented *does not* represent the order of presentation for each reader.

and $\quad SST = \dfrac{\displaystyle\sum_{i=1}^{p} T_i^2}{b} - CM$

The calculation of SSB follows the same pattern as the calculation of SST, namely, square each block total; sum the squares of each total; divide by p, the number of observations per total; and subtract the correction for the mean. If $B_1, B_2, \ldots, B_b$ represent the block totals, then

$$SSB = \dfrac{(B_1^2 + B_2^2 + \ldots + B_b^2)}{p} - CM$$

Using the additivity of the sums of squares, we can find SSE by subtraction.

$$SSE = \text{Total } SS - \underline{\hspace{2cm}} - \underline{\hspace{2cm}}$$
$\qquad\qquad\qquad\qquad\qquad\qquad\qquad\qquad\qquad$ *SSB; SST*

2. The analysis of variance table for a completely randomized block design with b blocks and p treatments follows.

Source	d.f.	SS	MS	
		ANOVA		
Blocks	_____	SSB	$SSB/(b-1)$	$(b-1)$
Treatments	_____	SST	$SST/(p-1)$	$(p-1)$
Error	_____	SSE	$SSE/(b-1)(p-1)$	$(b-1)(p-1)$
Total	$bp-1$	Total SS		

Using text notation $bp = n$, $bp - 1 = \underline{\hspace{2cm}}$ and $(b-1)(p-1)$ $\qquad$ *n - 1*
$= bp - b - p + 1$.

To test the null hypothesis: "there is no difference in treatment means," we use

$$F = \underline{\hspace{2cm}}$$
$\qquad\qquad\qquad\qquad\qquad\qquad\qquad\qquad\qquad$ *MST/MSE*

which has an F distribution with $v_1 = \underline{\hspace{2cm}}$ and $v_2 = \underline{\hspace{2cm}}$ $\qquad$ *p - 1; (p - 1)(b - 1)*
degrees of freedom when H_0 is true. If H_0 is false, the statistic will tend to be larger than expected; hence we would reject H_0 if

$$F > F_\alpha$$

3. Although a test of H_0: "there is no difference in block means" is not always required, we can test this hypothesis using

$$F = \underline{\hspace{2cm}}$$
$\qquad\qquad\qquad\qquad\qquad\qquad\qquad\qquad\qquad$ *MSB/MSE*

A. *Partitioning the Sums of Squares*

$$CM = \frac{(\text{Total})^2}{bp} = \frac{(\underline{\hspace{2cm}})^2}{20} = 5346.45$$

327

$$\text{Total } SS = \sum_{i=1}^{p} \sum_{j=1}^{b} y_{ij}^2 - CM$$

$$= 5555 - \underline{\hspace{2cm}}$$

5346.45

$$= \underline{\hspace{2cm}}$$

208.55

For *SST* and *SSB* remember that the respective totals are each squared and divided by the number of measurements per total. Block totals contain $p = 4$ measurements and treatment totals contain $b = 5$ measurements.

$$SSB = \sum_{j=1}^{b} \frac{B_j^2}{p} - CM$$

$$= \frac{58^2 + 75^2 + \ldots + 58^2}{4} - \underline{\hspace{2cm}}$$

5346.45

$$= 5484.75 - 5346.45$$

$$= \underline{\hspace{2cm}}$$

138.30

$$SST = \sum_{i-1}^{p} \frac{T_i^2}{b} - CM$$

$$= \frac{82^2 + 91^2 + 84^2 + 70^2}{5} - \underline{\hspace{2cm}}$$

5346.45

$$= \underline{\hspace{2cm}} - 5346.45$$

5392.20

$$= \underline{\hspace{2cm}}$$

45.75

$$SSE = \text{Total } SS - \underline{\hspace{2cm}} - \underline{\hspace{2cm}}$$

$SSB; SST$

$$= 208.55 - 138.30 - 45.75$$

$$= \underline{\hspace{2cm}}$$

24.50

B. *The Analysis of Variance Table*

Complete the following *ANOVA* table.

34.58; 16.95
15.25; 7.48
2.04

		ANOVA		
Source	d.f.	SS	MS	F
Blocks	4	138.30	_____	_____
Treatments	3	45.75	_____	_____
Error	12	24.50	_____	
Total	19	208.55		

In testing H_0: "no difference in treatment means," we use

7.48

$$F = \frac{MST}{MSE} = \frac{15.25}{2.04} = \underline{\quad\quad}$$

3.49

With $\nu_1 = 3$ and $\nu_2 = 12$ degrees of freedom, $F_{.05} = \underline{\quad\quad}$. Hence we reject H_0 and conclude that there is a significant difference among the mean reading times for the four type styles.

5. Because we expected significant differences in mean reading times for the five readers, we used a randomized block design with the readers as blocks. Let us test whether these five readers have significantly different mean reading times. To test H_0: "no difference in block means," we use

16.95

$$F = \frac{MSB}{MSE} = \frac{34.58}{2.04} = \underline{\quad\quad}$$

3.26; reject

more

The 5% critical value of F with $\nu_1 = 4$ and $\nu_2 = 12$ degrees of freedom is $\underline{\quad\quad}$; hence we $\underline{\quad\quad}$ H_0 and conclude that the mean reading times for the five readers are significantly different. A significant test of blocks indicates that our experiment has been made (more, less) precise by using the randomized block design with readers as blocks.

13.8 Estimation for the Randomized Block Design (13.8)

1. Since a randomized block design involves two classifications, not only can we estimate differences in treatment means, but we can also estimate the differences in block means. In either situation we can construct a confidence interval estimate based upon Student's t distribution with

$(b - 1)(p - 1)$

$\underline{\quad\quad}$ degrees of freedom. Hence $(1 - \alpha)$ 100% confidence intervals would be found using

$$(\bar{T}_i - \bar{T}_j) \pm t_{\alpha/2} \sqrt{\frac{2\,MSE}{b}}$$

which is equivalent to _____ , and

$$(\bar{B}_i - \bar{B}_j) \pm t_{\alpha/2} \sqrt{\frac{2MSE}{p}}$$

which is equivalent to _____ .

$$(\bar{T}_i - \bar{T}_j) \pm t_{\alpha/2} s \sqrt{\frac{2}{b}}$$

$$(\bar{B}_i - \bar{B}_j) \pm t_{\alpha/2} s \sqrt{\frac{2}{p}}$$

2. *Example:*

Refer to 13.7, Example 4. Estimate the difference in mean reading time for type styles 1 and 2 with a 95% confidence interval.

Solution:

a. Pertinent information:

$$\bar{T}_1 = 16.40 \qquad\qquad MSE = \text{_____}$$

2.04

$$\bar{T}_2 = 18.20 \qquad\qquad \text{d.f.} = \text{_____}$$

12

$$b = 5 \qquad\qquad t_{.025} = \text{_____}$$

2.179

b. Using

$$(\bar{T}_1 - \bar{T}_2) \pm t_{.025} \sqrt{\frac{2MSE}{b}}$$

we have

$$(16.40 - 18.20) \pm 2.179 \sqrt{\frac{2(2.04)}{5}}$$

or _____ ± _____ minutes.

−1.80; 1.97

3. *Example:*

For the same problem, find a 95% confidence interval for the difference in mean reading time for readers 2 and 3.

Solution:

To use the estimator

$$(\bar{B}_2 - \bar{B}_3) \pm t_{.025} \sqrt{\frac{2MSE}{p}}$$

we need the following additional information: $\bar{B}_2 = $ _____ ,

18.75

$\bar{B}_3 = $ _____ , $p = 4$. Then

13.75

$$(18.75 - 13.75) \pm 2.179 \sqrt{\frac{2(2.04)}{4}}$$

simplifies to

5.00; 2.20

_____ ± _____ minutes.

4. Confidence interval estimates for block means or the difference between two block means are not always required nor are they always useful. Oftentimes, however, blocks constitute an important factor in many experiments. For example, if a marketing research survey investigating potential sales for four products is carried out in six areas, the areas would constitute blocks for this experiment, and the differences in mean sales between areas would be of strong interest to the experimenter.

Self-Correcting Exercises 13B

1. In a study where the objective was to investigate methods of reducing fatigue among employees whose job involved a monotonous assembly procedure, twelve randomly selected employees were asked to perform their usual job under each of three trial conditions. As a measure of fatigue, the experimenter used the total length of time in minutes of assembly line stoppages during a four-hour period for each trial condition. The data follow.

	Conditions		
Employee	*1*	*2*	*3*
1	31	22	26
2	20	15	23
3	26	21	18
4	21	12	22
5	12	16	18
6	13	19	23
7	18	7	16
8	15	9	12
9	21	11	26
10	15	15	19
11	11	14	21
12	18	11	21

a. Perform an analysis of variance for these data, testing whether there is a significant difference among the mean stoppage times for the three conditions.
b. Is there a significant difference in mean stoppage times for the twelve employees? Was the "blocking" effective?
c. Estimate the difference in mean stoppage time for conditions 2 and 3 with 95% confidence.

2. In a brand identification experiment involving four brands, 10 subjects in each of 5 geographic areas were asked to listen to an advertising jingle associated with each of the four brands and identify the brand through its jingle. The length of time in seconds until correct identification was averaged for the 10 people with the following results.

		Brands		
Areas	1	2	3	4
1	3.7	3.9	4.2	4.0
2	4.2	4.8	4.6	4.7
3	2.9	3.5	3.0	3.4
4	5.0	5.4	5.0	5.5
5	3.3	4.3	4.1	3.9

a. Present an analysis of variance for these data, testing for significant differences among mean recognition times for the four brands. Test for a significant difference among mean recognition times for the 5 areas.

b. Estimate the difference in mean recognition times for brands 2 and 4 with a 95% confidence interval.

c. Find a 95% confidence interval estimate for the difference in mean recognition times for areas 1 and 4.

13.9 Comments on Blocking and on the Analysis of Variance Assumptions (13.9, 13.10)

1. There are _____ major steps in designing an experiment that must be kept conceptually separate: | two

  a. The first step encompasses the decision about what _____ to include in the experiment and the number of _____ per _____. Each setting of the independent variable, or each combination of settings of the independent variables if there are more than one, corresponds to a single _____. | treatments / observations / treatment / treatment

  b. The second step involves the decision of how to apply the _____ to the experimental _____. Here is where the choice between a _____ and a randomized _____ design should be made. | treatments / units / completely randomized; block

2. Blocking produces a gain in _____ if and only if the between-block variation is _____ than the _____ _____ variation. But blocking also costs information because it _____ the number of degrees of freedom associated with the sum of squares for _____, denoted by _____. | information / larger; within-block / reduces / error; SSE

3. Hence, blocking is beneficial only if the gain in _____ due to blocking outweighs the loss due to reduced degrees of freedom associated with SSE. | information

4. In order to use analysis of variance techniques, we must be able to assume that the probability distribution of y for any given treatment-block condition is _____, with _____ variance σ^2, and that the random errors associated with any pair of observations are _____. | normal; common / independent

5. While we can never be certain that the assumptions are satisfied, it is important to make sure they are _____ in a particular experiment. When the assumptions cannot even be approximately satisfied, the statistician must resort to _____ procedures. | reasonable / nonparametric

13.10 Summary (13.11)

independent; random
error

completely randomized

randomized block

error
large

one

1. An analysis of variance is a method for partitioning the total variation exhibited by a set of observations into portions associated with a set of _____ variables and one associated with _____ _____ .

2. When treatments constitute the only independent variable in the experiment, we have a one-way classification of the data known as a _____ _____ design.

3. When treatments and blocks constitute the independent variables in the experiment, we have a two-way classification of the data known as a _____ _____ design.

4. Testing for significant differences among treatment means (or block means) is accomplished by using as a statistic the ratio of the treatment (or block) mean square to the _____ mean square. The ratio of mean squares has an F distribution. A significantly _____ sample value of F is sufficient evidence to indicate the existence of differences among the treatment (or block) means. Analysis of variance F-tests are *always* _____ -tailed tests.

Exercises

1. A large piece of cotton fabric was cut into 12 pieces and randomly partitioned into three groups of four. Three different chemicals designed to produce resistance to stain were applied to the units, one chemical for each group. A stain was applied (as uniformly as possible) over all $n = 12$ units and the intensity of the stain measured in terms of light reflection.
   a. What type of experimental design was employed?
   b. Perform an analysis of variance and construct the *ANOVA* table for the following data:

	Chemical	
1	*2*	*3*
12	14	9
8	9	7
9	11	9
6	10	5

   c. Do the data present sufficient evidence to indicate a difference in mean resistance to stain for the three chemicals?
   d. Give a 95% confidence interval for the difference in means for chemicals 1 and 2.
   e. Approximately how many observations per treatment would be required to estimate the difference in mean response for two chemicals correct to within 1.0?

f. Obtain SSE directly for the data of Exercise 1 by calculating the sums of squares of deviations within each of the three treatments and pooling. Compare with the value found using $SSE = $ Total $SS - SST$.

g. Give a 90% confidence interval for the mean stain intensity for chemical 2.

2. A substantial amount of variation was expected in the amount of stain applied to the experimental units of Exercise 1. It was decided that greater uniformity could be obtained by applying the stain three units at a time. A repetition of the experiment produced the following results:

	Chemical		
Application	1	2	3
1	12	15	9
2	9	13	9
3	7	12	7
4	10	15	9

a. Give the type of design.

b. Conduct an analysis of variance for the data.

c. Do the data provide sufficient evidence to indicate a difference among chemicals?

d. Give the formula for a $(1 - \alpha) 100\%$ confidence interval for the difference in a pair of chemical means. Calculate a 95% confidence interval for $(\mu_2 - \mu_3)$.

e. Approximately how many blocks (applications) would be required to estimate $(\mu_1 - \mu_2)$ correct to within .5?

f. We noted that the chemist suspected an uneven distribution of stain when simultaneously distributed over the 12 pieces of cloth. Do the data support this view? (That is, do the data present sufficient evidence to indicate a difference in mean response for applications?)

3. Daily lost production from three production lines in a manufacturing operation were recorded for a ten-day period.

	Line		
Day	1	2	3
1	15	11	8
2	9	9	6
3	6	8	4
4	7	6	5
5	16	13	9
6	23	25	14
7	12	9	7
8	10	12	9
9	12	10	11
10	16	10	9

a. Give the type of experiment.

b. Give the analysis of variance for the data.

   c. Do the data present sufficient evidence to indicate a difference in mean lost daily production for the three production lines?

   d. Do the data provide sufficient evidence to indicate a difference in mean daily lost production between days?

   e. Find a 95% confidence interval for the difference in mean loss of production for lines 1 and 3.

4. Twenty college graduates selected by a large corporation were randomly separated into four equal groups and subjected to three months of executive training. A slightly different training program was administered to each group. At the end of the three-month period, progress of the participants was measured by a specially designed examination. The exam scores are shown below (one participant in group three dropped out of the training program).

		Group		
1	2	3	4
112	111	140	101
92	129	121	116
124	102	130	105
89	136	106	126
97	99		119

   a. Give the type of design which appears appropriate.

   b. Conduct an analysis of variance for the data.

   c. Do the data present sufficient evidence to indicate a difference in mean response on the examination for the four training programs?

   d. Find a 95% confidence interval for the difference in mean response on the exam for groups 1 and 2.

   e. How could one employ blocking to increase the information in this problem? Under what circumstances might a blocking design applied to this problem fail to achieve the objective of the experiment?

5. The Graduate Record Examination scores were recorded for students admitted to three different graduate programs in a university.

	Graduate Programs	
1	2	3
532	670	502
601	590	607
548	640	549
619	710	524
509		542
627		
690		

   a. Do these data provide sufficient evidence to indicate a difference in mean level of achievement on the GRE for applicants admitted to the three programs?

b. Find a 90% confidence interval for the difference in mean GRE scores for programs 1 and 2.

6. An experiment was conducted to compare the gasoline mileage using four different gasoline additives. To eliminate the effect of the type of automobile used, the experiment was blocked on automobiles. Five different automobiles were employed with each automobile using four different tankfuls of gasoline, each with a different additive. Each set of four measured runs by one type of automobile tended to represent a rather homogeneous set of measurements and was considered a block. The data, in miles per gallon, is shown below for each type of automobile and each gasoline additive.

	Additive			
Automobile	1	2	3	4
A	28	19	28	35
B	16	14	20	20
C	31	28	22	33
D	26	16	27	24
E	11	16	19	20

a. Give the analysis of variance for the data.

b. Do the data present sufficient evidence to indicate a difference in average gasoline mileage capability for the four gasoline additives?

c. Do the data present sufficient evidence to indicate a difference in average gasoline mileage capability among the automobiles? Was blocking desirable?

Chapter 14

ELEMENTS OF TIME SERIES ANALYSIS

14.1 Introduction (14.1)

1. The businessman is constantly faced with variables whose values are _____ over time. Many unmeasured and uncontrolled variables may cause a response to vary over time and thereby inflate the experimental error. The undesirable effect of time can be reduced by using _____ designs and by making experimental treatment comparisons within relatively _____ blocks of time. In other decision-making situations, time may be one of the most important variables.

    random

    block
    homogeneous

2. Any sequence of measurements taken on a process variable over time is called a _____ _____. The time series is usually represented by a mathematical _____ listing the process values as a function of _____, or by a curve on a graph whose vertical axis represents the value of the random response plotted against _____ on the horizontal axis.

    time series
    equation
    time
    time

3. It is the _____ generated by a time series that is of especial interest to a business planner or forecaster.

    pattern

4. The analysis of time series is a difficult task. Response measurements appearing in a time series are usually _____, with the correlation _____ as the time interval between a pair of measurements _____. As a result, time series data will often defy the basic assumption of _____ required for the methods we have learned thus far. Since the methodology of time series analysis has not yet been developed to an advanced state, analytical methods used are often quite subjective. Newer techniques of time series analysis are often very complex.

    correlated
    increasing
    decreases
    independence

14.2 Components of Time Series (14.2)

1. Time series are often conceptually divided into four component series. These are:

long-term trends
cyclic effects
seasonal effects
random variation
Long-term trends

Cyclic effects
long-
term

Seasonal effects

predictable

unpredictable
Random; upward
downward

short

cyclic effect; seasonal
effect; trend; random
variation; random
variation; nonrandom

signal
noise

components
causes; forecast

random variation
signal

smoothing techniques

a. _____ _____ _____ ,
b. _____ _____ ,
c. _____ _____ ,
d. _____ _____ .

2. _____ _____ _____ are often present in time series because of such things as a steady increase in population. Such factors do not cause sudden changes in the response, but produce steady change over time.

3. _____ _____ in a time series are apparent when the response rises and falls in a gentle, wavelike manner on a _____ _____ trend curve. Cyclic effects could be caused by many factors, for example, pulsations in the demand for a product or business cycles.

4. _____ _____ in time series are rises and falls that always occur at a particular time of year. The essential difference between seasonal and cyclic effects is that seasonal effects are _____ , occurring at a given interval of time from the last occurrence, while cyclic effects are completely _____ .

5. _____ variation represents the random _____ and _____ movement of the series after adjustment for the other components. It is the unexplained shifting and bobbing of the series in the _____ -term period. These variations are caused by factors such as weather and political events.

6. Any time series may contain any number of the following components:
   _____ _____ , _____ _____ ,
   long-term _____ , or _____ _____ ; however, all time series will contain _____ _____ .
   With most time series processes, the _____ components are not easily separable.

7. The communications engineer refers to the long-term, cyclic, and seasonal effects as the _____ of the time series. The random variations are called _____ . The amplitude, or strength, of the noise is an important consideration. It is possible for the noise to be so great that it completely hides the signal.

8. The objective of time series analysis is to identify the _____ which do exist in order to identify their _____ and to _____ future values of the time series.

9. Accurate estimation of future values of time series is possible only when the magnitude of the _____ _____ is small. Otherwise, its fluctuations may overwhelm or even cancel the _____ components.

14.3 Smoothing Methods (14.3)

1. Traditional methods of time series analysis have rested heavily upon _____ _____ . These techniques attempt to cancel out

the effect of random variation and reveal the underlying components. In the terms of the communications engineer, we filter out the small high frequency variations (noise) present on the signal, making the signal more easily detectable.

2. Smoothing can be accomplished by utilizing a _____ _____ of the response measurements over a set number of time periods. The moving average $\bar{y}_t$ at time t of the response measurements over M time periods is given by

$$\bar{y}_t = \frac{y_{t-(M-1)/2} + y_{t+1-(M-1)/2} + y_{t+2-(M-1)/2} + \cdots + y_{t+(M-1)/2}}{M}$$

when M is an _____ number. _____ is the process response at time t, _____ is the process response at time $t-1$, and so forth.

3. For example, with a five-period moving average, $\bar{y}_{10}$ is given by

$$\bar{y}_{10} = \underline{\hspace{3cm}}$$

4. When M is an even number, the moving averages will occur _____ the time points. Therefore, it is more useful to select _____ values for M.

5. The primary disadvantage of using a moving average for smoothing is that the technique will not produce a smoothed value corresponding to each response value (observation), unless $M =$ _____ . This can be a serious problem when the number of response measurements is _____ .

6. *Example:*
   The weekly sales of the Nomura Electronics Company are given in the table below. Compute the moving average of sales for the period shown when $M = 3$. The ten moving averages are computed in a manner similar to the computation shown for $\bar{y}_2$.

t	y_t	$\bar{y}_t$	
1	132		
2	100	116.3	$\bar{y}_2 = \dfrac{y_1 + y_2 + y_3}{3}$
3	117	102.3	
4	90	105.0	
5	108	_____	$= \dfrac{(132) + (100) + (117)}{3}$
6	130	_____	
7	123	_____	
8	142	_____	
9	96	_____	$= \dfrac{(349)}{3}$
10	121	_____	
11	70	_____	
12	102		$= 116.3$

7. Another method of smoothing which is more efficient than the moving-average method is the process of _____ smoothing.

---

moving
average

odd; y_t
y_{t-1}

$\dfrac{y_8 + y_9 + y_{10} + y_{11} + y_{12}}{5}$

between
odd

1
small

109.3
120.3
131.7
120.3
119.7
95.7
97.7

exponential

smoothed

$S_t; y_1$

$(1 - \alpha)$

$\alpha y_t + (1 - \alpha)S_{t-1}$

0; 1
basic
smoothing
constant

all

less

smoothing; α
α; 0
quickly
small
large

This technique is more efficient because it produces a _____ value corresponding to each response measurement—one does not "lose" observations.

8. The smoothed value, under exponential smoothing, at time period t is denoted by _____ . At the first period, we let $S_1 =$ _____ . For the second time period, we have

$$S_2 = \alpha y_2 + \underline{\hspace{2cm}} S_1$$

and for each succeeding time period t, we have,

$$S_t = \underline{\hspace{2cm}}$$

for _____ $\leqslant \alpha \leqslant$ _____ .

9. The above equation is called the _____ equation of exponential smoothing, and α is called the _____ _____ . It is interesting to note that whereas the moving average considers process values only over the M time periods, the exponential smoothing method considers _____ past process values at each stage in the computations. Even though remote responses are not dropped in the exponential smoothing scheme as they are in a moving average, their contribution to the smoothed value S_t becomes (greater, less) at each successive time point. The speed at which remote responses are dampened out is determined by the _____ constant, _____ . For values of _____ near _____ , remote values are dampened out slowly. For values of α near one, they are dampened out more _____ . For a volatile series, we would select a (large, small) smoothing constant. For a stable process, we would select a (large, small) constant.

10. *Example:*
The sales manager of the Nomura Electronics Company is dissatisfied with the results of the moving-average technique employed in the previous example. He has suggested that you try exponential smoothing with $\alpha = .5$ and $\alpha = .1$. On the graph following, plot the original data, the moving average for $M = 3$ from the previous exercise, and the exponentially smoothed curves for both α levels.

Solution:

a.

105.7
117.9
123.0; 120.5
124.9; 131.3
122.0; 113.7
121.9; 117.4
116.7; 93.7
115.2; 97.9

t	y_t	$S_t(\alpha = .1)$	$S_t(\alpha = .5)$
1	132	132	132
2	100	128.8	116.0
3	117	127.6	116.5
4	90	123.8	103.3
5	108	122.2	
6	130	123.0	
7	123		
8	142		
9	96		
10	121		
11	70		
12	102		

$$S_t(\alpha = .1) = (\alpha)y_t + (1 - \alpha)S_{t-1}$$
$$= .1y_t + 9S_{t-1}$$

$$S_2(\alpha = .1) = (.1)(y_2) + .9(S_1)$$
$$= 10 + 118.8$$
$$= 128.8$$

The 24 exponentially smoothed values are computed in a manner similar to the computation shown for $S_2(\alpha = .1)$.

b. Plot the smoothed series for $\alpha = .1$ and $\alpha = .5$.

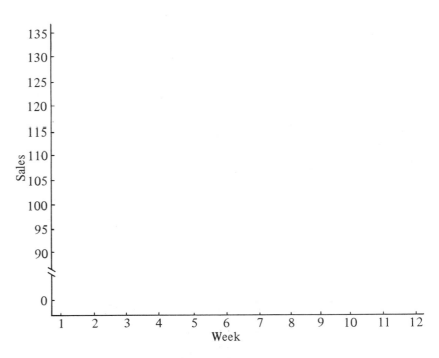

14.4 Adjustment of Seasonal Data (14.4)

1. When a time series exhibits a seasonal component, the _____ _____ smoothing technique can be used to remove the seasonal component by using a moving average of order M, where M is the number of time points in one complete seasonal _____. In most seasonal economic time series, the seasonal period usually consists of either 4 or 12 time periods, corresponding, respectively, to _____ and _____ cycles.

2. In using the moving-average technique to remove a seasonal component whose cycle consists of M time periods,
   a. Compute the M-period moving average for the series.
   b. If M is an _____ number, center the moving-average values by averaging adjacent moving averages.

3. The loss of _____ observations at each end of the time series is not a serious problem if the number of observations is _____. In any case, we should have observations over at least _____ complete seasons in order to apply the moving-average technique for deseasonalizing the data.

moving-average

period *or* cycle

quarterly
yearly

even

$M/2$
large
three

4. *Example:*

A newly founded community college operates on the basis of three academic terms each year. Enrollment at the college during the years 1968 through 1974 was as follows:

	Enrollment		
Academic year	*Fall*	*Winter*	*Spring*
1968–1969	910	1180	1580
1969–1970	1060	1210	2080
1970–1971	1720	2640	3320
1971–1972	3090	3250	3570
1972–1973	3730	3680	4690
1973–1974	3560	3760	4450

Use a moving average of order 3 to deseasonalize these data.

Solution:

a. The sequential time listing for these data together with the moving-average series are given as follows:

Time	*Enrollment*	*Moving average*	*Time*	*Enrollment*	*Moving average*
1	910	—	10	3090	_____
2	1180	1223	11	3250	_____
3	1580	1273	12	3570	_____
4	1060	1283	13	3730	_____
5	1210	1450	14	3680	_____
6	2080	1670	15	4690	_____
7	1720	2147	16	3560	_____
8	2640	2560	17	3760	_____
9	3320	3017	18	4450	—

Since $M = 3$ is odd, there is no reason to perform a second moving average for the purpose of centering the moving-average time series.

b. A plot of the original enrollment data is given below. Plot the moving-average series superimposed on this graph.

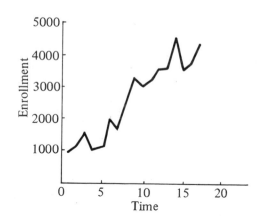

3220
3303
3517
3660
4033
3977
4003
3923

c. The moving-average series shows (more, less) variation than do the original data.

d. With the seasonal component removed, it appears that the rate of increase of enrollment is (increasing, leveling off).

Self-Correcting Exercises 14A

The owner of a suburban liquor store has indicated that the following represents his gross monthly sales (in thousands of dollars) for the years 1969 and 1970:

1969		1970	
Month	*Sales*	*Month*	*Sales*
Jan.	9.5	Jan.	11.3
Feb.	11.6	Feb.	12.7
Mar.	16.4	Mar.	15.9
Apr.	13.5	Apr.	14.3
May	17.6	May	18.0
June	21.3	June	23.1
July	19.7	July	20.3
Aug.	17.5	Aug.	18.6
Sept.	22.1	Sept.	23.4
Oct.	23.0	Oct.	24.1
Nov.	25.8	Nov.	27.6
Dec.	33.2	Dec.	35.0

1. Plot the sales values against time and construct the time series.
2. Which time series components appear to exist within the sales pattern?
3. Smooth the monthly sales values by computing a three-month moving average. Plot the smoothed series and the original series on the same set of graph paper. Has smoothing helped to identify the components of the series?
4. Smooth the sales data by computing an exponentially smoothed series using the smoothing constant $\alpha = .1$.
5. Smooth the sales data by computing an exponentially smoothed series using the smoothing constant $\alpha = .5$.
6. On a sheet of graph paper, superimpose the two smoothed series on the original series. Are any hidden time series components suggested?
7. Was the larger or the smaller smoothing constant most appropriate, or is there no detectable difference? Explain.

14.5   Index Numbers (14.5)

1. Because of the variability in the buying power of the dollar over time, it is necessary to deflate some values and inflate others in order to make meaningful comparisons. This is done through the use of _____ _____. The application of _____ _____

is not limited strictly to monetary comparisons, but in business problems any other use is uncommon.

2. An index number is a _____ or an average of _____. Two or more time periods are involved, one of which is called the _____ _____ _____. The value at the _____ _____ _____ serves as the standard point of comparison, while values at other time periods are used to show the _____ _____ in value from the standard value of the base period.

3. If we let

$$I_k = \frac{(\text{average dollar value of concern in year } k)\,(100)}{\text{average dollar value in year one}}$$

then we are using year one as our _____ _____. Each year's _____ is a percentage of the base year's combined dollar values.

4. *Example:*

You are employed as an hourly worker by Nomura Electronics, and have worked for the company for 10 years. Over this time period your average yearly wages have risen, but you suspect you have little more buying power than you had when you were hired. To find out, adjust your average hourly wages for each year, based on the consumer price index in your area, which is given below.

Year	Average hourly wages	Wage index	Adjusted wages
1	3.25	100.0	_____
2	3.37	104.3	_____
3	3.44	107.5	_____
4	3.57	112.2	_____
5	3.62	116.6	_____
6	3.75	121.4	_____
7	3.89	124.7	_____
8	3.96	128.3	_____
9	4.02	132.0	_____
10	4.17	137.4	_____

Solution:

We may use the formula

$$A_k = (100)W_k/I_k$$

to compute adjusted wages, where

A_k = adjusted dollar figure in year k

W_k = average dollar figure in year k

I_k = wage index for year k

Margin notes (left column):

ratio; ratios

base time period
base time period

percentage change

base period
index

$3.25
$3.23
$3.20
$3.18
$3.10
$3.09
$3.12
$3.09
$3.05
$3.03

Hence we have

$$A_2 = \frac{(100)\,(\underline{\hspace{2cm}})}{(104.3)} = \frac{(\underline{\hspace{2cm}})}{(104.3)} = \underline{\hspace{2cm}}$$

3.37; 337; 3.23

$$A_3 = \underline{\hspace{2cm}}$$

3.20

The other adjusted values are computed similarly.

5. A list of index numbers for two or more periods of time, where each index number employs the same base year, is called an _____ _____ _____.

index
time series

6. *Example:*

Plot the index time series in the previous example.

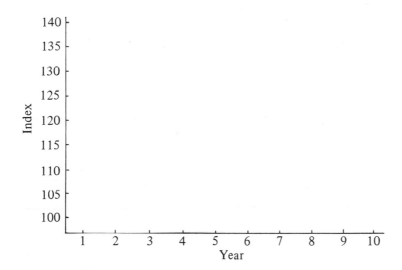

7. A commonly used index to compare two sets of prices from a wide variety of items is called a _____ _____ index. An aggregate index is the _____ of an aggregate (sum) of commodity prices for a given year k to an aggregate of the prices of the same commodities in some _____ _____. The index is computed by evaluating

simple aggregate
ratio

base year

$$I_k = \frac{\displaystyle\sum_{i=1}^{n} p_{ki}}{\displaystyle\sum_{i=1}^{n} p_{0i}}\ (100)$$

where

$$p_{ki} = \text{price in year } k \text{ of item } i \text{ where } i \text{ ranges from 1 to } n$$

$$p_{0i} = \text{base year price of the same item } i.$$

percentage

100
100
100
$I_k - 100$

deflation
inflation

100
percentage

8. An index number I_k measures the _____ changes in a set of monetary values at period k compared with a base period index of _____ . When computing an index number, one must multiply the monetary value ratios or averages by _____ so that the resultant index number is comparable to the base period index of _____ . The percentage change from the base period to period k is _____ . Thus, if I_k is equal to 100, no change is implied; if I_k is less than 100, (inflation, deflation) of the monetary values is implied; and if I_k is greater than 100, (inflation, deflation) of the monetary value is assumed.

9. Most formulas for the computation of an index number contain the constant multiple _____ to insure that the index number for period k is a _____ which is comparable to the base period monetary value index, 100.

10. *Example:*

You have decided to quit your job at Nomura Electronics (as a result of the previous example), and are accepting a job offer in Tokyo. A friend who lived in Tokyo during 1954 says the prices there are very low, and has produced an old account book to prove his point. The prices of some commodities listed in his book are given below. Another friend just returned from a vacation in Tokyo, says the prices are high, and quotes some prices he remembers. You are curious and wish to compute the price change over the 1954-to-1974 period, using 1954 as the base period. Using the data below, compute the aggregate price index for 1974. Prices are per pound.

Commodity	1954 Price	1974 Price
Gohan	10	35
Tofu	15	24
Miso	8	57
Nori	12	42
Sakana	17	63
Mochi	5	15

24; 57; 42; 63

15; 8; 12; 17

236; 67; 352

$$I_{1974} = \frac{(35) + (\underline{\quad}) + (\underline{\quad}) + (\underline{\quad}) + (\underline{\quad}) + (15)}{(10) + (\underline{\quad}) + (\underline{\quad}) + (\underline{\quad}) + (\underline{\quad}) + (5)}(100)$$

$$= \frac{(\underline{\quad})}{(\underline{\quad})}(100) = \underline{\qquad}$$

11. The simple aggregate index has its greatest weakness in that changes in the

measuring units

_____ _____ may drastically affect the value of the index. An index which gives a better indication of relative prices is called the _____ _____ index. A _____

_____ index is the ratio of an aggregate of weighted commodity

prices for a given year k to an aggregate of the weighted prices of the same

commodities in some base year. In this case, the prices do not contribute

_____ to the value of the index. Each price is weighted by the

_____ of the items produced or the _____ of units

purchased or consumed so as to include each item considered by the index

according to its _____ in the aggregate of prices of the items

being described by the index. The index is found by computing

$$I_k = \frac{\sum\limits_{i=1}^{n} p_{ki} q_{ki}}{\sum\limits_{i=1}^{n} p_{0i} q_{0i}} (100)$$

where

q_{ki} = relative quantity of item consumed in time period k

q_{0i} = relative quantity of item consumed in base time period.

12. *Example:*

After computing the simple aggregate index of the previous example, you

realize that your average diet has changed over the time period, as your

tastes changed. In order to make a more meaningful comparison, you assign

the following average q_{ki}'s, average quantities you might have bought per

month during the time the prices were in effect. Compute the aggregate

weighted index for the period, using 1954 as the base period.

Commodity	1954 Price	1974 Price	q_{1954}	q_{1974}
Gohan	10	35	5	3
Tofu	15	24	4	9
Miso	8	57	1	2
Nori	12	42	3	4
Sakana	17	63	15	12
Mochi	5	15	2	1

$$I_{1974} = \frac{(35)(3) + (24)(9) + (57)(2) + (42)(4) + (63)(12) + (15)(1)}{(10)(5) + (15)(4) + (8)(1) + (12)(3) + (17)(15) + (5)(2)} (100)$$

$$= \frac{(105) + (216) + (114) + (168) + (756) + (15)}{(50) + (60) + (8) + (36) + (255) + (10)} (100)$$

$$= \frac{(\underline{\quad\quad})}{(\underline{\quad\quad})} (100) = \underline{\quad\quad}$$

Laspeyres
weighted aggregate

13. The U.S. Department of Labor uses a special index, called the _____ Index. It is a special form of the _____ _____ index, and is found by computing

$$L = \frac{\displaystyle\sum_{i=1}^{n} p_{ki} q_{0i}}{\displaystyle\sum_{i=1}^{n} p_{0i} q_{0i}} (100)$$

all
price
buying power

price increases

less
more

Laspeyres
weighted average

where p_{ki}, q_{0i}, and p_{0i} are defined as before. In this index method, base year weights are used for _____ other years. By doing this, we can make more meaningful comparisons of changes in _____ and _____ _____ over time, since we are only considering the change in price per given number of units and not changing the number of units. One disadvantage of this method is that it tends to overstate the effect of _____ _____. This is because the demand for most goods shows some sensitivity to price changes. This means that as the prices of certain goods increase, consumers tend to buy _____ of these goods and to buy _____ of substitute goods whose prices have remained unchanged. This problem can usually be ignored in the case of necessities, which have no close substitutes. The (Laspeyres, weighted average) index is often cheaper to use than the (Paasche, weighted average) index because it is not necessary to measure quantities of items for each time period.

14. The index in the previous example was affected greatly by the change in diet over the period. We shall compute the Laspeyres Index for this data, given again below, and compare the resulting index with the one computed in the previous example.

Commodity	1954 Price	1974 Price	q_{1954}
Gohan	10	35	5
Tofu	15	24	4
Miso	8	57	1
Nori	12	42	3
Sakana	17	63	15
Mochi	5	15	2

$$L = \frac{(35)(5) + (24)(4) + (57)(1) + (42)(3) + (63)(15) + (15)(2)}{(10)(5) + (15)(4) + (8)(1) + (12)(3) + (17)(15) + (5)(2)} (100)$$

$$= \frac{(175) + (96) + (57) + (126) + (945) + (30)}{(50) + (60) + (8) + (36) + (255) + (10)} (100)$$

1429; 419; 341.1

$$= \frac{(\quad\quad)}{(\quad\quad)} (100) = \underline{\quad\quad}.$$

Due to the use of only base year quantities by the Laspeyres Index, the computed Laspeyres value is somewhat _____ than the previously computed simple aggregate index.

larger

15. Two other price indices sometimes used are the _____ Index and _____ _____ Index. The Paasche Index uses _____ year rather than _____ year quantities as weights for the weighted index. The Paasche Index tends to underweight rather than overweight commodities whose prices have _____.

Paasche
Fisher's Ideal; reference
base

increased

16. The _____ _____ Index is based on the supposition that since the _____ Index tends to give too much weight to those goods whose prices have increased and the _____ Index to give such goods too little weight, the price index should be between these two indices.

Fisher's ideal
Laspeyres
Paasche

17. The _____ _____ Index is the _____ mean of the Laspeyres and the Paasche Indices. It is found by computing

Fisher's ideal; geometric

$$I_F = \sqrt{I_L I_P}$$

where I_F = Fisher's Ideal Index

I_L = Laspeyres Index

I_P = Paasche Index

Although this method probably yields a more accurate value than either the Paasche or Laspeyres methods, it is seldom used in practice.

18. Two important indices computed regularly by the Bureau of Labor Statistics are the _____ _____ Index and the _____ _____ Index. Both of these can be somewhat misleading.

Consumer Price; Wholesale
Price

19. The Consumer Price Index (CPI) is published monthly. It is a(n) _____ _____ index. The year 1967 is currently used as the base period.

weighted aggregate

20. The following factors should be considered in examining the CPI.
    a. The CPI (is, is not) representative of all American families.
    b. The CPI says (little, much) about the cost of living for a professional man.
    c. The CPI (ignores, considers) taxation and product quality changes over time.

is not
little

ignores

21. Any computed price index, including the CPI, should always mention the relevant base period and the class of items or people for which the index has meaning.

22. Another index computed by the Bureau of Labor Statistics is the Wholesale Price Index (WPI). One difficulty in the use of this index is that it (is, is not) really an indicator of wholesale prices, but actually represents the change in _____ selling prices.

is not
producers'

23. Security market indices, such as the Dow Jones Industrial Average, are computed (similarly to, differently from) the wage and price indices we have discussed. Dow Jones Averages might be described as averages of a

differently from

30
mergers
stock splits
less

group of time series rather than as indicators of changes in value or price. The Dow Jones Industrial Average tries to compute the average of the daily closing prices of the securities of _____ predetermined industrial firms. The computations become involved when events such as _____ and _____ _____ occur. Each time these more involved computations are necessary, the index becomes (less, more) meaningful.

Self-Correcting Exercises 14B

1. Using 1970 as the base year, compute the simple price index for the manufacturer's suggested retail price for a table model color television set. The prices over the years 1970 through 1975 are listed below.

Year	1970	1971	1972	1973	1974	1975
Price	$340	$325	$350	$380	$400	$410

2. An accountant employed in the state auditor's office of a western state has earned the following annual salaries in his three years' employment.

Year	1972	1973	1974
Salary	$7880	$8400	$8850

During these three years, the state's wage indices were 121.4, 125.2, and 129.0, respectively, computed from 1960 as the base year. Have the accountant's real wages increased during his time of employment in his current position? Explain.

3. The cost of operating an automobile was compared for the years 1960 and 1970. It was decided that operating costs were to exclude the cost of insurance because of the many different types of insurance policies available to the automobile owner. The items, and their costs, included in the analysis were:

Item	1960 Price (p_0)	1970 Price (p_k)
Gasoline (gallon)	$ .29	$ .35
Oil (quart)	.54	.75
Mechanic's time (per hour)	2.50	4.25

These figures were computed as averages over the entire United States for the period of time under consideration. Using the prices for 1960 as the base year prices, compute the simple aggregate index for the cost of car care for 1970.

4. After further studying the problem of comparing the cost of operating an automobile in 1960 versus 1970, it was thought necessary to consider not only the cost per unit of gasoline, oil, and mechanic time but also the

quantity of each of these items used in a year's time. The average use of gasoline and oil and the average hours required of an automobile mechanic per car owner were computed for 1960 and 1970. They are:

Item	1960 Quantity (q_0)	1970 Quantity (q_k)
Gasoline (gallons)	500	700
Oil (quarts)	50	40
Mechanic's time (hours)	8	11

Using the price information given in Exercise 3 and the quantities of each item used given here, compute the weighted aggregate index of car cost for 1970 using 1960 as the base year. Comment on the difference between the index computed here and the index computed in Exercise 3. (That is, how do you account for their difference and what is the meaning of this difference?)

5. Refer to Exercises 3 and 4. Use these data to compute the Laspeyres Index for 1970 with 1960 data considered as base year data. Account for any difference between the Laspeyres Index computed here and the weighted aggregate index computed in Exercise 4.

6. Refer to Exercises 3 and 4. Use these data to compute the Paasche Index for 1970 with 1960 data considered as base year data. Account for any differences between the Paasche Index computed here, the Laspeyres Index computed in Exercise 5, and the weighted aggregate index computed in Exercise 4.

7. Refer to Exercises 5 and 6. Use the results obtained in these two exercises to compute Fisher's Ideal Index for the automobile cost data. Let the base year be 1960.

14.6 Summary (14.6)

1. A time series is a sequence of measurements taken on a _____ that varies over time. A time series may consist of several _____, such as a long-term _____, a _____ effect, or a _____ effect. All time series may contain any number of these components, while all contain _____ variation. This _____ variation tends to hide the underlying components. One method used to try to cancel out the random variation is to use _____ techniques.

process *or* response
components
trend; cyclic
seasonal
random
random

smoothing

2. Time-series process values can be misleading. This is often the case when monetary units are involved. This problem may be reduced through the use of _____ numbers. _____ numbers may be used to _____ or _____ process values so that more meaningful comparisons can be made. Index numbers measure the _____ in price or value of a single commodity or of an aggregate of commodities from some _____ time period to a reference time period.

index; Index
inflate; deflate
change

base

multiply; price

Weighted indices _____ each commodity _____ by a predetermined factor. These indices are the most common type.

3. Some indices, such as those computed by the Bureau of Labor Statistics, can be quite misleading. Care must be taken in the use of such indices, since they may not really measure what they try to measure, or they may have only limited application.

Chapter 15

FORECASTING MODELS

15.1 Introduction (15.1)

1. In previous chapters, we have been concerned with observations made on business and economic random variables called _____ _____. It is natural for businessmen and economists to try to _____ the future behavior of such time series.

2. Depending on how far into the future we are attempting to forecast, we distinguish between _____-term and _____-term forecasts. Short-term forecasts generally make predictions for _____ year(s) into the future, while long-term forecasts usually look from _____ to _____ years into the future.

3. The further one attempts to project a forecast into the future, the (less, more) speculative the forecast becomes. Because the future is always _____, we can never expect complete forecasting accuracy.

4. Forecasting the future behavior of a time series by the smoothing methods of Chapter 14 is highly speculative because such attempts require the very strong assumption that _____ trends and cycles will continue unchanged into the _____.

5. Due to uncertain future economic, political and business developments, such an assumption is very often unjustified and subjective _____ must be used in conjunction with mathematical forecasting techniques. For this reason, forecasting remains as much an art as a science.

6. There are three classes of forecasting models:
   a. _____ models.
   b. _____ _____ models.
   c. _____ _____ models.
   Only econometric and time series models, which involve the use of _____ data to make inferences about the future, will be considered in this text.

time
series
forecast

short; long
one

two; ten

more
uncertain

past
future

judgment

econometric
time series
qualitative forecasting

sample

15.2 Econometric Forecasting Models (15.2)

Econometric
probabilistic

1. _____ models consist of one or more equations which describe the _____ relationship between a dependent time series and one or more independent economic variables. The linear model of earlier chapters is an example of an econometric model.

2. Econometric forecasting models are distinguished from time series models in that the latter ignore any relationship between a given time series and other economic _____. Rather, time series models predict the future behavior of a time series solely on the basis of its own _____ behavior.

variables

past

linear trend

3. A simple long-term _____ _____ might be represented by

time

$$y = \beta_0 + \beta_1 x + \epsilon \qquad \text{where } x = \underline{\hspace{2cm}}.$$

We can estimate the values of β_0 and β_1 by the procedures of Chapter 11.

curvilinear

4. A _____ long-term trend might be represented by

$$y = \beta_0 + \beta_1 x + \beta_2 x^2 + \epsilon \qquad (x = \text{time})$$

We could estimate the parameters of this equation also by the method of least squares, as explained in Chapter 12.

5. On the graph below, plot a time series (real or imaginary) to which the linear model might appropriately be fitted.

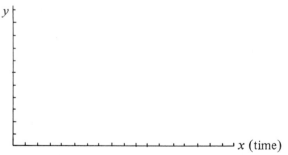

On the graph below, plot an imaginary or real time series to which the curvilinear model might appropriately be fitted.

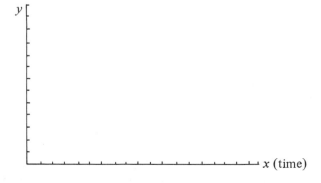

6. One problem generally encountered in practice is that the random error terms (denoted by ϵ_i) associated with the y_i's are often not _____ between successive measurements. As a result, any probabilistic intervals which might be constructed around the expected process value will be too _____. It is possible that an examination of the _____ patterns present in the series will enable one to improve the accuracy of prediction and estimation. If the response is an _____ over a period of time, serial correlation of the ϵ_i's will be reduced, and may enable us to assume the _____ required by the method of least squares.

independent

narrow; correlation

average

independence

7. A great deal of ingenuity can be shown in the choice of predictors in a multivariate regression prediction model. For instance, if

x_1 = price of tea

x_2 = price of coffee

x_3 = t, the index of time

x_4 = price of cream

x_5 = price of cream substitutes

$x_6 = x_1 x_2$

$x_7 = \sin\left(\dfrac{2\pi t}{12}\right)$

we might predict the monthly demand for cream by the additive prediction model

$$y = \beta_0 + \beta_1 x_1 + \beta_2 x_2 + \ldots + \beta_7 x_7 + \epsilon$$

where x_6 takes into account an _____ effect between tea and coffee prices, and x_7 allows for a _____ effect in sales, with a period of _____ year (_____ months). The term $\beta_3 x_3$ allows for a long-term _____ trend which is linear over time.

interaction
cyclic
one; 12
growth

8. It is very important to remember that the test of a model is how well it predicts the future. The fit of the model to the _____ response measurements, though important, is secondary.

past

9. A model is tested by computing the sum of _____ for _____ errors (_____), as given by the formula

squares
forecast; SSE

$$SSE - \sum_{t-1}^{n} \underline{\hspace{3cm}}$$

$(y_t - \hat{y}_t)^2$

where y_t is the _____ response measurement and $\hat{y}_t$ is the _____ response measurement.

observed
predicted

future; smallest

least
squares

Revise

sinusoidal

linear
cyclic

cyclic
period

10. *SSE* is computed for observed and predicted response measurements at
_____ points in time. The model yielding the _____
SSE is the one providing the best forecasting accuracy.

11. The general procedure most commonly employed in the development of a
time series forecasting model is as follows:

a. Select a number of variables which are believed to be closely related to
the process variable of interest.

b. Construct transformations of these variables in an attempt to model
observed patterns of the response variable over time or interactions
between predictors.

c. Estimate the parameters of the model by the method of _____
_____.

d. Test the model to see how well it fits the response measurements and
how well it forecasts the future.

e. _____ the model by adding new variables as predictors and
removing certain predictors currently in the model whenever it appears
appropriate.

12. The method of least squares, as used in the estimation of the parameters in
a regression model, requires, in a practical sense, the use of an electronic
computer. The computations involved make hand calculations or the use
of a desk calculator almost prohibitive.

15.3   A Least-Squares Sinusoidal Model (15.3)

1. A least-squares multiple linear regression model with periodic terms is
called a _____ model. An example of such a model is

$$y_t = \beta_0 + \beta_1 t + \beta_2 \sin\left(\frac{2\pi t}{p}\right) + \beta_3 \cos\left(\frac{2\pi t}{p}\right) + \beta_4 t \sin\left(\frac{2\pi t}{p}\right)$$

$$+ \beta_5 t \cos\left(\frac{2\pi t}{p}\right) + \epsilon_t$$

Within this model, $\beta_1 t$ accounts for a _____ growth trend over
time, $\beta_2 \sin(2\pi t/p)$ and $\beta_3 \cos(2\pi t/p)$ account for _____
(periodic) effects over time, but $\beta_4 t \sin(2\pi t/p)$ and $\beta_5 t \cos(2\pi t/p)$ account
for a _____ effect whose amplitude is increasing over time. The
symbol p in the equation is the _____ of the cycles present
within the time series.

2. *Example:*

Based on past data, the quarterly earnings of the Electromation Corporation were found to be modeled quite well by the sinusoidal model

$$\hat{y}_t = .15 + .03t + .22 \sin\left(\frac{2\pi t}{4}\right) + .03t \cos\left(\frac{2\pi t}{4}\right)$$

Use this forecasting equation to predict the quarterly earnings of Electromation over the next two years (next eight time periods).

Solution:

The values for $\sin(2\pi t/4)$ and $\cos(2\pi t/4)$ are listed below. The forecast for the first quarter would be

$$\hat{y}_1 = .15 + .03(1) + .22(1) + .03(1)(0)$$

$$= .40$$

For the second period,

$$\hat{y}_2 = .15 + .03(\underline{}) + .22(\underline{}) + .03(\underline{})(\underline{})$$

2; 0; 2; –1

$$= \underline{}$$

.15

Fill in the remaining values in the table below.

Year		t	$\sin(2\pi t/4)$	$\cos(2\pi t/4)$	$\hat{y}_t$	
1	Q1	1	1	0	.40	
	Q2	2	0	−1	.15	
	Q3	3	−1	0	_____	.02
	Q4	4	0	1	_____	.39
2	Q1	5	1	0	_____	.52
	Q2	6	0	−1	_____	.15
	Q3	7	−1	0	_____	.14
	Q4	8	0	1	_____	.63

3. Models such as the one we have just discussed are generally not too responsive to _____ processes. Often this situation can be improved through the use of another process-related variable in the equation, such as sales, prices of certain products, GNP, budget expenditures, or other financial-economic factors. The inclusion of additional predictors in a multiple linear regression model will _____ decrease forecast accuracy. If the added variables add only a negligible amount to the accuracy of the fit of the model in the presence of the other variables in the equation, the coefficients associated with the new variables will be _____, weighting out their effect in the equation. But recall that the best criterion of the goodness of a forecasting model is not how well it fits the sample data but how well it _____ the future.

volatile

never

small

predicts

4. Forecasting requires _____ of the model into the future. This can possibly lead to large forecasting _____. Invariably, not all relevant predictors which affect the process are included in the model. Some variables may have been overlooked because, during the period over which the data was being gathered, they were relatively _____ and hence were not apparent. In spite of the large errors sometimes caused by these dormant variables, least-squares forecasting equations can

extrapolation

errors

stable

short
is
errors

be quite useful. They are perhaps the most useful in predicting _____ term process values where relative stability (is, is not) more likely to exist within the system. The point to remember is that large _____ can occur when extrapolation is used.

15.4 The Autoregressive Forecasting Model (15.4)

correlation

correlation
autoregressive
past
greatest

autoregressive

1. A time series may sometimes exhibit a high degree of _____ between successive values. For such series, linear models may be employed which take advantage of this _____ in the forecast model. Such models are called _____ models. They use _____ process values as predictors in the model, using those lagged values associated with the _____ lag correlation. For example, if y_t and y_{t+1} denote the responses from a time series at times t and $t + 1$, respectively, we might use the _____ model

$$y_{t+1} = \beta_0 + \beta_1 y_t + \epsilon_{t+1}$$

successive
first
order

to predict y_{t+1} if a significant correlation between _____ process values appears to exist. Such a model is called a _____ _____ autoregressive model. In general, a p th order autoregressive model is given by

$\beta_p y_{t-p+1}$

$$y_{t+1} = \beta_0 + \beta_1 y_t + \beta_2 y_{t-1} + \beta_3 y_{t-2} + \ldots + \underline{\hspace{1cm}} + \epsilon_{t+1}$$

y_{t-2}

For example, if process values separated by three units of time are highly correlated, we must let p be large enough to include at least _____ as a predictor of y_{t+1} in the model.

correlation

poor

forecasts
sum
squares; error; SSE

2. Autoregressive terms can be used in a linear regression model in the presence of other, nonautoregressive predictor variables. Whether autoregressive terms are used alone or in the presence of nonautoregressive predictor variables in a linear regression model, the choice of which autoregressive terms to use is a very difficult one. The autoregressive model assumes _____ between process values over time. If this assumption is not valid for a particular time series, an autoregressive model may generate _____ forecasts, even though the model may fit the sample data fairly well. The only way we can determine whether the autoregressive model, or any other forecasting model for that matter, is a good forecasting model is to use that model in competition with other models to develop _____ for a process under study. The model which returns the most accurate forecast, as measured by its having the smallest _____ of _____ for forecast _____ (_____), is the best model and should be employed in further analyses.

3. *Example:*
Based on past data, it was determined that the autoregressive model

$$\hat{y}_{t+1} = -13.0 + 1.5y_t - 0.3y_{t-2}$$

is an acceptable model for forecasting the monthly sales volume (in thousands of dollars) of a certain growing company. Use the model to forecast the company's sales for the next 12 months. (The actual sales for each of the next 12 months are listed below.)

Solution:

Because of the nature of the autoregressive model which we have chosen to employ, forecasts cannot be computed until the fourth month, since the model assumes that process values lagged by _____ month and _____ months are used as predictors to estimate current process values. Thus, for month four, the forecast value is

one

three

$$\hat{y}_4 = -13.0 + 1.5(73.6) - 0.3(68.3)$$

$$= 76.91$$

For the fifth month,

$$\hat{y}_5 = -13.0 + 1.5(\underline{\hspace{1.5cm}}) - 0.3(\underline{\hspace{1.5cm}})$$

76.0; 69.1

$$= \underline{\hspace{2cm}}$$

80.27

Compute the remaining eight monthly forecasts and fill in the table which follows.

t	y_t	Forecast Model	$\hat{y}_t$	
1	68.3	$-13.0 + 1.5y_t - 0.3y_{t-2}$		
2	69.1			
3	73.6			
4	76.0	$-13.0 + 1.5(73.6) - 0.3(68.3) =$	76.91	
5	77.9	$-13.0 + 1.5(76.0) - 0.3(69.1) =$	_____	80.27
6	80.5	$-13.0 + 1.5(77.9) - 0.3(73.6) =$	_____	81.77
7	85.0	$-13.0 + 1.5(80.5) - 0.3(76.0) =$	_____	84.95
8	88.4	$-13.0 + 1.5(85.0) - 0.3(77.9) =$	_____	91.13
9	94.7	$-13.0 + 1.5(88.4) - 0.3(80.5) =$	_____	95.45
10	102.8	$-13.0 + 1.5(94.7) - 0.3(85.0) =$	_____	103.55
11	115.7	$-13.0 + 1.5(102.8) - 0.3(88.4) =$	_____	114.68
12	127.6	$-13.0 + 1.5(115.7) - 0.3(94.7) =$	_____	132.14

4. If the process which we wish to forecast is quite _____, a first- or second-order autoregressive model usually is appropriate. The more _____ the process, the less likely it is that an autoregressive model will provide a good forecasting model for the process.

stable

volatile

5. The greater the number of autoregressive predictors which are included within an autoregressive model, the _____ will be the resultant forecasts. There is a limit, though. One should not select so many pre-

better

dictors as to make the degrees of freedom associated with the residual sum of squares too small. As a rule of thumb, if n is the sample size, one should not use more than _____ predictors in a linear regression prediction model. Furthermore, autoregressive predictors usually tend to be less significant as predictors of y_t as they are lagged _____ from y_t. Economic factors, such as the cost of gathering extra data and the cost of the extra computations required by a larger model, must also be considered. As was mentioned earlier, a model which includes autoregressive predictors most likely also contains as predictors other variables which are believed to be related to y_t. Thus, a good model to forecast the sales of cream in year t might be

$$y_t = \beta_0 + \beta_1 x_1 + \beta_2 x_2 + \beta_3 x_3 + \beta_4 x_4 + \epsilon$$

where

$x_1 = y_{t-1}$, the sales of cream in the previous year

$x_2 = y_{t-2}$, the sales of cream two years ago

x_3 = the price of coffee

x_4 = the price of tea

6. One aid in the determination of which lag values to use as autoregressive predictors is the _____ , which is a graphical display of the correlations existing between responses in a time series separated by a constant interval of time. These time-lag correlations are called _____ . The _____ of process values separated by k units of time is computed by

$$r_k = \frac{\sum_{t=1}^{n} (y_t - \hat{y}_t)(y_{t+k} - \hat{y}_{t+k})}{\sum_{t=1}^{n} (y_t - \hat{y}_t)^2}, \quad -1 \leqslant r_k \leqslant 1$$

where $y_1, y_2, \ldots, y_n$ are the values for n consecutive time periods in a time series and $\hat{y}_t$ is the value at time period t of the linear trend line fitted to the time series data. The linear trend equation is of the type $\hat{y}_t = a_0 + a_1 t$ where a_0 and a_1 are estimates found using least-squares methods. The equation is used to eliminate _____ trends in the time series data over time so that autocorrelations can be more accurately estimated.

Margin answers:

n/4

farther

correlogram

autocorrelations
autocorrelation

linear

7. An example of a _____ is given below.

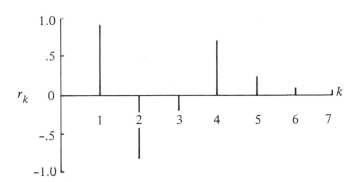

In this case, we would conclude that the model has relatively strong correlations between process values separated by _____, _____, and _____ units of time. The other autocorrelations appear to be quite weak. Thus, three autoregressive predictors which might appropriately be used to forecast y_{t+1} are _____, _____, and _____. It is important to remember that a negative correlation is just as important as a positive correlation. A negative value of r_k shows that process values separated by k units of time are likely to be on _____ sides of the linear trend line.

correlogram

one; two
four

$y_t; y_{t-1}; y_{t-3}$

opposite

Self-Correcting Exercises 15A

1. The Public Welfare Administrator for the state of Nevada claims that the number of people who will request funds each month in the next calendar year under the state's Aid to Families of Dependent Children can be predicted by the equation

$$\hat{y}_t = 33.0 + 0.5t + 11.5 \cos\left(\frac{2\pi t}{12}\right)$$

where the $\hat{y}_t$ is computed in thousands of claimants and t is the monthly index; $t = 1$ (January), $t = 2$ (February), . . . , $t = 12$ (December). Use the administrator's forecast equation to forecast the number of claims under the Nevada AFDC program for each month of the next calendar year.

2. Based on past sales data, the manager of a neighborhood grocery store claims that his gross monthly sales volume (in thousands of dollars) can be forecast by the autoregressive prediction equation

$$\hat{y}_{t+1} = 4.3 + 1.8y_t - 0.2y_{t-1}$$

Suppose that his gross monthly sales volumes (in thousands of dollars) over the next 12 months are:

Month	Sales
Jan.	10.0
Feb.	10.6
Mar.	10.9
Apr.	10.8
May	11.1
June	11.3
July	11.0
Aug.	11.5
Sept.	11.6
Oct.	11.2
Nov.	11.7
Dec.	11.5

Beginning with March, use the suggested autoregressive forecasting equation to estimate the monthly sales volume based on past sales data. Compare the forecasted sales volumes with the actual sales volumes.

3. Use the sales data given in Exercise 2 to construct a first-order autoregressive model for forecasting the grocer's gross monthly sales data. The model will be of the form

$$y_{t+1} = \beta_0 + \beta_1 y_t + \epsilon$$

Estimate the parameters of the model by the method of least squares. How does this model compare with the autoregressive model suggested in Exercise 2?

15.5   An Exponential-smoothing Forecasting Model (15.5)

smoothing
random variation
time
forecasts; future
exponential-smoothing

T

exponentially smoothed
first

S_t; $1 - \alpha$

smoothed; S_t
linear

1. In Chapter 14, we explored _____ methods which are used in an attempt to average out the effect of _____ _____ in a _____ series. Now we consider the direct use of smoothing methods to compute _____ of _____ process values.

2. We specifically consider Brown's _____ _____ forecasting model, which uses observations from a time series, $y_1, y_2, \ldots,$ y_t to compute a forecast of the time series process value y_{t+T}, i.e., _____ time periods ahead of the available data.

3. Brown's methods gives a convenient way of expressing this forecast in terms of easily computable _____ _____ statistics.

   a. If the time series appears constant over time, we would use a _____-order exponential-smoothing forecasting model given by

$$\hat{y}_{t+T} = \underline{\qquad} = \alpha y_t + (\underline{\qquad}) S_{t-1}$$

   That is, if the time series appears constant over time, the forecast is equal to the _____ statistic, _____.

   b. If the time series is _____ over time, we would employ a second-order exponential-smoothing forecasting model given by

$$\hat{y}_{t+T} = (\underline{\hspace{1.5cm}}) S_t - (\underline{\hspace{1.5cm}}) S_t(2)$$

$2 + \dfrac{\alpha T}{(1-\alpha)}; 1 + \dfrac{\alpha T}{(1-\alpha)}$

where $S_t(2)$ is called the _____-smoothed statistic and is found by computing

double

$$S_t(2) = \alpha \underline{\hspace{1.5cm}} + (1-\alpha) \underline{\hspace{1.5cm}}$$

$S_t; S_{t-1}(2)$

This statistic is a smoothing of the smoothed values, _____, and gives an indication of the _____ changes over time.

S_t
trend

c. If the time series is neither _____ nor _____ with time, we would use a third-order exponential-smoothing forecasting model given by

constant; linear

$$\hat{y}_{t+T} = [6(1-\alpha)^2 + (6-5\alpha)\alpha T + \alpha^2 T^2] \frac{(\underline{\hspace{1cm}})}{2(1-\alpha)^2}$$

S_t

$$- [6(1-\alpha)^2 + 2(5-4\alpha)\alpha T + 2\alpha^2 T^2] \frac{(\underline{\hspace{1cm}})}{2(1-\alpha)^2}$$

$S_t(2)$

$$+ [2(1-\alpha)^2 + (4-3\alpha)\alpha T + \alpha^2 T^2] \frac{(\underline{\hspace{1cm}})}{2(1-\alpha)^2}$$

$S_t(3)$

The statistic $S_t(3)$ is called the _____-smoothed statistic and measures the average rate of change of the trend over time. $S_t(3)$ is found by computing

triple

$$S_t(3) = \alpha \underline{\hspace{1.5cm}} + (1-\alpha) \underline{\hspace{1.5cm}}$$

$S_t(2); S_{t-1}(3)$

4. Thus, Brown's method provides a means by which forecasts can be computed based upon the three _____ _____ $S_t, S_t(2)$, and $S_t(3)$. The advantage of Brown's method is that it is a _____ scheme developing a new, updated forecast model each time new _____ become available. Updating of least-squares models each time new data become available is often too costly and, hence, becomes prohibitive.

smoothed statistics
recursive
process
data

5. The primary disadvantage of Brown's method is that it may tend to _____ _____ certain cycles or seasonal patterns within the process. Since the model is computed as a function of the smoothed statistics, these statistics tend to consider any departure of the process values from a constant or linear trend as _____ _____ in the time series. Thus, Brown's method should not be used to generate forecasts for a process in which a distinct _____ or _____ pattern exists.

smooth out

random variation

cyclic; seasonal

6. The forecast model is initiated by setting the smoothed statistics $S_t, S_t(2)$ and $S_t(3)$ all equal to _____, the _____ observation. The _____ _____, α, is then selected as a function of the

y_1; first
smoothing constant

small
larger
arbitrary
order
constant
linear; T

forecast
one

updated

apparent volatility of random variation within the process. If the process appears quite volatile, α is given a (large, small) value; if the process is rather stable, a (larger, smaller) value for α is selected. But in any case, the selection of the smoothing constant is _____, and the statistician must use his judgment in choosing α. One chooses the _____ of the model according to whether or not the time series is _____ or _____ over time. One chooses _____, the forecast lead time, according to the number of time points ahead one is attempting to _____. Care should be taken when attempting to forecast more than _____ time period(s) ahead. The values of T and α are substituted into the model of the appropriate order and the forecasting equation is computed as a function of the smoothed statistics S_t, $S_t(2)$ and $S_t(3)$. The smoothed statistics are _____ with each subsequent observation, and then entered into the forecasting equation to obtain the forecast for the next time period.

7. *Example:*

The following data represent the daily high temperature in Fahrenheit degrees recorded at O'Hare Field in Chicago for 15 consecutive days during the month of February. Use Brown's method to forecast the daily high temperatures one day ahead of available data over this period ($T = 1$) and then compare the forecasts with the actual, observed temperatures.

Temperature, y_t: 19.0, 24.5, 20.5, 25.0, 24.8, 30.1, 38.5, 33.0, 29.8, 27.0, 32.7, 42.5, 44.0, 48.2, 46.0.

Solution:

A plot of the temperature values against time would show that the relationship is nearly linear over small segments of time. Thus, an appropriate forecasting for this process is the

$$\hat{y}_{t+T} = \left(2 + \frac{\alpha T}{(1-\alpha)}\right) S_t - \left(1 + \frac{\alpha T}{(1-\alpha)}\right) S_t(2)$$

Suppose, for the sake of discussion, that we let $\alpha = .1$. Then, since $T = 1$, the forecast equation becomes

$$\hat{y}_{t+1} = \underline{\qquad} S_t - \underline{\qquad} S_t(2)$$

2.11; 1.11

For the time period $t = 1$, the smoothing statistics S_t and $S_t(2)$ are set equal to the first process value, _____. Thereafter, they are computed from the recursive equations

19.0

$$S_t = \alpha y_t + (1-\alpha)S_{t-1}$$

and

$$S_t(2) = \alpha S_t + (1-\alpha)S_{t-1}(2)$$

At the second time period ($t = 2$),

$$S_2 = (.1)(24.5) + (1 - .1)(19.0)$$

$$= 19.55$$

and

$$S_2(2) = (.1)(\underline{\hspace{2cm}}) + (1 - .1)(\underline{\hspace{2cm}})$$

$$= \underline{\hspace{2cm}}$$

19.55; 19.0

19.06

Compute the smoothed statistics S_t and $S_t(2)$ for the remaining 13 time periods and place them in the table below.

Day		Temperature	
t	y_t	S_t	$S_t(2)$
1	19.0	19.0	19.0
2	24.5	19.55	19.06
3	20.5	_____	_____
4	25.0	_____	_____
5	24.8	_____	_____
6	30.1	_____	_____
7	38.5	_____	_____
8	33.0	_____	_____
9	29.8	_____	_____
10	27.0	_____	_____
11	32.7	_____	_____
12	42.5	_____	_____
13	44.0	_____	_____
14	48.2	_____	_____
15	46.0	_____	_____

19.65; 19.12
20.19; 19.23
20.65; 19.37
21.60; 19.59
23.29; 19.96
24.26; 20.39
24.81; 20.83
25.03; 21.25
25.80; 21.70
27.47; 22.28
29.12; 22.96
31.03; 23.77
32.53; 24.65

Forecasts may now be computed directly by substituting into the forecasting equation. Computing the forecast for time $t = 2$ using the data available from time $t = 1$, we have

$$\hat{y}_2 = \underline{\hspace{2cm}}(19.0) - \underline{\hspace{2cm}}(19.0)$$

$$= \underline{\hspace{2cm}}$$

2.11; 1.11

19.0

Using data through $t = 2$ to forecast the temperature at $t = 3$,

$$\hat{y}_3 = 2.11(19.55) - 1.11(\underline{\hspace{2cm}})$$

$$= \underline{\hspace{2cm}}$$

19.06

20.09

Use the forecast equation and the smoothed statistics to compute the remaining forecasts for periods $t = 4$ through $t = 15$.

Day t	Actual Temperature y_t	Forecast Temperature $\hat{y}_t$
1	19.0	
2	24.5	19.00
3	20.5	20.09
4	25.0	
5	24.8	
6	30.1	
7	38.5	
8	33.0	
9	29.8	
10	27.0	
11	32.7	
12	42.5	
13	44.0	
14	48.2	
15	46.0	

8. *Example:*

The forecasts which were computed in Example 7 do not appear to be very accurate. Thus, if Brown's method is an appropriate device to use to generate forecasts for this process, either—

a. we should have used a _____ smoothing constant, or

b. we should have used the _____-order exponential-smoothing forecasting model. Use such a model with a smoothing constant of 0.2 to forecast the temperature data from Example 7 one period ahead of available data.

Solution:

The model we have chosen to use is

$$\hat{y}_{t+T} = [6(1 - \alpha)^2 + (6 - 5\alpha)\alpha T + \alpha^2 T^2]\,\frac{S_t}{2(1 - \alpha)^2}$$

$$- [6(1 - \alpha)^2 + 2(5 - 4\alpha)\alpha T + 2\alpha^2 T^2]\,\frac{S_t(2)}{2(1 - \alpha)^2}$$

$$+ [2(1 - \alpha)^2 + (4 - 3\alpha)\alpha T + \alpha^2 T^2]\,\frac{S_t(3)}{2(1 - \alpha)^2}$$

Since $\alpha = .2$ and $T = 1$, the coefficients of the model give us the forecasting equation

$$\hat{y}_{t+1} = \underline{\quad\quad} S_t - \underline{\quad\quad} S_t(2) + \underline{\quad\quad} S_t(3)$$

In order to forecast the process values, we must first compute the values for the _____ _____ S_t, $S_t(2)$, and $S_t(3)$. These statistics are computed _____ by first setting S_1, $S_1(2)$, and $S_1(3)$ equal to _____ and then employing the smoothing equations

20.24
21.26
22.07
23.83
26.99
28.56
29.23
29.23
30.35
33.23
35.96
39.09

larger
third

3.813; 4.375; 1.563

smoothed statistics
recursively
19.0

$$S_t \quad = \alpha y_t + (1 - \alpha)S_{t-1}$$

$$S_t(2) = \alpha S_t + (1 - \alpha)S_{t-1}(2)$$

and

$$S_t(3) = \alpha S_t(2) + (1 - \alpha)S_{t-1}(3)$$

Since $\alpha = .2$, at the second time period ($t = 2$), the smoothed statistics are

$$S_2 \quad = (.2)\,(\underline{\hspace{1.5cm}}) + (1 - .2)\,(\underline{\hspace{1.5cm}}) \qquad\qquad 24.5;\ 19.0$$

$$= \underline{\hspace{1.5cm}} \qquad\qquad 20.10$$

$$S_2(2) = (.2)\,(\underline{\hspace{1.5cm}}) + (1 - .2)\,(\underline{\hspace{1.5cm}}) \qquad\qquad 20.10;\ 19.0$$

$$= \underline{\hspace{1.5cm}} \qquad\qquad 19.22$$

and

$$S_2(3) = (.2)\,(\underline{\hspace{1.5cm}}) + (1 - .2)\,(\underline{\hspace{1.5cm}}) \qquad\qquad 19.22;\ 19.0$$

$$= \underline{\hspace{1.5cm}} \qquad\qquad 19.04$$

Compute the remaining 13 values for each of the smoothed statistics and enter them in the table below.

t	S_t	$S_t(2)$	$S_t(3)$	
1	19.0	19.0	19.0	
2	20.10	19.22	19.04	
3	___	___	___	20.18; 19.41; 19.11
4	___	___	___	21.14; 19.76; 19.24
5	___	___	___	21.87; 20.18; 19.43
6	___	___	___	23.52; 20.85; 19.71
7	___	___	___	26.52; 21.98; 20.16
8	___	___	___	27.82; 23.15; 20.76
9	___	___	___	28.22; 24.16; 21.44
10	___	___	___	27.98; 24.92; 22.14
11	___	___	___	28.92; 25.72; 22.86
12	___	___	___	31.64; 26.90; 23.67
13	___	___	___	34.11; 28.34; 24.60
14	___	___	___	36.93; 30.06; 25.69
15	___	___	___	38.74; 31.80; 26.91

Forecasts one period ahead of available data can now be generated by substituting the smoothed statistics computed above into the forecasting equation

$$\hat{y}_{t+1} = 3.813S_t - 4.375S_t(2) + 1.563S_t(3)$$

Thus, at $t = 1$, our forecast for the second period is

$$\hat{y}_2 = 3.813(19) - 4.375(19) + 1.563(19)$$

$$= 19.0$$

At time $t = 2$, our forecast for the third period is

20.10; 19.22; 19.04

$$\hat{y}_3 = 3.813 \,(\underline{\hspace{1cm}}) - 4.375 \,(\underline{\hspace{1cm}}) + 1.563 \,(\underline{\hspace{1cm}})$$

22.31

$$= \underline{\hspace{1cm}}$$

Compute the one period ahead of available data forecasts for time periods 4 through 15 and list them below.

t		y_t		$\hat{y}_t$
1		19.0		
2		24.5		19.0
3		20.5		22.31
4		25.0		_____
5		24.8		_____
6		30.1		_____
7		38.5		_____
8		33.0		_____
9		29.8		_____
10		27.0		_____
11		32.7		_____
12		42.5		_____
13		44.0		_____
14		48.2		_____
15		46.0		_____

21.90
24.23
25.47
29.27
36.47
37.24
35.41
32.27
33.48
39.95
44.52
49.46

Plot the actual values against the forecast values for the process on the graph below. Note the improved accuracy over the method of Example 7.

9. The multiple exponential-smoothing model can be used as a tracking
model to discover _____ points in a time series. According to
this interpretation, a time series has bottomed out when the true values
cut (<u>under</u>, <u>over</u>) the smoothing forecasts. A process has peaked out
when the _____ values cut under the _____ values.

turning

over

true; forecast

10. From the plot in Example 8, the temperature time series peaked out on the
____, ____ and ____ days. Similarly, the time series bottomed
out on the _____ and _____ days.

2nd; 7th; 14th

3rd; 10th

15.6 The Exponentially Weighted Moving-Average Forecasting Model (15.6)

1. An exponential-smoothing forecasting model is inappropriate to use when
the process values follow a _____ or _____ pattern
over time. The exponentially weighted moving average (EWMA) model is
quite often very effective for generating forecasts for a process with a definite _____ effect.

cyclic; seasonal

seasonal

2. The difference between a cyclic effect and a seasonal effect is that the
seasonal effect is recurrent and _____ and, hence, predictable.
The EWMA attempts to take advantage of this predictability by separately
estimating at each point in time (a) a smoothed process _____,
(b) the trend _____, and (c) the _____
_____. The model then combines these three statistics in a
unique fashion to compute a forecast of a future process value.

periodic

average

gain; seasonal

factors

3. Like the exponential-smoothing forecasting model, the EWMA is a recursive scheme and is therefore efficient in that each forecast is based upon
_____ available past process information. The three components
of the EWMA model are:

a. The smoothed process _____ at time t:

all

average

$$S_t = (\alpha)y_t/F_{t-L} + (\underline{\hspace{1cm}})(S_{t-1} + R_{t-1})$$

$1 - \alpha$

b. The _____ gain at time t:

trend

$$R_t = (\beta)(S_t - S_{t-1}) + (\underline{\hspace{1cm}})R_{t-1}$$

$1 - \beta$

c. The updated _____ factor at time t:

seasonal

$$F_t = (\gamma)y_t/S_t + (\underline{\hspace{1cm}})F_{t-L}$$

$1 - \gamma$

The constants α, β, and γ are arbitrarily selected _____ constants
having values between _____ and _____. Usually, the process
generates accurate forecasts when α and β are near _____ and γ is
near _____. The index L in the seasonal factor F_{t-L} is the _____
of the seasonal effect (the number of time periods required for the process
to complete one seasonal pattern). If the process under study represented
the monthly sales pattern of a department store, L would equal _____,
the number of months before the seasonal pattern would again repeat
itself.

smoothing

zero; one

.1

.4; period

12

S_t

R_t

$(T)R_t$

F_{t-L+T}

L

two

slope
trend
L

trend

initial

4. The EWMA develops a model by asking the following questions:
   a. What is the average value of the process at time t?
   b. What is the best estimate of the gain in the average trend over the fore-cast period?
   c. What is the multiplicative relationship between the process average and the actual process value during the forecast period?
5. All these questions can be answered by the above described components.
   a. _____ is the average value of the process at time t.
   b. _____ is the best estimate of the gain in average trend per unit of time based on all available process information. Thus, if we are fore-casting T time periods ahead, the best estimate of the gain in average trend over these T time periods is _____.
   c. The multiplicative relationship between the process average and the process value at time $t + T$ is _____, the multiplicative relationship computed during the last seasonal period.

   Thus, consistent with a rather logical development, the EWMA forecast model to forecast the value of a process T time periods ahead of available data is

$$\hat{y}_{t+T} = [S_t + (T)R_t] F_{t-L+T}$$

6. Initial values are needed for S and R so that S_t and R_t can be computed at time $t = 1$. Also, a total of _____ initial values are needed for the seasonal factors, F_t; one is computed for each partition (day, week, month, etc.) of the complete seasonal period.
7. It is usually best to derive these initial estimates from part of the process data available from past information. Hopefully, one has at least _____ complete periods of seasonal data from which to compute these estimates. A method for determining the original estimates was discussed in detail in Example 15.2 in the text. In this case, two complete periods of sample data from the past were used. Then,
   a. S_0, the original estimate for S was the first process value from the sample;
   b. R_0, the original value for R was selected as the _____ of the linear _____ line fitted to the sample data;
   c. the _____ seasonal factors were computed by taking the ratio, at each point in the first seasonal period, of the process value to the cor-responding value at that point in time on the _____ line fitted to the data.

   Reference to Example 15.2 should make these points more clear.
8. After the original estimates are developed, these values are then smoothed over the available sample data by use of the above smoothing equations for S_t, R_t, and F_t. The last values computed from the sample data for S, R, and the L-values of F are then used as the _____ estimates for the forecast period.
9. The EWMA model is useful only when the time series is seasonal and has a

predictable period. Furthermore, the peaks and valleys of each seasonal pattern must always occur at the same partitions through the seasonal pattern.

10. *Example:*

The data which appear below represent the monthly sales (in thousands of dollars) of a state liquor store in Eugene, Oregon. Use the EWMA forecasting method to forecast these sales figures one period ahead of available data. Let $\alpha = .1$, $\beta = .1$, and $\gamma = .4$.

Month	Year 1	Year 2
Jan.	15.07	16.91
Feb.	15.86	17.08
Mar.	20.24	20.63
Apr.	18.33	18.64
May	19.87	21.15
June	20.93	20.43
July	17.16	18.67
Aug.	18.93	20.42
Sept.	18.80	19.40
Oct.	22.58	23.83
Nov.	25.35	26.71
Dec.	28.32	29.83

Solution:

Suppose that based upon preliminary sales data, initial estimates have been obtained for S_0, R_0, and the 12 initial values of the seasonal factor, F. These values are as follows:

$$S_0 = 17.53, \qquad R_0 = 0.05$$

and

$$F_{\text{Jan.}} = 0.89 \qquad F_{\text{Feb.}} = 0.93 \qquad F_{\text{Mar.}} = 1.10 \qquad F_{\text{Apr.}} = 1.03$$

$$F_{\text{May}} = 1.10 \qquad F_{\text{June}} = 1.09 \qquad F_{\text{July}} = 0.98 \qquad F_{\text{Aug.}} = 1.04$$

$$F_{\text{Sept.}} = 1.04 \qquad F_{\text{Oct.}} = 1.25 \qquad F_{\text{Nov.}} = 1.35 \qquad F_{\text{Dec.}} = 1.56$$

Suppose we arbitrarily label the months beginning with January of Year 1 and ending with December of Year 2, $t = 1, 2, 3, \ldots, 24$. Our forecast for $t = 1$ based on the initial estimates is then

$$\hat{y}_1 = (S_0 + R_0)F_{\text{Jan.}}$$

$$= \underline{\qquad\qquad} \qquad\qquad (17.53 + 0.05)(0.89)$$

$$= \underline{\qquad\qquad} \qquad\qquad 15.65$$

which compares to the actual January sales figure of \underline{\qquad}. To find $\qquad$ 15.07

further forecasts, we must first find the smoothed estimates for the values of S_t, R_t, and F_{t-L}. Let us compute the forecast of sales for February of Year 1 ($t = 2$), based on available sales data through January of Year 1 ($t = 1$).

The smoothed process average at time $t = 1$ is

$$S_1 = (.1) \frac{y_1}{F_{\text{Jan.}}} + (1 - .1)(S_0 + R_0)$$

$$= (.1) \frac{15.07}{0.89} + (.9)(17.53 + 0.05)$$

$$= 17.52$$

The trend gain at time $t = 1$ is

$$R_1 = (.1)(S_1 - S_0) + (1 - .1)R_0$$

$$= (.1)(17.52 - 17.53) + (.9)(0.05)$$

$$= 0.044$$

The updated seasonal factor to use during the next January is

$$F_1 = (.4) \frac{y_1}{S_1} + (1 - .4)F_{\text{Jan.}}$$

$$= (.4) \frac{(15.07)}{17.52} + (.6)(0.89)$$

$$= 0.88$$

The forecast of sales for February of the first year ($t = 2$) is then

$$\hat{y}_2 = (S_1 + R_1)F_{\text{Feb.}}$$

$$= (17.52 + 0.044)(0.93)$$

$$= 16.33$$

which compares to the actual value of $y_2 = 15.86$.

To find $\hat{y}_3$ based upon sales data through $t = 2$, we need values for S_2 and R_2. They are obtained as follows:

$$S_2 = (.1) \frac{y_2}{F_{\text{Feb.}}} + (.9)(S_1 + R_1)$$

$$= (.1) \frac{(\underline{\hspace{2cm}})}{(0.93)} + (.9) \, (\underline{\hspace{1.5cm}} + \underline{\hspace{1.5cm}})$$

15.86; 17.52; 0.044

$$= \underline{\hspace{2cm}}$$

17.51

and

$$R_2 = (.1) \, (S_2 - S_1) + (.9)R_1$$

$$= (.1) \, (\underline{\hspace{1.5cm}} - \underline{\hspace{1.5cm}}) + (.9) \, (\underline{\hspace{1.5cm}})$$

17.51; 17.52; 0.044

$$= \underline{\hspace{2cm}}$$

0.039

The forecast of sales for time period $t = 3$ is then

$$\hat{y}_3 = (S_2 + R_2)F_{\text{Mar.}}$$

$$= (\underline{\hspace{1.5cm}} + \underline{\hspace{1.5cm}}) \, (\underline{\hspace{1.5cm}})$$

17.51; 0.039; 1.10

$$= \underline{\hspace{2cm}}$$

19.30

which compares to the true sales at $t = 3$ of $y_3 = 20.24$. For each of the remaining time periods, $t = 4$ through $t = 24$, compute the smoothed process average S_t, the trend gain R_t, and the seasonal factor, F_t. Then use the EWMA forecasting method to find the estimate of sales in period $t + 1$ based on sales data through period t. List the values in the table below.

t	S_t	R_t	F_t	$\hat{y}_t$	y_t
1	17.52	0.044	0.88	15.65	15.07
2	17.51	0.039	0.92	16.33	15.86
3				19.30	20.24
4					18.33
5					19.87
6					20.93
7					17.16
8					18.93
9					18.80
10					22.58
11					25.35
12					28.32
13					16.91
14					17.08
15					20.63
16					18.64
17					21.15
18					20.43
19					18.67
20					20.42
21					19.40
22					23.83
23					26.71
24					29.83

The correct values are given in the table which follows.

t		S_t	R_t	F_t	$\hat{y}_t$	y_t
1		17.52	0.044	0.88	15.65	15.07
2		17.51	0.039	0.92	16.33	15.86
3		17.63	0.047	1.12	19.30	20.24
4		17.69	0.048	1.03	18.21	18.33
5		17.77	0.051	1.11	19.51	19.87
6		17.96	0.065	1.12	19.42	20.93
7		17.97	0.060	0.97	17.66	17.16
8		18.05	0.062	1.04	18.75	18.93
9		18.11	0.062	1.04	18.84	18.80
10		18.16	0.061	1.25	22.72	22.58
11		18.28	0.067	1.36	24.60	25.35
12		18.33	0.065	1.55	28.62	28.32
13		18.48	0.074	0.89	16.19	16.91
14		18.56	0.075	0.92	17.07	17.08
15		18.61	0.073	1.12	20.87	20.63
16		18.62	0.067	1.02	19.24	18.64
17		18.72	0.070	1.12	20.74	21.15
18		18.74	0.065	1.11	21.04	20.43
19		18.85	0.070	0.98	18.24	18.67
20		18.99	0.077	1.05	19.68	20.42
21		19.03	0.073	1.03	19.83	19.40
22		19.10	0.073	1.25	23.88	23.83
23		19.22	0.078	1.37	26.08	26.71
24		19.29	0.077	1.55	29.91	29.83

15.7 Other Forecasting Models and Procedures (15.7)

A. *The Growth Model*

1. If a growth process shows little or no _____ or _____ effect, and the trend appears to be _____, then a growth model might suitably be used to forecast the time series.

   cyclic; seasonal
   exponential

2. In such a time series, the process values are increasing at an increasing rate over time.

3. The model for an exponential growth model is

   $$g = \underline{\hspace{2cm}}$$

   $ae^{bt}\epsilon'$

   where t = the unit of time

   e = 2.71828 . . .

   ϵ' = random error

   and a and b are the model constants which determine the fit of the process values, g, to the units of time, t.

4. Notice that the model is a _____ model. If we take the natural

   multiplicative

_____ of both sides of the model equation, the model reduces to

$$\ln g = \ln a + bt + \ln \epsilon'$$

which is an _____ model. If we let

$$y = \underline{\hspace{2cm}}$$

$$\beta_0 = \underline{\hspace{2cm}}$$

$$\beta_1 = \underline{\hspace{2cm}}$$

and

$$\epsilon = \underline{\hspace{2cm}}$$

we have the simple _____ regression model of Chapter 11:

$$y = \beta_0 + \beta_1 t + \epsilon$$

5. The _____ growth model can then be fitted to time series data by:
   a. transforming the process values by computing their _____
   _____,
   b. computing the coefficients for the linear regression model relating
   $y = \underline{\hspace{2cm}}$ to the units of time, t.
6. Future process values can then be forecast by substituting the proper value for t into the regression model and estimating the value of y. Since $\hat{y}$ is in terms of the natural logarithm of the process value, the process value would be

$$\hat{g} = \underline{\hspace{2cm}}$$

7. An appropriate _____ _____ can similarly be found for the estimate (forecast) value of the process. One would first use the methods of Section 12.7 to find a confidence interval using the regression estimate, $\hat{y}$. Confidence intervals for g, the forecast value, can be found by transforming the confidence interval for y, say

$$k_1 < y < k_2$$

to

$$\underline{\hspace{2cm}} < g < \underline{\hspace{2cm}}$$

---

logarithm

additive

$\ln g$

$\ln a$

b

$\ln \epsilon'$

linear

exponential

natural
logarithms

$\ln g$

$e^{\hat{y}}$

confidence interval

$e^{k_1}; e^{k_2}$

B. *The Box-Jenkins Forecasting Procedure*

Box-Jenkins

1. When the patterns in a time series are very complex or difficult to discern, the _____ _____ forecasting procedure can be a useful and efficient technique.

autocorrelations

2. The Box-Jenkins technique uses an analysis of the _____ present in the time series to provide the basis for a forecasting model which combines—

autoregressive

    a. a(n) _____ component, composed of a linear combination of lagged values of the underlying time series, and

moving-average

    b. a(n) _____ _____ component, composed of a linear combination of current and past error terms.

trend

3. Differencing is applied to the time series as many times as is necessary to remove any inherent _____. The autocorrelation analysis is actually performed on the time series which is generated by first-differencing the underlying time series.

4. Any particular Box-Jenkins forecasting model belongs to a class of such models which is specified by three numbers: the maximum lag on the autoregressive terms, the maximum lag on the moving-average terms, and the number of applications of first-differencing needed to eliminate any trends.

least squares
residuals

5. Once the Box-Jenkins model has been specified, the model parameters are estimated using _____ _____. But before a forecast can be made, the model must be checked. If the _____ generated by the forecasting model do not exhibit any distinct pattern, but rather appear random, the fit of the model is presumed adequate. Otherwise, a new _____ of Box-Jenkins models must be considered.

class

6. There are limitations on the usefulness of Box-Jenkins forecasting models:

    a. The necessary computer programs can be very expensive to use.

    b. The EWMA model will give at least as good results when applied to a time series with a clear _____ component.

seasonal

    c. Such models rely heavily on subjective judgment and forecasting experience at the model specification stage.

C. *Qualitative Forecasting Models*

1. Qualitative forecasting models should be considered when the relevant historical _____ _____ is not available as an aid in forecasting the future.

data base

2. Qualitative forecasting models include the _____ _____ method, the _____ method, the _____ analogy, and, in situations concerning customer behavior, _____ research methods.

panel consensus
delphi; historical
market

Self-Correcting Exercises 15B

1. Refer to Self-Correcting Exercises 15A, problem 2. Assume the sales data for the year given are linear over time. Use a first-order multiple exponential smoothing (Brown's method) forecasting model to forecast the sales volume one month ahead of available information. Let $\alpha = .1$.
2. Refer to the data given in Self-Correcting Exercises 14A. Since the sales volume for the liquor store appears to be quite seasonal, use the exponentially weighted moving-average model to forecast the monthly sales volume of the liquor store one month ahead of available sales data. Based upon earlier sales data, initial values for the process average and trend gain are $S_0 = 18.0$ and $R_0 = 0.2$, respectively, while initial values for the seasonal indices are:

Jan. .53	May .92	Sept. 1.12
Feb. .61	June 1.11	Oct. 1.16
Mar. .89	July 1.02	Nov. 1.30
Apr. .72	Aug. .90	Dec. 1.66

Let the smoothing constants be $\alpha = .1, \beta = .1, \gamma = .4$.

15.8 Summary (15.8)

1. At best, statistical methods provide only a _____ _____ in the computation of the forecast of a process value because of the uncertainties which exist over time. Certain variables may lie _____ for a period of time only later to exhibit a considerable influence on a time series. Other variables may simply _____ their apparent relationship with a time series. Thus, a model which _____ a set of sample data may not accurately forecast future process values.

2. The ultimate criterion of a forecasting model is how well it _____ the future. Model selection can be aided by observing the relationship of the process variable with _____ and with other variables over time.

3. The most commonly used forecasting model is the _____ _____ model. Such a model uses an _____ combination of related variables to generate a forecast. Trigonometric terms can also be used in the model to track _____ patterns of the process value over time.

4. When _____ process values are used in a linear regression model as predictors, the model is called an _____ model. The determination of which _____ process values to use as predictors is often aided by the construction of a _____.

starting point

dormant

change
fits

forecasts

time

linear
regression; additive

cyclic

lagged
autoregressive
lagged
correlogram

exponential-smoothing

seasonal; exponen-
tially weighted

same
seldom

5. Recursive forecasting methods do not employ predictor variables formally in the model. The multiple _____ _____ model (Brown's method) is useful when the time series can be considered a polynomial over time. For processes which exhibit a pronounced _____ effect, the _____ _____ moving-average model often generates accurate forecasts.

6. Only a few of the available forecasting methods were presented in Chapter 15. It must be remembered that the development of a good forecasting model requires a great deal of ingenuity on the part of the statistician. Seldom would two statisticians select the _____ model for a particular process and _____ would one particular model be found appropriate for forecasting two different time series.

Chapter   16

SURVEY SAMPLING

16.1   Introduction (16.1)

1. The topics presented in previous chapters were mainly concerned with methods for describing and analyzing available sets of data, with the major emphasis on analysis and interpretation of results. In this chapter, the emphasis will be on the methods used to select the sample that gives rise to the sample observations. Methods for selecting the sample are called sampling designs.

2. The objective of a sampling design is to produce a sample that is representative of the _____ from which it was drawn. The type of sampling design chosen depends mainly on the _____ of the population with regard to the characteristic under investigation; however, other factors may also affect the sampling design ultimately chosen.

   population
   uniformity

3. A _____ is an enumeration of every element contained in the population, whereas a sample survey involves only those elements of the population included in the _____. Although a census certainly provides more information than would a sample survey, a sample survey has many advantages when compared to a complete census. In addition to economy and feasibility, a sample survey has the following advantages.

   census

   sample

   a. Sampling provides the opportunity for rapid information retrieval not usually available with a complete census.

   b. When the evaluation of the characteristics under study results in the destruction of the elements tested, a census is not reasonable.

   c. A complete census will not necessarily provide complete information since, for example, people may refuse to answer what they feel are sensitive or very personal questions, or the sheer volume of data may cause careless recording and/or handling of results.

4. In order to ensure that the sample is representative of the population sampled, and that the sample is chosen so that valid inferences can be made about the population, the sample must be drawn in a _____ manner. A random sample is a sample selected in such a way that every sample of n observations has the same probability of being selected. When

   random

sample

element
does not

may not
frame

frame

larger

two

5%

a sample is not random, only descriptive statements about the (sample, population) can be made.

5. A sampling design or a survey design specifies the method for collecting the elements in the sample. An _____ is an object on which a measurement is taken. The design itself (does, does not) specify the method in which an element in the sample will give rise to an observation. Sampling units are nonoverlapping collections of elements from the population. A sampling unit (may, may not) be an individual element. A list of all sampling units contained in the population is called a _____ .

6. In conducting a sample survey, the sampling units must first be identified, and an appropriate frame constructed. The sampling units to be included are then randomly chosen from the _____ in accordance with the desired sampling design.

16.2 Bias and Error in Sampling (16.2)

1. The reliability of an inference concerning a population parameter θ is measured by the error in estimation, defined as $|\hat{\theta} - \theta|$, the absolute difference between the estimate and the true value of the parameter estimated. When the experimenter can specify a tolerable bound B on the error of estimation, a minimum sample size can be found that will ensure that the estimate $\hat{\theta}$ will not differ from θ by more than B with a high probability. The smaller the value of B, the (smaller, larger) will be the sample size required to achieve the specified bound on the error of estimation.

2. Three factors that may affect the validity of the results of a sample survey are random variation, misspecification, and nonresponse. Misspecification and nonresponse may cause estimates to be biased, while random variation introduces the possibility that the sample observations constitute one of the very unlikely samples possible under random sampling.

3. *Random Variation:*
When sampling has been done in a random manner, so that every combination of n elements from the population has an equal chance of being selected, the distribution of sample estimates can be determined, and confidence interval estimates for the parameter under investigation can be constructed. When, for example, the estimator is unbiased and the distribution of estimates is approximately normal, a 95% confidence interval estimate means that approximately 95% of such estimates will be within _____ standard deviations of the true value of the parameter. However, it also means that approximately _____ of such estimates will lie farther than two standard deviations from the true value of the parameter. Since random sampling always introduces random variation into the estimation scheme, there is always the possibility that any single estimate will be farther than two standard deviations from the true value of the parameter. For example, if a random sampling plan implemented to determine the average assessed value of single-family residences in a given area happened to produce a sample containing only those homes with four or more bed-

rooms when the area has a preponderance of residences with at most three bedrooms, the sample average would lead the sampler to conclude that the average assessed value in the area is (lower, higher) than it actually is. Hence, random variation introduces the probability of error in estimation.

higher

4. *Misspecification:*

In order to make valid inferences from sample information, the sample must be drawn from the target population of interest. If a sample drawn from a related, but essentially different, population is used to make inferences about the target population, any resulting inferences about the target population will be _____ in some way. When the frame used to select a sample does not accurately contain the elements in the target population, we have the problem of _____. Using a telephone directory as a frame for all family residences in a given city systematically excludes residences without phones or residences with unlisted telephone numbers. Such a systematic exclusion could produce bias in inferences made from sample data collected using this frame. It may be that the frame contains elements not in the population, or perhaps contains incorrect information concerning these elements. In either case, misspecification can produce _____ in the survey sample results.

biased

misspecification

bias

5. *Nonresponse:*

Another major source of error in sample surveys is due to nonresponse by some members of the sample. Nonresponse is quite common in telephone surveys, in surveys in which a questionnaire is mailed to a household, and in door-to-door surveys involving individual households. Nonresponse results in bias because researchers in general assume that respondents and nonrespondents would provide _____ information in the survey when this is rarely the case. In preference surveys, very often nonrespondents are satisfied with the status quo, or have no strong feelings about a given matter. In door-to-door surveys, nonrespondents are usually those employed outside the home, while respondents are homemakers, retired persons, and others who can perform their work at home. Some control over nonresponse can be accomplished by revisiting nonrespondents or randomly choosing an _____ sampling unit.

similar

alternate

6. Errors due to random variation can be controlled to some extent by the choice of sample _____ and by the choice of the survey _____ to be used. Careful definition of the target population and the associated frame can eliminate bias due to _____. Attempts to contact nonrespondents or the random selection of an alternate will help reduce bias due to _____. In light of these sources of error, great care should be exercised in designing a sample survey and in the interpretation of the results.

size
design
misspecification

nonresponse

16.3 How to Select a Random Sample (16.3)

1. The selection of a simple random sample is a basic technique that is used in all sampling designs. Therefore, it is important to know in detail how to

select a simple random sample of size n from a *finite* population consisting of N elements.

2. When a sample is drawn in such a way that every possible sample of size n has the same probability of being selected, the sampling is said to be _____ and the resulting sample is called a simple _____.

random; random sample

3. Although random sampling is difficult to achieve in practice, the use of a _____ _____ table in selecting a random sample is the best way to implement a random sampling design. A random number table contains the digits _____ through _____ with equal frequency and in a random order. The digits are in random order if there is no pattern of any kind with respect to their occurrence. For example, in a random number table you would not find the digit 9 always followed by a 1 or 2. Neither, for example, would you find a two-digit combination such as 57 or 75 always followed by a combination such as 68 or 86. When a random number table is used to select a simple random sample, the choice of elements to be included in the sample reflects the properties of the random number table used in the selection. We illustrate the procedure with the next example.

random number

0; 9

4. *Example:*

In order to estimate the number of visits to a doctor per household in an area containing $N = 1000$ households, an investigator has decided to select a simple random sample of size 20 households. Use the random number table in your text to select a sample of size $n = 20$ drawn in such a way as to satisfy a simple random sampling plan.

Solution:

The frame to be used in this problem consists of a list of the 1000 households in the given area. Since each of the numbers 1 through 1000 corresponds to one and only one household in the area, we need to select 20 numbers between 1 and 1000 from the random number table to identify the households to be included in the sample.

a. Suppose we decide to use the first three digits of the five-digit numbers appearing in the columns of the table. We must first randomly select a line and column in the table as a starting point and then decide in which direction we will move within the table. This can be done by turning to a page containing the random numbers and setting your pencil point on the page. In pinpointing a five-digit block of numbers, we can use the first two digits to find the row and the next two digits to find the column in which to begin. Suppose that our pencil pointed to the five-digit group 21361 in line 81, column 7. The first two digits in the group 21361 can identify the line as line _____, while the second two digits in the group 21361 can identify the column. Since there are only 14 columns, divide 36 by 14 and use the *remainder* to identify the column. Since 36/14 is 2 with a remainder of _____, we begin with column _____.

21

8
8

b. Using line 21, column 8 as a starting point, we can now list the five-digit entries by moving in any direction we wish. Let us list lines 21 through

25 for columns 8, 9, 10 and 11 to produce the 20 random numbers required to identify the sample elements. We will associate households 1 through 999 with the entries 001 through 999 in the table and household 1000 with the entry 000.

04734	59193	22178	30421
26384	58151	06646	21524
28728	35806	06912	17012
15398	46557	41135	10367
61280	50001	67658	32586

By reading the first three digits in each five-digit group, we have identified the households to be included in the sample.

c. If a household number appeared more than once in the list of random numbers, that household would only appear *once* in the sample. Further entries in the table would be used until 20 distinct households had been identified for inclusion in the sample.

5. *Example:*

How would the selection procedure in Example 4 be modified if the area contained $N = 500$ households?

Solution:

a. By using three-digit entries to identify the $n = 20$ households when the population size is $N = 500$, we could associate households 1 through 500 with the digits _____ through _____ and discard or not record 000 and any random digits between 501 and 999.

b. Alternatively, to avoid excessive table listings, we could use the random digits 001 through 500 directly, and for any number in the range 501 through 999, use its remainder upon division by _____. Under this scheme, household 228 would be associated with the three-digit random numbers 228 and _____. Finally, by associating household 500 with the random numbers 000 and _____, our sample will be drawn so that every household has a 2 in 1000 or 1 in 500 chance of being included in the sample.

001; 500

500

728
500

Self-Correcting Exercises 16A

1. An auditing firm has been hired by a company to examine its accounts receivable. If the company has 100 current accounts and the auditing firm proposes to examine 20 of those accounts, explain how you would randomly select 20 accounts from the 100 accounts using a random number table.

2. To investigate employee satisfaction with regard to company fringe benefits, the management of a company employing 250 workers proposes to survey 30 workers concerning their views on company fringe benefits. If these 30 workers are to be randomly chosen from the 250 workers employed by the company, provide an efficient selection scheme for choosing

the 30 workers, using random number tables. Implement the sampling plan and record the 30 workers who are to be interviewed.

16.4 Estimation Based on a Simple Random Sample (16.4)

1. The objective of any sampling design is to produce valid inferences about the population sampled. Most investigations are concerned with estimating the population mean, μ, or a population total, τ. For example, a large wholesale firm might be interested in the mean sales per account as well as the total sales. This same firm would also be interested in the proportion of delinquent accounts. In addition to a point estimator for each of these population parameters, we need the variance of these estimators in order to place bounds on the error of estimation. We shall consistently use two standard deviations as the bound on error, implying minimally that at least _____% (and more likely _____%) of such estimates will lie within two standard deviations of the true value of the estimated parameter.

75; 95

A. *Estimation of the Population Mean and Total for a Simple Random Sample*

1. The estimator of the population mean μ of a finite population of size N based on a simple random sample of size n is

$$\bar{y} = \frac{\Sigma y_i}{n}$$

with variance

$$\hat{\sigma}_{\bar{y}}^2 = \frac{s^2}{n}\left(\frac{N-n}{N}\right)$$

The point estimate with bounds on the error of estimation is $\bar{y} \pm 2\hat{\sigma}_{\bar{y}}$. The quantity s^2 is the sample variance of the n sample observations, discussed earlier in this text.

2. The estimator of the population total τ uses the information contained in $\bar{y}$ by inflating this average by a factor of _____, the population size. Hence,

N

$$\hat{\tau} = N\bar{y}$$

with variance

$$\hat{\sigma}_{\hat{\tau}}^2 = N^2 \hat{\sigma}_{\bar{y}}^2$$

The point estimate with bounds on the error of estimation is given as

$$N\bar{y} \pm 2\sigma_{\hat{\tau}}$$

3. Notice that the variance of $\bar{y}$ when sampling from a finite population of size N is

$$\frac{s^2}{n}\left(\frac{N-n}{N}\right)$$

the same as the quantity given in earlier chapters multiplied by _____.
The quantity $(N-n)/N$ is called the finite population _____
_____ and accounts for the fact that sampling does deplete a
finite population. When n is small relative to N, $(N-n)/N$ is close to
_____. When $N \geqslant 20n$, the correction factor is often ignored and
the quantity s^2/n is used as the variance of $\bar{y}$. However, we will use the
finite population correction factor where appropriate, regardless of the
population and sample sizes.

$(N-n)/N$	
correction	
factor	
one	

4. *Example:*
A wholesale firm that has 325 active accounts is interested in estimating
the average sales per account as well as the total sales over the last four
weeks. In a random sample of 20 accounts, the average sales per account
was found to be $\bar{y} = \$849$ with a sample standard deviation of $s = \$89$.
Estimate the average sales per account and the total sales for the last four
weeks. Place bounds of error on these estimates.
Solution:
A summary of the pertinent information follows.

$$\bar{y} = 849 \qquad\qquad n = 20$$

$$s = 89 \qquad\qquad N = 325$$

a. The estimate of the mean sales per account is $\bar{y} = $ _____. To place
bounds of error on this estimate, we need to evaluate $\hat{\sigma}_{\bar{y}}$.

849

$$\hat{\sigma}^2_{\bar{y}} = \frac{s^2}{n}\left(\frac{N-n}{N}\right)$$

$$= \frac{(89)^2}{20}\left(\frac{325-20}{325}\right)$$

$$= \frac{(89)^2}{20}\;(\underline{\hspace{1.5cm}})$$

.9385

$$= \underline{\hspace{2cm}}$$

371.6929

Hence,

$$\hat{\sigma}_{\bar{y}} = \sqrt{371.6929}$$

19.28

$$= \underline{\hspace{2cm}}$$

The estimate of the mean sales per account with a bound on the error of estimation is

$$849 \pm 2(19.28)$$

$849; $38.56

$$\underline{\hspace{2cm}} \pm \underline{\hspace{2cm}}$$

b. The estimate of the total sales is given by

$$\hat{\tau} = N\bar{y}$$

325

$$= \underline{\hspace{2cm}}(849)$$

275,928

$$= \underline{\hspace{2cm}}$$

Evaluating $\hat{\sigma}_{\hat{\tau}}$, we have

$$\hat{\sigma}_{\hat{\tau}}^2 = N^2 \hat{\sigma}_{\bar{y}}^2$$

325

$$= (\underline{\hspace{2cm}})^2(371.6929)$$

$$= 39,260,062.56$$

with

$$\hat{\sigma}_{\hat{\tau}} = \sqrt{39,260,062.56}$$

6265.79

$$= \underline{\hspace{2cm}}$$

The estimate of total sales with bounds on the error of estimation is given as

$$275,928 \pm 2(6265.79)$$

or

$275,928; $12,532

$$\underline{\hspace{2cm}} \pm \underline{\hspace{2cm}}$$

B. *Estimation of the Population Proportion for a Simple Random Sample*

1. In estimating the proportion p of the population that possesses a given characteristic, we use the computational procedures of Chapter 8 with a modification to account for sampling from a finite population of size N.
2. If y is the number of elements in the sample of size n possessing the specified characteristic, the estimate of p is

$$\hat{p} = \underline{\hspace{2cm}}$$

$\dfrac{y}{n}$

with variance

$$\hat{\sigma}_{\hat{p}}^2 = \frac{\hat{p}\hat{q}}{(n-1)}\left(\frac{N-n}{N}\right)$$

where $\hat{q} = \underline{\hspace{2cm}}$. The point estimate for p with bounds on the error or estimation is

$1 - \hat{p}$

$$\hat{p} \pm 2\hat{\sigma}_{\hat{p}}$$

3. *Example:*
Refer to Example 4 in Section A. Suppose that 2 of the 20 sampled accounts were found to be delinquent. Estimate the proportion of the firm's accounts that are delinquent.
Solution:
a. The estimate of the proportion of delinquent accounts is

$$\hat{p} = \frac{y}{n} = \frac{2}{20} = \underline{\hspace{2cm}}$$

.1

and

$$\hat{q} = 1 - \hat{p} = \underline{\hspace{2cm}}$$

.9

b. The estimated variance of $\hat{p}$ is

$$\hat{\sigma}_{\hat{p}}^2 = \frac{\hat{p}\hat{q}}{(n-1)}\left(\frac{N-n}{N}\right)$$

$$= \frac{(.1)(.9)}{19}\left(\frac{325-20}{325}\right)$$

$$= \frac{.09}{19} (.9385)$$

.004445

$$= \underline{\hspace{2cm}}$$

and

$$\hat{\sigma}_{\hat{p}} = \sqrt{.004445}$$

.0667

$$= \underline{\hspace{2cm}}$$

c. The point estimate of the proportion of delinquent accounts with bounds on the error of estimation is

$$.1 \pm 2(.0667)$$

.1; .1334

$$\underline{\hspace{2cm}} \pm \underline{\hspace{2cm}}$$

Self-Correcting Exercises 16B

1. To estimate the average assessed value of $N = 1000$ single-family residences within a given area of a city, a simple random sample of $n = 25$ residences provided the following information.

$$\bar{y} = \$46,500 \qquad\qquad s = \$8,600$$

a. Estimate the average assessed value of the 1000 homes in this area, and place a bound on the error of estimation.
b. Estimate the total assessed value of the homes in this area, and place a bound on the error of estimation.
2. A quality control scheme required that a random sample of $n = 50$ items be selected from each incoming lot of $N = 1000$ items. If 8 defective items were found in a sample of 50 items from lot number 18, estimate the percentage of defective items in lot 18, and place a bound on the error of estimation.

16.5 Stratified Random Sampling (16.5)

1. In many situations the population of interest consists of one or more subpopulations. Workers within a given industry may be grouped into several natural job categories; business firms or cities may be grouped according to size; areas may be classified as urban, suburban or rural. In such cases, it is desirable to have each subpopulation represented in the sample. A stratified random sample is a sample obtained by dividing a population into nonoverlapping subpopulations called _____ and then selecting

strata

a _____ _____ sample within each stratum.

2. Stratified random sampling, when appropriate, has three major advantages over simple random sampling.
   a. The cost of collecting and analyzing data is often reduced by stratifying a population into homogeneous subgroups, which are different from one another.
   b. The variance of the estimator is also reduced by stratification, since the variation within subgroups is usually (smaller, larger) than the overall population variance.

smaller

   c. Stratified sampling provides separate estimates for parameters in each _____ , without selecting a separate sample.

stratum

3. The cost of sampling and the bound on the error of estimation are two factors that determine the sample allocation across the strata. In general, one takes a larger sample if
   a. the stratum is (small, large)

large

   b. the variance within that stratum is (small, large), or

large

   c. sampling costs (less, more) in that stratum.

less

   One method of allocation, called the proportional allocation procedure, partitions the sample size across the strata proportional to the _____ of the strata. We will use this procedure throughout this chapter because of its simplicity and because of inherent problems usually encountered in optimum allocation procedures.

size

4. In allocating a sample of size n across L strata using the proportional allocation procedure, n_i elements are selected from the ith stratum, where

$$n_i = n\left(\frac{N_i}{N}\right)$$

   when the ith stratum contains N_i elements and the total population size is

$$N = \sum_{i=1}^{L} N_i$$

5. *Example:*
   An investigator has sufficient funds to include 50 wholesale dealers of farm implements in a products liability insurance survey. Of the 1000 dealers, 600 have annual sales under $5 million, 300 have annual sales between $5 and $25 million, and the remaining 100 have annual sales in excess of $25 million. Produce the proportional sample allocation appropriate for this situation.
   Solution:
   The population size is $N = 1000$, with stratum sizes N_1 = _____ ,

600

   N_2 = _____ , N_3 = _____ .

300; 100

   a. The sample size for stratum 1 is

$$n_1 = n\left(\frac{N_1}{N}\right)$$

$$= 50\left(\frac{600}{1000}\right)$$

30

$$=\underline{\hspace{2cm}}$$

b. For stratum 2,

$$n_2 = 50\left(\frac{300}{1000}\right)$$

15

$$=\underline{\hspace{2cm}}$$

c. For stratum 3,

$$n_3 = 50\left(\frac{100}{1000}\right)$$

5

$$=\underline{\hspace{2cm}}$$

30; 15
5

Proportional allocation would allot $n_1 = \underline{\hspace{2cm}}, n_2 = \underline{\hspace{2cm}}$, and $n_3 = \underline{\hspace{2cm}}$.

6. *Estimation of the Mean and Variance of Each Stratum:*
If y_{ij} is the jth observation in the ith stratum, $j = 1, 2, \ldots, n_i$, the mean and variance for the ith stratum are estimated by

$$\bar{y}_i = \frac{\displaystyle\sum_{j=1}^{n_i} y_{ij}}{n_i}$$

and

$$s_i^2 = \frac{\displaystyle\sum_{j=1}^{n_i} (y_{ij} - \bar{y}_i)^2}{n_i - 1}$$

respectively, where $i = 1, 2, \ldots, L$. The sum of squared deviations is calculated as usual:

$$\sum_{j=1}^{n_i} (y_{ij} - \bar{y}_i)^2 = \sum_{j=1}^{n_i} y_{ij}^2 - \frac{\left(\sum\limits_{j=1}^{n_i} y_{ij}\right)^2}{n_i}$$

7. *Estimation of the Population Mean for a Stratified Random Sample:*
   The estimator of the population mean is the weighted average of the strata means, using the strata sizes as weights. This estimator is

$$\bar{y}_{st} = \frac{1}{N} \sum_{i=1}^{L} N_i \bar{y}_i$$

with variance

$$\hat{\sigma}_{\bar{y}_{st}}^2 = \frac{1}{N^2} \sum_{i=1}^{L} N_i^2 \left(\frac{N_i - n_i}{N_i}\right) \left(\frac{s_i^2}{n_i}\right)$$

Two standard deviations are used as bounds on the error of estimation.

8. *Example:*
   The following tabulation provides a partial summary of the results of the products liability insurance survey of Example 5. The amount of products liability insurance carried by each dealer was recorded in units of one million dollars. Stratum 1 included all dealers with annual sales under $5 million, stratum 2 included those dealers with annual sales between $5 and $25 million, and stratum 3 included those dealers whose annual sales exceeded $25 million.

	Stratum 1	Stratum 2	Stratum 3
N_i	600	300	100
n_i	30	15	5
y_i	6.2	47.3	150.2
s_i^2	2.5	25.4	100.8

Estimate the average amount of products liability insurance carried, and place bounds on the error of estimation.
Solution:
a. Using the tabled information, the estimate of the average amount of products liability insurance carried is found using

$$\bar{y}_{st} = \frac{1}{N} \sum_{i=1}^{L} N_i \bar{y}_i$$

There are $L = 3$ strata with $N = 1000$. Hence,

$$\bar{y}_{st} = \frac{1}{1000} [600(6.2) + 300(47.3) + 100(150.2)]$$

15,020

$$= \frac{1}{1000} [3720 + 14{,}190 + \underline{}]$$

32,930

$$= \frac{1}{1000} (\underline{})$$

32.93

$$= \underline{}$$

b. To calculate bounds on error, we need to evaluate the variance of $\bar{y}_{st}$. Using proportional allocation, the finite population correction factors should be equal within each stratum. For stratum 1,

.95

$$\frac{N_1 - n_1}{N_1} = \frac{600 - 30}{600} = \underline{}$$

For stratum 2,

.95

$$\frac{N_2 - n_2}{N_2} = \frac{300 - 15}{300} = \underline{}$$

For stratum 3,

.95

$$\frac{N_3 - n_3}{N_3} = \frac{100 - 5}{100} = \underline{}$$

Hence,

$$\hat{\sigma}_{\bar{y}_{st}}^2 = \frac{1}{N^2} \sum_{i=1}^{L} N_i^2 \left(\frac{N_i - n_i}{N_i} \right) \left(\frac{s_i^2}{n_i} \right)$$

$$= \frac{.95}{(1000)^2} \left[(600)^2 \left(\frac{2.5}{30} \right) + (300)^2 \left(\frac{25.4}{15} \right) + (100)^2 \left(\frac{100.8}{5} \right) \right]$$

$$= \frac{.95}{(1000)^2} [30{,}000 + 151{,}800 + 201{,}600]$$

$$= \frac{.95}{(1000)^2} [\underline{\hspace{2cm}}] \qquad\qquad 383{,}400$$

$$= \underline{\hspace{2cm}} \qquad\qquad .36423$$

and

$$\hat{\sigma}_{\bar{y}_{st}} = \sqrt{.36423} - \underline{\hspace{2cm}} \qquad\qquad .6035$$

c. The estimate of the average amount of liability insurance carried is

$$\$32{,}930{,}000 \pm 2(603{,}500)$$

or

$$\underline{\hspace{2cm}} \pm \underline{\hspace{2cm}} \qquad\qquad \$32{,}930{,}000; \$1{,}207{,}000$$

9. *Example:*
Using the information in Example 8, estimate the total amount of products liability insurance carried by these dealers and place a bound on the error of estimation.
Solution:
From Example 8, we have $\bar{y}_{st} = \underline{\hspace{2cm}}$ with estimated variance $\underline{\hspace{2cm}}$. Therefore, $\qquad\qquad$ 32.93 .6035

$$\hat{\tau} = N\bar{y}_{st}$$

$$= 1000(32.93)$$

$$= \underline{\hspace{2cm}} \qquad\qquad 32{,}930$$

and

$$\hat{\sigma}_{\hat{\tau}} = \sqrt{N^2 \hat{\sigma}_{\bar{y}_{st}}^2}$$

$$= \sqrt{(1000)^2(.6035)}$$

$$= \sqrt{\underline{\hspace{2cm}}} \qquad\qquad 603{,}500$$

$$= \underline{\hspace{2cm}} \qquad\qquad 776.85$$

The estimate of the total amount of products liability insurance carried is

$$\$32,930MM \pm 2(\$776.85MM)$$

$$\$32,930MM \pm \$1,553.70MM$$

where MM represents 1 million.

10. *Estimation of the Population Proportion for a Stratified Random Sample:*
The estimator of the population proportion p for a stratified random sample is the weighted average of the sample proportions in each stratum using the strata sizes as weights.

$$\hat{p}_{st} = \frac{1}{N} \sum_{i=1}^{L} N_i \hat{p}_i$$

with

$$\hat{\sigma}^2_{\hat{p}_{st}} = \frac{1}{N^2} \sum_{i=1}^{L} N_i^2 \left(\frac{N_i - n_i}{N_i}\right) \left(\frac{\hat{p}_i \hat{q}_i}{n_i - 1}\right)$$

Again, two standard deviations are used as bounds on the error of estimation.

11. *Example:*
In addition to the amount of products liability insurance carried, each dealer in the survey was asked whether or not he carried excess or "umbrella" coverage, which covers claims in excess of the usual products liability insurance. The number in each stratum carrying umbrella coverage is given in the following table.

Strata	Sample Size	Number Having Umbrella Coverage	$\hat{p}_i$
1	30	21	
2	15	9	
3	5	4	

.70
.60
.80

Estimate p, the proportion of dealers who carry excess coverage, and place bounds on the error estimation.

Solution:

a. In the table, fill in the values for $\hat{p}_1, \hat{p}_2$ and $\hat{p}_3$. The estimate for p is

$$\hat{p}_{st} = \frac{1}{N} \sum_{i=1}^{3} N_i \hat{p}_i$$

$$= \frac{1}{1000} [600(\underline{\hspace{1.5cm}}) + 300(\underline{\hspace{1.5cm}}) + 100(\underline{\hspace{1cm}})]$$

$.70; .60; .80$

$$= \frac{1}{1000} (420 + 180 + 80)$$

$$= \underline{\hspace{2cm}}$$

$.68$

b. In evaluating the variance of $\hat{p}_{st}$, we can use the fact that the finite population correction factor $(N_i - n_i)/N_i = .95$ for $i = 1, 2, 3$. Hence,

$$\hat{\sigma}^2_{\hat{p}_{st}} = \frac{1}{N^2} \sum_{i=1}^{3} N_i^2 \left(\frac{N_i - n_i}{N_i} \right) \left(\frac{p_i q_i}{n_i - 1} \right)$$

$$= \frac{.95}{(1000)^2} \left[(\underline{\hspace{1cm}})^2 \frac{(.7)(.3)}{29} + (\underline{\hspace{1cm}})^2 \frac{(.6)(.4)}{14} \right.$$

$600; 300$

$$\left. + (\underline{\hspace{1cm}})^2 \frac{(.8)(.2)}{4} \right]$$

100

$$= \frac{.95}{(1000)^2} (2606.8966 + 1542.8571 + 400)$$

$$= \underline{\hspace{2cm}}$$

$.004322$

and

$$\hat{\sigma}_{\hat{p}_{st}} = \underline{\hspace{2cm}}$$

$.066$

c. The estimate of the proportion of dealers who carry excess coverage with bounds on the error of estimation is

$$.68 \pm 2(.066)$$

which, correct to 2 decimal accuracy, is $\underline{\hspace{1.5cm}} \pm \underline{\hspace{1.5cm}}$.

$.68; .13$

12. Using a stratified random sampling procedure allows an investigator to estimate parameters within a stratum, as well as parameters of the total population. If, for example, we wished to estimate the percentage of dealers in the first stratum (less than \$5 million annual sales) carrying umbrella coverage, we would use

$$\hat{p}_1 \pm 2 \sqrt{ \left(\frac{N_1 - n_1}{N_1} \right) \left(\frac{\hat{p}_1 \hat{q}_1}{n_1 - 1} \right) }$$

or

.70

$$\underline{\hspace{2cm}} \pm 2 \sqrt{(.95)\frac{(.7)(.3)}{29}}$$

.70; .08

$$\underline{\hspace{2cm}} \pm \underline{\hspace{2cm}}$$

Self-Correcting Exercises 16C

1. The home office would like to estimate the value of the items on the machine inventory lists at its four branch offices. If $n = 60$ items are to be sampled, use proportional allocation to determine the number of inventory items to be sampled at each branch office if the inventory lists at the four branch offices contain $N_1 = 1100, N_2 = 600, N_3 = 800$ and $N_4 = 500$ items, respectively.

2. When the stratified sampling plan in Exercise 1 was implemented, the following information was obtained.

	Branch Office			
	1	*2*	*3*	*4*
Number of items, N_i	1,100	600	800	500
Sample size, n_i	22	12	16	10
Sample mean, $\bar{y}_i$	1,050	820	990	1,280
Sample variance, s_i^2	1,210	930	1,080	1,510

a. Estimate the average value of the inventoried items on all four branch office inventory lists, and place a bound on the error of estimation.

b. Estimate the total value of the inventoried items on all four branch office inventory lists, and place a bound on the error of estimation.

c. Estimate the average value of the inventoried items at branch office 1 and place a bound on the error of estimation.

3. In addition to the value of the inventoried items, the number of items five years old or older at each branch office was also recorded.

	Branch Office			
	1	*2*	*3*	*4*
Sample size	22	12	16	10
Number of items 5 years old or older	12	5	6	3

Estimate the proportion of inventoried items five years old or older on all branch office inventory lists, and place a bound on the error of estimation.

16.6 Cluster Sampling (16.6)

1. In order to select a simple random sample or a stratified random sample, an investigator must have available a frame listing all of the elements in the population to be sampled. When an appropriate frame is not available or is very costly to obtain, a _____ sampling design can be used.

2. A cluster is a simple random sample in which the _____ _____ are collections or clusters of elements in the population. A cluster sample is obtained by randomly selecting m _____ from the population and then conducting a complete _____ within each cluster. In sampling households in a given city, an appropriate cluster of households might be a city block or a political ward. In sampling airline passengers, an appropriate cluster would be an arriving or departing plane load. In sampling students within a large school, an appropriate cluster would be a classroom.

3. Although a current frame listing all the households in a given city may not exist, a frame listing arriving or departing passengers should be fairly complete, and a frame listing the students in a given school certainly exists. However, the selection of a simple or stratified random sample would not be practically feasible in any large airport because of the large number of flights and the distance between gates. The administrators of a large school would probably allow some classrooms to be disrupted for a short time, but would be adverse to disrupting all classrooms in order to obtain a simple or stratified random sample.

4. Cluster sampling provides an effective design when
   a. a frame listing all the elements in the population (is, is not) available or (is, is not) costly to obtain, or
   b. the population is (small, large) and spread over a wide area and/or the cost of obtaining an observation (increases, decreases) as the distance between elements increases.

5. In preparing a cluster sampling design, an experimenter is often faced with choosing between a design involving a small number of large clusters and a design involving a large number of small clusters. When costs are not prohibitive, the (former, latter) design should be chosen since it is more likely to include a more representative cross-section of the sampled population.

6. *Estimation of a Population Mean for a Cluster Sample.*
   In cluster sampling, m clusters are randomly selected from a frame listing the _____ and a complete _____ census of the n_i elements in the ith cluster is conducted. The value of n_i (is always, may not be) known in advance. (The number of airline passengers may vary from

cluster
sampling units

clusters
census

is not
is
large
increases

latter

clusters; census

may not be

flight to flight.) Let t_i represent the total of the measurements in the ith cluster. The estimator of the population mean μ is

$$\bar{y}_{cl} = \frac{\displaystyle\sum_{i=1}^{m} t_i}{\displaystyle\sum_{i=1}^{m} n_i}$$

an aggregate mean based on the grand total of all observations divided by the total number of elements in the sample. Let M denote the number of clusters in the population, and let the average cluster size be denoted by

$$\bar{n} = \frac{1}{m} \sum_{i=1}^{m} n_i$$

The variance of the estimator $\bar{y}_{cl}$ is

$$\hat{\sigma}^2_{\bar{y}_{cl}} = \left(\frac{M-m}{Mm\bar{n}^2}\right)\left(\frac{\displaystyle\sum_{i=1}^{m}(t_i - \bar{y}_{cl}n_i)^2}{m-1}\right)$$

Two standard deviations are used as bounds on the error of estimation.

7. *Estimation of the Population Total for a Cluster Sample:*
   Let $\bar{t}$ be the average cluster total defined as

$$\bar{t} = \frac{1}{m} \sum_{i=1}^{m} t_i$$

The estimator of the population total τ is given as

$$\hat{\tau} = M\bar{t}$$

with variance

$$\hat{\sigma}^2_{\hat{\tau}} = M^2\left(\frac{M-m}{Mm}\right)\left(\frac{\displaystyle\sum_{i=1}^{m}(t_i - \bar{t})^2}{m-1}\right)$$

Two standard deviations are used as a bound on the error of estimation.

8. *Example:*

A dealer in electronic equipment offers his customers a twelve-month service contract at a fixed annual cost. In order to update cost estimates for the 200 installations under service contracts, the dealer randomly selected 20 installations and recorded the number of service calls, including regular maintenance, and the actual cost incurred for each call during the last six months. For sampling purposes, each installation represents a cluster, and each repair call at a given installation constitutes an element in the population of interest. The data follow.

Installation	Service Calls	Cost	Installation	Service Calls	Cost
1	6	$1,250	11	6	$1,050
2	4	600	12	9	1,700
3	5	1,150	13	7	1,250
4	6	1,550	14	9	2,150
5	8	2,000	15	5	850
6	6	1,150	16	6	1,000
7	4	750	17	4	850
8	10	2,250	18	6	1,100
9	4	900	19	7	1,650
10	5	950	20	10	1,950

$$\sum_{i=1}^{20} n_i = \underline{\hspace{2cm}} \qquad \sum_{i=1}^{20} t_i = \underline{\hspace{2cm}}$$

127; $26,100

Estimate the average cost per repair call, and place bounds on the error of estimation.

Solution:

a. The estimate of the average cost per repair call is

$$\bar{y}_{cl} = \frac{\sum\limits_{i=1}^{m} t_i}{\sum\limits_{i=1}^{m} n_i}$$

$$= \frac{26,100}{127}$$

$$= \underline{\hspace{2cm}}$$

$205.51

b. To calculate the variance of the estimator $\bar{y}_{cl}$, we need the following sum of squares.

$$\sum_{i=1}^{m} (t_i - \bar{y}_{cl} n_i)^2 = \sum_{i=1}^{m} t_i^2 - 2\bar{y}_{cl} \sum_{i=1}^{m} t_i n_i + \bar{y}_{cl}^2 \sum_{i=1}^{m} n_i^2$$

Now

$$\sum_{i=1}^{20} t_i^2 = 1250^2 + 600^2 + \ldots + 1950^2 = 38{,}665{,}000$$

$$\sum_{i=1}^{20} t_i n_i = (1250)(6) + (600)(4) + \ldots + (1950)(10)$$
$$= 182{,}700$$

$$\sum_{i=1}^{20} n_i^2 = 6^2 + 4^2 + \ldots + 10^2 = 879$$

Therefore,

182,700

$$\sum_{i=1}^{20} (t_i - \bar{y}_{cl} n_i)^2 = 38{,}665{,}000 - 2(205.51)(\underline{\hspace{2cm}})$$

879

$$+ (205.51)^2(\underline{\hspace{2cm}})$$

695,648.5279

$$= \underline{\hspace{2cm}}$$

The average cluster size is

6.35

$$\bar{n} = \frac{1}{m} \sum_{i=1}^{m} n_i = \frac{1}{20}(127) = \underline{\hspace{2cm}}$$

With $M = 200$ clusters in the population,

$$\hat{\sigma}^2_{\bar{y}_{cl}} = \left(\frac{(M-m)}{(Mm\bar{n}^2)}\right)\left(\frac{\sum_{i=1}^{m} (t_i - \bar{y}_{cl} n_i)^2}{m-1}\right)$$

$$-\frac{(200-20)}{(200)(20)(6.35)^2}\frac{(695,648.5279)}{19}$$

$$= \underline{\hspace{1.5cm}}$$ 40.8603

Hence,

$$\hat{\sigma}_{\bar{y}_{cl}} = \sqrt{\underline{\hspace{2cm}}}$$ 40.8603

$$= \underline{\hspace{1.5cm}}$$ $6.39

c. The estimate of the average cost per repair call with a bound on the error of estimation is

$$\$205.51 \pm 2(\underline{\hspace{2cm}})$$ 6.39

or

$$\$205.51 \pm \underline{\hspace{2cm}}$$ $12.78

9. *Example:*
Estimate the total cost of repair calls for all 200 installations in Example 8 and place a bound on the error of estimation.
Solution:
a. The estimate of the population total is

$$\hat{\tau} = \frac{M}{m}\sum_{i=1}^{m} t_i$$

$$= \frac{200}{20}(26,100)$$

$$= \underline{\hspace{1.5cm}}$$ $261,000

Equivalently, the average repair cost per cluster is

$$\bar{t} = \frac{1}{m}\sum_{i=1}^{m} t_i$$

$$= \frac{1}{20}(26,100)$$

$$= \underline{\hspace{1.5cm}}$$ $1305

and the estimate of the population total based on $M = 200$ clusters is

$$\hat{\tau} = M\bar{t}$$

$$= (200)(1305)$$

$261,000

$$=\underline{\hspace{3cm}}$$

b. To evaluate the variance of $\hat{\tau}$, we need to calculate

$$\sum_{i=1}^{m}(t_i - \bar{t})^2 = \sum_{i=1}^{m} t_i^2 - \frac{\left(\sum_{i=1}^{m} t_i\right)^2}{m}$$

26,100

$$= 38{,}665{,}000 - \frac{(\underline{\hspace{2cm}})^2}{20}$$

34,060,500

$$= 38{,}665{,}000 - \underline{\hspace{2cm}}$$

4,604,500

$$=\underline{\hspace{2cm}}$$

Therefore,

$$\hat{\sigma}_{\hat{\tau}}^2 = \left(\frac{M-m}{Mm}\right)\left(\frac{\sum_{i=1}^{m}(t_i - \bar{t})^2}{m-1}\right)$$

$$= \frac{(200-20)}{(200)(20)}\left(\frac{4{,}604{,}500}{19}\right)$$

10,905.3947

$$=\underline{\hspace{2cm}}$$

and

$$\hat{\sigma}_{\hat{\tau}} = \sqrt{10{,}905.3947}$$

$104.43

$$=\underline{\hspace{2cm}}$$

c. The estimate of the total cost with a bound on the error of estimation is

$261,000 \pm 2(\underline{\hspace{2cm}})$ $104.43

or

$261,000 \pm \underline{\hspace{2cm}}$ $208.86

10. *Estimation of the Population Proportion for a Cluster Sample:*
In estimating the population p of those elements in the population possessing a specified characteristic from a cluster sample, a_i, the number of elements in the ith cluster possessing that characteristic is tabulated for each cluster. The estimate of p is

$$\hat{p}_{cl} = \frac{\sum\limits_{i=1}^{m} a_i}{\sum\limits_{i=1}^{m} n_i}$$

with variance

$$\hat{\sigma}^2_{\hat{p}_{cl}} = \left(\frac{M-m}{Mm\bar{n}^2}\right)\left(\frac{\sum\limits_{i=1}^{m}(a_i - \hat{p}_{cl}n_i)^2}{m-1}\right)$$

Notice that the formula for the variance of $\hat{p}_{cl}$ is the same as that for $\bar{y}_{cl}$ with t_i replaced by \underline{\hspace{2cm}}. Further, an equivalent form for the sum of squares in this formula can be calculated as a_i

$$\sum_{i=1}^{m}(a_i - \hat{p}_{cl}n_i)^2 = \sum_{i=1}^{m} a_i^2 - 2\hat{p}_{cl}\sum_{i=1}^{m} a_i n_i + \hat{p}_{cl}^2 \sum_{i=1}^{m} \underline{\hspace{1.5cm}}$$ n_i^2

11. The variance formula in Number 10 is an unbiased estimator when the cluster sizes are all \underline{\hspace{2cm}}. When the cluster sizes are unequal, the estimator of the variance is a good estimator only when the number of clusters is greater than or equal to \underline{\hspace{1cm}}.   equal

20

12. *Example:*
In conducting the survey reported in Example 8, the number of service calls requiring only adjustments with no replacement parts was also recorded.

Installation	Service Calls	Adjustments Only	Installation	Service Calls	Adjustments Only
1	6	4	11	6	0
2	4	2	12	9	5
3	5	2	13	7	5
4	6	5	14	9	4
5	8	3	15	5	3
6	6	4	16	6	3
7	4	0	17	4	2
8	10	7	18	6	1
9	4	2	19	7	4
10	5	3	20	10	4

127; 63

$$\Sigma n_i = \underline{\hspace{2cm}} \qquad\qquad \Sigma a_i = \underline{\hspace{2cm}}$$

Estimate the proportion of service calls involving adjustments only, and place a bound on the error of estimation.

Solution:

This problem is similar to Example 8 except that the quantities $t_1, t_2, \ldots, t_{20}$ are replaced with the quantities $a_1, a_2, \ldots a_{20}$. A summary of relevant information follows.

200; 63

$$M = \underline{\hspace{2cm}} \qquad \Sigma a_i = \underline{\hspace{2cm}} \qquad \Sigma a_i^2 = 257$$

20; 127

$$m = \underline{\hspace{2cm}} \qquad \Sigma n_i = \underline{\hspace{2cm}} \qquad \Sigma n_i^2 = 879$$

6.35

$$\bar{n} = \underline{\hspace{2cm}} \qquad \Sigma a_i n_i = 444$$

a. The estimate of the proportion of service calls requiring only adjust-ments is

.4961

$$\hat{p}_{cl} = \frac{\Sigma a_i}{\Sigma n_i} = \frac{63}{127} = \underline{\hspace{2cm}}$$

b. Evaluate

$$\Sigma(a_i - \hat{p}_{cl} n_i)^2 = \Sigma a_i^2 - 2\hat{p}_{cl} \Sigma a_i n_i + \hat{p}_{cl}^2 \Sigma n_i^2$$

.4961; .4961

$$= 257 - 2(\underline{\hspace{1.5cm}})(444) + (\underline{\hspace{1.5cm}})^2(879)$$

32.7985

$$= \underline{\hspace{2cm}}$$

The variance of $\hat{p}_{cl}$ is

$$\hat{\sigma}_{\hat{p}_{cl}}^2 = \left(\frac{M-m}{Mm\bar{n}^2}\right)\left(\frac{\displaystyle\sum_{i=1}^{m}(a_i - \hat{p}_{cl} n_i)^2}{m-1}\right)$$

$$= \frac{(200-20)}{200(20)(\underline{\quad})^2} \frac{(\underline{\qquad})}{19}$$

32.7985

6.35

$$= \underline{\qquad}$$

.001926

with

$$\hat{\sigma}_{\hat{p}_{cl}} = \sqrt{.001926}$$

$$= \underline{\qquad}$$

.0439

c. The estimate of the number of service calls requiring only adjustments is

$$\underline{\qquad} \pm 2(\underline{\qquad})$$

.4961; .0439

or

$$\underline{\qquad} \pm \underline{\qquad}$$

.50; .08

Self-Correcting Exercises 16D

1. A survey was designed to estimate the amount spent on utilities during the year for households in a city. Because a list of households was not available, a cluster sampling design was used with blocks as the clusters. From the $M = 200$ city blocks within the city limits, a random sample of $m = 10$ blocks produced the following information.

City Block	Number of Households	Amount for Utilities
1	16	$19,210
2	10	9,130
3	14	12,340
4	20	16,480
5	15	9,570
6	8	10,420
7	15	12,290
8	30	20,920
9	10	9,980
10	18	16,750

a. Estimate the average yearly amount spent on utilities per household, and place a bound on the error of estimation.
b. Estimate the total amount spent on utilities in this city, and place a bound on the error of estimation.

2. A cancer research organization wishes to determine whether recent advances made in the treatment of cancer are being implemented in hospitals having radiation therapy units. In designing the survey, it was decided to randomly sample $m = 10$ of the possible $M = 75$ geographic areas designated as clusters. In the following tabulation, a_i is the number of hospitals having radiation units that have implemented at least one recent recommendation in the treatment of cancer. (Data are fictitious.)

Cluster	n_i	a_i
1	20	8
2	10	5
3	30	16
4	8	2
5	15	7
6	28	17
7	48	19
8	64	38
9	22	10
10	13	4

Estimate the proportion of hospitals utilizing new treatment recommendations, and place a bound on the error of estimation.

16.7 Finding the Sample Size (16.7)

1. An effective sampling plan is one in which a specified amount of information is obtained at a minimum _____. The number of elements to be included in a sample will depend upon the specified bound on the error of estimation as well as the _____ of the elements in the population to be sampled. In general, small bounds on error require (small, large) sample sizes, while small sample sizes are required when the population is fairly uniform and exhibits (small, large) variability. Formulas for determining the sample size required to achieve a given precision in estimation vary from one sampling design to another. In every case, however, B, the maximum tolerable bound on the error of estimation must be specified, and the variability of the elements in the population must be _____, or a reasonable _____ must be available.

2. When using a *simple random sampling design,* the sample size required to estimate the population mean μ with a bound B on the error of estimation is

$$n = \frac{N\sigma^2}{(N-1)D + \sigma^2}$$

cost

variability

large
small

known; estimate

where $D = B^2/4$, N is the size of the population, and σ^2 is the population variance. When N is very large (so that the finite population correction factor can be ignored), this formula reduces to

$$n = \frac{4\sigma^2}{B^2}$$

When σ is unknown and a prior estimate is not available, a rough estimate of σ based upon the Empirical Rule is $\hat{\sigma} = $ (range)/4. When estimating the population total τ, earlier formulas apply with $D = B^2/4N^2$.

3. *Example:*

A department store would like to estimate the average monthly sales for its 10,000 credit-card customers. How many credit-card accounts should be included in the sample in order to estimate μ, the average monthly credit-card sales with a bound on the error of estimation of $B = \$20$. It is known that monthly credit-card sales in general range from $20 to $500.

Solution:

a. Since the standard deviation is unknown, we will use the range to estimate σ. The range is \$500–\$20 = \$480. Therefore, $\sigma = \$480/4 = \$120$ and $\hat{\sigma}^2 = 120^2 = 14{,}400$.

b. $N = $ _____ and $B = $ _____. The quantity D used in finding | 10,000; \$20
   the sample size is $D = B^2/4 = (20)^2/4 = $ _____. Then, | 100

$$n = \frac{N\sigma^2}{(N-1)D + \sigma^2}$$

$$= \frac{(10{,}000)(\underline{\quad\quad\quad})}{(9999)100 + \underline{\quad\quad}}$$ | 14,400
   | 14,400

$$= \frac{144{,}000{,}000}{1{,}014{,}300}$$

$$= \underline{\quad\quad\quad}$$ | 141.97

A random sample of _____ accounts should be selected in order | 142
to estimate the average monthly credit-card sales to within \$20.

c. Since $N = 10{,}000$ is large, we can use the approximate solution

$$n = \frac{4\sigma^2}{B^2}$$

$$= \frac{4(14{,}400)}{400}$$

$$= \underline{\quad\quad\quad}$$ | 144

pq

.25

This result differs only slightly from the sample size found using the exact formula.

4. In estimating the population proportion *p,* the sample size formulas for the population mean μ can be used with σ^2 replaced by _____. However, since *p* is unknown, some estimate for *p* must be available. This estimate could be in the form of an educated guess, or one can assume maximum variation, attained when $p = q = 1/2$, and take $\sigma^2 =$ _____.

5. In determining the total sample size *n* to be allocated among the *L* strata in a *stratified random sampling design,* in addition to *B,* the bound on the error of estimation, we must also know the strata sizes, $N_1, N_2, \ldots, N_L$ as well as the variances within the strata, $\sigma_1^2, \sigma_2^2, \ldots, \sigma_L^2$. Previous samples or the range approximation can be used to estimate the variances if they are unknown. The sample size required to estimate the population mean μ with a bound *B* on the error of estimation is

$$n = \frac{\displaystyle\sum_{i=1}^{L} N_i \sigma_i^2}{ND + \dfrac{1}{N} \displaystyle\sum_{i=1}^{L} N_i \sigma_i^2}$$

where $D = B^2/4$. By substituting $D = B^2/4N^2$ into this formula, the sample size required to estimate the population total τ with a bound *B* on the error of estimation can be found.

6. *Example:*

In order to update the current group life insurance plan, the personnel department of a company was asked to estimate the average amount of group life insurance held be the company's $N = 2000$ employees. The company employs $N_1 = 1500$ machine operators, $N_2 = 350$ support personnel, and $N_3 = 150$ persons in managerial positions. The latest available information indicates that $\sigma_1 = \$3000$, $\sigma_2 = \$1500$ and $\sigma_3 = \$5000$. How large a sample should be taken to ensure that the bound on the error of estimation be no larger than $B = \$1000$? Using proportional allocation, how many persons from each stratum would be included in the sample? *Solution:*

a. Large intermediate values in the calculation of *n* can be avoided by recording *B,* σ_1, σ_2, and σ_3 in units of $\$1000$. Complete the following summary.

3

350

$$\sigma_1 = \underline{\hspace{2cm}} \qquad\qquad N_1 = 1500$$

$$\sigma_2 = 1.5 \qquad\qquad N_2 = \underline{\hspace{2cm}}$$

$$\sigma_3 = \underline{\hspace{2cm}} \qquad\qquad N_3 = \underline{\hspace{2cm}} \qquad\qquad 5; 150$$

$$B = 1 \qquad\qquad N = 2000$$

We also need to evaluate the quantity D and $\sum_{i=1}^{3} N_i \sigma_i^2$.

$$D = B^2/4 = (1)^2/4 = \underline{\hspace{2cm}} \qquad\qquad .25$$

$$\sum_{i=1}^{3} N_i \sigma_i^2 = 1500(3)^2 + 350(1.5)^2 + 150(5)^2$$

$$= 13{,}500 + 787.5 + 3750$$

$$= \underline{\hspace{2cm}} \qquad\qquad 18{,}037.5$$

Then

$$n = \frac{\displaystyle\sum_{i=1}^{3} N_i \sigma_i^2}{ND + \dfrac{1}{N}\displaystyle\sum_{i=1}^{3} N_i \sigma_i^2}$$

$$= \frac{18{,}037.5}{2000(.25) + \dfrac{18{,}037.5}{2000}}$$

$$= \frac{18{,}037.5}{(\underline{\hspace{2cm}})} \qquad\qquad 509.01875$$

$$= \underline{\hspace{2cm}} \qquad\qquad 35.44$$

The sample size required to estimate the average amount of group life insurance per employee with bound on the error of estimation equal to $1000 is $n = \underline{\hspace{2cm}}$.

b. Using proportional allocation,

$$n_1 = 36\left(\frac{1500}{2000}\right) = \underline{\hspace{2cm}} \qquad\qquad 27$$

36

6.3

$$n_2 = 36\left(\frac{350}{2000}\right) = \underline{\hspace{2cm}}$$

2.7

$$n_3 = 36\left(\frac{150}{2000}\right) = \underline{\hspace{2cm}}$$

27; 6
3

We would randomly select $n_1 = \underline{\hspace{2cm}}$, $n_2 = \underline{\hspace{2cm}}$, and $n_3 = \underline{\hspace{2cm}}$ people from strata 1, 2, and 3, respectively.

7. To find the sample size required to estimate a population proportion using stratified random sampling, we substitute $\sigma_i^2 = p_i q_i$, the variance of the ith stratum, and $D = B^2/4$. A prior estimate or guess can be substituted for

.25

p_i or the maximum variation of $p_i q_i = \underline{\hspace{2cm}}$ can be used. Using maximum variation and proportional allocation, the sample size required to estimate the population proportion p with a bound on error equal to B is

$$n = \frac{N}{NB^2 + 1}$$

For example, the sample size required to estimate p in a population of $N = 2000$ elements with a bound on error equal to $B = 0.1$ is

$$n = \frac{2000}{2000(.01) + 1}$$

$$= \frac{2000}{(\underline{\hspace{2cm}})}$$

21

95.24

$$= \underline{\hspace{2cm}}$$

96

or $n = \underline{\hspace{2cm}}$ elements.

8. Simple random sampling and stratified random sampling both require the

frame

existence of a _____ listing the elements in the population. In contrast, cluster sampling utilizes a frame in which the sampling units are

clusters

_____ of elements. The size of the clusters in many situations are actually random quantities. However, the information in a cluster sample depends not only on m, the number of clusters, but also on the size of the clusters. Rather than present appropriate formulas here, we refer the reader to a text on survey sampling such as *Elementary Survey Sampling* by Mendenhall, Ott, and Scheaffer. In general, however, more information can be obtained in a cluster sample by selecting a (smaller,

larger

larger) number of smaller-sized clusters.

Self-Correcting Exercises 16E

1. A professional organization listing approximately 12,000 members on its national roster would like to conduct a mail survey of its members in order to estimate the proportion of its members favoring the establishment of a second journal to be made available to its members. Assuming maximum variation within a simple random sampling design, how large a sample should be taken in order that the estimate of p be no farther than $B = .05$ from the true value?

2. Suppose that the professional organization in Exercise 1 can actually classify its members into the following three strata.

Stratum	Classification	N_i
1	Employed by academic institution	6,000
2	Employed by industrial organization	4,000
3	Self-employed	2,000

   a. Using a stratified random design with proportional allocation, how large a sample should be taken to estimate the proportion of members favoring a second journal to within $B = .05$ if it is assumed that the proportions for the three strata would be approximately $p_1 = .7, p_2 = .6$, and $p_3 = .5$?

   b. What is the resulting proportional allocation among the three strata?

   c. How would your results differ if you were to assume that $p_1 = p_2 = p_3 = .5$?

3. A bank offering two kinds of checking accounts would like to estimate the average monthly balance in the checking accounts of its customers. In the $N_1 = 10,000$ "no minimum balance" accounts, the average monthly balance is between $25 and $500, while in the $N_2 = 5000$ "$300 minimum balance" accounts, the average monthly balance ranges between $300 and $1500. How large a sample should be taken in order to estimate the average monthly balance to within $30? What is the proportional allocation across the two strata?

16.8 Other Sampling Designs and Procedures (16.8)

1. We have described the three most commonly used sampling designs. In this section, we will briefly review some other sampling designs and some procedures that can be used within any design.

2. *Systematic Sampling:*

A systematic sample is obtained by randomly selecting one of the first k elements in the frame and then selecting every _____ element thereafter. Systematic sampling is especially useful when the elements (or information) in the population are recorded in some systematic way. Computer-stored data, for example, is easily sampled using systematic samples. Systematic sampling (should, should not) be used when periodicities exist in the population. Periodicities or cyclical behavior may be present in financial records or in production records kept over _____. By systematically sampling either the peaks or the troughs in such records, we may obtain a biased sample that is not representative of the total population.

kth

should not

time

3. *Two-Stage Cluster Sampling:*

A two-stage cluster sample is obtained by selecting a simple random sample of clusters and then selecting a random sample of elements within each _____. For example, in a study of overtime expenditures, a large company might randomly select m of its subsidiaries and then randomly select several departments within each subsidiary to be included in the sampling. When clusters constitute _____ areas, cluster sampling of the areas is referred to as *area sampling.* The chief advantage of two-stage or multistage sampling designs over other designs is cost savings, since a frame listing only _____ is required and the elements sampled within a cluster would be physically nearer each other than would be elements selected at random from the population. However, any type of cluster sampling may result in biased estimates because of the intentional exclusion of part of the population from our sample.

cluster

geographic

clusters

4. *Ratio Estimation:*

Ratio estimation is a procedure that can be used within any appropriate sampling design. This procedure uses an observed relationship between two variables, x and y, measured on the same set of sample elements, to predict μ_y or τ_y. For example, one might wish to estimate the selling price of a home using the square footage of the home, or one might wish to predict the juice content of fruit, using its observed weight. Ratio estimation assumes that the relationship between two variables is of the form

$$R = \frac{\tau_y}{\tau_x}$$

so that $\tau_y = R\tau_x$. Two variables, x and y, are measured for each element in the sample, and the quantity R is estimated as

$$\hat{R} = \frac{\sum\limits_{i=1}^{n} y_i}{\sum\limits_{i=1}^{n} x_i}$$

The population total τ_y can be estimated using

$$\hat{\tau}_y = \underline{\hspace{2cm}}$$

$\hat{R}\tau_x$

provided τ_x is known. When there is a strong positive correlation between x and y (greater than $1/2$), the variance of the ratio estimator $\hat{R}\tau_x$ is (smaller, larger) than the variance of the estimator $N\bar{y}$. We would expect the ratio estimator to be more precise in this case, since we are using the additional information provided by the variable _____ in estimating τ_y.

smaller

x

5. *Randomized Response Sampling:*

Two nonsampling errors that frequently bias the results of sample surveys are the refusal of a respondent to answer all, or part of, a questionnaire or the deliberate falsification of information. These errors often result when the questionnaire, or certain parts of the questionnaire, deal with sensitive or potentially embarrassing topics. _____ _____ sampling is an attempt to alleviate this problem by pairing a sensitive question with another question that the respondent should feel comfortable in answering. The respondent then answers one of the questions, which he or she selects at random using some randomization device. For example, the question "Have you ever smoked marijuana?" could be paired with the question "Have you ever drunk coffee?" The interviewer receives an answer but is unaware of which question is being answered by the respondent. The analysis of randomized response data utilizes the fact that the randomization device selects the sensitive question with a known _____. Randomized response sampling is a procedure that can be utilized within any of the sampling designs.

Randomized response

probability

16.9 Summary and Comments (16.9)

1. In addition to random sampling designs, there are some nonrandom sampling designs that are commonly used. However, with nonrandom sampling designs, only _____ statements can be made. Convenience sampling, judgment sampling, and quota sampling are three forms of nonrandom sampling.

descriptive

2. A *convenience sample* consists of elements that can easily be obtained. A group of volunteer subjects (would, would not) comprise a convenience sample.

would

3. *Judgment sampling* involves the selection of the elements in the sample by "experts" so that the sample is "representative" of the _____ of interest. For example, one city in the United States might be picked as a typical city to represent all the cities in the United States.

population

4. *Quota sampling* involves the selection of a predetermined number of elements from specific portions of the population so as to construct a sample _____ to the population with respect to certain variables. National opinion polls might rely on quota sampling to insure that given ethnic, socioeconomic, religious, political, and other groups are represented

proportional

population
nonrandom

can

random

ratio estimation

randomized response

in the sample in roughly the same proportions that they appear in the _____. The selection of the elements within the quotas often depends upon the sampler and usually results in a _____ sample.

5. Samples arising from the use of random, stratified, cluster, and systematic sampling designs (can, cannot) be used to make inferential statements about the population from which they were drawn because these designs produce _____ samples with a known probability of including or excluding elements of the population in the sample.

6. Within these sampling designs, the _____ _____ procedure can be used when observations on a highly correlated auxiliary variable are available, while the _____ _____ technique can be used to elicit responses to embarrassing or sensitive topics within the sample survey.

Exercises

1. When is a sample a random sample? Why is a random sample preferred to a nonrandom sample?
2. What are the sources of error in a sample survey?
3. Differentiate between an element, a cluster, and a sampling unit.
4. In a random sample of $n = 20$ accounts, the average amount due was $\bar{y} = \$130.25$ with a standard deviation of $s = \$15.30$.
   a. Estimate μ, the average amount due for all $N = 100$ current accounts held by this company, and place a bound on the error of estimation.
   b. Estimate the total amount due for all $N = 100$ accounts, and place a bound on the error of estimation.
5. Refer to Exercise 4. If 3 of the 20 accounts sampled are delinquent, estimate the proportion of delinquent accounts, and place a bound on the error of estimation.
6. Refer to Exercise 5. Estimate the total number of delinquent accounts using the estimator $N\hat{p}$, and place a bound on the error of estimation. (The variance of $N\hat{p}$ is $N^2 \sigma_{\hat{p}}^2$.)
7. Using simple random sampling, how large a sample is required to estimate the population mean with a bound $B = 15$ if the range of the observations for the $N = 9000$ elements in the population is expected to be approximately 400?
8. Refer to Exercise 2, *Self-Correcting Exercises 16E*. The following information resulted when a stratified random sample survey involving $n = 350$ of the 12,000 members of the professional organization was conducted.

	Strata		
	1	*2*	*3*
Stratum size, N_i	6,000	4,000	2,000
Sample size, n_i	175	117	58
Number favoring second journal	130	76	32

Estimate the proportion of the members favoring the establishment of a second journal, and place a bound on the error of estimation.

9. A stratified random sampling design involving three strata is to be used in estimating the population mean. From the following information determine the sample size required to estimate μ with a bound on error of $B = 10$ if proportional allocation is to be used.

Strata	1	2	3
N_i	2300	1200	4500
σ_i^2	4250	2500	5750

Determine the allocation of the sample across the three strata.

10. In order to obtain travel information concerning its passengers, an airline randomly selected $n = 10$ departing flights from its $N = 180$ flight listings and asked all the passengers on these ten flights to complete a questionnaire. The following data was extracted from the questionnaire. The third column records the ground distance between the terminal airport and the passengers' ultimate destination. (Data are fictitious.)

Flight	Number of Passengers	Total Distance	Number with Distance over 50 Miles
1	131	3,275	27
2	103	3,090	21
3	189	8,505	57
4	93	2,046	10
5	205	7,175	52
6	148	7,400	26
7	172	6,880	69
8	110	3,520	23
9	165	6,270	64
10	193	9,071	87

By considering the flights included in the sample as $m = 10$ clusters randomly selected from $M = 180$ clusters,

a. Estimate the average ground distance between the terminal airport and ultimate destination per passenger, and place a bound on the error of estimation.

b. Estimate the proportion of passengers who will travel over 50 ground miles to their ultimate destination, and place a bound on the error of estimation.

11. In order to update the actual dollar value of its inventory, a firm randomly selects $n = 10$ of the $N = 600$ types of items from its inventory list and determines the actual dollar value per type of item sampled. Computer-stored records are used to determine the actual dollar value and the inventoried dollar value of the types of items included in the sample. These data are summarized in units of $100.

Item	Computer Value (x)	Actual Value (y)
1	6.1	5.4
2	48.6	45.0
3	3.2	2.9
4	25.4	22.4
5	43.9	37.3
6	68.6	62.4
7	187.4	172.1
8	45.2	33.9
9	5.1	4.4
10	170.9	153.6

a. Estimate the ratio of the actual inventory value to the computer inventory value.

b. If the total of the computer inventory value is τ_x = 34,920, use the ratio estimator to estimate τ_y, the total actual value of the inventoried items.

c. Estimate τ_y using the estimator $N\bar{y}$ and compare this estimate with that found in part b.

12. A bank having 10,000 checking accounts would like to estimate the average monthly balance using a 1-in-100 systematic sample from its list of accounts.

a. What is the size of the sample using this scheme?

b. Describe how the sample should be drawn from the 10,000 checking accounts.

c. Implement your plan in part b, and indicate which accounts would be included in the sample.

Chapter   17

ANALYSIS OF
ENUMERATIVE DATA

17.1   A Description of the Multinomial Experiment (17.1)

1. Examine the following experimental situations for any general similarities.
   a. Two hundred people are classified according to their ages. The number of people in each of the age groups 0-20, 21-40, 41-60, and over 60 is recorded.
   b. A sample of 100 items is randomly selected from a production line. Each item is classified as belonging to one of three groups: acceptables, seconds, or rejects, and the number in each group is recorded.
   c. A random sample of 50 people holding valid driver's licenses is selected from state records and each person is classified as having: no previous accidents, one accident, two accidents, or three or more accidents.
2. Each of these situations is similar to the others in that classes or categories are defined and the number of items falling into each category is recorded. Hence, these experiments result in enumerative or _____ data — count and have the following general characteristics which define the _____ experiment. — multinomial
   a. The experiment consists of _____ identical trials. — n
   b. The outcome of each trial falls into one of k _____ or _____. — classes; cells
   c. The probability that the outcome of a single trial falls into cell i is p_i, $i = 1, 2, \ldots, k$, where p_i is _____ from trial to trial and — constant

$$\sum_{i=1}^{k} p_i = \underline{\quad\quad}$$ 1

   d. The trials are _____. — independent
   e. We are interested in $n_1, n_2, n_3, \ldots, n_k$, where n_i is the number of trials in which the outcome falls in cell i, and

$$\sum_{i=1}^{k} n_i = \underline{\quad\quad}$$ n

2

3. The binomial experiment is a special case of the multinomial experiment. This can be seen by letting $k =$ _____ , and noting the following correspondences.

	Binomial	Multinomial ($k = 2$)
a.	n	n
b.	p	p_1
c.	q	_____
d.	y	n_1
e.	$n - y$	
f.	$E(y) = np$	$E(n_1) = np_1$
g.	$E(n - y) = nq$	$E(n_2) = $ _____

p_2

n_2

np_2

4. For the multinomial experiment, we wish to make inferences about the associated population parameters, $p_1, p_2, \ldots, p_k$. A statistic that allows us to make inferences of this sort was developed by the British statistician, Karl Pearson, around 1900.

17.2   The Chi-square Test (17.2)

1. For a multinomial experiment consisting of n trials with known (or hypothesized) cell probabilities, $p_i, i = 1, 2, \ldots, k$, we can find the expected number of items falling into the ith cell by using

$$E(n_i) = \underline{\hspace{2cm}} \qquad i = 1, 2, \ldots, k$$

np_i

2. The cell probabilities are rarely known in practical situations. Consequently, we wish to estimate, or test hypotheses concerning, their values. If the hypothesized cell probabilities are the correct values, then the *observed* number of items falling in each of the cells, n_i, should differ but slightly from the expected number, $E(n_i) = np_i$. Pearson's statistic (given below) utilizes the _____ of the deviations of the _____ from the _____ number in each cell.

squares; observed
expected

$$X^2 = \sum_{i=1}^{k} \frac{[n_i - E(n_i)]^2}{E(n_i)}$$

or

$$X^2 = \sum_{i=1}^{k} \underline{\hspace{2cm}}$$

$\dfrac{(n_i - np_i)^2}{np_i}$

3. When n, the number of trials, is large, this statistic has an approximate _____ distribution. A requirement on the expected numbers in each cell is that $E(n_i) \geqslant$ _____ $, i = 1, 2, \ldots, k$. This requirement

chi-square
5

can be satisfied by combining classes or cells until $E(n_i) \geqslant$ _____ for every cell.

4. For small deviations from the expected cell counts, the value of the statistic would be _____ , supporting the hypothesized cell probabilities. However, for large deviations from the expected counts, the value of the statistic would be _____ , and the hypothesized values of the cell probabilities would be _____ . Hence, a (one, two)-tailed test is used, rejecting H_0 when X^2 is large.

5. To find a critical value for χ^2, the degrees of freedom, v, must be known. Since v will change as the X^2-statistic is applied to different situations, a general rule for finding v is used. The degrees of freedom is equal to the number of cells less one degree of freedom for each independent linear restriction placed upon the cell counts. One linear restriction that will always be present is

$$\sum_{i=1}^{k} n_i = n_1 + n_2 + \ldots + n_k = \underline{\hspace{2cm}}$$

17.3 A Test of an Hypothesis Concerning Specified Cell Probabilities (17.3)

1. Let us consider the following application of Pearson's statistic to a problem concerning cell probabilities:

A manufacturer claims that his production line produces 85% Grade A items, 10% Grade B items, and 5% rejects. A random sample of 100 items from this production line included 80 Grade A's, 9 Grade B's, and 11 rejects. Does this sample contain sufficient evidence to refute the manufacturer's claim at the $\alpha = .05$ level?

2. This experiment consists of classifying 100 items by assigning them to one of three cells, cell 1 (Grade A's), cell 2 (Grade B's), and cell 3 (rejects) where $p_1 = .85, p_2 = .10$, and $p_3 = .05$. The expected cell numbers are found to be

a. $\quad E(n_1) = np_1 = 100(.85) = \underline{\hspace{1.5cm}}$

b. $\quad E(n_2) = np_2 = 100\,(\underline{\hspace{1.5cm}}) = \underline{\hspace{1.5cm}}$

c. $\quad E(n_3) = np_3 = (\underline{\hspace{1.5cm}})\,(\underline{\hspace{1.5cm}}) = \underline{\hspace{1.5cm}}$

3. Tabulating the results of 2 we have:

	Cell		
	1	*2*	*3*
Expected cell frequency	85	10	5
Observed cell frequency	80	9	11

Answers (right margin):
5
small
large
rejected
one
n
85
.10; 10
100; .05; 5

4. Using Pearson's statistic, X^2, we can test the manufacturer's claim *against* the hypothesis that *at least one* cell probability, p_i, is different from the value, p_{i0}, claimed by the manufacturer. We will compare the value of X^2 with a critical value of $\chi_{.05}^2$. The degrees of freedom is equal to the number of cells ($k = 3$) less one degree of freedom for the linear restriction, $n_1 + n_2 + n_3 = n = 100$. Therefore, $\nu = k - 1 = $ _____ and the critical χ^2 will be based on 2 degrees of freedom. Hence, $\chi_{.05}^2 = $ _____ .

5. Formalizing this discussion we have the following statistical test of the manufacturer's claim at the $\alpha = .05$ level.

a. $\quad H_0 : p_1 = .85, p_2 = .10, p_3 = .05$

b. $\quad H_a : p_i \neq p_{i0}$ for at least one i, $i = 1, 2, 3$

c. Test statistic:

$$X^2 = \sum_{i=1}^{3} \frac{[n_i - E(n_i)]^2}{E(n_i)}$$

d. Rejecton region: Reject H_0 if

$$X^2 > \chi_{.05}^2 = 5.991$$

e. $\quad X^2 = \dfrac{(80 - 85)^2}{85} + \dfrac{(9 - 10)^2}{10} + \dfrac{(11 - 5)^2}{5}$

$= .2941 + .1 + 7.2$

$= $ _____

f. Decision: $X^2 = 7.594 > 5.991$; hence, we (reject, do not reject) H_0. Therefore, the data produce sufficient evidence to contradict the manufacturer's statement that $p_1 = .85, p_2 = .10$, and $p_3 = .05$.

6. *Example:*

A botanist performs a secondary cross of petunias involving independent factors controlling leaf shape and flower color where the factor "A" represents red color, "a" represents white color, "B" represents round leaves, and "b" represents long leaves. According to the Mendelian Model, the plants should exhibit the characteristics AB, Ab, aB, and ab in the ratio 9:3:3:1. Of 160 experimental plants, the following numbers are observed: AB, 95; Ab, 30; aB, 28; ab, 7. Is there sufficient evidence to refute the Mendelian Model at the $\alpha = .01$ level?

Solution:

Translating the ratios into proportions, we have

(margin answers)

2

5.991

7.5941

reject

$P(AB) = p_1 = 9/16$

$P(Ab) = p_2 = 3/16$

$P(aB) = p_3 = $ _____ 3/16

$P(ab) = p_4 = $ _____ 1/16

Now we can tabulate our data as follows:

	Cell			
	AB	Ab	aB	ab
Expected	90	30			30; 10
Observed	95	30	28	7	

Perform a statistical test of the Mendelian Model using Pearson's statistic.

a. $H_0 : p_1 = 9/16, p_2 = 3/16, p_3 = 3/16, p_4 = 1/16$

b. $H_a : p_i \neq p_{i0}$ for at least one value of $i = 1, 2, 3, 4$

c. Test statistic:

$$X^2 = \sum_{i=1}^{4} \frac{[n_i - E(n_i)]^2}{E(n_i)}$$

d. Rejection region: With $v = 3$, we shall reject H_0 if

$X^2 > X_{.01}^2 = $ _____ 11.3449

e. $X^2 = \dfrac{(95 - 90)^2}{90} + \dfrac{(30 - 30)^2}{30} + \dfrac{(28 - 30)^2}{30} + \dfrac{(7 - 10)^2}{10}$

$= .2778 + .0000 + .1333 + .9000$

$= $ _____ 1.3111

f. Decision: _____.

Do not reject H_0 since $X^2 = 1.3111 < 11.3449$

g. Therefore we can say that there is not sufficient evidence to refute the Mendelian Model.

Self-Correcting Exercises 17A

1. A company specializing in kitchen products has produced a mixer in five different colors. A random sample of $n = 250$ sales has produced the following data:

Color	White	Copper	Avocado	Rose	Gold
Number sold	62	48	56	39	45

Test the hypothesis that there is no preference for color at the $\alpha = .05$ level of significance. (Hint: if there is no color preference, then $p_1 = p_2 = p_3 = p_4 = p_5 = 1/5$.)

2. The number of Caucasians possessing the four blood types, A, B, AB, and O, are said to be in the proportions .41, .12, .03 and .44, respectively. Would the observed frequencies of 90, 16, 10 and 84, respectively, furnish sufficient evidence to refute the given proportions at the $\alpha = .05$ level of significance?

17.4 Contingency Tables (17.4)

1. We now examine the problem of determining whether *independence* exists between two methods for classifying observed data. If we were to classify people first according to their incomes, and second according to their brand preference, would these methods of classification be independent of each other? We might classify salesmen first according to their age class, where age classes range from 20 to 65, and second according to their average weekly sales volume. Would these methods of classification be independent? In each problem we are asking whether one method of classi- fication is _____ on another. We investigate this problem by displaying our data according to the two methods of classification in an array called a _____ table.

contingent

contingency

2. A criminologist studying criminal offenders under age 25 who have a record of one or more arrests is interested in knowing whether the educa- tional achievement level of the offenders influences the frequency of arrests. He has classified his data using four educational achievement level classifications:

  A: completed 6th grade or less

  B: completed 7th, 8th, or 9th grade

  C: completed 10th, 11th, or 12th grade

  D: education beyond 12th grade

Number of Arrests	Educational Achievement				Totals
	A	*B*	*C*	*D*	
1	55 (45.39)	40 (43.03)	43 (43.03)	30 (36.55)	168
2	15 (21.61)	25 (20.49)	18 (20.49)	22 (17.40)	80
3 or more	7 (10.00)	8 (9.48)	12 (9.48)	10 (8.05)	37
Totals	77	73	73	62	285

The contingency table shows the number of offenders in each cell together with the expected cell frequency (in parentheses). The expected frequencies are obtained as follows:

a. Define p_A as the unconditional probability that a criminal offender will have completed grade 6 or less. Define p_B, p_C, and p_D in a similar manner.

b. Define p_1, p_2, p_3 to be the unconditional probability that the offender has 1, 2, or 3 or more arrests, respectively.

c. Remember that if two events, A and B, are independent, then $P(AB) =$ _____ . Hence, if the two classifications are independent, a cell probability will equal the _____ of the two respective unconditional row and column probabilities.

$P(A) \cdot P(B)$
product

d. For example, the probability that an offender who has completed grade 6 is arrested 3 or more times is

$$p_{A3} = \underline{\qquad}$$

$p_A \cdot p_3$

whereas the probability that a person with a 10th grade education is arrested twice is

$$p_{C2} = \underline{\qquad}$$

$p_C p_2$

3. Since the row and column probabilities are unknown, they must be estimated from the _____ data. The estimators for these probabilities are defined in terms of r_i, the row totals, c_j, the column totals, and n.

sample

a. $\hat{p}_A = c_1/n = \underline{\qquad}/285$ 77

$\hat{p}_B = c_2/n = \underline{\qquad}/285$ 73

$\hat{p}_C = c_3/n = \underline{\qquad}/285$ 73

$\hat{p}_D = c_4/n = \underline{\qquad}/285$ 62

b. $\hat{p}_1 = r_1/n - \underline{\qquad}/285$ 168

$\hat{p}_2 = r_2/n = \underline{\qquad}/285$ 80

$\hat{p}_3 = r_3/n = \underline{\qquad}/285$ 37

4. If the observed cell frequency for the cell in row i and column j is denoted by n_{ij}, then an estimate for the expected cell number in the ijth cell under the hypothesis of independence can be calculated by using the estimated cell probabilities.

$$E(n_{ij}) = n(p_{ij})$$

$$= n(p_i)(p_j)$$

$$\hat{E}(n_{ij}) = n(r_i/n)(c_j/n)$$

$r_i c_j/n$

$$= \underline{\hspace{2cm}}$$

5. The expected cell numbers enclosed in parentheses for the contingency table in 1 are found in this way. For example,

45.39

a. $\quad \hat{E}(n_{11}) = \dfrac{(168)(77)}{285} = \underline{\hspace{2cm}}$

43.03

b. $\quad \hat{E}(n_{12}) = \dfrac{(168)(73)}{285} = \underline{\hspace{2cm}}$

8.05

c. $\quad \hat{E}(n_{34}) = \dfrac{(37)(62)}{285} = \underline{\hspace{2cm}}$

80; 62; 17.40

d. $\quad \hat{E}(n_{24}) = \dfrac{(\underline{\hspace{1.5cm}})(\underline{\hspace{1.5cm}})}{285} = \underline{\hspace{2cm}}$

6. Now Pearson's statistic can be calculated accordingly as

$$X^2 = \sum_{i=1}^{3} \sum_{j=1}^{4} \frac{[n_{ij} - \hat{E}(n_{ij})]^2}{\hat{E}(n_{ij})}$$

$$= \frac{(55 - 45.39)^2}{45.39} + \frac{(40 - 43.03)^2}{43.03} + \ldots$$

$$+ \frac{(12 - 9.48)^2}{9.48} + \frac{(10 - 8.05)^2}{8.05}$$

10.23

$$= \underline{\hspace{2cm}}$$

one
restriction
n; one

1

7. Recall that the number of degrees of freedom associated with the χ^2-statistic used in testing X^2 equals the number of cells less \underline{\hspace{2cm}} degree of freedom for each independent linear \underline{\hspace{2cm}} on the cell counts. The first restriction is that $\Sigma n_i = \underline{\hspace{2cm}}$; hence \underline{\hspace{2cm}} degree of freedom is lost here. Then $(r - 1)$ independent linear restrictions have been placed on the cell counts due to the estimation of $(r - 1)$ row probabilities. Note that we need only estimate $(r - 1)$ independent row probabilities since their sum must equal \underline{\hspace{2cm}}. In like manner, $(c - 1)$ independent linear restrictions have been placed on the cell counts due to the estimation of the column probabilities.

a. Since there are _____ cells, the number of degrees of freedom for testing χ^2 in an $r \times c$ contingency table is

$$v = rc - (1) - (r - 1) - (c - 1)$$

which can be factored algebraically as

$$v = \underline{\hspace{2cm}}$$

rc

$(r - 1)(c - 1)$

b. In short, the number of degrees of freedom for an $r \times c$ contingency table, where all expected cell frequencies must be estimated from sample data (that is, from estimated row and column probabilities), is the number of rows minus one, times the number of columns minus one.

c. For our problem concerning criminal offenders under age 25,

$$v = (r - 1)(c - 1) = (\underline{\hspace{1.5cm}})(\underline{\hspace{1.5cm}}) = \underline{\hspace{1.5cm}}$$

$2; 3; 6$

8. We can now write the test of the hypothesis of independence of the two methods of classification at the $\alpha = .05$ level.
   a. H_0: the two classifications are independent
   b. H_a: the two classifications are not independent
   c. Test statistic:

   $$X^2 = \sum_{i=1}^{3} \sum_{j=1}^{4} \frac{[n_{ij} - \hat{E}(n_{ij})]^2}{\hat{E}(n_{ij})}$$

   d. Rejection region: With $v = 6$, we shall reject H_0 if $X^2 > \chi^2_{.05} =$ _____.

   12.5916

   e. The calculation of X^2 results in the value $X^2 = 10.23$
   f. Decision:

   _____.

   Since $X^2 < 12.5916$, do not reject H_0

   g. Since we were unable to reject H_0, the data do not present sufficient evidence to indicate that educational achievement and the number of arrests are dependent.

9. *Example:*

   A marketing research director wishes to test the hypothesis that the number of children in a family is independent of the family income. A random sample of 385 families resulted in the following contingency table.

Number of Children	Income Brackets in Thousands of Dollars				
	0-$4	$4-8	$8-12	Above $12	Total
0	10 (14.26)	9 (15.05)	18 (16.48)	24 (15.21)	61
1	8 (17.77)	12 (18.75)	25 (20.53)	31 (18.95)	76
2	14 (21.74)	28 (22.95)	23 (25.12)	28 (23.19)	93
3	26 (17.77)	24 (18.75)	20 (20.53)	6 (18.95)	76
4 or more	32 (18.47)	22 (19.49)	18 (21.34)	7 (19.70)	79
Totals	90	95	104	96	385

If the number in parentheses is the estimated expected cell number, do these data present sufficient evidence at the $\alpha = .01$ level to indicate an independence of family size and family income?

Solution:

The estimated cell counts have been found using

$$\hat{E}(n_{ij}) = \frac{r_i c_j}{n}$$

and are given in parentheses within each cell. The degrees of freedom are

$(r - 1)(c - 1) = $ _____ .

a. H_0: the two classifications are independent
b. H_a: the classifications are not independent
c. Test statistic:

$$X^2 = \sum_{i=1}^{5} \sum_{j=1}^{4} \frac{[n_{ij} - \hat{E}(n_{ij})]^2}{\hat{E}(n_{ij})}$$

d. Rejection region: With $\nu = 12$, we shall reject H_0 if

$$X^2 > \chi_{.01}^2 = \underline{\hspace{2cm}} .$$

e. Calculate X^2:

$$X^2 = \frac{(10 - 14.26)^2}{14.26} + \frac{(9 - 15.05)^2}{15.05} + \dots$$

$$+ \frac{(18 - 21.34)^2}{21.34} + \frac{(7 - 19.70)^2}{19.70}$$

$$= \underline{\hspace{2cm}}$$

12

26.2170

63.4783

f. Decision:

<u>   </u>.

Therefore, we can conclude that family size and family income (<u>are</u>, <u>are not</u>) independent classifications.

Reject H_0
are not

Self-Correcting Exercises 17B

1. On the basis of the following data, is there a significant relationship between levels of income and political party affiliation at the $\alpha = .05$ level of significance?

		Income	
Party Affiliation	Low	Average	High
Republican	33	85	27
Democrat	19	71	56
Other	22	25	13

2. Three hundred people were interviewed to determine their opinions regarding a uniform driving code for all states.

	Opinion	
Sex	For	Against
Male	114	60
Female	87	39

Is there sufficient evidence to indicate that the opinion expressed is dependent upon the sex of the person interviewed?

17.5   r X c Tables with Fixed Row or Column Totals (17.5)

1. To avoid having rows or columns that are absolutely empty, it is sometimes desirable to fix the row or column totals of a contingency table in the design of the experiment. In Example 17.4 (9) the design could have been to randomly sample 100 families in each of the four income brackets, thereby insuring that each of the income brackets would be represented in the sample. On the other hand, a random sample of 80 families in each of the family size categories could have been taken so that all family size categories would appear in the overall sample.

2. When using fixed row or column totals the number of independent linear restrictions on the cell counts is the same as for an $r \times c$ contingency table. Therefore the data is analyzed in the same way that an $r \times c$ contingency table is analyzed, using Pearson's χ^2 based on $\nu = $ _____ degrees of freedom.

$(r-1)(c-1)$

3. In this example we examine a case where the column totals are fixed in advance.

Example:

A manufacturer of ladies' garments wished to determine whether the percentage of unacceptable dresses differed for three different styles produced in his factory. A lot of 300 dresses of each style was produced in his factory with the following results:

Style	1	2	3
Number Unacceptable	9	4	11

Is there sufficient evidence to indicate that the percentage of unacceptable dresses varies from style to style at the $\alpha = .05$ level?

Solution:

a. The above table displays only half of the pertinent information. Extend the table as follows, allowing space for the expected cell frequencies.

	Style			
	1	*2*	*3*	*Totals*
Unacceptable	9 (_____)	4 (_____)	11 (_____)	24
Acceptable	291 (292)	296 (292)	289 (292)	876
Totals	300	300	300	900

8; 8; 8

b. By fixing the column totals at 300, we have assured that the unconditional probability of selecting style 1, 2, or 3 is a constant and equal to _____ for each style.

1/3

　　If the percentage of unacceptable dresses does not vary from style to style, then the probability of observing an unacceptable dress for a given style is the *same* for each style and is equal to a common value, *p*. Therefore, the unconditional probability of observing an unacceptable dress is *p,* and in like manner, the unconditional probability of observing an acceptable dress is *q*.

　　If the percentage of defective dresses *is the same for the three styles,* then the probability of observing an unacceptable dress in a given style will be

$$p_{1j} = (1/3)(p) \qquad \text{for } j = 1, 2, 3$$

while the probability of observing an acceptable dress in a given style will be

$$p_{2j} = (1/3)(q) \qquad \text{for } j = 1, 2, 3$$

However, if the probability of observing an unacceptable dress varies from style to style, then

$p_{1j} \neq (1/3)\,(p)$ for at least one value of $j = 1, 2, 3$

$p_{2j} \neq (1/3)\,(q)$ for at least one value of $j = 1, 2, 3$

But, this is the same as asking whether the row and column classifications are independent; hence, this test is equivalent to a test of independence of the two classifications based on $(r - 1)\,(c - 1)$ degrees of freedom.

c. The test proceeds as follows:

$$H_0 : p_1 = p_2 = p_3 = p$$

$$H_a : p_i \neq p \quad \text{for at least one value of } i = 1, 2, 3$$

Test statistic:

$$X^2 = \sum_i \sum_j \frac{[n_{ij} - \hat{E}(n_{ij})]^2}{\hat{E}(n_{ij})}$$

Rejection region: Reject H_0 if $X^2 > \chi^2_{.05} = $ _____ .   5.991
Calculate the estimated expected cell frequencies.

$$\hat{E}(n_{1j}) = \frac{24\,(300)}{900} = \text{_____} \quad j = 1, 2, 3$$ 8

$$\hat{E}(n_{2j}) = \frac{876\,(300)}{900} = \text{_____} \quad j = 1, 2, 3$$ 292

Then

$$X^2 = \frac{(9-8)^2}{8} + \frac{(4-8)^2}{8} + \frac{(\text{_____})^2}{8}$$ 11 – 8

$$+ \frac{(291-292)^2}{292} + \frac{(296-292)^2}{292} + \frac{(\text{_____})^2}{292}$$ 289 – 292

$$= \frac{(\text{_____})}{8} + \frac{(\text{_____})}{292}$$ 26; 26

$$= \text{_____}$$ 3.3390

Decision:

_____ . We can conclude that the percentage of   Do not reject H_0
defectives (does, does not) vary from style to style.   does not

Self-Correcting Exercises 17C

1. A survey of voter sentiment was conducted in four mid-city political wards to compare the fraction of voters favoring a "city manager" form of government. Random samples of 200 voters were polled in each of the four wards with results as follows:

	Ward			
	1	*2*	*3*	*4*
Favor	75	63	69	58
Against	125	137	131	142

Can you conclude that the fractions favoring the city manager form of government differ in the four wards?

2. A personnel manager of a large company investigating employee satisfaction with their assigned jobs collected the following data for 200 employees in each of four job categories:

	Categories				
Satisfaction	*I*	*II*	*III*	*IV*	*Totals*
High	40	60	52	48	200
Medium	103	87	82	88	360
Low	57	53	66	64	240
Totals	200	200	200	200	800

Do these data indicate that the satisfaction scores are dependent upon the job categories at the $\alpha = .05$ level?

17.6 Other Applications (17.6)

1. *Goodness of Fit Tests*
   a. Section 17.3(1) dealt with a problem that comes under the category of goodness of fit tests, since we tested whether the observed data fitted the hypothesized model. In fact, since the observed cell frequencies deviated significantly from this model, we rejected the model.
   b. We may encounter the problem of testing whether a population possesses a given probability distribution _____. For example, if we wished to test the hypothesis that a population has a normal distribution with a specified mean and variance, we would select a random sample from this population and construct a sample frequency histogram. The k cells of the histogram would correspond to the k cells of the multinomial experiment and the number in each cell would be the number falling in each cell of the histogram. From the table of normal areas, the probability of falling into each cell could be found, and the expected number of measurements in each cell computed using $E(n_i) = np_i$ _____. Then

distribution

np_i

Pearson's statistic with $(k - 1)$ degrees of freedom could be applied to test the hypothesis of normality.

2. *Tests of Independence*

   a. Example 17.4(9) shows in great detail how a test of the independence of two methods of classification can be constructed.

   b. The independence of three or more methods of classifications can be tested by constructing a test in a manner analogous to that for _____ two methods of classification by first estimating the expected cell frequencies and applying Pearson's statistic with the proper degrees of freedom.

3. *Tests Concerning Proportions*

   a. The χ^2-test can be used to test the equality of several binomial proportions as we did in Example 17.5(3).

   b. A problem very similar to Example 17.5(3) would be one in which the change in a multinomial population is investigated over time. For example, an advertising campaign may be conducted over a period of three months by a dairy products company in a large city. During the first month, only newspaper advertisements will be used; in the next month, television ads will be used; and during the third month, mail circulars. The percentage of all dairy sales within the city which accrue to the dairy conducting the advertising campaign could be investigated over time. Thus, an investigation of the effectiveness of the three modes of advertising is examined.

   c. Specific problems could be investigated using sophisticated statistical techniques involving the χ^2-test. For example: In an advertising experiment, the number of customers, n, buying a particular brand available in a supermarket is said to be linearly related to the amount spent the previous week to advertise the brand in the region of the supermarket. Thus, $n = \alpha + \beta A$, where A is the amount spent on advertising. An experiment was conducted using four different amounts of advertising, $1000, $2000, $3000, and $4000.

   The method of maximum likelihood or minimum-χ^2 could be used to estimate α and β from which the expected cell frequencies could be estimated. Then the hypothesis of linearity could be tested using Pearson's statistic with the proper degrees of freedom.

Self-Correcting Exercises 17D

1. A company producing wire rope has recorded the number of "breaks" occurring for a given type of wire rope within a four-hour period. These records were kept for 50 four-hour periods. If y is the number of "breaks" recorded for each four-hour period and μ is the mean number of "breaks" for a four-hour period, does the following Poisson model adequately describe this data when $\mu = 2$?

$$p(y) = \frac{\mu^y e^{-\mu}}{y!} \qquad y = 0, 1, 2, \ldots$$

y	0	1	2	3 or more
Number Observed	4	15	16	15

Hint: Find $p(0), p(1)$, and $p(2)$ by means of Table 2 of your text. Use the fact that $p[y \geqslant 3] = 1 - p(0) - p(1) - p(2)$. After finding the expected cell numbers, you can test the model by applying Pearson's χ^2-test.

2. In standardizing a score, the mean is subtracted and the result divided by the standard deviation. If 100 scores are so standardized and then grouped, test at the $\alpha = .05$ level of significance whether these scores were drawn from the standard normal distribution.

Interval	Frequency
Less than –1.5	8
–1.5 to –0.5	20
–0.5 to 0.5	40
0.5 to 1.5	29
Greater than 1.5	3

17.7 Summary (17.7)

1. We have investigated a test of an hypothesis concerning the cell probabilities associated with the _____ experiment.

multinomial

2. The test statistic used in testing such an hypothesis was developed by _____ and is given by

Pearson

$$X^2 = \sum_{\text{cells}} \frac{(\text{Observed-Expected})^2}{(\text{Expected})}$$

3. For large values of n, X^2 has an approximate _____ distribution

chi-square (χ^2)

4. This test is a _____ -tailed test, where H_0 is rejected for _____ values of X^2.

one
large

5. The degrees of freedom associated with χ^2 is equal to the number of _____ , less one degree of freedom for each independent linear _____ on the cell counts.

cells
restriction

6. In order that the approximation to the χ^2-statistic be reasonably good, the expected cell frequency must be greater than or equal to _____ for every cell.

five

Exercises

1. What are the characteristics of a multinomial experiment?
2. Do the following situations possess the properties of a multinomial experiment?

a. A shipment of 40 pairs of shoes from a manufacturer contained men's shoes, women's shoes, and children's shoes. The number of men's shoes, women's shoes, and children's shoes are recorded.

b. An investor has the option of choosing among three portfolios, one of which hedges against inflation, one which is best under a stable economy, and one which provides protection in time of recession. The payoff to the investor is dependent upon the portfolio he selects and the state of nature which results.

c. Four production lines are checked for defectives during an eight-hour period and the number of defectives for each production line recorded.

3. The probability of receiving grades of A, B, C, D, and E are .07, .15, .63, .10, and .05, respectively, in a certain business course. In a class of 120 students,

a. what is the expected number of A's?

b. what is the expected number of B's?

c. what is the expected number of C's?

4. A department store manager claims that his store has twice as many customers on Fridays and Saturdays as on any other day of the week (the store is closed on Sundays). That is, the probability that a customer visits the store Friday is 2/8, the probability that a customer visits the store Saturday is 2/8, while the probability that a customer visits the store on each of the remaining weekdays is 1/8. During an average week, the following numbers of customers visited the store:

Monday	95	Thursday	75
Tuesday	110	Friday	181
Wednesday	125	Saturday	214

Can the manager's claim be refuted at the $\alpha = .05$ level of significance?

5. If the probability of a female birth is 1/2, according to the binomial model, in a family containing four children, the probability of 0, 1, 2, 3, or 4 female births is 1/16, 4/16, 6/16, 4/16, and 1/16, respectively. A sample of 80 families each containing four children resulted in the following data:

Female births	0	1	2	3	4
Number of families	7	18	33	16	6

Do the data contradict the binomial model with $p = 1/2$ at the $\alpha = .05$ level of significance?

6. A sales training program thought to be effective in increasing sales activity is administered to 500 real estate salesmen. Their weekly sales immediately after the training program were compared to those of 500 salesmen of the same sales area who did not participate in the training program. The results were as follows:

	More Than One Sale	One Sale	No Sale
Trained	252	146	102
Untrained	224	136	140

Test the hypothesis that the two classifications are independent at the $\alpha = .05$ level of significance.

7. A manufacturer wished to know whether the number of defectives produced varied for four different production lines. A random sample of 100 items was selected from each line and the number of defectives recorded.

Production lines	1	2	3	4
Defectives	8	12	7	9

Do these data produce sufficient evidence to indicate that the percentage of defects is varying from line to line?

8. In a random sample of 50 male and 50 female undergraduates, each member was asked if he was for, against, or indifferent to the practice of having unannounced in-class quizzes. Do the following data indicate that attitude toward this practice is dependent upon the sex of the student interviewed?

	Male	Female
For	20	10
Against	15	30
Indifferent	15	10

9. In an experiment performed in a laboratory, a ball is bounced within a container whose bottom (or floor) has holes just large enough for the ball to pass through. The ball is allowed to bounce until it passes through one of the holes. For each of 100 trials, the number of bounces until the ball falls through one of the holes is recorded. If y is the number of bounces until the ball does fall through a hole, does the model

$$p(y) = (.6)(.4)^y \qquad y = 0, 1, 2, 3, \ldots$$

adequately describe the following data?

y	0	1	2	3 or more
Number observed	65	28	4	3

Hint: First find $p(0)$, $p(1)$, $p(2)$, and $p(y \geq 3)$ from which the expected numbers for the cells can be calculated using np_0, np_1, np_2, etc. Then a goodness of fit test will adequately answer the question posed.

Chapter 18

NONPARAMETRIC STATISTICS

18.1   Introduction (18.1)

1. In earlier chapters, we tested various hypotheses concerning the parameters of populations. In this chapter, we shall be concerned with hypotheses that do not involve population parameters directly, but rather deal with the _____ of the population frequency distribution. These latter hypotheses are termed _____, and the techniques for making inferences in such cases are called _____ tests.

   form
   nonparametric
   nonparametric

2. Nonparametric tests are appropriate when one or more of the following conditions exist:
   a. The experimental measurements cannot be quantified, but can be _____ on an arbitrary scale.

   ranked _or_ ordered

   b. Only directional _____ between test items are available, without any measure of the _____ of the difference.

   differences
   size

   c. One is concerned only with the question of whether or not a given population possesses a particular _____, or whether two populations have the same _____.

   distribution
   distribution

   d. One has serious doubts that the _____ required for parametric tests are satisfied.

   assumptions

3. Several null hypotheses are given below. Indicate whether each is best tested by parametric or nonparametric methods.
   a. H_0:   The population is normally distributed
   b. H_0:   The mean, μ, is greater than 1.39
   c. H_0:   The two populations have the same standard deviation
   d. H_0:   The two populations have the same frequency distribution

   nonparametric
   parametric
   parametric
   nonparametric

18.2   The Sign Test for Comparing Two Population Distributions (18.2)

1. The _____ test is most often employed for observations that have been randomly selected in pairs, using a _____ _____ experiment. The sign test is based on the signs of the observed _____.

   sign
   paired-difference
   differences

omitted

18

identical
distribution

1/2

binomial

$p = 1/2$
large

small
large
small

< 1/2
> 1/2

2. Thus in a paired-difference experiment, we may observe in each pair only whether the first element is larger than the second. If the first element is larger (smaller), we assign a plus (minus) sign to the difference. We will define the test statistic, y, to be the number of plus signs observed.

3. It is worth emphasizing that the sign test *does not* require a numerical measure of a response, but merely a statement of which of two responses within a matched pair is larger. Thus the sign test is a convenient and even necessary tool in many brand preference investigations. If within a given pair it is impossible to tell which response is larger (a tie occurs), the pair is _____. Thus if 20 differences are analyzed and two of them are impossible to classify as plus or minus, we shall base our inference on _____ (give number) differences.

4. The sign test is used in testing whether or not two population distributions are _____. The sign test is completely independent of the form of the _____ of differences.

5. Let p denote the probability that a difference selected at random from the population of differences would be given a plus sign. If the two population distributions are identical, the probability of a plus sign for a given pair would equal _____. Then the null hypothesis, "the two populations are identical," could be stated in the form $H_0 : p = 1/2$. The test statistic, y, will have a _____ distribution whether H_0 is true or not. If H_0 is true, then the number of trials, n, will be the number of pairs in which a difference can be detected and the probability of success (i.e., a plus sign) on a given trial will be _____. If the alternative hypothesis is $H_a : p > 1/2$, then (large, small) values of y would be placed in the rejection region. If the alternative hypothesis is $H_a : p < 1/2$, then _____ values of y would be used in the rejection region. With $H_a : p \neq 1/2$, the rejection region would include both _____ and _____ values of y.

6. *Example:*

In an experiment designed to compare the relative effectiveness of two alloys with respect to their resistance to corrosion, fifteen pairs of metal strips were subjected to corrosive elements, and at the end of a specified time, a measure of the amount of corrosion that had taken place was recorded for each strip. A preliminary investigation of the 15 pairs revealed that in 12 of the 15 pairs, alloy number one showed more corrosion. Does this constitute sufficient evidence to indicate that the alloys differ in their resistance to corrosion?

Solution:

If there is no difference in ability to resist corrosion, then the probability that a strip of alloy number one shows more corrosion than a strip of alloy number two is $p = 1/2$. If alloy number one is more resistant than alloy number two, then p _____, while if alloy number one is less resistant than two, then p _____. Using this information, the test proceeds as follows.

a. $H_0: p = \dfrac{1}{2}$

b. $H_a:$ _____ $p \neq \dfrac{1}{2}$

c. The test statistic is y, the number of pairs in which alloy one showed
   more corrosion than alloy two. The number of pairs is $n = 15$, and the
   observed value of y is _____.   12

d. Rejection region: The alternative hypothesis indicates that we should
   reject H_0 for very large or very small values of y. Using the table of
   binomial probabilities in your text with $p = 1/2$ and $n = 15$, evaluate
   the following possible rejection regions.

Rejection region	α	
$y = 0, 1, 2, 13, 14, 15$	_____	.008
$y = 0, 1, 2, 3, 12, 13, 14, 15$	_____	.036
$y = 0, 1, 2, 3, 4, 11, 12, 13, 14, 15$	_____	.118

   Choosing the rejection region so that the probability of a Type I error is
   less than or equal to .05, we would agree to reject $H_0: p = 1/2$ if $y = 0$,
   1, 2, 3, 12, 13, 14, or 15 with $\alpha =$ _____.   .036

e. With the observed value of $y = 12$, we (accept, reject) H_0 and conclude   reject
   that there is a difference in resistance to corrosion for these two alloys.
   In fact, it appears that of the two alloys, alloy number _____   two
   is the more resistant to corrosion.

7. We observed in Chapter 7 that the normal approximation to binomial
   probabilities is reasonably accurate if $p = 1/2$ even when n is as small as
   _____. Thus, the normal distribution can ordinarily be used to   10
   approximate _____ for a given rejection region. α

8. Furthermore, when n is at least _____, the test can be based on the   25
   statistic

$$z = \frac{y - .5n}{.5\sqrt{n}}$$

   which will have approximately the standard normal distribution when H_0
   is _____.   true

9. *Example:*
   The productivity of 25 employees was observed and measured both before
   and after the installation of new lighting in a workroom. The productivity
   of 18 of the 25 workers was observed to have improved while the productivity of the others appeared to show no perceptible gain as a result of the
   new lighting. Test whether the new lighting was effective in increasing
   employee productivity.

Solution:

Let p denote the probability that one of the 25 employees selected at random exhibits increased productivity after the installation of new lighting. This constitutes a paired-difference test where the productivity measures are paired on the employees. Such pairing tends to block out employee variations.

= 1/2

a. The null hypothesis is $H_0: p$ _____.

> 1/2

b. The appropriate one-sided alternative hypothesis is $H_a: p$ _____.

c. If y denotes the number of employees who show improved productivity after the installation of the new lighting, then y has a binomial distribution with mean $np = 25(1/2) =$ _____ and a variance equal to

12.5

6.25

$npq = 25(1/2)(1/2) =$ _____ . Therefore the test statistic can be taken to be

$$z = \frac{y - 12.5}{\sqrt{6.25}}$$

d. We would reject H_0 at the $\alpha = .05$ level of significance if the calculated

1.645

value of z is greater than $z_{.05} =$ _____ .

e. Since $y = 18$,

2.2

$$z = \frac{18 - 12.5}{2.5} =$$ _____

would; has

Hence we (would, would not) reject H_0; the new lighting (has, has not) improved employee productivity.

18.3 The Mann-Whitney U Test: Two Populations and Independent Random Samples (18.3)

1. When the actual magnitudes of the observations are known, more information than that used by the sign test can be gleaned from the data for use in hypothesis testing. However, in order to make more efficient use of this information, the simplicity of the sign test must be sacrificed and a slightly more complex testing procedure introduced.

independent

2. If an experimenter has two _____ random samples in which the observations can be ranked in order of magnitude, the Mann-Whitney U statistic can be used to test whether the samples have been drawn from

identical

_____ populations.

3. The Mann-Whitney U test is appropriate when we have two independent samples of size n_1 and n_2 from populations A and B, respectively. If the null hypothesis is true, and both samples have been drawn from the same population, we then have one sample of size $N = n_1 + n_2$ from the same population.

a. All $N = n_1 + n_2$ observations are ranked from small to large with the smallest observation assigned rank 1 and the largest assigned rank $N = n_1 + n_2$. Tied observations are assigned the average of the ranks they would have been assigned if there were no ties. For example, if the sixth and seventh smallest observations have the same magnitude, each is assigned the value _____.

6.5

    If the null hypothesis is true, we would expect to see the A and B observations randomly mixed in the ranking positions. If H_0 is false and the A observations come from a population whose values tend to be larger than the B observations, the A's will tend to occupy the _____ rank positions. If the B's tend to be larger than the A's, then the A observations will tend to occupy the _____ rank positions

higher
lower

  b. A statistic that reflects the positions in the total ranking of the observations from population A and from population B is the sum of the rank positions occupied by the first sample or the sum of the rank positions occupied by the second sample, denoted by _____ and _____, respectively.

T_A ; T_B

4. The stronger the discrepancy between T_A and T_B, the greater is the evidence to indicate that the samples have been drawn from two _____ populations. The Mann-Whitney U statistic uses this information in testing for a difference in the population frequency distributions giving rise to the sample observations.

different

5. The Mann-Whitney U statistic is the smaller of U_A and U_B where

$$U_A = n_1 n_2 + \frac{n_1(n_1 + 1)}{2} - T_A$$

$$U_B = n_1 n_2 + \frac{n_2(n_2 + 1)}{2} - T_B$$

with $U_A + U_B =$ _____. The quantity U_A counts the number of times that an A observation precedes a B observation in the ranking while U_B counts the number of times that a B observation precedes an A observation.

$n_1 n_2$

6. Since U is the smaller of U_A and U_B, the smaller the value of U, the (more, less) likely it is that the underlying distributions are different.

more

7. The Mann-Whitney U statistic is used in testing whether population A and population B have identical frequency distributions. The specification of the rejection region depends upon the alternative hypothesis. A (one, two) -tailed test is used when the alternative hypothesis is that the two populations are not identical. If the alternative hypothesis is that the frequency distribution for population A lies to the right (or left) of the frequency distribution for population B, a (one, two) -tailed test is used.

two

one

8. The selection of the rejection region depends upon the value of α, the sample sizes, n_1 and n_2, and the alternative hypothesis. Tabled values for

A

α

α/2

5; 6; 2; 1; 9
3; 7; 8; 10; 4

23

10; 4; 32

17

8

$n_1 n_2$

$P(U \leq U_0)$ when n_1 and n_2 are less than or equal to 10 are given in Table 8 in the Appendix of your text. Notice that the entries in Table 8 are indexed with $n_1 \leq n_2$. When the sample sizes are not equal, always designate the population with the smaller sample size as population _____.

a. A one-tailed rejection region consists of the values of $U \leq U_0$ where U_0 is chosen from Table 8 such that $P(U \leq U_0) =$ _____. In this case the U statistic will be chosen specifically to be U_A or U_B.

b. The rejection region for a two-tailed test consists of the values $U \leq U_0$ where $P(U \leq U_0) =$ _____. In this case U is the smaller of U_A or U_B.

9. *Example:*

Five sample observations for each of two samples are given below:

Sample A: 19 (___) 20 (___) 16 (___) 12 (___) 23 (___)
Sample B: 17 (___) 21 (___) 22 (___) 25 (___) 18 (___)

In the space provided, fill in the rank of each of the 10 observations and calculate T_A and T_B.

$$T_A = 5 + 6 + 2 + 1 + 9 = \underline{\qquad}$$

$$T_B = 3 + 7 + 8 + \underline{\qquad} + \underline{\qquad} = \underline{\qquad}$$

10. *Example:*

Use the data in Example 9 to test H_0: the population frequency distributions for A and B are identical against H_a: the population frequency distributions are not identical.

Solution:

a. We must first calculate U_A and U_B.

$$U_A = n_1 n_2 + \frac{n_1(n_1 + 1)}{2} - T_A$$

$$= 5(5) + \frac{5(6)}{2} - 23 = \underline{\qquad}$$

and

$$U_B = n_1 n_2 + \frac{n_2(n_2 + 1)}{2} - T_B$$

$$= 5(5) + \frac{5(6)}{2} - 32 = \underline{\qquad}$$

As a check on our calculations, notice that

$$U_A + U_B = \underline{\qquad} = 25$$

b. The Mann-Whitney U statistic is equal to _____, the _____ of | 8; smaller
U_A and U_B.

c. For a two-tailed test the rejection region consists of values of $U \leqslant U_0$
such that $P(U \leqslant U_0) \approx$ with U_0 found in Table 8 of the text when
$n_1 = n_2 =$ _____. An appropriate choice is $U_0 =$ _____, since | 5; 3
that insures that $P(U \leqslant U_0) =$ _____, which is approximately | .0278
equal to $\alpha/2$ for $\alpha = .05$.

d. Since $U = 8$ is greater than $U_0 = 3$, we (reject, do not reject) the null | do not reject
hypothesis of identical population frequency distributions.

11. *Example:*

Before filling several new managerial positions which were created due to
company expansion, the personnel director of the company formed a
review board consisting of five people who were asked to interview the
twelve qualified applicants and rank them in order of merit. Seven of the
twelve applicants held college degrees but had limited on-the-job experience. Of the remaining five applicants, all did not necessarily have college
degrees, but all did have substantial experience. The review board's rankings follow.

Limited experience	*Substantial experience*
4	1
6	2
7	3
9	5
10	8
11	
12	

Do these rankings indicate that the review board considers on-the-job
experience to be more important than formal education?

Solution:

a. In testing the null hypothesis that the underlying populations are
identical versus the alternative hypothesis that the population consisting of applicants having substantial experience is better qualified (will
receive low ranks), we require a _____ -tailed test. | one

b. In deciding upon the test statistic and the rejection region, we must
take care to note that the tables are given with $n_1 \leqslant n_2$. Hence we take
$n_1 = 5$ and $n_2 = 7$ and identify the five applicants with substantial
experience as A's and the remaining seven applicants as B's. If H_a is
true, the A's will occupy the _____ ranks and U_A will | lower *or* smaller
be _____ because T_A is _____. Similarly, the B's | large; small
will have generally higher ranks, making T_B _____ and U_B | large
_____. Hence, if H_a is true, (U_A, U_B) will be smaller than | small; U_B
_____, and will be used as our test statistic U. | U_A

c. $T_B = 4 + 6 + 7 +$ _____ $+$ _____ $+$ _____ $+$ _____ $=$ _____. | 9; 10; 11; 12; 59

d. Using U_B as the test statistic, with $\alpha \approx .05$, $n_1 = 5$ and $n_2 = 7$, an
appropriate rejection region would consist of the values $U \leqslant$ _____ | 7
with $\alpha =$ _____, using Table 8 in the text. | .0530

$$U_B = n_1 n_2 + \frac{n_2(n_2 + 1)}{2} - T_B$$

59

$$= 5\,(7) + \frac{7(8)}{2} - \underline{\hspace{2cm}}$$

4

$$= \underline{\hspace{2cm}}$$

4; 7; reject

e. Since $U = \underline{\hspace{2cm}}$ is less than $U_0 = \underline{\hspace{2cm}}$, we (reject, do not reject) H_0 and conclude that the review board does consider on-the-job experience to be more important than formal education alone.

12. When the sample sizes both exceed ten, Table 8 can no longer be used to locate rejection regions for tests involving the Mann-Whitney U statistic.

10

normal

However, when the sample sizes exceed $\underline{\hspace{2cm}}$, the distribution of U can be approximated by a $\underline{\hspace{2cm}}$ distribution with mean

$$E(U) = \frac{n_1 n_2}{2}$$

and variance

$$\sigma_U^2 = \frac{n_1 n_2 (n_1 + n_2 + 1)}{12}$$

Therefore, we can use as a test statistic:

$$z = \frac{U - E(U)}{\sigma_U}$$

standard normal

with the appropriate one- or two-tailed rejection region expressed in terms of z, the $\underline{\hspace{2cm}}$ $\underline{\hspace{2cm}}$ random variable.

13. *Example:*

A manufacturer uses a large amount of a certain chemical. Since there are just two suppliers of this chemical, the manufacturer wishes to test whether the percent of contaminants is the same for the two sources against the alternative that there is a difference in the percent of contaminants for the two suppliers. Data from independent random samples are given below.

Supplier	Percent contaminants				
A	.86	.69	.72	.65	1.13
	.65	1.18	.45	1.41	.50
	1.04	.41			
B	.55	.40	.22	.58	.16
	.07	.09	.16	.26	.36
	.20	.15			

Solution:

a. We combine the obtained contaminant percentages in a single ordered arrangement, and identify each percentage by letter.

Percent	.07	.09	.15	.16	.16	.20	.22	.26
Rank	1	2	3	4.5	4.5	6	7	8
Supplier	B	B	B	B	B	B	B	B
Percent	.36	.40	.41	.45	.50	.55	.58	.65
Rank	9	10	11	12	13	14	15	16.5
Supplier	B	B	A	A	A	B	B	A
Percent	.65	.69	.72	.86	1.04	1.13	1.18	1.41
Rank	16.5	18	19	20	21	22	23	24
Supplier	A	A	A	A	A	A	A	A

b. Since the sample sizes of $n_1 = 12$ and $n_2 = 12$ are beyond those given in Table 8, we can use the normal approximation to the distribution of U. The manufacturer, in asking whether there is a difference between the two suppliers, has specified a _____-tailed test. Therefore we would reject H_0 if U were either too large or too small. (For a two-tailed test using the normal approximation, we are at liberty to use either U_A or U_B as the value of U to be tested.)

two

c. Using $n_1 = n_2 = 12$, $E(U) = $ _____ and $\sigma_U^2 = $ _____.

72; 300

$$U_A = n_1 n_2 + \frac{1}{2} n_1 (n_1 + 1) - T_A$$

$$= 144 + 78 - \underline{\quad\quad}$$

216

$$= \underline{\quad\quad}$$

6

while

$$U_B = n_1 n_2 + \frac{1}{2} n_2 (n_2 + 1) - T_B$$

$$= 144 + 78 - \underline{\quad\quad}$$

84

$$= \underline{\quad\quad}$$

138

d. The rejection region in terms of $z = (U - E(U))/\sigma_U$ would be to reject H_0 if $|z| > $ _____. With U_A as the value of U,

1.96

$$z = \frac{6 - 72}{\sqrt{300}} = \frac{-66}{17.32} = \underline{\quad\quad}$$

-3.81

Hence we would conclude that there (is, is not) a significant difference in percent contaminants for the two suppliers.

is

3.81

normal; equal

e. Had we used U_B as the value of U, our result would have been

$$z = \frac{138 - 72}{\sqrt{300}} = \frac{66}{17.32} = \underline{\hspace{2cm}}$$

and we would have arrived at the same conclusion.

14. Use of the Mann-Whitney U test eliminates the need for the restrictive assumptions of Student's t-test which requires that the samples be randomly drawn from _____ populations having _____ variances.

Self-Correcting Exercises 18A

1. An experiment was designed to compare the durabilities of two highway paints, Paint A and Paint B, under actual highway conditions. An A strip and a B strip were painted across a highway at each of 30 locations. At the end of the test period, the experimenter observed the following results. At 8 locations Paint A showed the least wear, at 17 locations Paint B showed the least wear, and at the other 5 locations the paint samples showed the same amount of wear. Can we conclude (use $\alpha = .05$) that Paint B is more durable?

2. Refer to Chapter 9, Exercise 15. Use the sign test to test the null hypothesis that there is no difference in brightness scores versus the alternative hypothesis that dye 1 produces higher brightness scores than does dye 2. Select the rejection region so that α is as close to .05 as possible.

3. An investigation was conducted to determine whether a state's strict charter regulations for forming a new business are effective in minimizing the chance of the new business's failing. To investigate this question, ten small businesses who had applied for a business charter at least three years ago were randomly selected from the state, and ten were selected from a neighboring state without such restrictive regulations. Recorded below is the number of days each small business survived for the 10 businesses selected from each state. An S is recorded for each business in the sample which is solvent (has not failed) at the time of the investigation.

State with strict regulations	State without strict regulations
315	45
474	112
737	251
894	340
S	412
S	533
S	712
S	790
S	845
S	974

Use the Mann-Whitney U and $\alpha = .0526$ to obtain a one-tailed test of whether the state with the strict charter requirements charters businesses which are more likely to succeed than those chartered by its neighboring state.

4. The score on a certain psychological test, P, is used as an index of status frustration. The scale ranges from $P = 0$ (low frustration) to $P = 10$ (high frustration). This test was administered to independent random samples of seven corporate executives and eight Federal government administrators with the following results:

	Status frustration score							
Corporate executives	6	10	3	8	8	7	9	
Federal govt. administrators	3	5	2	0	3	1	0	4

Use the Mann-Whitney U statistic with α as close to .05 as possible to test whether the distribution of status frustration scores is the same for the two groups against the alternative that the status frustration scores are higher among corporate executives.

18.4 The Wilcoxon Rank Sum Test for a Paired Experiment (18.4)

1. We have previously discussed the sign test, a nonparametric test which can be used for a paired-difference experiment. The sign test utilizes only the _____ of the difference within each matched pair. A more efficient test (that is, one which makes better use of the information contained in the sample data) would also consider the _____ of the differences if they are available. Such a test is the Wilcoxon rank sum test.

direction or sign

size or magnitude

2. The Wilcoxon rank sum test employs as a test statistic, T, the (smaller, larger) sum of ranks for differences of the same sign where the differences are ranked in order of their _____ _____. In calculating T, zero differences are _____ and ties in the absolute values of nonzero differences are treated in the same manner as prescribed for the _____ test. Critical values of T are given in Table 9 of the text.

smaller
absolute values
omitted

Mann-Whitney U

3. *Example:*
Twelve office machinery salesmen were sent to a three-week training program in hopes of improving their sales efficiency. The average weekly sales volume for each salesman was computed before entering the training program and after a considerable lapse of time following the training program. The results follow. The differences in average sales volume (Before-After) have been ranked according to their absolute values and appear in the fifth column. It is these ranks which are important in a rank sum test such as the Wilcoxon test.

Salesman	Average weekly sales		Difference	Rank for the absolute value of the difference
	Before	After		
1	$380	$520	−$140	9
2	330	400	− 70	5
3	310	290	20	1.5
4	400	440	− 40	4
5	350	370	− 20	1.5
6	410	410	*	*
7	350	450	− 100	7
8	310	430	− 120	8
9	375	375	*	*
10	290	440	− 150	10
11	345	425	− 80	6
12	370	405	− 35	3

*Zero differences (not included in ranks)

For a one-sided test with $\alpha = .05$, we should reject H_0: "training program has no effect on average weekly sales volume" when $T \leqslant$ _____. The sample value of T is _____. Hence, we _____ the null hypothesis, H_0.

4. When n, the number of _____ in the experiment, is large $(n \geqslant$ _____$)$, T is approximately _____ distributed with mean

$$E(T) = \frac{n(n + 1)}{4}$$

and variance

$$\sigma_T^2 = \frac{n(n + 1)(2n + 1)}{24}$$

5. In such cases, we may employ the test statistic

$$z = \frac{T - E(T)}{\sigma_T}$$

which will have approximately the standard normal distribution when H_0 is _____.

6. *Example:*

A drug was developed for reducing the cholesterol level in heart patients. The cholesterol levels before and after drug treatment were obtained for a random sample of 25 heart patients with the following results:

11
1.5; reject

pairs
25; normally

true

	Cholesterol level			Cholesterol level	
Patient	Before	After	Patient	Before	After
1	257	243	13	364	343
2	222	217	14	210	217
3	177	174	15	263	243
4	258	260	16	214	198
5	294	295	17	392	388
6	244	236	18	370	357
7	390	383	19	310	299
8	247	233	20	255	258
9	409	410	21	281	276
10	214	216	22	294	295
11	217	210	23	257	227
12	340	335	24	227	231
			25	385	374

Test whether this drug has an effect on the cholesterol level of heart patients.

Solution:

Differences, Before-After, arranged in order of their absolute values are shown below together with the corresponding ranks. Fill in the missing ranks.

Difference	Rank	Difference	Rank
−1	2	7	14
−1	2	−7	14
−1	2	7	14
−2	4.5	8	16
−2	4.5	11	_____
3	6.5	11	_____
−3	6.5	13	19
−4	8.5	14	_____
4	8.5	14	_____
5	11	16	_____
5	11	20	23
5	11	21	24
		30	25

Answers in margin: 17.5, 17.5, 20.5, 20.5, 22

Suppose the alternative hypothesis of interest to the experimenter is the statement, "the drug has the effect of reducing cholesterol levels in heart patients." Thus, the appropriate rejection region for $\alpha = .05$ is $z <$ _____ where, in calculating z, we take T to be the smaller sum of ranks (the sum of ranks of the _____ differences).

Answers in margin: −1.645, negative

When H_0 is true,

$$E(T) = \frac{1}{2} n(n + 1) - \text{_____}$$

Answer in margin: 325

and

1381.25

$$\sigma_T^2 = \frac{1}{24} n(n + 1)(2n + 1) = \underline{\hspace{2cm}}$$

Thus, we shall reject H_0 at the $\alpha = .05$ significance level if

$$z = \frac{T - 325}{\sqrt{1381.25}} < -1.645$$

44
−7.56
reject

Summing the ranks of the negative differences, we obtain $T = \underline{\hspace{1.5cm}}$ and hence, $z = \underline{\hspace{1.5cm}}$. Comparing z with its critical value, we $\underline{\hspace{2cm}}$ H_0 in favor of the alternative hypothesis that the drug has the effect of reducing cholesterol levels in heart patients.

It is interesting to see what conclusion is obtained by using the sign test. Recall that y is equal to the number of positive differences and that the test statistic

$$z = \frac{y - .5n}{.5\sqrt{n}}$$

> 1.645; 1.8

has approximately the $\underline{\hspace{2cm}}$ $\underline{\hspace{2cm}}$ distribution when n is greater than ten and $H_0: p = 1/2$ is true. With $\alpha = .05$ the rejection region for z is z $\underline{\hspace{1.5cm}}$. But $y = 17$, so that $z = \underline{\hspace{1.5cm}}$. Thus, we obtain the same conclusion as before, though the sample value of the test statistic does not penetrate as deeply into the rejection region as when the Wilcoxon test was used. Since the Wilcoxon test makes fuller use of the information available in the experiment, we say that the Wilcoxon

efficient

test is more $\underline{\hspace{2cm}}$ than the sign test.

Self-Correcting Exercises 18B

1. Two real estate appraisers, call them A and B, were asked to each independently appraise ten properties. The results of the appraisals are shown below. (All appraisals are dollar values of assessed valuation.)

Property	1	2	3	4	5	6	7	8	9	10
Appr. A	4630	2680	8710	7300	4740	4320	5380	3050	1730	5920
Appr. B	2770	1300	5220	6100	4820	3400	3190	2660	2050	5400

Can it be said (use a two-tailed sign test with $\alpha = .02$) that appraisers A and B differ in their assessed valuation of different properties?

2. The sign test is not as efficient as the Wilcoxon rank sum test for data of the type presented in Exercise 1. Analyze the data of Exercise 1 by using the two-tailed Wilcoxon test with $\alpha = .02$. Can it be said that appraisers A and B differ in their assessed valuation of different properties?

3. Analyze the data of Exercise 15, Chapter 9 by use of the two-sided Wilcoxon test with $\alpha = .05$. Is there sufficient evidence to indicate a difference in mean brightness scores for the two dyes?

4. The sign test is sometimes used as a "quick and dirty" substitute for more powerful tests which require lengthy computations. The following differences were obtained in a paired-difference experiment: -.93, .95, .52, -.26, -.75, .25, 1.08, 1.47, .60, 1.20, -.65, -.15, 2.50, 1.22, .80, 1.27, 1.46, 3.05, -.43, 1.82, -.56, 1.08, -.16, 2.64.
Use the sign test with α = .05 to test $H_0: \mu_D = 0$ against the one-sided alternative $H_a: \mu_D > 0$.

5. Refer to problem 4. Use the large sample Wilcoxon test with α = .05 to test $H_0: \mu_D = 0$ against the alternative hypothesis $H_a: \mu_D > 0$. Compare (in efficiency and in computational requirements) the sign test and the Wilcoxon test as substitute tests in a paired differences experiment.

18.5 The Runs Test: A Test for Randomness (18.5)

1. The data for a runs test is obtained in the form of a _____ where each element in the _____ is either a "success" (S) or a "failure" (F). A run is defined as a _____ sequence of like elements. R is the number of _____ in a sequence. The number of runs in the sequence SSFSFFFSSS is _____. A very small or very large number of runs in a sequence would indicate nonrandomness. If there is at least one failure and at least one success then the minimum value for R is _____.

2. We let n_1 be the number of S elements and n_2 be the number of F elements in the sequence. The probability distribution for R when $n_1 \leqslant n_2$ and both n_1 and n_2 are less than or equal to 10 is provided by Table 10 in the text. If $n_1 \geqslant n_2$, simply interchange these symbols.

3. The runs test is used to test the null hypothesis: the sequence of S's and F's has been produced in a _____ manner. The alternative hypothesis will determine whether one is performing a one- or two-tailed test.

4. When the alternative hypothesis is H_a: the sequence has been produced in a nonrandom manner, a two-tailed rejection region is used, since too many runs is indicative of overmixing while too few runs is indicative of undermixing in which like elements tend to follow one another. A two-tailed rejection region consists of values of R such that $R \leqslant k_1$ and $R \geqslant k_2$ where k_1 and k_2 are appropriately chosen from Table 10 so that

$$P(R \leqslant k_1) + P(R \geqslant k_2) = \underline{\hspace{1in}}$$

the probability of a Type _____ error.

5. If the alternative hypothesis specifies that the sequence is nonrandom due to overmixing, the rejection region would consist of _____ values of R, since overmixing would lead to a larger number of runs than would be expected in a random sequence. The appropriate rejection region consists of values of R _____ k_2 where $P(R \geqslant k_2) = $ _____.

sequence

sequence

maximal

runs

5

2

random

α

I

large

$\geqslant; \alpha$

$\leqslant$

10

If the alternative hypothesis specifies that the sequence is nonrandom due to undermixing, the rejection region would consist of values of R _____ k_1 where $P(R \leqslant k_1) = \alpha$.

6. When n_1 and n_2 are both greater than _____ one may use the large-sample test statistic,

$$z = \frac{R - E(R)}{\sigma_R}$$

in which the expected value and variance of R are

$$E(R) = 1 + \frac{2n_1 n_2}{n_1 + n_2}$$

and

$$\sigma_R^2 = \frac{2n_1 n_2 (2n_1 n_2 - n_1 - n_2)}{(n_1 + n_2)^2 (n_1 + n_2 - 1)}$$

1.96

The rejection region for a two-tailed test with $\alpha = .05$ is $|z| \geqslant$ _____.

7. *Example:*

A salesman has contacted 12 customers on a certain day. Let S represent a sale and F a failure to make a sale. The sequential record for the day was: SSSFFFFSSSSF. Is there evidence of nonrandomness in this sequence?

Solution:

5; 7
.06
would not

$n_1 =$ _____ and $n_2 =$ _____. If we agree to reject when $R \leqslant 3$ and when $R \geqslant 10$ then $\alpha =$ _____. With this rejection region we (would, would not) reject the hypothesis of randomness.

8. *Example:*

Refer to the previous example. A lower tail test could be justified in the following situation. Suppose the district sales manager had reason to believe that this particular salesman was unusually sensitive to success and failure. Thus, a failure to sell seemed to reduce his confidence which in turn reduced his selling effectiveness. The opposite effect seemed to be true when a sale was consummated. If this theory were correct, the num-

less

ber of runs would tend to be considerably (more, less) than if H_0 were true. Hence, an appropriate test would utilize the rejection region $R \leqslant 3$

.015; .076

for $\alpha =$ _____ or the rejection region $R \leqslant 4$ for $\alpha =$ _____. If the latter rejection region were used, the district sales manager would

reject

_____ H_0 and perhaps enroll his salesman in a Dale Carnegie school.

9. *Example:*

A control chart is widely used in industry to provide a sequential record on some measured characteristic. This chart has a central line representing the process average. A measurement shall be classified as S if above this line and F if below. Does the following sequence indicate a lack of randomness in the distribution of this measured characteristic over time?

SSSFFFSSSSSSSFFFSFFFFSSSSSF

Solution:

Though n_1 and n_2 are too large to allow use of Table 10, both n_1 and n_2 are greater than ten. Hence, the statistic, z, can be used in a test of randomness. Now $n_1 = $ _____, $n_2 = $ _____. Hence, | 15; 11

$$E(R) = \underline{\hspace{2cm}} \text{ (give formula)}$$ | See 17.6(3)

$$= \underline{\hspace{2cm}} \text{ (evaluate)}$$ | 13.7

and $\quad \sigma_R^2 = \underline{\hspace{2cm}} \text{ (give formula)}$ | See 17.6(3)

$$= \underline{\hspace{2cm}} \text{ (value)}$$ | 5.94

Hence, $\sigma_R = \underline{\hspace{2cm}}$. | 2.44

The test statistic is thus

| $\dfrac{R - 13.7}{2.44}$.

$$z = \underline{\hspace{2cm}}$$

With $\alpha = .05$ a two-sided test would reject when $|z| > 1.96$. The sample value of R is _____ and hence the sample value of z is _____. | 8; –2.34
The decision is to _____ H_0. | reject

10. *Example:*

A runs test can be used to study the example of paragraph (4) in Section 17.5. We shall use the label S for a positive difference and F for a negative difference. The sequence of ordered differences produces the arrangement: FFFFFSFFSSSSSFSSSSSSSSSSS. The number of runs is $R = $ _____. | 6
n_1 (the number of S elements) = _____. n_2(the number of F elements) = _____. Though n_2 is less than ten we shall for illustrative purposes employ the large sample test statistic, | 17
| 8

$$z = \frac{R - E(R)}{\sigma_R}$$

Now

$$E(R) = 1 + \frac{2n_1 n_2}{n_1 + n_2} = \underline{\hspace{2cm}}$$ | 11.9

$$\sigma_R^2 = \frac{2n_1 n_2 (2n_1 n_2 - n_1 - n_2)}{(n_1 + n_2)^2 (n_1 + n_2 - 1)} = \underline{\hspace{2cm}}$$ | 4.48

$\dfrac{R - 13.7}{2.44}$

8; –2.34
reject

ranks

r
sample
random

y
ranks

$\Sigma x_i y_i - \dfrac{(\Sigma x_i)(\Sigma y_i)}{n}$

$\Sigma x_i^2 - \dfrac{(\Sigma x_i)^2}{n}$

$\Sigma y_i^2 - \dfrac{(\Sigma y_i)^2}{n}$

ties

To compare the runs test with the one-tailed Wilcoxon test we shall reject H_0 at the level $\alpha = .05$ when $z <$ _____. The sample value of z is _____, and hence we _____ H_0.

18.6 Rank Correlation Coefficient (18.6)

1. The Spearman rank correlation coefficient, r_s, is a numerical measure of the association between two variables, y and x. As implied in the name of the test statistic, r_s makes use of _____ and hence the exact value of numerical measurements on y and x need not be known. Conveniently r_s is computed in exactly the same manner as _____, the _____ correlation coefficient of Chapter 11.

2. To determine whether variables y and x are related, we select a _____ sample of n experimental units (or items) from the population of interest. Each of the n items is ranked first according to the variable x and then according to the variable _____. Thus, for each item in the experiment we obtain two _____. (Tied ranks are treated as in other parts of this chapter.) Let x_i and y_i denote the respective ranks assigned to item i. Then,

$$r_s = \frac{SS_{xy}}{\sqrt{SS_x SS_y}}$$

and

$$SS_{xy} = \sum_{i=1}^{n} (x_i - \bar{x})(y_i - \bar{y}) = \underline{\hspace{2cm}}$$

$$SS_x = \sum_{i=1}^{n} (x_i - \bar{x})^2 = \underline{\hspace{2cm}}$$

$$SS_y = \sum_{i=1}^{n} (y_i - \bar{y})^2 = \underline{\hspace{2cm}}$$

3. When there are no _____ in either the x observations or the y observations, r_s is given by the simpler expression:

$$r_s = 1 - \frac{6\Sigma d_i^2}{n(n^2 - 1)}$$

where $d_i =$ _____.

$x_i - y_i$

This formula can be used as a good approximation for r_s even when ties are present, provided their number is (large, small) in comparison with the number of pairs.

small

4. *Example:*

An investigator wished to determine whether "leadership ability" is related to the amount of a certain hormone present in the blood. Six individuals were selected at random from the membership of the Junior Chamber of Commerce in a large city and ranked on the characteristic "leadership ability." A determination of hormone content for each individual was made from blood samples. The leadership ranks and hormone measurements are recorded below. Fill in the missing hormone ranks. Note that no difference in leadership ability could be detected for individuals 2 and 5.

Individual	Leadership ability rank (y_i)	Hormone content	Hormone rank (x_i)	
1	6	131	1	
2	3.5	174	_____	3
3	1	189	_____	5
4	2	200	6	
5	3.5	186	_____	4
6	5	156	_____	2

To calculate r_s, form an auxiliary table which facilitates the calculation of SS_{xy}, SS_x and SS_y.

Fill in the missing quantities:

Individual	y_i	y_i^2	x_i	x_i^2	$x_i y_i$	
1	6	_____	1	1	6	36
2	3.5	12.25	3	9	_____	10.5
3	1	1	5	_____	5	25
4	2	4	_____	36	12	6
5	_____	12.25	4	16	14	3.5
6	5	25	2	4	_____	10
Total	_____	90.5	21	91	57.5	21

Thus, $SS_{xy} = 57.5 - \dfrac{(21)(21)}{6} = $ _____

-16

$SS_x = 91 - \dfrac{(21)^2}{6} = $ _____

17.5

17

$$SS_y = 90.5 - \frac{(21)^2}{6} = \underline{\hspace{1.5cm}}$$

and finally,

-16

17.5; 17

$$r_s = \frac{\underline{\hspace{2cm}}}{\sqrt{(\underline{\hspace{1.5cm}})(\underline{\hspace{1.5cm}})}} = -.93$$

Thus high leadership ability (reflected in a low rank) seems to be associated with higher amounts of hormone.

5. The Spearman rank correlation coefficient may be employed as a test statistic to test an hypothesis of _____ between two character-

no association

istics. Critical values of r_s are given in Table 11 of the text. The tabulated quantities are values of r_0 such that $P[r_s > r_0] = .05, .025, .01$ or $.005$ as indicated. For a lower tail test, reject H_0: "no association between the two characteristics" when $r_s < \underline{\hspace{2cm}}$.

$-r_0$

Two-tailed tests require doubling the stated values of α, and hence critical values for two-tailed tests may be read from Table 11 if $\alpha = $ _____,

0.10

0.05; 0.02; 0.01

_____, _____, or _____.

6. *Example:*

Continuing the example of Number 4 of this section, we may wish to test whether leadership ability is associated with hormone level. If the experimenter had designed the experiment with the objective of demon-strating that low leadership ranks (high leadership abilities) are associated

a lower

with high hormone levels, the appropriate test would be (a lower, an upper) tail test.

.829

For $\alpha = .05$ the critical value of r_s is $r_0 = $ _____. Hence, we reject

-.829

H_0 if $r_s < $ _____. Since the sample value of r_s found in Number 4

does; do

(does, does not) fall in the rejection region we (do, do not) reject H_0.

Self-Correcting Exercises 18C

1. An automobile agency wished to study whether advertising has an effect on sales. The sales manager advertised only model A during the first week and only model B during the second week of the study. The sequential record of sales during the two-week period was A, A, B, B, B, A, A, A, A, B, A, A, A, A, A, B, B, B, A, B, B, B, B, B, B, A, A. If advertising increases the sales of the model advertised, the number of runs would tend to be less than the number expected in a random sequence. State the null hypothesis and test H_0 against the alternative that advertising increases sales of the model advertised. Use $\alpha = .05$.

2. Refer to Self-Correcting Exercises 18A, problem 4. Use a one-sided runs test, with α as close to .05 as possible, to test whether the distribution of status frustration scores is the same in the two groups. The alternative hypothesis is that status frustration scores are higher among the corporate executives.

3. An interviewer was asked to rank seven applicants as to their suitability for a given position. The same seven applicants took a written examination that was designed to rate an applicant's ability to function in the given position. The interviewer's ranking and the examination score for each applicant are given below.

Applicant	Interview rank	Examination score
1	4	49
2	7	42
3	5	58
4	3	50
5	6	33
6	2	65
7	1	67

Calculate the value of Spearman's rank correlation for these data. Test for a significant negative rank correlation at the $\alpha = .05$ level of significance.

4. Nine salespeople from the Apex Co. were randomly selected and ranked according to their average monthly sales. These same nine people were also ranked on a personality measure that integrated friendliness, extroversion and a keen sense for details. The following rankings resulted.

Salesperson	1	2	3	4	5	6	7	8	9
Sales rank	6	4	2	9	7	8	5	3	1
Personality rank	4	7	6	3	2	1	5	9	8

Calculate r_s for these data. Is there a significant negative rank correlation between sales and personality measure at the .05 level of significance?

18.7 Summary (18.7)

1. Nonparametric methods are appropriate when experimental observations cannot be _____ exactly or when the _____ required by parametric tests cannot be met.

   measured; assumptions

2. Nonparametric tests may be used in spite of the fact that a corresponding parametric test would be valid, to avoid lengthy _____ and thus shorten the _____ required to come to a decision. If used in this manner, it should be kept in mind that the nonparametric test may be less _____ than the corresponding parametric test.

   calculations
   time

   efficient

3. The data for a sign test is a set of related pairs. The difference within a given matched pair is given either a plus sign or a minus sign. The test statistic is the _____ of plus signs observed.

   number

4. The Mann-Whitney U statistic is used when (related, independent) samples have been drawn from populations A and B. All sample observations are combined into a sequence arranged in order of magnitude. The test statistic is U, the _____ of U_A and U_B, which in turn depend on the rank _____ T_A and T_B, respectively.

   independent

   smaller
   sums

absolute values
magnitude
sign

sequence

maximal
sequence; many
few

ranks
+1; –1
related

5. The Wilcoxon rank sum test for a paired experiment can be used if the
_____ _____ of the differences within matched pairs
can be ranked in order of _____. The test statistic, T, is the
smaller sum of ranks for differences of the same _____.

6. A test with a variety of applications is the runs test. Letters "S" and "F"
are associated with the elements of a _____ depending on
whether the element does or does not possess a given property. A run is a
_____ subsequence of like letters. The test statistic, R, is the
number of runs in the given _____. Too _____ or too
_____ runs would indicate a lack of randomness in the
sequence, and thus the presence of some disturbing mechanism.

7. The Spearman rank correlation coefficient, r_s, employs two sets of
_____ assigned to the same set of individuals. Sample values of
r_s near enough to _____ or _____ provide evidence that the
criteria producing the two rankings are _____.

Exercises

1. For each of the following tests, state whether the test would be used for
related samples or for independent samples: sign test, Mann-Whitney U
test, Wilcoxon test, runs test.

2. About 1.2% of our combat forces in a certain area develop combat fatigue.
To find identifying characteristics of men who are predisposed to this
breakdown, the level of a certain adrenal chemical was measured in samples from two groups: men who had developed battle fatigue and men who
had adjusted readily to combat conditions. The following determinations
were recorded:

Battle fatigue group	23.35	21.08	22.36	20.24
	21.69	21.54	21.26	20.71
	20.00	23.40	21.43	21.54
	22.21			
Well-adjusted group	21.66	21.85	21.01	20.54
	20.19	19.26	21.16	19.97
	20.40	19.92	20.52	19.78
	21.15			

Use a large-sample one-tailed Mann-Whitney U test with α approximately
equal to .05 to test whether the distributions of levels of this chemical are
the same in the two groups against the alternative that the mean level is
higher in the combat fatigue group.

3. Refer to Self-Correcting Exercises 18A, problem 3. Use a one-tailed runs
test with α = .051 to test whether strict charter requirements enhance the
chance of a business's success. What do you surmise about the efficiency of
the runs test relative to the Mann-Whitney U test for detecting a difference
in population means?

4. Refer to Self-Correcting Exercises 9C, problem 1. Use Wilcoxon's signed rank to test if the quality of items produced under the per unit rate is inferior to the quality of those items produced under the hourly rate.

5. Refer to Self-Correcting Exercises 9C, problem 2. Use the sign test to test if the per unit rate has the effect of increasing the mean number of items produced per worker.

6. The value of r (defined in Chapter 11) for the following data is .636.

x	y
.05	1.08
.14	1.15
.24	1.27
.30	1.33
.47	1.41
.52	1.46
.57	1.54
.61	2.72
.67	4.01
.72	9.63

Calculate r_s for this data. What advantage of r_s was brought out in this example?

7. A ranking of the quarterbacks in the top eight teams of the National Football League was made by polling a number of professional football coaches and sports writers. This "true ranking" is shown below with my ranking.
   a. Calculate r_s.
   b. Do the data provide evidence at the $\alpha = .05$ level of significance to indicate a positive correlation between my ranking and that of the experts?

Quarterback	A	B	C	D	E	F	G	H
True ranking	1	2	3	4	5	6	7	8
My ranking	3	1	4	5	2	8	6	7

8. Construction firms A and B are the only firms bidding for contracts in a certain area. Any cooperative arrangement between these firms would assure that any run of bids favorable to a given firm would be kept short (and thus the number of runs would be high). Does the following sequence of winning bids indicate that the two firms are acting in collusion? Use $\alpha \leqslant .05$. A, B, B, A, B, A, B, A, A, B, A, B, A, B, B, A.

SOLUTIONS TO
SELF-CORRECTING EXERCISES

Set 3A

1. a. Range = 59 − 18 = 41

   b.-c. Each student will obtain slightly different results. Dividing the range by 10 produces intervals of length slightly more than 4. A more convenient choice is to use 11 intervals of length 4, beginning at 17.5.

Class	Class Boundaries	Tally	f_i
1	17.5 – 21.5	1111	4
2	21.5 – 25.5	1111	4
3	25.5 – 29.5	11111 1	6
4	29.5 – 33.5	11111 11	7
5	33.5 – 37.5	11111 1	6
6	37.5 – 41.5	1111	4
7	41.5 – 45.5	1111	4
8	45.5 – 49.5	11	2
9	49.5 – 53.5	111	3
10	53.5 – 57.5	1	1
11	57.5 – 61.5	1	1

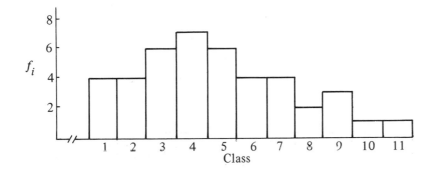

d. Dividing the range by 6, each interval must be of length 7.

Class	Class Boundaries	Tally	f_i
1	17.5 – 24.5	11111 11	7
2	24.5 – 31.5	11111 11111	10
3	31.5 – 38.5	11111 11111 1	11
4	38.5 – 45.5	11111 11	7
5	45.5 – 52.5	11111	5
6	52.5 – 59.5	11	2

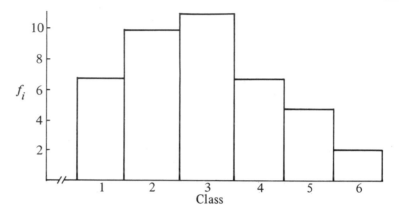

e. The second histogram is more informative, since it exhibits the piling up of the data in the middle classes. Using too many classes tends to flatten out the histogram, producing nearly equal frequencies in each class.

2. a. An extra column in the tabulation is used to calculate relative frequency.

Class	Class Boundaries	Tally	f_i	f_i/n
1	5.55 – 7.55	11111	5	5/32
2	7.55 – 9.55	11111	5	5/32
3	9.55 – 11.55	11111 11111 11	12	12/32
4	11.55 – 13.55	11111	5	5/32
5	13.55 – 15.55	111	3	3/32
6	15.55 – 17.55	1	1	1/32
7	17.55 – 19.55	1	1	1/32

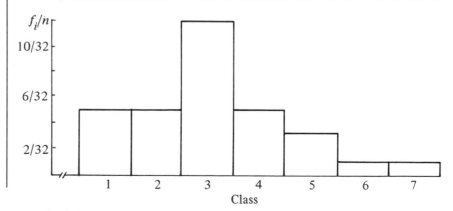

b. $\dfrac{1}{32} + \dfrac{1}{32} = \dfrac{2}{32}$;   c. $\dfrac{5}{32} + \dfrac{5}{32} - \dfrac{10}{32}$;   d. $\dfrac{12}{32} + \dfrac{5}{32} + \dfrac{3}{32} = \dfrac{20}{32}$

Set 3B

1. a. The height of each bar represents the total civilian labor force for the year of interest and the shaded area represents the proportion employed.

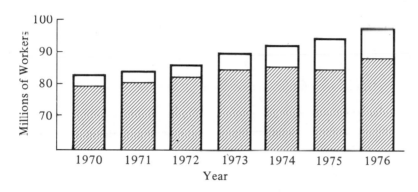

b. In order to make the drop in employment in 1975 look large, the vertical scale must be stretched and perhaps should begin at the point "70 million workers."

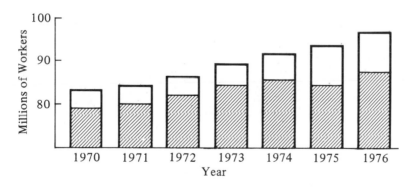

2. For each subdivision, the number of degrees in the central angle of its sector is given below.

Group	Degrees
White collar	(39.1) (360) / 81.8 = 172
Blue collar	(28.6) (360) / 81.8 = 126
Service worker	(11.0) (360) / 81.8 = 48
Farm worker	(3.1) (360) / 81.8 = 14

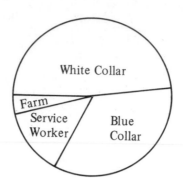

Set 3C

1. a. Arrange the set of data in order of ascending magnitude.

6	9	11	13	16
8	10	12	13	17
9	10	12	15	19

$$\text{median} = 12 \qquad \bar{y} = \frac{\sum\limits_{i=1}^{n} y_i}{n} = \frac{180}{15} = 12$$

b. There are 4 modes (9, 10, 12, 13) making it impossible to clearly locate the center of the data.

c. Range = 19 – 6 = 13

d.

y_i	$(y_i - \bar{y})$	$(y_i - \bar{y})^2$
6	−6	36
8	−4	16
9	−3	9
9	−3	9
10	−2	4
10	−2	4
11	−1	1
12	0	0
12	0	0
13	1	1
13	1	1
15	3	9
16	4	16
17	5	25
19	7	49
180	0	180

$$s^2 = \frac{\sum\limits_{i=1}^{n} (y_i - \bar{y})^2}{n - 1}$$

$$= \frac{180}{14} = 12.8571$$

$$s = \sqrt{12.8571} = 3.59$$

2. a.

y_i	$(y_i - \bar{y})$	$(y_i - \bar{y})^2$
3	0	0
5	2	4
2	−1	1
7	4	16
2	−1	1
4	1	1
3	0	0
1	−2	4
0	−3	9
4	1	1
2	−1	1
33	0	38

$$\bar{y} = \frac{\sum_{i=1}^{n} y_i}{n} = \frac{33}{11} = 3$$

$$s^2 = \frac{\sum_{i=1}^{n} (y_i - \bar{y})^2}{n - 1} = \frac{38}{10} = 3.8$$

$$s = \sqrt{3.8} = 1.95$$

b. Arrange the data in order of ascending magnitude.

0	2	3	5
1	2	4	7
2	3	4	

median = 3 $\bar{y} = 3$

Set 3D

1. Display the data in a table as follows.

y_i	y_i^2
9	81
15	225
10	100
8	64
12	144
13	169
16	256
6	36
19	361
17	289
12	144
11	121
10	100
13	169
9	81
180	2340

$$s^2 = \frac{\sum y_i^2 - \frac{(\sum y_i)^2}{n}}{n - 1}$$

$$= \frac{2340 - \frac{(180)^2}{15}}{14} = \frac{2340 - 2160}{14}$$

$$= \frac{180}{14} = 12.8571$$

2.

y_i	y_i^2
3	9
5	25
2	4
7	49
2	4
4	16
3	9
1	1
0	0
4	16
2	4
33	137

$$s^2 = \frac{\sum y_i^2 - \dfrac{(\sum y_i)^2}{n}}{n-1}$$

$$= \frac{137 - \dfrac{(33)^2}{11}}{10} = \frac{137 - \dfrac{1089}{11}}{10}$$

$$= \frac{137 - 99}{10} = \frac{38}{10} = 3.8$$

3. If $\bar{y}$ has been rounded off, then rounding error occurs each time $\bar{y}$ is subtracted from y_i in part a. Hence, there are n possible rounding errors. If part b is used, only one rounding error occurs when $(\sum y_i)^2$ is divided by n. Hence, part b is less subject to rounding errors and results in a more accurate computation.

Set 3E

1. The groupings used in this exercise are set up in this manner due to the fact that number of journeys can only be integer-valued. Hence, the group 1–3 would be equivalent to the group 0.5–3.5 if the methods of section 3.2 were used. The midpoint of this group, in either case, is 2. The data is displayed in the following table:

Class	Class Boundaries	f_i	m_i	$f_i m_i$	$f_i m_i^2$
1	1–3	6	2	12	24
2	4–6	8	5	40	200
3	7–9	4	8	32	256
4	10–12	2	11	22	242
		20		106	722

$$\bar{y} \approx \frac{\sum\limits_{i=1}^{4} f_i m_i}{n} = \frac{106}{20} = 5.3$$

$$s^2 \approx \frac{\Sigma f_i m_i^2 - \dfrac{(\Sigma f_i m_i)^2}{n}}{n-1} = \frac{722 - \dfrac{(106)^2}{20}}{19} = \frac{722 - 561.8}{19}$$

$$= \frac{160.2}{19} = 8.4316$$

$$s = \sqrt{8.4316} = 2.90$$

2. In this case, each group consists of one and only one value of the measured variable, rather than a group of several measurements within each class. Hence, the class midpoint is simply that value.

m_i	f_i	$f_i m_i$	$f_i m_i^2$
0	10	0	0
1	18	18	18
2	13	26	52
3	6	18	54
4	2	8	32
5	1	5	25
	50	75	181

a. $\bar{y} = \dfrac{\Sigma f_i m_i}{n} = \dfrac{75}{50} - 1.5$ $s^2 = \dfrac{\Sigma f_i m_i^2 - \dfrac{(\Sigma f_i m_i)^2}{n}}{n-1} = \dfrac{181 - \dfrac{(75)^2}{50}}{49}$

$$= \frac{181 - 112.5}{49} = 1.3980$$

$$s = \sqrt{1.3980} = 1.18$$

b. Since each class midpoint is *exactly* the arithmetic mean of the measurements within each class, all of which are the same, there is no approximation necessary, and the formulas become exact.

Set 3F

1. Let y_i be the height in centimeters and let x_i be the height in inches. Then $x_i = (1/2.54) y_i$. It is given that $\bar{y} = 171.7$ and $s_y = 6.6$. Then, with $a = 0$, $b = 1/2.54$,

$$\bar{x} = \frac{171.7}{2.54} = 67.60 \qquad s_x = b s_y = \frac{6.6}{2.54} = 2.60$$

2. Let y_i be the measurement in gallons and let x_i be the measurement in liters. Then $3.785\, y_i = x_i$. It is given that $\bar{y} = 10.2$ and $s_y = 1.6$. Then, with $a = 0, b = 3.785$,

$$\bar{x} = 3.785\,(10.2) = 38.607 \qquad s_x = bs_y = 3.785\,(1.6) = 6.056$$

3. a. If the value 165.0 were subtracted from each measurement, the trans-formed measurements would have values recorded to the nearest tenth, all lying between –5 and 5. If each measurement were next multiplied by 10, the resulting measurements would be integers between –50 and 50. The most difficult arithmetic calculation would now be squaring a number between 0 and 50.

   b. Let x_i be the transformed measurement, and let y_i be the original measurement. Then

$$x_i = 10\,(y_i - 165) = 10 y_i - 1650.$$

Using the Coding Theorem,

$$\bar{x} = 10\bar{y} - 1650 \qquad s_x = 10 s_y$$

Set 4A

1. Denote the four good items as G_1, G_2, G_3, G_4, and the two defectives as D_1 and D_2.

   a. $E_1: G_1 G_2 \qquad E_4: G_1 D_1 \qquad E_7: G_2 G_4 \qquad E_{10}: G_3 G_4 \qquad E_{13}: G_4 D_1$

   $E_2: G_1 G_3 \qquad E_5: G_1 D_2 \qquad E_8: G_2 D_1 \qquad E_{11}: G_3 D_1 \qquad E_{14}: G_4 D_2$

   $E_3: G_1 G_4 \qquad E_6: G_2 G_3 \qquad E_9: G_2 D_2 \qquad E_{12}: G_3 D_2 \qquad E_{15}: D_1 D_2$

   b. "At least one defective" implies one or two defectives, while "no more than one defective" implies zero or one defective.

   $A: \{E_4, E_5, E_8, E_9, E_{11}, E_{12}, E_{13}, E_{14}, E_{15}\}$;

   $B: \{E_4, E_5, E_8, E_9, E_{11}, E_{12}, E_{13}\,E_{14}\}$;

   $C: \{E_1, E_2, E_3, E_4, E_5, E_6, E_7, E_8, E_9, E_{10}, E_{11}, E_{12}, E_{13}, E_{14}\}$

   c. Each sample point is assigned equal probability; that is, $P(E_i) = 1/15$.

   $$P(A) = 9/15 = 3/5; \;\; P(B) = 8/15; \;\; P(C) = 14/15$$

2. a. $E_1: FFFF \qquad E_5: FFFM \qquad E_9: MFFM \qquad E_{13}: MFMM$

   $E_2: MFFF \qquad E_6: FFMM \qquad E_{10}: MFMF \qquad E_{14}: MMFM$

$E_3: FMFF \qquad E_7: FMFM \qquad E_{11}: MMFF \qquad E_{15}: MMMF$

$E_4: FFMF \qquad E_8: FMMF \qquad E_{12}: FMMM \qquad E_{16}: MMMM$

b. $A: \{E_6, E_7, E_8, E_9, E_{10}, E_{11}\}; \qquad B: \{E_1\};$

$C: \{E_2, E_3, E_4, E_5, E_6, E_7, E_8, E_9, E_{10}, E_{11}, E_{12}, E_{13}, E_{14}, E_{15}, E_{16}\};$

$D = A \cup B: \{E_1, E_6, E_7, E_8, E_9, E_{10}, E_{11}\}; E = BC:$ no sample points;

$F = A \cup C:$ same as C.

c. Since each sample point is equally likely,

$$P(A) = \frac{6}{16} = \frac{3}{8}; \quad P(B) = \frac{1}{16}; \quad P(C) = \frac{15}{16}; \quad P(D) = \frac{7}{16}; \quad P(E) = 0; \quad P(F) = \frac{15}{16}$$

3. a. $E_1: HH \qquad\qquad E_4: TT \qquad\qquad E_7: GT$

$E_2: HT \qquad\qquad E_5: TG \qquad\qquad E_8: GH$

$E_3: TH \qquad\qquad E_6: GG \qquad\qquad E_9: HG$

b. $A: \{E_1, E_2, E_3, E_4\} \qquad B: \{E_1, E_2, E_3, E_8, E_9\}$

$C: \{E_1, E_4, E_6\}$

c. Since each sample point is equally likely,

$$P(A) = \frac{4}{9}; \quad P(B) = \frac{5}{9}; \quad P(C) = \frac{3}{9} = \frac{1}{3};$$

$$P(A \cup C) = \frac{5}{9}; \quad P(BC) = \frac{1}{9}.$$

d.

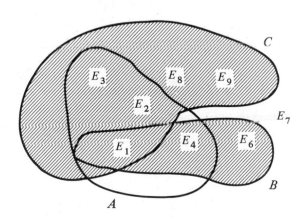

4. a. $E_1: HHH$ $\quad E_3: NHN$ $\quad E_5: HHN$ $\quad E_7: NHH$

$\quad E_2: HNN$ $\quad E_4: NNH$ $\quad E_6: HNH$ $\quad E_8: NNN$

b. $P(A) = \dfrac{3}{8}$; $\; P(B) = \dfrac{4}{8} = \dfrac{1}{2}$; $\; P(C) = \dfrac{1}{8}$; $\; P(D) = \dfrac{4}{8} = \dfrac{1}{2}$.

c. $P(A \cup D) = \dfrac{4}{8} = \dfrac{1}{2}$; $\; P(BD) = \dfrac{3}{8}$.

Set 4B

1. a. $D = A \cup B$; $\; E = BC$; $\; F = A \cup C$

b. AB: no sample points; $\; B \cup C: \{E_1, E_2, \dots, E_{16}\} = S$;

$AC \cup BC: \{E_6, E_7, E_8, E_9, E_{10}, E_{11}\}$; $\; \bar{C}: \{E_1\}$;

$\overline{AC}: \{E_1, E_2, \dots, E_5, E_{12}, E_{13}, \dots E_{16}\}$;

c. $P(A \cup B) = P(A) + P(B) - P(AB) = \dfrac{3}{8} + \dfrac{1}{16} - 0 = \dfrac{7}{16}$

$P(\bar{C}) = 1 - P(C) = 1 - \dfrac{15}{16} = \dfrac{1}{16}$

$P(\overline{BC}) = 1 - P(BC) = 1 - 0 = 1$

d. $P(A/C) = P(AC)/P(C) = \dfrac{6}{16} \bigg/ \dfrac{15}{16} = \dfrac{6}{15}$ while $P(A) = \dfrac{3}{8}$.

A and C are dependent but are not mutually exclusive.

e. $P(B/C) = P(BC)/P(C) = 0 \bigg/ \dfrac{15}{16} = 0$ while $P(B) = \dfrac{1}{16}$ and $P(BC) = 0$.

B and C are dependent and mutually exclusive.

2. a. $P(A) = P[\text{the executive represents a small corporation}] = \dfrac{75}{200} = \dfrac{3}{8}$.

$P(F) = P[\text{the executive favors gas rationing}] = \dfrac{15}{200} = \dfrac{3}{40}$.

$P(AF) = \dfrac{3}{200}$.

$P(A \cup G) = P[$executive favors conversion or represents a small corporation or both$|$

$$= P(A) + P(G) - P(AG) = \frac{75 + 22 - 10}{200} = \frac{87}{200}.$$

$P(AD) = \frac{20}{200} = P[$executive represents a small corporation and favors car pooling$]$.

$$P(\bar{F}) = 1 - P(F) = 1 - \frac{3}{40} = \frac{37}{40}.$$

b. $P(A|F) = P(AF)/P(F) = \dfrac{3/200}{15/200} = \dfrac{3}{15} \qquad P(A|D) = \dfrac{20/200}{55/200} = \dfrac{20}{55}.$

Neither A and F nor A and D are mutually exclusive.
A and F and A and D are both dependent.

3. Let S represent a sale on a particular contact, and N represent no sale. There are 8 sample points in the experiment; however, they are not all equally likely.

SSS	SNS	NNS	SNN
SSN	NSS	NSN	NNN

$P(A) = P(SSS) + P(SSN) + P(SNS) + P(NSS)$

For contact 1, $P(S) = P(N) = \dfrac{1}{2}.$

For contact 2, $P(S|S$ on 1$) = \dfrac{3}{4}, \quad P(S|N$ on 1$) = \dfrac{1}{3}.$

Similarly for contact 3, so that

$$P(A) = \left(\frac{1}{2}\right)\left(\frac{3}{4}\right)\left(\frac{3}{4}\right) + \left(\frac{1}{2}\right)\left(\frac{3}{4}\right)\left(\frac{1}{4}\right) + \left(\frac{1}{2}\right)\left(\frac{1}{4}\right)\left(\frac{1}{3}\right) + \left(\frac{1}{2}\right)\left(\frac{1}{3}\right)\left(\frac{3}{4}\right)$$

$$= \frac{12}{32} + \frac{4}{24} = \frac{13}{24}$$

4. Define A: Company A shows an increase
   B: Company B shows an increase
   C: Company C shows an increase

It is given that $P(A) = .4$, $P(B) = .6$, $P(C) = .7$ and A, B, and C are independent events.

a. $P(ABC) = P(A) P(B) P(C) = (.4) (.6) (.7) = .168$

b. $P(\bar{A}\bar{B}\bar{C}) = P(\bar{A}) P(\bar{B}) P(\bar{C}) = [1 - P(A)]\ [1 - P(B)]\ [1 - P(C)]$

$$= (.6) (.4) (.3) = .072$$

c. $P[\text{at least one shows profit}] = 1 - P[\text{none show profit}]$

$$= 1 - P(\bar{A}\bar{B}\bar{C}) = 1 - .072 = .928$$

Set 4C

1. Define D: item is defective
         M_1: item came from machine I
         M_2: item came from machine II
It is given that $P(D/M_1) = .015, P(D/M_2) = .02, P(M_1) = .40, P(M_2) = .60$.
Using Bayes' Law,

$$P(M_1/D) = \frac{P(D/M_1) P(M_1)}{P(D/M_1) P(M_1) + P(D/M_2) P(M_2)}$$

$$= \frac{.015(.40)}{.015(.40) + .02(.60)} = \frac{.006}{.018} = \frac{1}{3}$$

2. Using the *mn* rule, there are a total of $4(5)(3)(6)$ or 360 different systems which can be built. The total number of systems which do not include the one brand of receiver, the one brand of turntable, and so on, is $(4-1)(5-1)(3-1)(6-1) = 120$. Hence, the probability that the dealer will make a profit is

$$120/360 = \frac{1}{3}$$

3. Assuming that one account is assigned to each executive, order is important, and the total number of permutations is $P_6^6 = 6! = 720$.

4. There are two models to be selected from a total of four models (since two of the models have already been chosen to appear). The order of choice is unimportant, and the number of ways is

$$C_2^4 = \frac{4!}{2!2!} = \frac{4(3)}{2(1)} = 6$$

Set 5A

1. Each sample point consists of four elements, each representing the state of a particular component. Let S denote a successfully operating component and F denote a failure. Since components are independent, the Multiplicative Law of Probability can be used to find $P(E_i)$ with $P(S) = .99$ and $P(F) = .01$.

E_i	$P(E_i)$	y	E_i	$P(E_i)$	y
SSSS	.96059601	0	FSSF	.00009801	2
FSSS	.00970299	1	FSFS	.00009801	2
SFSS	.00970299	1	FFSS	.00009801	2
SSFS	.00970299	1	SFFF	.00000099	3
SSSF	.00970299	1	FSFF	.00000099	3
SSFF	.00009801	2	FFSF	.00000099	3
SFSF	.00009801	2	FFFS	.00000099	3
SFFS	.00009801	2	FFFF	.00000001	4

The probability distribution in compact form is

y	$p(y)$
0	.96059601
1	.03881196
2	.00058806
3	.00000396
4	.00000001

a. Reliability $= P[\text{system works}] = P[y = 0] = .9606$

b. Reliability $= P[\text{at least three components work}]$

$$= P[y \leq 1] = p(0) + p(1) = .9994$$

2. Let M represent a candidate with a masters degree and let C represent a candidate without such a degree. Define the following events:
   CM: C ranked first, M ranked second
   CC: C ranked first, C ranked second
   MM: M ranked first, M ranked second
   MC: M ranked first, C ranked second

$$p(0) = P[y = 0] = P(CC) = \frac{3}{5}\left(\frac{2}{4}\right) = \frac{6}{20};$$

$$p(1) = P[y = 1] = P(CM) + P(MC) = \frac{3}{5}\left(\frac{2}{4}\right) + \frac{2}{5}\left(\frac{3}{4}\right) = \frac{12}{20};$$

$$p(2) = P[y = 2] = P(MM) = \frac{2}{5}\left(\frac{1}{4}\right) = \frac{2}{20}$$

y	$p(y)$
0	3/10
1	6/10
2	1/10

3. Using the procedure in 2, define the event FC as "Ford chosen first, Chevrolet chosen second." Then

$$P[y = 0] = P(CC) = \frac{2}{5}\left(\frac{1}{4}\right) = \frac{1}{10} ;$$

$$P[y = 1] = P(CF) + P(FC) = \frac{2}{5}\left(\frac{3}{4}\right) + \frac{3}{5}\left(\frac{2}{4}\right) = \frac{6}{10} ;$$

$$P[y = 2] = P(FF) = \frac{3}{5}\left(\frac{2}{4}\right) = \frac{3}{10}$$

y	$p(y)$
0	.1
1	.6
2	.3

Set 5B

1. $\mu = E(y) = \sum\limits_{y} y\, p(y) = 5000(.30) + 10000(.35) + 15000(.20)$

$$+ 20000(.10) + 25000(.05)$$

$$= 11250$$

$\sigma^2 = E(y^2) - \mu^2 = (1000)^2\ [25(.3) + 100(.35) + 225(.20) + 400(.10)$

$$+ 625(.05)] - (11250)^2$$

$$= 158750000 - 126562500 = 32187500$$

$\sigma = \sqrt{32187500} = 5673.4$

2. Note that $R = 10y$ so that, for example, $P[R = 50,000] = P[y = 5000]$ = .30. The probability distribution for R is

R	$p(R)$
50,000	.30
100,000	.35
150,000	.20
200,000	.10
250,000	.05

$E(R) = 10E(y) = 112,500$

$\sigma^2 = (10,000)^2\ [158.75] - (112500)^2$

$$= 3218750000$$

$\sigma\ = 56734.0$

3. $P[R \leqslant 100,000] = .35 + .30 = .65$

4. Let y be the gain to the insurance company and let r be the premium charged by the company.

y	$p(y)$
r	.9900
$-15000 + r$	.0075
$-30000 + r$	.0025

In order to break even, $E(y) = 0$, or

$$E(y) = \sum_y y\, p(y) = .99r + .0075\,(-15,000 + r)$$

$$+ (-30,000 + r)(.0025) = 0$$

$$r - 112.50 - 75.00 = 0$$

$$r = \$187.50$$

Set 6A

1. Let y be the number of apartment dwellers who move within a year. Then $p = P[\text{move within a year}] = .2$ and $n = 7$.

   a. $P[y = 2] = C_2^7\,(.2)^2\,(.8)^5 = .27525$

   b. $P[y \leqslant 1] = C_0^7\,(.2)^0\,(.8)^7 + C_1^7\,(.2)^1\,(.8)^6 = .209715 + .367002$

   $$= .576717$$

2. Let y be the number of letters delivered within 4 days. Then $p = P[\text{letter delivered within 4 days}] = .7$ and $n = 20$.

   a. $P[y \geqslant 15] = 1 - P[y \leqslant 14] = 1 - .584 = .416$

   b. $P[y \geqslant 10] = 1 - P[y \leqslant 9] = 1 - .017 = .983$.

   Notice that if 10 or fewer letters arrive later than 4 days then $20 - 10 = 10$ or more will arrive within 4 days.

3. Let y be the number of contracts awarded, so that $p = .6$ and $n = 5$.

   a. $P[y = 5] = P[y \leqslant 5] - P[y \leqslant 4] = 1 - .922 = .078$

   b. $P[y \geqslant 3] = 1 - P[y \leqslant 2] = 1 - .317 = .683$

4. Let y be the number of satisfactory pieces of lumber, so that $p = .6$ and $n = 10$.

   a. $P[y \leqslant 3] = .055$

   b. $P[y \geqslant 8] = 1 - P[y \leqslant 7] = 1 - .833 = .167$

   c. $P[y \geqslant 7] = 1 - P[y \leqslant 6] = 1 - .618 = .382$

Set 6B

1. y = number of stockholders favoring the proposal
   $p = P[\text{stockholder favors a proposal}] = .3$
   $n = 100$

   $\mu = np = 100(.3) = 30; \quad \sigma^2 = npq = 100(.3)(.7) = 21; \quad \sigma = \sqrt{21} = 4.58$

   Calculate $\mu \pm 2\sigma = 30 \pm 2(4.58) = 30 \pm 9.16$. We would expect between 20.84 and 39.16 (between 21 and 39) stockholders to favor the proposal.
2. y = number of registered voters belonging to a minority group
   $p = .2$
   $n = 80$

   $\mu = np = 80(.2) = 16; \quad \sigma^2 = npq = 80(.2)(.8) = 12.8; \quad \sigma = \sqrt{12.8} = 3.58$

   As in Exercise 1, calculate $\mu \pm 2\sigma = 16 \pm 2(3.58) = 16 \pm 7.16$ or 8.84 to 23.16. We would expect to see between 9 and 23 minority group members on the jury lists.
3. y = number watching the T.V. program
   $p = .4$
   $n = 400$

   $\mu = 400(.4) = 160; \quad \sigma^2 = 400(.4)(.6) = 96; \quad \sigma = \sqrt{96} = 9.80$

   Calculate $\mu \pm 2\sigma = 160 \pm 2(9.8) = 160 \pm 19.6$ or 140.4 to 179.6. Since we would expect the number watching the show to be between 141 and 179 with probability .95, it is highly unlikely that only 96 people would have watched the show *if* the 40% claim is correct. It is more likely that the percentage of viewers for this particular show is less than 40%.

Set 6C

1. Let y be the number of fires observed so that $p = P[\text{fire}] = .005$ and $n = 1000$. The random variable is binomial; however, since n is large and p is small with $\mu = np = 5$, the Poisson approximation is appropriate.

   a. $P[y = 0] = \dfrac{\mu^0 e^{-\mu}}{0!} = e^{-5} = .006738$

   b. $P[y \leqslant 3] = \dfrac{5^0 e^{-5}}{0!} + \dfrac{5^1 e^{-5}}{1!} + \dfrac{5^2 e^{-5}}{2!} + \dfrac{5^3 e^{-5}}{3!}$

   $= .006738 (1 + 5 + 12.5 + 20.833) = .2650$

2. Let y be the number of defective panels with $\mu = 2$.

a. $P[y = 3] = \dfrac{2^3 \, e^{-2}}{3!} = 1.33(.135335) = .180$

b. $P[y \geqslant 2] = 1 - P[y \leqslant 1] = 1 - \dfrac{2^0 \, e^{-2}}{0!} - \dfrac{2^1 \, e^{-2}}{1!}$

$$= 1 - e^{-2}(1 + 2) = 1 - 3(.135335)$$

$$= .594$$

3. We are now concerned with the random variable y, the number of defective panels in a bundle of 200, with $\mu = 2(2) = 4$. Then

$$P[y \leqslant 4] = \dfrac{4^0 \, e^{-4}}{0!} + \dfrac{4^1 \, e^{-4}}{1!} + \dfrac{4^2 \, e^{-4}}{2!} + \dfrac{4^3 \, e^{-4}}{3!} + \dfrac{4^4 \, e^{-4}}{4!}$$

$$= .018316(1 + 4 + 8 + 10.67 + 10.67) = .629$$

4. Four employees will be chosen from 15, nine of whom are men and six of whom are women. Hence, $N = 15, k = 9, n = 4, N - k = 6$.

a. $P[\text{two or more men}] = P[y \geqslant 2] = \dfrac{C_2^9 \, C_2^6}{C_4^{15}} + \dfrac{C_3^9 \, C_1^6}{C_4^{15}} + \dfrac{C_4^9 \, C_0^6}{C_4^{15}}$

$$= \dfrac{36}{1365} + \dfrac{84(6)}{1365} + \dfrac{126}{1365} = \dfrac{666}{1365} = .488$$

b. $P[\text{exactly three women}] = P[\text{exactly one man}]$

$$= P[y = 1] = \dfrac{C_1^9 \, C_3^6}{C_4^{15}}$$

$$= \dfrac{9(20)}{1365} = .132$$

5. Define y to be the number of defective units chosen. Then $N = 50, k = 3,$ $N - k = 47, n = 5$.

$$P[y = 0] = \dfrac{C_0^3 \, C_5^{47}}{C_5^{50}} = \dfrac{47!5!45!}{5!42!50!} = \dfrac{47(46)(45)(44)(43)}{50(49)(48)(47)(46)} = .724$$

Set 6D

1. a. $P(\text{acceptance}) = C_0^4 \, p^0 \, q^4 + C_1^4 \, p^1 \, q^3$ for various values of p.
   When $p = 0$, $P(\text{acceptance}) = 1$; $p = .3$, $P(\text{acceptance}) = (.7)^4 + 4(.3)(.7)^3$

   $$= .2401 + .4116$$

   $$= .6517$$

   When $p = 1$, $P(\text{acceptance}) = 0$. The graph follows the procedures used in 6.7 (10) and is omitted here.
   b. Keep $n = 4$, take $a > 1$; keep $a = 1$, take $n < 4$.

2. a.

p	0	.1	.3	.5	1.0
$n = 10, a = 1$	1	.736	.149	.011	0
$n = 25, a = 1$	1	.271	.002	.000	0

   c. If the student will graph the 3 *OC* curves as given in part a and problem 1, he will see that increasing n has the effect of decreasing the probability of acceptance.

3. a.

p	0	.1	.3	.5	1.0
$n = 25, a = 3$	1	.764	.033	.000	0
$n = 25, a = 5$	1	.967	.193	.002	0

   c. Increasing a has the effect of increasing the probability of acceptance.

Set 6E

1. Let y be the number of shirt sales of the new color, so that $p = P[\text{shirt sale}$ will be of the new color] and $n = 25$. The hypothesis to be tested is

   $$H_0: p = .4$$
   $$H_a: p < .4$$

   Small values of the test statistic, y, would favor rejection of H_0 in favor of H_a. Hence, we seek a rejection region of the form $y \leqslant a$ so that

   $$\alpha = P[y \leqslant a \,|\, p = .4] \leqslant .05$$

   From Table 1, with $p = .4$, the rejection region is $y \leqslant 5$ with $\alpha = .029$.
   Since the observed value of y ($y = 6$) does not fall in the rejection region, H_0 cannot be rejected. There is insufficient evidence to doubt the 40% figure. Note that we cannot "accept H_0" unless β, the probability of a Type II error, is assessed for meaningful alternative values of $p < .4$.

2. y = number of defectives
p = proportion defective
$n = 20$
Since the manufacturer claims that the proportion defective is at most .05, his claim will be rejected if it can be shown that the proportion defective is more than .05.

$H_0: p = .05$

$H_a: p > .05$

Large values of y suggest that H_a is true, and the rejection region must be of the form $y \geq a$, with

$$\alpha = P[y \geq a \mid p = .05] \leq .05$$

$$1 - P[y \leq a - 1] \leq .05$$

$$P[y \leq a - 1] \geq .95$$

From Table 1, the necessary value of $a - 1$ is $a - 1 = 3$ and the rejection region will be $y \geq a$ or $y \geq 4$, with

$$\alpha = P[y \geq 4] = 1 - .984 = .016$$

The observed value of $y(y = 4)$ falls in the rejection region. Hence, H_0 is rejected and we conclude that $p > .05$. The manufacturer's claim is incorrect. The chance that this conclusion is incorrect is $\alpha = .016$.

3. y = number preferring Brand A
$p = P[\text{person favors Brand A}]$
$n = 15$
If neither brand is preferred, then $p = .5$.

$H_0: p = .5$

$H_a: p \neq .5$

Either large or small values of y will favor rejection of H_0, and the rejection region must be of the form

$$y \leq a \quad \text{or} \quad y \geq b \quad \text{with}$$

$$\alpha = P[y \leq a \mid p = .5] + P[y \geq b \mid p = .5] \leq .05$$

Choosing the rejection region,

$$y \leq 3 \quad \text{or} \quad y \geq 12$$

gives

$$\alpha = .018 + .018 = .036$$

The student may verify by trial and error that this is the necessary region.
Since the observed value is $y = 12$, the null hypothesis is rejected. There is a difference in preference for the two brands. The chance that this conclusion is incorrect is $\alpha = .036$.

Set 7A

Note: The student should illustrate each problem with a diagram and list all pertinent information before attempting the solution. Diagrams are omitted in order to conserve space.

1. a. $P[z > 2.1] = .5000 - A(2.1) = .5000 - .4821 = .0179$

   b. $P[z < -1.2] = .5000 - A(1.2) = .5000 - .3849 = .1151$

   c. $P[.5 < z < 1.5] = P[0 < z < 1.5] - P[0 < z < .5]$

$$= A(1.5) - A(.5) = .4332 - .1915 = .2417$$

   d. $P[-2.75 < z < -1.70] = A(2.75) - A(1.7) = .4970 - .4554 = .0416$

   e. $P[-1.96 < z < 1.96] = A(1.96) + A(1.96) = 2(.4750) = .95$

   f. $P[z > 1.645] = .5000 - A(1.645) = .5000 - .4500 = .05$

   Notice that linear interpolation was used. That is, since the value $z = 1.645$ is halfway between two tabled values, $z = 1.64$ and $z = 1.65$, the appropriate area is taken to be halfway between the two tabled areas, $A(1.64) = .4495$ and $A(1.65) = .4505$. As a general rule, values of z will be rounded to two decimal places, except for this particular example, which will occur frequently in our calculations.

2. a. We know that $P[z > z_0] = .10$, or $.5000 - A(z_0) = .10$ which implies that

$$A(z_0) = .4000$$

   The value of z_0 which satisfies this equation is $z_0 = 1.28$, so that $P[z > 1.28] = .10$

   b. $P[z < z_0] = .01$ so that $.5000 - A(z_0) = .01$ and

$$A(z_0) = .4900$$

The value of z_0 which satisfies this equation is $z_0 = -2.33$ so that $P[z < -2.33] = .01$. The student who draws a diagram will see that z_0 must be negative, since it must be in the left-hand portion of the curve.

c. $P[-z_0 < z < z_0] = A(z_0) + A(z_0) = .95$ so that

$$A(z_0) = .4750$$

The necessary value of z_0 is $z_0 = 1.96$ and $P[-1.96 < z < 1.96] = .95$.

d. $P[-z_0 < z < z_0] = 2 A(z_0) = .99$ so that

$$A(z_0) = .4950$$

The necessary value of z_0 is $z_0 = 2.58$ and $P[-2.58 < z < 2.58] = .99$.

3. The random variable of interest has a standard normal distribution and hence may be denoted as z.

a. $P[z > 1] = .5000 - A(1) = .5000 - .3413 = .1587$

b. $P[z > 1.5] = .5000 - A(1.5) = .5000 - .4332 = .0668$

c. $P[-1 < z < -.5] = A(1) - A(.5) = .3413 - .1915 = .1498$

d. The problem is to find a value of z, say z_0, such that

$$P[-z_0 < z < z_0] = .95$$

This was done in problem 2c and $z_0 = 1.96$. Hence, 95% of the billing errors will be between $-1.96 and $1.96.

e. Undercharges imply negative errors. Hence, the problem is to find z_0 such that

$$P[z < z_0] = .05.$$

That is,

$$.5000 \quad A(z_0) - .05 \quad \text{or} \quad A(z_0) = .4500$$

The value of z_0 is $z_0 = -1.645$ (see problem 1f) and hence, 5% of the undercharges will be at least $1.65.

Set 7B

1. We have $\mu = 10$, $\sigma = \sqrt{2.25} = 1.5$.

a. $P[y > 8.5] = P\left[\dfrac{y - \mu}{\sigma} > \dfrac{8.5 - 10}{1.5}\right] = P[z > -1]$

$$= .5000 + A(1) = .5000 + .3413 = .8413$$

b. $P[y < 12] = P\left[z < \dfrac{12 - 10}{1.5}\right] = P[z < 1.33] = .5000 + A(1.33)$

$$= .5000 + .4082 = .9082$$

c. $P[9.25 < y < 11.25] = P\left[\dfrac{9.25 - 10}{1.5} < z < \dfrac{11.25 - 10}{1.5}\right]$

$$= P[-.5 < z < .83] = .1915 + .2967 = .4882$$

d. $P[7.5 < y < 9.2] = P[-1.67 < z < -.53] = .4525 - .2019 = .2506$

e. $P[12.25 < y < 13.25] = P[1.5 < z < 2.17] = .4850 - .4332 = .0518$

2. The random variable of interest is y, the length of life for a standard house-hold lightbulb. It is normally distributed with $\mu = 250$ and $\sigma = \sqrt{2500} = 50$.

a. $P[y > 300] = P\left[z > \dfrac{300 - 250}{50}\right] = P[z > 1] = .5000 - .3413 = .1587$

b. $P[190 < y < 270] = P[-1.2 < z < .4] = .3849 + .1554 = .5403$

c. $P[y < 260] = P[z < .2] = .5000 + .0793 = .5793$

d. It is necessary to find a value of y, say y_0, such that

$$P[y > y_0] = .90$$

Now,

$$P[y > y_0] = P\left[\dfrac{y - \mu}{\sigma} > \dfrac{y_0 - 250}{50}\right] = .90 \quad \text{so that}$$

$$P\left[z > \dfrac{y_0 - 250}{50}\right] = .5 + A\left(\dfrac{y_0 - 250}{50}\right) = .90 \quad \text{or}$$

$$A\left(\frac{y_0 - 250}{50}\right) = .40$$

By looking at a diagram, the student will notice that the value satisfying this equation must be negative. From table 3, this value, $(y_0 - 250)/50$, is

$$\frac{y_0 - 250}{50} = -1.28$$

or $y_0 = -1.28(50) + 250 = 186$. Ninety percent of the bulbs have a useful life in excess of 186 hours.

e. Similar to part d. It is necessary to find y_0 such that $P[y < y_0] = .95$. Now,

$$P[y < y_0] = P\left[z < \frac{y_0 - 250}{50}\right] = .95$$

$$.5000 + A\left(\frac{y_0 - 250}{50}\right) = .95$$

$$A\left(\frac{y_0 - 250}{50}\right) = .45$$

Hence,

$$\frac{y_0 - 250}{50} = 1.645 \quad \text{or} \quad y_0 = 332.25.$$

That is, 95% of all bulbs will burn out before 332.25 hours.

3. The random variable is y, scores on a personnel evaluation, and has a normal distribution with $\mu = 50$ and $\sigma = 5$.

a. $P[y > 60] = P\left[z > \frac{60 - 50}{5}\right] = P[z > 2] = .5000 - .4772 = .0228$

h. $P[y < 45] = P[z < -1] = .5000 - .3413 = .1587$

c. $P[35 < y < 65] = P[-3 < z < 3] = .4987 + .4987 = .9974$

d. It is necessary to find y_0 such that $P[y < y_0] = .95$. As in problem 2 e,

$$A\left(\frac{y_0 - 50}{5}\right) = .45$$

$$\frac{y_0 - 50}{5} = 1.645 \quad \text{or} \quad y_0 = 58.225$$

Set 7C

1. $n = 100$, $p = .15$, and the probability of interest is $P[y \geq 23]$. Since the probabilities associated with the values $y = 23, 24, \ldots, 100$ are needed, the area of interest is the area to the right of 22.5. Further, $\mu = np = 100(.15) = 15$, $\sigma^2 = npq = 100(.15)(.85) = 12.75$.

$$P[y \geq 23] \approx P[y > 22.5] = P\left[z > \frac{22.5 - 15}{\sqrt{12.75}}\right]$$

$$= P[z > 2.1] = .5000 - .4821 = .0179$$

This event is one which we would expect to observe about one time in one hundred. It is a very unlikely event, given that $p = .15$. Perhaps the company is incorrect, and p is in fact greater than .15.

2. Let $p = P[\text{income is less than } 12,000] = \frac{1}{2}$, since 12,000 is the median income. Also, $n = 100$, $\mu = np = 50$, $\sigma^2 = npq = 25$.

$$P[y \leq 37] \approx P[y < 37.5] = P\left[z < \frac{37.5 - 50}{5}\right]$$

$$= P[z < -2.5] = .5000 - .4938 = .0062$$

The observed event is highly unlikely under the assumption that $12,000 is the median income. The $12,000 does not seem reasonable.

3. $n = 100$, $p = .1$, $\mu = np = 10$, $\sigma^2 = npq = 9$. For a normal random variable, 95% of the measurements will be within the interval $\mu \pm 2\sigma$ and, using the normal approximation to the binomial, this should be true for the binomial random variable as well. Hence, $\mu \pm 2\sigma = 10 \pm 2(3)$ and the number of failures should lie between 4 and 16.

4. $n = 100$, $p = .25$, $\mu = 25$, $\sigma^2 = 18.75$.

$$P[y \geq 30] \approx P[y > 29.5] = P\left[z > \frac{29.5 - 25}{4.33}\right] = P[z > 1.04] = .1492$$

Set 8A

1. $\bar{y} = 89.50$ with approximate bound on error $2\dfrac{s}{\sqrt{n}} = 2\dfrac{(25.10)}{\sqrt{50}} = 7.1$

2. $\bar{y} \pm z_{\alpha/2}\dfrac{s}{\sqrt{n}}$; $8750 \pm 1.96\dfrac{3050}{\sqrt{50}}$; 8750 ± 845.54;   or   7904.46 to

9595.54

Set 8B

1. $\hat{p} = \dfrac{y}{n} = \dfrac{25}{100} = .25$ with approximate bound on error $2\sqrt{\dfrac{\hat{p}\hat{q}}{n}} = 2\sqrt{\dfrac{.25(.75)}{100}}$

$$= 2(.0433) = .0866$$

2. $\bar{y}_1 - \bar{y}_2 = 150.5 - 160.2 = -9.7$ with approximate bound on error

$$2\sqrt{\dfrac{s_1^2}{n_1} + \dfrac{s_2^2}{n_2}} = 2\sqrt{\dfrac{23.72}{35} + \dfrac{36.37}{35}} = 2\sqrt{1.7169} = 2.62$$

3. $\hat{p}_1 - \hat{p}_2 = \dfrac{y_1}{n_1} - \dfrac{y_2}{n_2} = \dfrac{31}{204} - \dfrac{41}{191} = .15 - .21 = -.06$

Approximate bound on error: $2\sqrt{\dfrac{\hat{p}_1\hat{q}_1}{n_1} + \dfrac{\hat{p}_2\hat{q}_2}{n_2}} = 2\sqrt{.000625 + .000869}$

$$= 2(.039) = .078$$

4. a. $\hat{p} = \dfrac{y}{n} = \dfrac{86}{200} = .43$ with approximate bound on error,

$$2\sqrt{\dfrac{\hat{p}\,\hat{q}}{n}} = 2\sqrt{\dfrac{.43(.57)}{200}} = 2(.035) = .07$$

   b. $\hat{p} \pm z_{\alpha/2}\sqrt{\dfrac{\hat{p}\,\hat{q}}{n}}$; $.43 \pm 1.645\sqrt{\dfrac{.43(.57)}{200}}$; $.43 \pm .058$;   or $.372$ to $.488$

5. a. Of the total number of accidents ($32 + 41 = 73$), 23 involved injury and $200 or more damage. Hence,

$$\hat{p} = \dfrac{y}{n} = \dfrac{23}{73} = .32.$$

The 95% confidence interval is

$$\hat{p} \pm z_{\alpha/2}\sqrt{\dfrac{\hat{p}\,\hat{q}}{n}}$$

$$.32 \pm 1.96\sqrt{\dfrac{.32(.68)}{73}}$$

$.32 \pm .11$ or .21 to .43

b. $\hat{p}_1 = \dfrac{10}{32} = .31$, $\hat{p}_2 = .56$

$$(\hat{p}_1 - \hat{p}_2) \pm 1.96 \sqrt{\dfrac{\hat{p}_1 \hat{q}_1}{n_1} + \dfrac{\hat{p}_2 \hat{q}_2}{n_2}}$$

$$-.25 \pm 1.96 \sqrt{\dfrac{.31(.69)}{32} + \dfrac{.56(.44)}{41}}$$

$-.25 \pm .22$ or $-.47$ to $-.03$

4. a. $(\bar{y}_1 - \bar{y}_2) \pm z_{\alpha/2} \sqrt{\dfrac{s_1^2}{n_1} + \dfrac{s_2^2}{n_2}}$

$$(10520 - 9210) \pm 2.58 \sqrt{\dfrac{(1510)^2}{90} + \dfrac{(950)^2}{60}}$$

$1310 \pm 2.58 \,(200.938)$

1310 ± 518.42 or 791.58 to 1828.42

b. If the two plants belonged to populations having the same mean annual income, then $\mu_1 = \mu_2$, or $\mu_1 - \mu_2 = 0$. This value of $\mu_1 - \mu_2$ does not fall in the confidence interval obtained above. Hence, it is unlikely that the two plants belong to populations having the same mean annual income.

Set 8C

1. The estimator of μ is $\bar{y}$, with standard deviation $\sigma/\sqrt{n}$. Hence, solve

$$2\,\sigma/\sqrt{n} = B, \quad 2\,\dfrac{8}{\sqrt{n}} = 3, \quad \sqrt{n} = \dfrac{16}{3}, \quad n = 28.4$$

The experimenter should obtain $n = 29$ measurements.

2. The estimator of p is $\hat{p} = y/n$ with standard deviation $\sqrt{pq/n}$. Since it is given that $0 \leqslant p \leqslant .1$, maximum variation will occur when $p = .1$ and the sample size must be large enough to account for this maximum variation. Hence, solve

$$2\sqrt{\dfrac{pq}{n}} = B, \quad 2\sqrt{\dfrac{.1(.9)}{n}} = .01, \quad \sqrt{n} = \dfrac{2(.3)}{.01}, \quad n = 3600$$

3. For each subsidiary, the range of overtime hours is 150, so that $\sigma_1 \approx \sigma_2$ $\approx$ Range/4 = 37.5. Hence, assuming equal sample sizes are acceptable, solve

$$2\sqrt{\frac{\sigma_1^2}{n} + \frac{\sigma_2^2}{n}} = 10, \quad 2\sqrt{\frac{2(37.5)^2}{n}} = 10$$

$$\sqrt{n} = \frac{\sqrt{2812.5}}{5}, \quad n = 112.5$$

Hence, 113 weekly records from each subsidiary should be checked.

4. Maximum variation occurs when $p_1 = p_2 = .5$. Again assuming equal sample sizes, solve

$$2\sqrt{\frac{p_1 q_1}{n} + \frac{p_2 q_2}{n}} = .01, \quad 2\sqrt{\frac{2(.5)(.5)}{n}} = .01$$

$$\sqrt{n} = \frac{2\sqrt{.5}}{.01}, \quad n = 20,000$$

Set 8D

1. $H_0: p = .5$ $H_a: p > .5$ Test statistic: $z = \dfrac{\hat{p} - p_0}{\sqrt{\dfrac{p_0 q_0}{n}}}$

With $\alpha = .05$, reject H_0 if $z > 1.645$. Since $\hat{p} = \dfrac{34}{65} = .52$,

$$z = \frac{.52 - .50}{\sqrt{\dfrac{.5(.5)}{65}}} = \frac{.02}{.062} = .32$$

H_0 is not rejected. There is insufficient evidence to conclude that the proportion favoring the merger is greater than .5.

2. $H_0: \mu_1 - \mu_2 = 0$ $H_a: \mu_1 - \mu_2 \neq 0$ Test statistic: $z = \dfrac{(\bar{y}_1 - \bar{y}_2) - 0}{\sqrt{\dfrac{s_1^2}{n_1} + \dfrac{s_2^2}{n_2}}}$

With $\alpha = .01$, reject H_0 if $|z| > 2.58$. Calculate

$$z = \frac{21.1 - 18.0}{\sqrt{\frac{(3.5)^2}{30} + \frac{(4.2)^2}{40}}} = \frac{3.1}{\sqrt{.8493}} = \frac{3.1}{.92} = 3.37$$

H_0 is rejected. There is a significant difference in the mean assembly times for these two methods.

3. $H_0: p_1 - p_2 = 0$ $H_a: p_1 - p_2 \neq 0$ Test statistic: $z = \dfrac{(\hat{p}_1 - \hat{p}_2) - 0}{\sqrt{\hat{p}\hat{q}\left(\dfrac{1}{n_1} + \dfrac{1}{n_2}\right)}}$

Note that if $p_1 = p_2$ as proposed under H_0, the best estimate of this common value of p is

$$\hat{p} = \frac{y_1 + y_2}{n_1 + n_2} = \frac{160 + 90}{400 + 250} = \frac{250}{650} = .38$$

With $\alpha = .05$, reject H_0 if $|z| > 1.96$. Calculate

$$z = \frac{\dfrac{160}{400} - \dfrac{90}{250}}{\sqrt{.38(.62)\left(\dfrac{1}{400} + \dfrac{1}{250}\right)}} = \frac{.04}{\sqrt{.0015314}} = \frac{.04}{.039} = 1.03$$

H_0 is not rejected. There is insufficient evidence to conclude that there is a difference in the proportions for Cities 1 and 2.

4. $H_0: \mu = 25$ $H_a: \mu > 25$ Test statistic: $z = \dfrac{\bar{y} - \mu_0}{\sigma/\sqrt{n}}$

With $\alpha = .01$, reject H_0 if $z > 2.33$. It is given that $\sigma = 3$ for the normal inspection procedure. Hence,

$$z = \frac{29 - 25}{3/\sqrt{30}} = \frac{4}{.548} = 7.30$$

H_0 is rejected. The first inspector is not working up to company standards.

Set 9A

1. $\Sigma y_i = 131.8$, $\Sigma y_i^2 = 2487.9$, $\bar{y} = \dfrac{\Sigma y_i}{n} = \dfrac{131.8}{7} = 18.8$

$$s^2 = \frac{2487.9 - \frac{(131.8)^2}{7}}{6} = \frac{6.2943}{6} = 1.049 \qquad s = \sqrt{1.049} = 1.024$$

a. $\bar{y} \pm t_{.025} \dfrac{s}{\sqrt{n}}$, $\quad 18.8 \pm 2.447 \dfrac{1.024}{\sqrt{7}}$, $\quad 18.8 \pm .95 \quad$ or $\quad 17.85$ to 19.75

b. $H_0: \mu = 17.5 \quad H_a: \mu > 17.5 \quad$ Test statistic: $t = \dfrac{\bar{y} - \mu}{s/\sqrt{n}}$

With $\alpha = .05$ and $n - 1 = 6$ degrees of freedom, reject H_0 if $t > t_{.05}$ = 1.943. Calculate

$$t = \frac{18.8 - 17.5}{1.024/\sqrt{7}} = \frac{1.3}{.39} = 3.33$$

H_0 is rejected. The modification has significantly increased the average number of miles per gallon at the $\alpha = .05$ level of significance.

2. a. $H_0: \mu = .050 \quad H_a: \mu > .050 \quad$ Test statistic: $t = \dfrac{\bar{y} - \mu}{s/\sqrt{n}}$

With $\alpha = .01$ and $n - 1 = 24$ degrees of freedom, reject H_0 if $t > t_{.01}$ = 2.492. Calculate

$$t = \frac{.057 - .050}{.008/\sqrt{25}} = \frac{.007\,(5)}{.008} = 4.375$$

H_0 is rejected. Wednesday's production has an excess amount of impurities.

b. $\bar{y} \pm t_{.025} \dfrac{s}{\sqrt{n}}$, $\quad .057 \pm 2.064 \dfrac{.008}{5}$, $\quad .057 \pm .0033 \quad$ or $.0537$ to $.0603$

Set 9B

1. See Section 9.4(1).

2. $H_0: \mu_1 - \mu_2 = 0 \quad H_a: \mu_1 - \mu_2 \neq 0 \quad$ Test statistic: $t = \dfrac{(\bar{y}_1 - \bar{y}_2) - D_0}{s\sqrt{\dfrac{1}{n_1} + \dfrac{1}{n_2}}}$

With $\alpha = .05$ and $n_1 + n_2 - 2 = 10 + 8 - 2 = 16$ degrees of freedom, reject H_0 if $|t| > t_{.025} = 2.120$. Calculate

$$s^2 = \frac{(n_1 - 1) s_1^2 + (n_2 - 1) s_2^2}{n_1 + n_2 - 2} = \frac{9(1.1)^2 + 7(2.2)^2}{16} = \frac{10.89 + 33.88}{16}$$

$$= 2.798$$

$$t = \frac{(6.3 - 7.2) - 0}{\sqrt{2.798 \left(\frac{1}{10} + \frac{1}{8} \right)}} = \frac{-.9}{.793} = -1.13$$

Do not reject H_0. There is insufficient evidence to conclude that the two teams are significantly different.

3. a. $H_0: \mu_1 - \mu_2 = 0$ $H_a: \mu_1 - \mu_2 \neq 0$ Test statistic: $t = \dfrac{(\bar{y}_1 - \bar{y}_2) - D_0}{s \sqrt{\dfrac{1}{n_1} + \dfrac{1}{n_2}}}$

With $\alpha = .05$ and $n_1 + n_2 - 2 = 28$ degrees of freedom, reject H_0 if $|t| > t_{.025} = 2.048$. Calculate

$$s^2 = \frac{14(6.2)^2 + 14(9.3)^2}{28} = 62.47$$

$$t = \frac{(80.3 - 68.7) - 0}{\sqrt{62.47 \left(\frac{1}{15} + \frac{1}{15} \right)}} = \frac{11.6}{2.89} = 4.01$$

Reject H_0. There is a significant difference in mean scores for the two presentations.

b. $(\bar{y}_1 - \bar{y}_2) \pm t_{.025} \, s \sqrt{\dfrac{1}{n_1} + \dfrac{1}{n_2}}$, $11.6 \pm 2.048 (2.89)$, 11.6 ± 5.92

or $5.68 < \mu_1 - \mu_2 < 17.52$. Since it is possible that $(\mu_1 - \mu_2) < 10$ according to the confidence interval, approval should not be given for campaign number one to proceed to the next stage.

Set 9C

1. $H_0: \mu_d = \mu_P - \mu_H = 0$ $H_a: \mu_d = \mu_P - \mu_H < 0$ Test statistic: $t = \dfrac{\bar{d} - \mu_d}{s_d / \sqrt{n}}$

With $\alpha = .05$ and $n - 1 = 10 - 1 = 9$ degrees of freedom, reject H_0 if

$t < -t_{.05} = -1.833$. The 10 differences and the calculation of the test statistic are given below.

d_i	d_i^2
-5	25
-2	4
4	16
-3	9
-3	9
1	1
-1	1
0	0
-5	25
1	1
-13	91

$$\bar{d} = \frac{-13}{10} = -1.3 \quad s_d^2 = \frac{91 - \frac{(-13)^2}{10}}{9} = \frac{74.1}{9} = 8.2333$$

$$s_d = \sqrt{8.2333} = 2.869$$

$$t = \frac{-1.3 - 0}{2.869/\sqrt{10}} = -1.43$$

Do not reject H_0.

2.

d_i	d_i^2
4.6	21.16
1.8	3.24
-1.0	1.00
2.2	13.84
1.0	1.00
1.2	1.44
2.6	6.76
2.8	7.84
2.0	4.00
3.0	9.00
20.2	69.28

$$\bar{d} = \frac{20.2}{10} = 2.02 \quad s_d^2 = \frac{69.28 - 40.804}{9} = \frac{28.476}{9} = 3.164$$

$$s_d = 1.78$$

a. $\bar{d} \pm t_{.025} \dfrac{s_d}{\sqrt{n}}$, $2.02 \pm 2.262 \dfrac{1.78}{\sqrt{10}}$,

2.02 ± 1.27 or $.75 < \mu_d < 3.29$

b. $H_0: \mu_P - \mu_H = 0 \quad H_a: \mu_P - \mu_H > 0$

Test statistic: $t = \dfrac{\bar{d} - \mu_d}{s_d/\sqrt{n}}$

With $\alpha = .05$ and $n - 1 = 10$ degrees of freedom, reject H_0 if $t > t_{.05} = 1.833$. Calculate

$$t = \frac{2.02}{.563} = 3.59$$

Reject H_0. Per-unit scale increases production.

Set 9D

1. $H_0: \sigma^2 = 1 \quad H_a: \sigma^2 > 1$ Test statistic: $\chi^2 = \dfrac{(n-1)s^2}{\sigma_0^2}$

With $\alpha = .05$ and $n - 1 = 19$ degrees of freedom, reject H_0 if $\chi^2 > \chi_{.05}^2 = 30.1435$. Calculate $\chi^2 = [19(1.5)^2]/1 = 42.75$. Reject H_0. There is reason to stop and adjust the machine.

2. $H_0: \sigma^2 = 100$ $H_a: \sigma^2 < 100$ Test statistic: $\chi^2 = \dfrac{(n-1)s^2}{\sigma_0^2}$.

With $\alpha = .05$ and $n - 1 = 29$ degrees of freedom, reject H_0 if $\chi^2 < \chi^2_{.95}$ = 17.7083. Calculate

$$\chi^2 = \frac{29(8.9)^2}{100} = 22.97.$$

Do not reject H_0.

3. a. $H_0: \sigma = 5$ $H_a: \sigma > 5$ Test statistic: $\chi^2 = \dfrac{(n-1)s^2}{\sigma_0^2}$

With $\alpha = .05$, reject H_0 if $\chi^2 > 42.5569$. Since

$$\chi^2 = \frac{29(7.3)^2}{25} = 61.81,$$

reject H_0. The new technique is less sensitive.

b. $\dfrac{(n-1)s^2}{\chi_U^2} < \sigma^2 < \dfrac{(n-1)s^2}{\chi_L^2}$, $\dfrac{29(7.3)^2}{45.7222} < \sigma^2 < \dfrac{29(7.3)^2}{16.0471}$,

$33.80 < \sigma^2 < 96.30$, $5.81 < \sigma < 9.82$

Set 9E

1. $H_0: \sigma_1^2 = \sigma_2^2$ $H_a: \sigma_1^2 \neq \sigma_2^2$ $F = \dfrac{s_1^2}{s_2^2}$ where population 1 represents adver-

tising campaign two. With $\alpha = .10$, and $\nu_1 = \nu_2 = 14$, reject if $F > 2.48$. Calculate

$$F = \frac{(9.3)^2}{(6.2)^2} = 2.25.$$

Do not reject H_0. Assumption has been met.

2. $H_0: \sigma_1^2 = \sigma_2^2$ $H_a: \sigma_1^2 \neq \sigma_2^2$ Test statistic: $F = s_1^2/s_2^2$ where population 1 represents commodity 2. With $\alpha = .10$ and $\nu_1 = \nu_2 = 9$, reject H_0 if $F > 3.18$. Calculate

$$F = \frac{(2.49)^2}{(1.59)^2} = 2.45.$$

Do not reject H_0. The commodities exhibit the same basic variation.

Set 10A

1. For each truck purchased, the company will incur a loss of 250 + 500 = 750, whether or not the truck is in service. If the truck is in service, it will earn 1250 – 150 = $1100, so that the total profit will be 1100 – 750 = 350.

Profit Table

		Number in Service		
		1	2	3
Number of	1	350	350	350
trucks	2	–400	700	700
bought	3	–1150	–50	1050

Opportunity Loss Table

		Number in Service		
		1	2	3
	1	0	350	700
	2	750	0	350
	3	1500	750	0

2. If one bid is submitted, he spends $85,000 and earns $100,000 for a profit of $15,000. If two bids are submitted, he initially spends $10,000; if one bid is awarded he earns $20,000, while if two bids are awarded he earns $200,000 – 155,000 = $45,000. Similarly, the profits for three bids may be calculated.

Profit Table

		Number of Contracts Awarded			
		0	1	2	3
No. of	1	– 5,000	15,000	15,000	15,000
Bids	2	–10,000	10,000	35,000	35,000
Submitted	3	–15,000	5,000	30,000	60,000

Opportunity Loss Table

		Number of Contracts Awarded			
		0	1	2	3
No. of	1	0	0	20,000	45,000
Bids	2	5,000	5,000	0	25,000
Submitted	3	10,000	10,000	5,000	0

Set 10B

1.

s_j	$p(s_j)$
1	.3
2	.6
3	.1

a. $E(L_1) = 0(.3) + 350(.6) + 700(.1) = 280$

$E(L_2) = 750(.3) + 350(.1) = 260$

$E(L_3) = 1500(.3) + 750(.6) = 900$

To minimize $E(L_i)$, purchase two trucks.

b. Cost of uncertainty is $E(L_2) = \$260$

2. a. Profit = (Price per unit) × (No. of units) = $60.

		Profit Table					Opportunity Loss Table		

Profit Table

		Weather	
Crop	Dry	Avg.	Excess
1	165	390	465
2	240	440	240
3	290	240	140

Opportunity Loss Table

		Weather	
Crop	Dry	Avg.	Excess
1	125	50	0
2	50	0	225
3	0	200	325

b. $E(L_1) = 125(.2) + 50(.7) = \$60$

$E(L_2) = 50(.2) + 225(.1) = \$32.50$

$E(L_3) = 200(.7) + 325(.1) = \$172.50$

To minimize $E(L_i)$, plant crop 2.

c. Cost of uncertainty is $E(L_2) = \$32.50$

Set 10C

1. a. **Profit Table**

Available Equipment	Demand			
	0	1	2	3
1	−50	450	450	450
2	−100	400	900	900
3	−150	350	850	1350

Note: We assume that if a contractor demands more equipment than is available, he will rent the available equipment, and go elsewhere for the rest.

b. **Opportunity Loss Table**

Available Equipment	Demand				Available	Max.Opp.Loss
	0	1	2	3		
1	0	0	450	900	1	900
2	50	50	0	450	2	450
3	100	100	50	0	3	100

The minimax decision is to keep 3 large pieces of equipment.

2.

No. Bought	Max. Opp. Loss
1	700
2	750
3	1500

Referring to Self-Correcting Exercises 10A, problem 1, the maximum opportunity losses are shown at the left. The minimax decision is to buy 1 truck.

3.

Crop	Max. Opp. Loss
1	125
2	225
3	325

Referring to Self-Correcting Exercises 10B, problem 2, the minimax decision is to plant crop 1.

4. Substitute utility values for monetary values in problem 1, Self-Correcting Exercises 10A.

$$E(U_1) = .30(.3) + .30(.6) + .30(.1) = .30$$

$$E(U_2) = .05(.3) + .60(.6) + .60(.1) = .435$$

$$E(U_3) = 0(.3) + .05(.6) + 1.00(.1) = .13$$

5. In order to maximize the expected utility, two trucks should be bought.

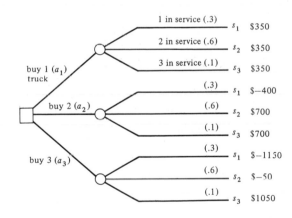

Set 11A

1. a.

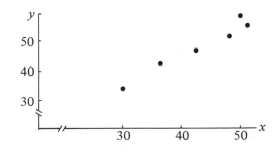

The trend appears to be linear.

b. $\Sigma x_i = 256$ $\qquad\qquad$ $\Sigma x_i y_i = 12608$

$\Sigma y_i = 286$ $\qquad\qquad$ $n = 6$

$\Sigma x_i^2 = 11294$ $\qquad\qquad$ $\Sigma y_i^2 = 14096$

$SS_{xy} = 12608 - 12202.667 = 405.333$

$SS_x = 11294 - 10922.667 = 371.333$

$$\hat{\beta}_1 = \frac{SS_{xy}}{SS_x} = \frac{405.333}{371.333} = 1.09$$

$$\hat{\beta}_0 = \frac{286}{6} - 1.09 \left(\frac{256}{6} \right) = 47.6667 - 46.5067 = 1.16$$

$$\hat{y} = 1.16 + 1.09x$$

c. $\hat{y} = 1.16 + 1.09(50) = 55.66$ or 5566 students.

2. a. $\Sigma x_i = 31.6$ $\quad \Sigma x_i y_i = 624.6$ $\quad SS_{xy} = 624.6 - 609.429 = 15.171$

$\Sigma y_i = 135$ $\quad n = 7$ $\qquad\qquad SS_x = 149.82 - 142.651 = 7.169$

$\Sigma x_i^2 = 149.82$ $\quad \Sigma y_i^2 = 2645$

$$\hat{\beta}_1 = \frac{15.171}{7.169} = 2.12$$

$$\hat{\beta}_0 = 19.29 - 2.12(4.51) = 9.73$$

$$\hat{y} = 9.73 + 2.12x$$

b.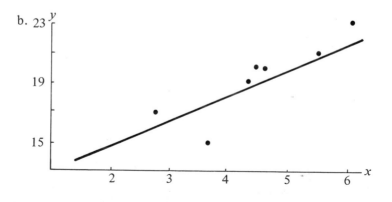

3. a. $\Sigma x_i = 96$ $\Sigma x_i y_i = 1799$ $SS_{xy} = 1799 - 1851.429 = -52.429$

$\Sigma y_i = 135$ $n = 7$ $SS_x = 1402 - 1316.571 = 85.429$

$\Sigma x_i^2 = 1402$ $\Sigma y_i^2 = 2645$ $\hat{\beta}_1 = -0.61$

$\hat{\beta}_0 = 19.29 - (-.61)(13.71) = 27.65$

$\hat{y} = 27.65 - .61x$

b.

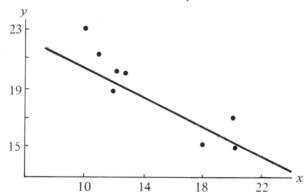

Set 11B

1. $SS_y = 14096 - 13632.667 = 463.333$

$SSE = SS_y - \hat{\beta}_1 SS_{xy} = 463.333 - (1.09)(405.333) = 20.87$

Note that the unrounded value of $\hat{\beta}_1$ has been used for the sake of accuracy.

$$s^2 = \frac{20.87}{4} = 5.22 \quad s - \sqrt{5.22} - 2.28$$

a. $H_0: \beta_1 = 0$ $H_a: \beta_1 \neq 0$ Reject H_0 if $|t| > t_{.025,4} = 2.776$

Test statistic: $t = \dfrac{\hat{\beta}_1 - \beta_1}{s/\sqrt{SS_x}} = \dfrac{1.09}{\sqrt{\dfrac{5.22}{371.33}}} = \dfrac{1.09}{.12} = 9.08$. Reject H_0.

b. $\hat{\beta}_1 \pm t_{.025} \dfrac{s}{\sqrt{SS_x}} = 1.09 \pm 2.776(.12) = 1.09 \pm .33$

or $.76 < \beta_1 < 1.42$

2. $SS_y = 2645 - 2603.571 = 41.429$

$SSE = 41.429 - 2.12(15.171) = 9.33$

$s^2 = \dfrac{9.33}{5} = 1.87 \qquad s = \sqrt{1.87} = 1.37$

$H_0: \beta_1 = 0 \qquad H_a: \beta_1 \neq 0$

Rejection region: With 5 degrees of freedom and $\alpha = .05$, reject H_0 if $|t| > t_{.025} = 2.571$

Test statistic: $t = \dfrac{\hat{\beta}_1 - 0}{s/\sqrt{SS_x}} = \dfrac{2.12}{\sqrt{\dfrac{1.87}{7.17}}} = \dfrac{2.12}{.51} = 4.16.$

Reject H_0.

3. $SS_y = 2645 - 2603.571 = 41.429$

$SSE = 41.429 - (-0.61)(-52.429) = 9.25$

$s^2 = \dfrac{9.25}{5} = 1.85 \qquad s = 1.36$

$H_0: \beta_1 = 0 \qquad H_a: \beta_1 \neq 0$

Reject H_0 if $|t| > t_{.025,5} = 2.571$

$t = \dfrac{-.61 - 0}{\sqrt{\dfrac{1.85}{85.43}}} = \dfrac{-.61}{.15} = -4.067 \qquad$ Reject H_0.

Set 11C

1. $H_0: E(y \mid x = 0) = 0 \qquad$ Test statistic: $t = \dfrac{\hat{y} - E_0}{s\sqrt{\dfrac{1}{n} + \dfrac{(x_0 - \bar{x})^2}{SS_x}}}$

$H_a: E(y \mid x = 0) \neq 0$

Rejection region: With $\alpha = .05$, reject H_0 if $|t| > t_{.025} = 2.776$. Calculate:

$\hat{y} = 1.16 + 1.09(0) = 1.16$

$$t = \frac{1.16 - 0}{\sqrt{5.22 \left\{ \frac{1}{7} + \frac{(42.67)^2}{371.33} \right\}}} = \frac{1.16}{\sqrt{26.34}} = \frac{1.16}{5.13} = .226$$

Do not reject H_0. Note that $\hat{y} = 1.16 + 1.09x$ does not pass through the origin, even though we could not reject the hypothesis, $H_0 : E(y \mid x = 0) = \beta_0 = 0$. We would not expect that it would though, with only 6 observations, due to random variation.

2. $(\hat{y} \mid x = 4.5) = 9.73 + 2.12(4.5) = 9.73 + 9.54 = 19.27$

$$V(\hat{y} \mid x) = 1.87 \left\{ \frac{1}{7} + \frac{(4.50 - 4.51)^2}{7.17} \right\}$$

$$= 1.87(.14) = .2618$$

The 90% confidence interval is $\hat{y} \pm t_{.05} \sqrt{V(\hat{y} \mid x)}$

$$= 19.27 \pm 2.015 \sqrt{.2618}$$

$$= 19.27 \pm 1.03$$

or $18.24 < E(y \mid x = 4.5) < 20.30$.
Since $x = 250$ is outside the limits for the observed x, one should not predict for that value.

3. $(\hat{y} \mid x = 12) = 27.65 - .61(12) = 20.33$;

$$V(\hat{y} \mid x = 12) = 1.85 \left[\frac{1}{7} + \frac{(12 - 13.71)^2}{85.43} \right] = 1.85(.18) = .33$$

The 90% confidence interval is

$$20.33 \pm 2.015 \sqrt{.33} = 20.33 \pm 2.015(.57) = 20.33 \pm 1.15 \quad \text{or}$$

$$19.18 < E(y \mid x = 0) < 21.48.$$

Note that this interval predicts a slightly higher expected yield.

4. $(\hat{y} \mid x = 40) = 1.16 + 1.09(40) = 44.76$;

$$V(\hat{y} \mid x) = 5.22 \left[\frac{1}{6} + \frac{(40 - 42.67)^2}{371.33} \right] = 5.22(.19) = .99.$$

The 95% confidence interval is

$$44.76 \pm 2.776 \sqrt{.99} = 44.76 \pm 2.776 \quad \text{or}$$

$$41.98 < E(y \mid x = 40) < 47.54.$$

Enrollment will be between 4198 and 4754 with 95% confidence.

Set 11D

1. a. Total $SS = \Sigma y_i^2 - \dfrac{(\Sigma y_i)^2}{n} = 41.43;$ $\quad SSE = 9.33;$ therefore,

$$SSR = 41.43 - 9.33 = 32.10$$

b. $r^2 = \dfrac{SSR}{\text{Total } SS} = \dfrac{32.10}{41.43} = .7748;$ $\quad$ c. $r = \sqrt{.7748} = .88$

2. a. $SSR = 41.43 - 9.25 = 32.18;$ $\quad r^2 = \dfrac{32.18}{41.43} = .7767 \quad$ while

$r = -\sqrt{.7767} = -.88.$ Total variation is reduced by 77.67% by using number of damaging insects to aid in prediction.

b. The predictors are equally effective.

3.

x_1 (Bolls)	x_2 (Insects)
5.5	11
2.8	20
4.7	13
4.3	12
3.7	18
6.1	10
4.5	12

$\Sigma x_1 = 31.6$ $\qquad \Sigma x_2 = 96$

$\Sigma x_1^2 = 149.82$ $\qquad \Sigma x_2^2 = 1402$

$n = 7$ $\qquad \Sigma x_1 x_2 = 410.80$

$$r = \frac{410.80 - (31.6)(96)/7}{\sqrt{[149.82 - (31.6)^2/7][1402 - (96)^2/7]}}$$

$$= \frac{-22.571}{\sqrt{7.169\,(85.429)}} = -.91$$

High correlation explains the fact that either variable is equally effective in predicting cotton yield.

Set 12A

1. $\Sigma x_i = 0$ $\qquad \Sigma x_i y_i = 6.3$

$\Sigma x_i^2 = 10$ $\qquad \Sigma x_i^2 y_i = 87.9$

$\Sigma y_i = 49.4$ $n = 5$

$\Sigma x_i^3 = 0$ $\Sigma x_i^4 = 34$

a. The normal equations with $x_1 = x$ and $x_2 = x^2$ are:

$$5\hat{\beta}_0 \qquad\qquad + 10\hat{\beta}_2 = 49.4$$
$$\qquad 10\hat{\beta}_1 \qquad\qquad = 6.3$$
$$10\hat{\beta}_0 \qquad\qquad + 34\hat{\beta}_2 = 87.9$$

b. From equation 2, $\hat{\beta}_1 = .63$. Then solving equations 1 and 3 simultaneously, $\hat{\beta}_0 = 11.4371$ and $\hat{\beta}_2 = -.7786$.

c. Using the prediction equation,

$$\hat{y} = 11.4371 + .63x - .7786x^2$$

when $x = 1$ yields

$$\hat{y} = 11.4371 + .63 - 7786 = 11.2885$$

2. a. $H_0: \beta_2 = 0; \qquad H_a: \beta_2 \neq 0$

Test statistic: $F = \left(\dfrac{\hat{\beta}_2}{s_{\hat{\beta}_2}}\right)^2 = 5.9086$

Rejection region: With $v_1 = 1$ and $v_2 = 2$ degrees of freedom, reject H_0 if $F > 18.51$. Do not reject H_0. The quadratic regression is not significant.

b. $\hat{\beta}_1 \pm t_{.025,\, 2}\, s_{\hat{\beta}_1}$

$.63 \pm 4.303\,(.3790)$

$.63 \pm 1.631$ or $-1.001 < \beta_1 < 2.261$

c. $\hat{\beta}_2 \pm t_{.025,\, 2}\, s_{\hat{\beta}_2}$

$-.7786 \pm 4.303\,(.3203)$

$-.7786 \pm 1.3783$ or $-2.1569 < \beta_2 < .5997$

3. a.

y_i	$x_{1i} - \bar{x}_1$	$x_{2i} - \bar{x}_2$
21	.986	-2.714
17	-1.714	6.286
20	0.186	-0.714
19	-0.214	-1.714
15	-0.814	4.286
23	1.586	-3.714
20	-0.014	-1.714

$\Sigma(x_{1i} - \bar{x}_1) = 0 \qquad \Sigma y_i = 135 \qquad \Sigma(x_{1i} - \bar{x}_1)(x_{2i} - \bar{x}_2) = -22.57$

$\Sigma(x_{2i} - \bar{x}_2) = 0 \qquad n = 7$

$\Sigma(x_{1i} - \bar{x}_1)^2 = 7.17$

$\Sigma(x_{2i} - \bar{x}_2)^2 = 85.43 \qquad\qquad \Sigma y_i(x_{1i} - \bar{x}_1) = 15.17$

$\qquad\qquad\qquad\qquad\qquad\qquad \Sigma y_i(x_{2i} - \bar{x}_2) = -52.43$

The normal equations are:

$7\hat{\beta}_0 \qquad\qquad\qquad\quad = 135$

$\qquad 7.17\hat{\beta}_1 - 22.57\hat{\beta}_2 \quad = 15.17$

$\quad -22.57\hat{\beta}_1 + 85.43\hat{\beta}_2 \quad = -52.43$

Solving the second and third equations yields $\hat{\beta}_1 = 1.09$ and $\hat{\beta}_2 = -.32$ while $\hat{\beta}_0 = 19.29$. The predictor line is

$$\hat{y} = 19.29 + 1.09(x_1 - \bar{x}_1) - .32(x_2 - \bar{x}_2)$$

$$= 19.29 + 1.09x_1 - 1.09(4.514) - .32x_2 + .32(13.714)$$

$$= 18.76 + 1.09x_1 - .32x_2$$

b. For $x_1 = 4.4$ and $x_2 = 16, \hat{y} = 18.44$.

4. a. $H_0: \beta_1 = 0 \qquad H_a:\beta_1 \neq 0$

Test statistic: $F = \left(\dfrac{\hat{\beta}_1}{s_{\hat{\beta}_1}}\right)^2 = .7411$

Reject H_0 if $F > F_{1,\,4} = 7.71$. Do not reject H_0.

b. $H_0: \beta_2 = 0 \qquad H_a: \beta_2 \neq 0$

Test statistic: $F = \left(\dfrac{\hat{\beta}_2}{S_{\hat{\beta}_2}}\right)^2 = .7746$

Reject H_0 if $F > F_{1,\,4} = 7.71$. Do not reject H_0.

c. $\hat{\beta}_1 \pm t_{.05,\,4}\, s_{\hat{\beta}_1}$

$1.0948 \pm 2.132\,(1.2729)$

1.0948 ± 2.7138 or $-1.6190 < \beta_1 < 3.8086$

Set 12B

1. a. $H_0: \beta_1 = \beta_2 = 0 \qquad H_a$: at least one of β_1 or β_2 is non zero

Test statistic: $F = \dfrac{MSR}{MSE} = \dfrac{6.2277}{1.4363} = 4.336$

Reject H_0 if $F > F_{2,2} = 19.00$. Do not reject H_0.

The regression is not significant.

  b. $R^2 = .8126$ or 81.26% of the variation in y is accounted for by x_1 and x_2.

2. a. $R^2 = .8115$; therefore, 81.15% of the variation in y is accounted for by x_1 and x_2.

  b. $H_0: \beta_1 = \beta_2 = 0$ H_a: at least one of β_1 or β_2 is non-zero

    Test statistic: $F = \dfrac{MSR}{MSE}$

    With $\nu_1 = 2$ and $\nu_2 = 4$ degrees of freedom, reject H_0 if $F > F_{.05} = 6.94$
    Calculate

$$F = \dfrac{16.8101}{1.9521} = 8.6112$$

    Reject H_0. There is a significant regression of y on x_1 and x_2.

  c. Additional percentage $= 100(.8115 - .7748) = 100(.0367) = 3.67\%$

  d. Each variable, x_1 or x_2, adds very little to the model (given that the other is already present) because of their high correlation. Hence, each partial regression is non-significant. Together however, much of the variation in y is explained by x_1 and x_2; hence, the significant multiple regression.

Set 12C

1.

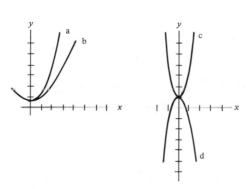

2. $y = \beta_0 + \beta_1 x_1 + \beta_2 x_2 + \beta_3 x_1 x_2 + \epsilon$

3. $y = \beta_0 + \beta_1 x_1 + \beta_2 x_2 + \beta_3 x_1 x_2 + \beta_4 x_3 + \beta_5 x_1 x_3 + \epsilon$

4. The three lines corresponding to areas 1, 2, and 3 are

$$\text{Area 1}: \hat{y} = 2 + x_1$$

$$\text{Area 2}: \hat{y} = 2 + x_1 + 1 + 3x_1 = 4x_1 + 3$$

$$\text{Area 3}: \hat{y} = 2 + x_1 + 2 + x_1 = 2x_1 + 4$$

The graphs are omitted, but the student is referred to Chapter 11, where the graph of a straight line is discussed.

Set 12D

1. a. $H_0: \beta_1 = \beta_2 = \beta_3 = 0$ H_a: at least one of the β_i is non-zero.

Test statistic: $F = \dfrac{MSR}{MSE} = \dfrac{70.4296}{11.1519} = 6.3155$

Reject H_0 if $F > F_{3, 6} = 4.76$. There is a significant regression of y on x_1, x_2 and x_3 since H_0 is rejected.

b. $H_0: \beta_2 = \beta_3 = 0$ H_a: at least one of β_2 or β_3 is non-zero.

Test statistic: $F = \dfrac{MS(\text{Drop})}{MSE_2} = \dfrac{(SSE_1 - SSE_2)/(k - g)}{MSE_2}$

Calculate $MSE_2 = \dfrac{SSE_2}{6} = 11.1519$

$$MS(\text{Drop}) = \dfrac{(120.2263 - 66.9112)}{3 - 1} = 26.6576$$

Then $F = \dfrac{26.6576}{11.1519} = 2.390$

Reject H_0 if $F > F_{2, 6} = 5.14$. Do not reject H_0. The variables x_2 and x_3 contribute no information.

c. $H_0: \beta_1 = 0$ $H_a: \beta_1 \neq 0$

Test statistic: $F = \dfrac{MS(\text{Drop})}{MSE_2}$

where $MS(\text{Drop}) = \dfrac{176.3438 - 66.9112}{3 - 2} = 109.4326$

Then $F = \dfrac{109.4326}{11.1519} = 9.8129$

Reject H_0 if $F > F_{1,6} = 5.99$. Reject H_0. The variable x_1 contributes significant information. Note that this test is equivalent to the test presented in Section 12.4, and that the F-value appears in the printout.

d. Number in family unit and area are not relevant to predicting amount of money in a savings account, but income is.

Set 13A

1. $CM = \dfrac{(93.8)^2}{15} = 586.5627$; Total $SS = 596.26 - CM = 9.6973$;

$SST = \dfrac{32.3^2 + 28.2^2 + 33.3^2}{5} - CM = 589.484 - CM = 2.9213$;

$SSE = 9.6973 - 2.9213 = 6.7760$

ANOVA

Source	d.f.	SS	MS	F
Treatments	2	2.9213	1.4607	2.5867
Error	12	6.7760	.5647	
Total	14	9.6973		

a. $H_0: \mu_1 = \mu_2 = \mu_3$ Test statistic: $F = \dfrac{MST}{MSE}$

   H_a: at least one of the equalities is incorrect.

With $\nu_1 = 2$ and $\nu_2 = 12$ degrees of freedom, reject H_0 if $F > F_{.05} = 3.89$. Since $F = 2.5867$, do not reject H_0 We cannot find a significant difference.

b. $(\bar{T}_2 - \bar{T}_3) \pm t_{.025} \sqrt{MSE\left(\dfrac{1}{n_2} + \dfrac{1}{n_3}\right)} = (5.64 - 6.66) \pm 2.179 \sqrt{\dfrac{2(.5647)}{5}}$

$$= -1.02 \pm 2.179(.4753) = -1.02 \pm 1.04 \qquad \text{or}$$

$$-2.06 < \mu_2 - \mu_3 < .02 \quad \text{with 95\% confidence.}$$

2. $CM = \dfrac{(105)^2}{14} = 787.5;$ Total $SS = 895 - CM = 107.5;$

$$SST = \dfrac{43^2}{4} + \dfrac{21^2}{3} + \dfrac{25^2}{4} + \dfrac{16^2}{3} - CM = 850.8333 - CM = 63.3333$$

$$SSE = 107.5 - 63.3333 = 44.1667$$

ANOVA

Source	d.f.	SS	MS	F
Periods	3	63.3333	21.1111	4.78
Error	10	44.1667	4.4167	
Total	13	107.5000		

a. $F = 4.78 > F_{.05} = 3.71.$ Reject H_0. There is a difference in mean time to assemble for the four lengths of time.

b. $(\bar{T}_2 - \bar{T}_4) \pm t_{.025} \sqrt{MSE\left(\dfrac{1}{n_2} + \dfrac{1}{n_4}\right)} = (7 - 5.33) \pm 2.228 \sqrt{4.4167\left(\dfrac{2}{3}\right)}$

$$= 1.67 \pm 2.228(1.7159) = 1.67 \pm 3.82 \quad \text{or} \quad -2.15 < \mu_2 - \mu_4 < 5.49$$

c. $(7 - 6.25) \pm 2.228 \sqrt{4.4167\left(\dfrac{1}{3} + \dfrac{1}{4}\right)} = .75 \pm 2.228(1.6051) = .75 \pm 3.58$

$$\text{or} \quad -2.83 < \mu_2 - \mu_3 < 4.33$$

Set 13B

1. $CM = \dfrac{638^2}{36} = 11306.7778;$ Total $SS = 12340 - CM = 1033.2222$

$$SST = \dfrac{221^2 + 172^2 + 245^2}{12} - CM = \dfrac{138450}{12} - CM = 11537.5 - CM$$

$$= 230.7222$$

$$SSB = \frac{79^2 + 58^2 + \ldots + 46^2 + 50^2}{3} - CM = \frac{35354}{3} - CM = 477.8889$$

$$SSE = 1033.2222 - 230.7222 - 477.8889 = 324.6111$$

ANOVA

Source	d.f.	SS	MS	F
Employees	11	477.8889	43.4444	2.9444
Conditions	2	230.7222	115.3611	7.8184
Error	22	324.6111	14.7551	
Total	35			

a. $F = 7.8184 > 3.44$. Reject H_0. There is a significant difference between conditions.

b. $F = 2.9444 > F_{.05} = 2.27$. Reject H_0. There is a significant difference between employees. Blocking was effective.

c. $(\bar{T}_2 - \bar{T}_3) \pm t_{.025} \sqrt{MSE\left(\frac{2}{b}\right)} = (14.33 - 20.42) \pm 2.074 \sqrt{14.7551\left(\frac{2}{12}\right)}$

$$= -6.09 \pm 2.074(1.5682) = -6.09 \pm 3.25 \quad \text{or}$$

$$-9.34 < \mu_2 - \mu_3 < 2.84.$$

2. $CM = \frac{(83.4)^2}{20} = 347.778$;   Total $SS = 358.5 - CM = 10.722$

$$SST = \frac{(19.1)^2 + (21.9)^2 + (20.9)^2 + (21.5)^2}{5} - CM = 348.696 - CM = 0.918$$

$$SSB = \frac{(15.8)^2 + (18.3)^2 + (12.8)^2 + (20.9)^2 + (15.6)^2}{4} - CM$$

$$= 357.135 - CM = 9.357$$

$$SSE = 10.722 - .918 - 9.357 = .447.$$

ANOVA

Source	d.f.	SS	MS	F
Brands	3	0.918	.306	8.215
Areas	4	9.357	2.339	62.799
Error	12	0.447	.037	
Total	19	10.722		

a. $F = \dfrac{MS \text{ Brands}}{MSE} = 8.215 > 3.49 \qquad F = \dfrac{MS \text{ Areas}}{MSE} = 62.799 > 3.26$

Both areas and brands are significant.

b. $(4.38 - 4.18) \pm 2.179 \sqrt{\dfrac{2}{5}(.037)} = .20 \pm 2.179(.122) = .20 \pm .27$ or

$$-.07 < \mu_2 - \mu_4 < .47$$

c. $(3.95 - 5.23) \pm 2.179 \sqrt{\dfrac{2}{4}(.037)} = -1.28 \pm 2.179(.136) = -1.28 \pm .30$

or $-1.58 < \mu_{A1} - \mu_{A4} < -.98$

Set 14A

1.

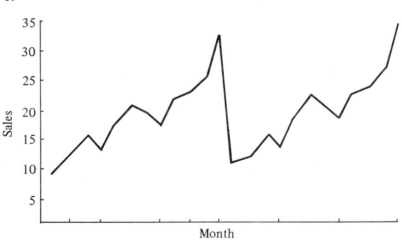

2. The seasonal component, with a period of 12 months.
3. Calculate:

$$\bar{y}_2 = \frac{y_1 + y_2 + y_3}{3} = \frac{37.5}{3} = 12.5 \qquad \bar{y}_3 = \frac{y_2 + y_3 + y_4}{3} = \frac{41.5}{3} = 13.8$$

The 22 averages are given below.

12.5, 13.8, 15.8, 17.5, 19.5, 19.5, 19.8, 20.9, 23.6, 27.3, 23.4,
19.1, 13.3, 14.3, 16.1, 18.5, 20.5, 20.7, 20.8, 22.0, 25.0, 28.9

The moving-average smoothed series is the series connected with the dotted line below.

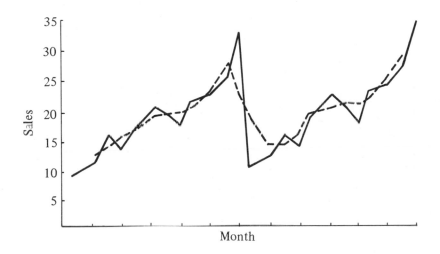

The seasonal component is even more apparent in the smoothed series since some random variation has been eliminated.

4. Let $S_1 = y_1 = 9.5$. Then calculate:

$$S_2 = .1y_2 + .9S_1 = .1(11.6) + .9(9.5) = 9.71$$

Similarly,

$$S_3 = .1(16.4) + .9(9.71) = 10.38,$$

$$S_4 = .1(13.5) + .9(10.38) = 10.69.$$

The 23 exponentially smoothed values are given below.

9.50, 9.71, 10.38, 10.69, 11.38, 12.37, 13.10, 13.54, 14.40, 15.26, 16.31, 18.00, 17.33, 16.87, 16.77, 16.52, 16.67, 17.31, 17.61, 17.71, 18.28, 18.86, 19.73, 21.26.

5. Let $S_1 = 9.5$. Then $S_2 = .5y_2 + .5S_1 = 10.55, S_3 = .5(16.4) + .5(10.55) = 13.48$. The 23 exponentially smoothed values follow.

9.50, 10.55, 13.48, 13.49, 15.55, 18.43, 19.07, 18.29, 20.20, 21.60, 23.70, 28.45, 19.88, 16.29, 16.10, 15.20, 16.60, 19.85, 20.08, 19.34, 21.37, 22.74, 25.17, 30.09.

6. The original series is the dotted line in the graph below.

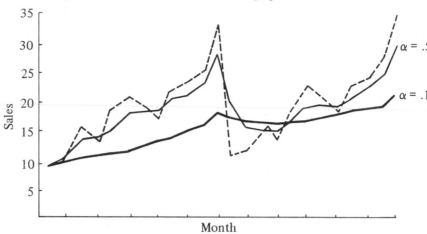

7. The smaller constant smooths the series too much, leaving little information, while the larger constant removes random variation, leaving the seasonal trend visible.

Set 14B

1. Let $I_k = \dfrac{\text{price in year } k}{\text{price in 1970}}$ (100). Then

$$I_{1971} = \frac{325}{340}(100) = 95.6; \ I_{1972} = \frac{350}{340}(100) = 102.9; \ I_{1973} = \frac{380}{340}(100) = 111.8$$

$$I_{1974} = \frac{400}{340}(100) = 117.6; \ \ I_{1975} = \frac{410}{340}(100) = 120.6$$

2. Compute adjusted wages as in 14.5(4).

$$A_{1972} = \frac{100(7880)}{121.4} = 6490.94; \ \ A_{1973} = \frac{100(8400)}{125.2} = 6709.27;$$

$$A_{1974} = \frac{100(8850)}{129.0} = 6860.47$$

Thus, the real wages, $A_{1972}, A_{1973}, A_{1974}$ have increased over the three-year period.

3. $I_k = \dfrac{\Sigma p_{ki}}{\Sigma p_{oi}}(100) = \dfrac{.35 + .75 + 4.25}{.29 + .54 + 2.50}(100) = \dfrac{535}{3.33} = 160.66$

4. $I_k = \dfrac{\Sigma p_{ki}q_{ki}}{\Sigma p_{oi}q_{oi}}(100) = \dfrac{.35(700) + .75(40) + 4.25(11)}{.29(500) + .54(50) + 2.50(8)}(100) = \dfrac{32175}{192} = 167.58$

Gasoline and mechanic's time increased in quantity, the second quite expensive, an average priced item (oil) decreased only slightly; hence the index increased.

5. $I_L = \dfrac{\Sigma p_{ki}q_{oi}}{\Sigma p_{oi}q_{oi}}(100) = \dfrac{.35(500) + .75(50) + 4.25(8)}{192}(100) = \dfrac{24650}{192} = 128.39$

Comparisons made per given number of units sold; increase in mechanic's time and gasoline are not considered. Hence, index is lower.

6. $I_P = \dfrac{\Sigma p_{ki}q_{ki}}{\Sigma p_{oi}q_{ki}}(100) = \dfrac{32175}{.29(700) + .54(40) + 2.50(11)} = \dfrac{32175}{252.1} = 127.63$

Slightly different from I_L in 5 due to different weights.

7. $I_F = \sqrt{I_P I_L} = \sqrt{16386.4157} = 128.01$

Set 15A

1.

t	$\dfrac{2\pi t}{12}$	$\cos \dfrac{2\pi t}{12}$	$11.5 \cos \dfrac{2\pi t}{12}$	$\hat{y}_t$
1	$\pi/6$	$\sqrt{3}/2$	9.96	43.46
2	$\pi/3$	$1/2$	5.75	39.75
3	$\pi/2$	0	0	34.50
4	$2\pi/3$	$-1/2$	-5.75	29.25
5	$5\pi/6$	$-\sqrt{3}/2$	-9.96	25.54
6	π	-1	-11.5	24.50
7	$7\pi/6$	$-\sqrt{3}/2$	-9.96	26.54
8	$4\pi/3$	$-1/2$	-5.75	31.25
9	$3\pi/2$	0	0	37.50
10	$5\pi/3$	$1/2$	5.75	43.75
11	$11\pi/3$	$\sqrt{3}/2$	9.96	48.46
12	2π	1	11.50	50.50

2.

t	y_t	y_{t-1}	y_{t-2}	$\hat{y}_t$
3	10.9	10.6	10.0	$4.3 + .8(10.6) - .2(10) = 10.78$
4	10.8	10.9	10.6	$4.3 + .8(10.9) - .2(10.6) = 10.90$
5	11.1	10.8	10.9	$4.3 + .8(10.8) - .2(10.9) = 10.76$
6	11.3	11.1	10.8	$4.3 + .8(11.1) - .2(10.8) = 11.02$
7	11.0	11.3	11.1	$4.3 + .8(11.3) - .2(11.1) = 11.12$
8	11.5	11.0	11.3	$4.3 + .8(11.0) - .2(11.3) = 10.84$
9	11.6	11.5	11.0	$4.3 + .8(11.5) - .2(11.0) = 11.30$
10	11.2	11.6	11.5	$4.3 + .8(11.6) - .2(11.5) = 11.28$
11	11.7	11.2	11.6	$4.3 + .8(11.2) - .2(11.6) = 10.94$
12	11.5	11.7	11.2	$4.3 + .8(11.7) - .2(11.2) = 11.42$

3. Let $y_{t+1} = y$ and $y_t = x$, so that the notation will be consistent with that of Chapter 12. There are $n = 11$ data points.

$y = y_{t+1}$	10.6 10.9 10.8 11.1 11.3 11.0 11.5 11.6 11.2 11.7 11.5
$x = y_t$	10.0 10.6 10.9 10.8 11.1 11.3 11.0 11.5 11.6 11.2 11.7

$n = 11$ $\Sigma x^2 = 1348.85$

$\Sigma x = 121.7$ $\Sigma y^2 = 1381.1$

$\Sigma y = 123.2$ $\Sigma xy = 1364.28$

$$\hat{\beta}_1 = \frac{1364.28 - 121.7(123.2)/11}{1348.85 - (121.7)^2/11}$$

$$= \frac{1.24}{2.4055} = .515$$

$$\hat{\beta}_0 = \bar{y} - \hat{\beta}_1 \bar{x} = \frac{1}{11}\,[123.2 - (.515)\,121.7] = 5.502$$

$$\hat{y}_{t+1} = \hat{\beta}_0 + \hat{\beta}_1 y_t = 5.502 + .515\, y_t$$

The residual sum of squares is $SSE = \Sigma(y_t - \hat{y}_t)^2$

$$= SS_y - \hat{\beta}_1 SS_{xy}$$

$$= 1381.1 - \frac{(123.2)^2}{11} - (.515)(1.24)$$

$$= 1.26 - .6386 = .6214$$

The residual sum of squares for the model of problem 2 (which includes one *less* term) is $SSE = \Sigma(y_t - \hat{y}_t)^2 = 1.0288$. Hence, the model of problem 3 is superior.

Set 15B

1. Since $T = 1$, $\alpha = .1$, the forecasting equation will be identical to that given in example 15.5(8); namely,

$$\hat{y}_{t+1} = 2.11S_t - 1.11S_t(2),$$

with $S_t = .1y_t + .9S_{t-1}$ and $S_t(2) = .1S_t + .9S_{t-1}(2)$.

The smoothed statistics and the appropriate forecasts are given below.

t	y_t	S_t	$S_t(2)$	$\hat{y}_t$
1	10.0	10.000000	10.000000	—
2	10.6	10.060000	10.006000	10.00
3	10.9	10.144000	10.019800	10.12
4	10.8	10.209600	10.038780	10.28
5	11.1	10.298640	10.064766	10.40
6	11.3	10.398776	10.098166	10.56
7	11.0	10.458898	10.134238	10.73
8	11.5	10.563008	10.177114	10.82
9	11.6	10.666707	10.226072	10.99
10	11.2	10.720036	10.275467	11.16
11	11.7	10.818032	10.329723	11.21
12	11.5	10.886228	10.385372	11.36

2. Similar to Example 15.6(10). Given that $S_0 = 18.0$ and $R_0 = .20$, the necessary formulas are:

$$S_t = .1\frac{y_t}{F_{t-L}} + .9(S_{t-1} + R_{t-1}); \quad F_t = .4\frac{y_t}{S_t} + .6F_{t-L}$$

$$R_t = .1(S_t - S_{t-1}) + .9R_{t-1}; \quad \hat{y}_{t+1} = (S_t + R_t)F_{t-L+1}$$

The calculations are shown in the table on the following page:

Set 16A

1. Assign random numbers 01 through 99 to accounts no. 1 through no. 99 and assign random number 00 to account no. 100. Randomly select 20 random numbers and sample the associated accounts.

2. a. Using three digit numbers 001 through 250 to identify the $N = 250$ workers, we could use the random digits 001 through 250 to identify the workers to be included in the sample, and for any three digit random number in the range 251 through 999 use its remainder upon division by 250. For example, worker number 200 would be associated with the random numbers 200, 450, 700 and 950. Worker number 250 would be associated with the random digits 250, 500, 750 and 000.

   b. Suppose a random starting point was determined as line 66, column 5 of the random number table in your text. The first three digits of lines 66–70 in columns 5–10 are

t	y_t	S_t	R_t	F_t	$\hat{y}_t$
1	9.5	1.7925 + 16.38 = 18.17	.017 + .18 = .197	.2091 + .318 = .53	18.200(.53) = 9.65
2	11.6	1.9016 + 16.5303 = 18.43	.026 + .177 = .203	.2518 + .366 = .62	18.367(.61) = 11.20
3	16.4	1.8427 + 16.7697 = 18.61	.018 + .183 = .201	.3525 + .534 = .89	18.633(.89) = 16.58
4	13.5	1.8750 + 16.9299 = 18.80	.019 + .181 = .200	.2872 + .432 = .72	18.811(.72) = 13.54
5	17.6	1.9130 + 17.1000 = 19.01	.021 + .180 = .201	.3703 + .552 = .92	19.000(.92) = 17.48
6	21.3	1.9189 + 17.2899 = 19.21	.020 + .181 = .201	.4435 + .666 = 1.11	19.211(1.11) = 21.32
7	19.7	1.9314 + 17.4699 = 19.40	.019 + .181 = .200	.4062 + .612 = 1.02	19.411(1.02) = 19.80
8	17.5	1.9444 + 17.6400 = 19.58	.018 + .180 = .198	.3575 + .540 = .90	19.600(.90) = 17.64
9	22.1	1.9732 + 17.8902 = 19.86	.028 + .178 = .206	.4451 + .672 = 1.12	19.878(1.12) = 22.26
10	23.0	1.9828 + 18.0594 = 20.04	.018 + .185 = .203	.4591 + .696 = 1.16	20.066(1.16) = 23.28
11	25.8	1.9846 + 18.2187 = 20.20	.016 + .183 = .199	.5109 + .780 = 1.29	20.243(1.30) = 26.32
12	33.2	2.0000 + 18.3591 = 20.36	.027 + .176 = .203	.6523 + .996 = 1.65	20.399(1.66) = 33.86
13	11.3	2.1321 + 18.4995 = 20.63	.017 + .183 = .200		20.555(.53) = 10.89
14	12.7	2.0484 + 18.7497 = 20.80	.011 + .180 = .169		20.833(.62) = 12.92
15	15.9	1.7865 + 18.9000 = 20.69	.016 + .179 = .195		21.000(.89) = 18.69
16	14.3	1.9861 + 18.7731 = 20.76	.007 + .152 = .159		20.859(.72) = 15.02
17	18.0	1.9565 + 18.8271 = 20.78	.002 + .143 = .145		20.919(.92) = 19.25
18	23.1	2.0811 + 18.8325 = 20.91	.013 + .131 = .144		20.925(1.11) = 23.23
19	20.3	1.9902 + 18.9486 = 20.94	.003 + .130 = .133		21.054(1.02) = 21.48
20	18.6	2.0667 + 18.9657 = 21.03	.009 + .120 = .129		21.073(.90) = 18.97
21	23.4	2.0893 + 19.0431 = 21.13	.010 + .116 = .126		21.159(1.12) = 23.70
22	24.1	2.0776 + 19.1304 = 21.21	.008 + .113 = .121		21.256(1.16) = 24.66
23	27.6	2.1395 + 19.1979 = 21.34	.013 + .109 = .122		21.331(1.29) = 27.52
24	35.0				21.462(1.65) = 35.41

294	218	150	345	333	061
173	376	470	420	974	486
058	248	869	603	164	032
844	605	793	934	688	254
379	610	439	152	806	439

The remainders after division by 250 are

44	218	150	95	83	61
173	126	220	170	224	236
58	248	119	103	164	32
94	105	43	184	188	4
129	110	189	152	56	189

Since 189 appeared twice, the next 3 digit number, 952, which reduces to 202, is included. Therefore, the 30 workers associated with the above numbers are to be included in the sample.

Set 16B

1. a. The estimate of average assessed value with bound on error is

$$\bar{y} \pm 2 \sqrt{\left(\frac{N-n}{N}\right)\left(\frac{s^2}{n}\right)}$$

$$\$46500 \pm 2 \sqrt{\left(\frac{975}{1000}\right)\left(\frac{8600^2}{25}\right)}$$

$$\$46500 \pm \$3396$$

b. The estimate of total assessed value is

$$\hat{\tau} = N\bar{y} = 1000(46500) = 46,500,000$$

with

$$\sigma_{\hat{\tau}} = \sqrt{N^2 \hat{\sigma}_{\bar{y}}^2} = 1000 \sqrt{\frac{(8600)^2}{25}} = 1,698,000$$

The estimate of τ with bound on error is

$$\$46,500,000 \pm 2(1,698,000)$$

$$\$46,500,000 \pm \$3,396,000$$

2. Calculate $\hat{p} = \dfrac{y}{n} = \dfrac{8}{50} = .16$. Then

$$\hat{p} \pm 2 \sqrt{\left(\frac{N-n}{N}\right)\frac{\hat{p}\hat{q}}{n-1}}$$

$$.16 \pm 2 \sqrt{\left(\frac{950}{1000}\right)\frac{.16(.84)}{49}}$$

$$.16 \pm 2(.0510)$$

$$.16 \pm .1020$$

Set 16C

1. Calculate $N = \displaystyle\sum_{i=1}^{L} N_i = 3000$. Then

$$n_1 = n\left(\frac{N_1}{N}\right) = 60\left(\frac{1100}{3000}\right) = 22$$

$$n_2 = n\left(\frac{N_2}{N}\right) = 60\left(\frac{600}{3000}\right) = 12$$

$$n_3 = n\left(\frac{N_3}{N}\right) = 60\left(\frac{800}{3000}\right) = 16$$

$$n_4 = n\left(\frac{N_4}{N}\right) = 60\left(\frac{500}{3000}\right) = 10$$

2. a. Calculate $\bar{y}_{st} = \dfrac{\Sigma N_i \bar{y}_i}{N} = \dfrac{1100(1050) + 600(820) + 800(990) + 500(1280)}{3000}$

$$= \frac{3,079,000}{3000} = \$1026.33$$

Since $(N_i - n_i)/N_i = .98$ for $i = 1, 2, 3, 4$

$$\hat{\sigma}^2_{\bar{y}_{st}} = \frac{.98}{N^2} \Sigma \frac{N_i^2 s_i^2}{n_i}$$

$$= \frac{.98}{(3000)^2} \left[\frac{(1100)^2(1210)}{22} + \frac{(600)^2(930)}{12} + \frac{(800)^2(1080)}{16} \right.$$

$$\left. + \frac{(500)^2(1510)}{10} \right]$$

$$= \frac{.98}{(3000)^2} (175,400,000)$$

$$= 19.0991$$

Then

$$\bar{y}_{st} \pm 2\hat{\sigma}_{\bar{y}_{st}} = \$1026.33 \pm 2(4.37)$$

$$= \$1026.33 \pm 8.74$$

b. $\quad N\bar{y}_{st} \pm 2N\hat{\sigma}_{\bar{y}_{st}}$

$3000(1026.33) \pm 2(3000)(4.37)$

$\$3,079,000 \pm \$26,221.52$

c. For stratum 1,

$$\bar{y}_1 \pm 2 \sqrt{\left(\frac{N_1 - n_1}{N_1} \right) \frac{s_1^2}{n_1}}$$

$$\$1050 \pm 2 \sqrt{.98 \left(\frac{1210}{22} \right)}$$

$\$1050 \pm 2(7.34)$

$\$1050 \pm \$14.68$

3. Calculate $\hat{p}_1 = \frac{12}{22} = .5454, \hat{p}_2 = \frac{5}{12} = .4167, \hat{p}_3 = \frac{6}{16} = .3750, \hat{p}_4 = \frac{3}{10}$

$= .3000.$ Then

$$\hat{p}_{st} = \frac{1}{N} \Sigma N_i \hat{p}_i$$

$$= \frac{1}{3000} [1100(.5454) + 600(.4167) + 800(.3750) + 500(.3000)]$$

$$= \frac{1300}{3000} = .4333$$

$$\hat{\sigma}^2_{\hat{p}_{st}} = \frac{.98}{(3000)^2} \, \Sigma N_i^2 \left(\frac{\hat{p}_i \hat{q}_i}{n_i - 1} \right)$$

$$= \frac{.98}{(3000)^2} \, (38,074.0604)$$

$$= .00415$$

and

$$\hat{p}_{st} \pm 2 \hat{\sigma}_{\hat{p}_{st}}$$

$$.4333 \pm 2 \sqrt{.00415}$$

$$.43 \pm .13$$

Set 16D

1. a. Calculate $\Sigma t_i = 137,090$ $\Sigma n_i = 156$

$\Sigma t_i^2 = 2,045,261,700$ $\Sigma n_i^2 = 2790$

$\Sigma t_i n_i = 2,341,180$

Then

$$\bar{y}_{cl} = \frac{\Sigma t_i}{\Sigma n_i} = \frac{137,090}{156} = \$878.78$$

Also,

$$\Sigma(t_i - \bar{y}_{cl} n_i)^2 = 2,045,261,700 - 2(878.78)(2,341,180)$$

$$+ (878.78)^2 (2790)$$

$$= 85,086,843.84$$

and $\bar{n} = \dfrac{1}{m} \, \Sigma n_i = \dfrac{1}{10} \, (156) = 15.6$

With $M = 200$,

$$\hat{\sigma}^2_{\bar{y}_{cl}} = \frac{(M-m)}{Mm\bar{n}^2}\left(\frac{\Sigma(t_i - \bar{y}_{cl}n_i)^2}{m-1}\right)$$

$$= \frac{(200-10)}{200(10)(15.6)^2}\left(\frac{85,086,843.84}{9}\right)$$

$$= 3690.5774$$

and $\hat{\sigma}_{\bar{y}_{cl}} = \sqrt{3690.5774} = 60.75$

Therefore, $\bar{y}_{cl} \pm 2\hat{\sigma}_{\bar{y}_{cl}}$

$$\$878.78 \pm 2(60.75)$$

$$\$878.78 \pm \$121.50$$

b. $\hat{\tau} = \frac{M}{m}\Sigma t_i = \frac{200}{10}(137,090) = \$2,741,800$

Calculate

$$\Sigma(t_i - \bar{t})^2 = \Sigma t_i^2 - \frac{(\Sigma t_i)^2}{m}$$

$$= 2,045,261,700 - 1,879,366,810$$

$$= 165,894,890$$

Then

$$\hat{\sigma}^2_{\hat{\tau}} = M^2\left(\frac{M-m}{Mn}\right)\left(\frac{\Sigma(t_i - \bar{t})^2}{m-1}\right)$$

$$= (200)^2\left(\frac{190}{2000}\right)\left(\frac{165,894,890}{9}\right)$$

$$= 70,044,509,110$$

and $\hat{\sigma}_{\hat{\tau}} = 264,659.23$.

Therefore, $\hat{\tau} \pm 2\hat{\sigma}_{\tau} = \$2,741,800 \pm 2(264,659.23)$

or $\$2,741,800 \pm \$529,318.46$

2. Calculate $\Sigma a_i = 126$ $\qquad$ $\Sigma n_i = 258$

$$\Sigma a_i^2 = 2608 \qquad \Sigma n_i^2 = 9526$$

$$\Sigma a_i n_i = 4903$$

Then $\hat{p}_{cl} = \dfrac{\Sigma a_i}{\Sigma n_i} = \dfrac{126}{258} = .4883$

To determine the value for $\hat{\sigma}_{\hat{p}_{cl}}^2$, calculate

$$\Sigma(a_i - \hat{p}_{cl} n_i)^2 = \Sigma a_i^2 - 2\hat{p}_{cl}\Sigma n_i a_i + \hat{p}_{cl}^2 \Sigma n_i^2$$

$$= 2608 - 2(.4883)(4903) + (.4883)^2(9526)$$

$$= 91.08001414$$

and $\bar{n} = \dfrac{1}{m}\Sigma n_i = \dfrac{258}{10} = 25.8$

Then

$$\hat{\sigma}_{\hat{p}_{cl}}^2 = \left(\frac{M - m}{Mm\bar{n}^2}\right)\frac{\Sigma(a_i - \hat{p}_{cl}n_i)^2}{m - 1}$$

$$= \left(\frac{(75 - 10)}{750(25.8)^2}\right)\frac{91.08001414}{9}$$

$$= .001317629$$

and $\hat{\sigma}_{\hat{p}_{cl}} = \sqrt{.001317629} = .0363$

Therefore,

$$\hat{p}_{cl} \pm 2\hat{\sigma}_{\hat{p}_{cl}}$$

$$.4883 \pm 2(.0363)$$

or $\qquad .49 \pm .07$

Set 16E

1. With $B = .05$, and $\sigma^2 = pq \approx (.5)(.5) = .25$, and $D = \dfrac{B^2}{4} = .000625$,

$$n = \frac{N\sigma^2}{(N-1)D + \sigma^2} = \frac{12000(.25)}{11999(.000625) + .25}$$

$$= \frac{300}{7.749375} = 387.13 \text{ or } 388 \text{ members.}$$

2. a. Calculate

$$D = \frac{B^2}{4} = \frac{.0025}{4} = .000625$$

$$\Sigma N_i \sigma_i^2 = 6000(.7)(.3) + 4000(.6)(.4) + 2000(.5)(.5)$$

$$= 2720$$

Then

$$n = \frac{\Sigma N_i \sigma_i^2}{ND + \dfrac{1}{N} \Sigma N_i \sigma_i^2}$$

$$= \frac{2720}{12000(.000625) + (2720/12000)}$$

$$= \frac{2720}{7.7267} = 352.03 \text{ or } 353 \text{ members}$$

b. $n_1 = 353 \left(\dfrac{6000}{12000} \right) = 176.01 \quad \text{or} \quad n_1 = 176$

$\quad n_2 = 353 \left(\dfrac{4000}{12000} \right) = 117.67 \quad \text{or} \quad n_2 = 118$

$\quad n_3 = 353 \left(\dfrac{2000}{12000} \right) = 58.83 \quad \text{or} \quad n_3 = 59$

c. If $p_1 = p_2 = p_3 = .5$,

$$n = \frac{N}{NB^2 + 1} = \frac{12000}{12000(.0025) + 1} - 387.10$$

or $\quad n = 388$ members.

3. Calculate

$$\sigma_1 \approx \frac{(500 - 25)}{4} = 118.75, \sigma_2 \approx \frac{(1500 - 300)}{4} = 300.$$

Then

$$\Sigma N_i \sigma_i^2 = (10000)(118.75)^2 + (5000)(300)^2$$

$$= 591{,}015{,}625$$

and

$$n = \frac{\Sigma N_i \sigma_i^2}{ND + \dfrac{1}{N} \Sigma N_i \sigma_i^2}$$

$$= \frac{591{,}015{,}625}{15000(30)^2/4 + (591{,}015{,}625/15000)}$$

$$= \frac{591{,}015{,}625}{3{,}414{,}401.042} = 173.09 \text{ or } n = 174$$

The proportional allocation is

$$n_1 = 174\left(\frac{10000}{15000}\right) = 116 \text{ and } n_2 = 174\left(\frac{5000}{15000}\right) = 58$$

Set 17A

1. $H_0: p_1 = p_2 = p_3 = p_4 = p_5 = \dfrac{1}{5}$

H_a: at least one of the above equalities is incorrect.

$E(n_i) = np_i = 250\left(\dfrac{1}{5}\right) = 50 \quad \text{for} \quad i = 1, 2, \ldots, 5$

With $k - 1 = 5 - 1 = 4$ degrees of freedom, reject H_0 if $X^2 > \chi_{.05}^2 = 9.49$.
Test statistic:

$$X^2 = \Sigma \frac{[n_i - E(n_i)]^2}{E(n_i)}$$

$$= \frac{(62 - 50)^2 + (48 - 50)^2 + (56 - 50)^2 + (39 - 50)^2 + (45 - 50)^2}{50}$$

$$= \frac{144 + 4 + 36 + 121 + 25}{50} = 6.6$$

Do not reject H_0. We cannot say there is a preference for color.

2. $H_0: p_1 = .41, \quad p_2 = .12, \quad p_3 = .03, \quad p_4 = .44$

H_a: at least one equality is incorrect.

	Blood Type			
	A	B	AR	Q
Observed n_i	90	16	10	84
Expected $E(n_i)$	82	24	6	88

With $k - 1 = 3$ degrees of freedom, reject H_0 if $X^2 > \chi^2_{.05} = 7.81$.
Test statistic:

$$X^2 = \frac{(90 - 82)^2}{82} + \frac{(16 - 24)^2}{24} + \frac{(10 - 6)^2}{6} + \frac{(84 - 88)^2}{88}$$

$$= .7805 + 2.6667 + 2.6667 + .1818 = 6.30$$

Do not reject H_0. There is insufficient evidence to refute the given proportions.

Set 17B

1. H_0: independence of classifications.
   H_a: classifications are not independent.
   Expected and observed cell counts are:

	Income			
Party Affiliation	Low	Average	High	Totals
Republican	33(30.57)	85(74.77)	27(39.66)	145
Democrat	19(30.78)	71(75.29)	56(39.93)	146
Other	22(12.65)	25(30.94)	13(16.41)	60
Totals	74	181	96	351

With $(r - 1)(c - 1) = 2(2) = 4$ degrees of freedom, reject H_0 if $X^2 > \chi^2_{.05} = 9.49$.
Test statistic:

$$X^2 = \frac{(2.43)^2}{30.57} + \frac{(10.23)^2}{74.77} + \ldots + \frac{(-3.41)^2}{16.41} = 25.61$$

Reject H_0. There is a significant relationship between income levels and political party affiliation.

2. H_0: opinion independent of sex.
H_a: opinion dependent upon sex.
Expected and observed cell counts are:

	Opinion		
Sex	For	Against	Totals
Male	114(116.58)	60(57.42)	174
Female	87(84.42)	39(41.58)	126
Totals	201	99	300

With $(r - 1)(c - 1) = 1$ degree of freedom and $\alpha = .05$, reject H_0 if $X^2 > \chi^2_{.05} = 3.84$. Test statistic is

$$X^2 = \frac{(-2.58)^2}{116.58} + \frac{(2.58)^2}{57.42} + \frac{(2.58)^2}{84.42} + \frac{(-2.58)^2}{41.58} = .4119$$

Do not reject H_0. There is insufficient evidence to show that opinion is dependent upon sex.

Set 17C

1. $H_0: p_1 = p_2 = p_3 = p_4 = p$
$H_a: p_i \neq p$ for at least one $i = 1, 2, 3, 4$.

	Ward				
	1	2	3	4	Totals
Favor	75(66.25)	63(66.25)	69(66.25)	58(66.25)	265
Against	125(133.75)	137(133.75)	131(133.75)	142(133.75)	535
Totals	200	200	200	200	800

With $(r - 1)(c - 1) = 3$ degrees of freedom and $\alpha = .05$, reject H_0 if $X^2 > \chi^2_{.05} = 7.81$.
Test statistic:

$$X^2 = \frac{(8.75)^2}{66.25} + \frac{(-3.25)^2}{66.25} + \ldots + \frac{(8.25)^2}{133.75} = \frac{162.75}{66.25} + \frac{162.75}{133.75} = 3.673$$

Do not reject H_0. There is insufficient evidence to suggest a difference from ward to ward.

2. H_0: independence of classifications
H_a: dependence of classifications

Satisfaction	Categories			
	I	*II*	*III*	*IV*
High	40(50)	60(50)	52(50)	48(50)
Medium	103(90)	87(90)	82(90)	88(90)
Low	57(60)	53(60)	66(60)	64(60)

With $(r-1)(c-1) = 6$ degrees of freedom, reject H_0 if $X^2 > \chi^2_{.05} = 12.59$. Test statistic:

$$X^2 = \frac{(-10)^2}{50} + \frac{10^2}{50} + \ldots + \frac{4^2}{60} = 8.727.$$

Do not reject H_0.

Set 17D

1. With $e^{-2} = .135335$, $p(0) = .135335$, $p(1) = 2e^{-2} = .270670$, $p(2) = 2e^{-2} = .270670$, and $P[y \geqslant 3] = 1 - p(0) - p(1) - p(2) = .323325$. The observed and expected cell counts are shown below.

n_i	4	15	16	15
$E(n_i)$	6.77	13.53	13.53	16.17

With $k - 1 = 3$ degrees of freedom, reject H_0 if $X^2 > \chi^2_{.05} = 7.81$. Test statistic:

$$X^2 = \frac{(-2.77)^2}{6.77} + \frac{(1.47)^2 + (2.47)^2}{13.53} + \frac{(-1.17)^2}{16.17}$$

$$= 1.133 + .611 + .085 = 1.829$$

Do not reject the model.

2. Expected numbers are $E(n_i) = np_i = 100p_i$, where $p_i = P[\text{observation falls in cell } i \mid \text{score drawn from the standard normal distribution}]$. Hence, using Table 3,

$$p_1 = P[z < -1.5] = .0668$$

$$p_2 = P[-1.5 < z < -0.5] = .2417 \quad p_3 = P[-0.5 < z < 0.5] = 2(.1915)$$

$$= .3830,$$

$$p_4 = .2417, \quad p_5 = .0668$$

Observed and expected cell counts are shown below.

n_i	8	20	40	29	3
$E(n_i)$	6.68	24.17	38.30	24.17	6.68

With $k - 1 = 4$ degrees of freedom, reject H_0 if $X^2 > \chi^2_{.05} = 9.49$.
Test statistic:

$$X^2 = \frac{1.32^2}{6.68} + \frac{(-4.17)^2}{24.17} + \ldots + \frac{(-3.68)^2}{6.68}$$

$$= .2608 + .7194 + .0755 + .9635 + 2.0273 = 4.047$$

Do not reject the model.

Set 18A

1. Let $p = P[\text{paint A shows less wear}]$ and $y = $ number of locations where paint A shows less wear. Since no numerical measure of a response is given, the sign test is appropriate.

$$H_0: p = \frac{1}{2}$$
$$H_a: p < \frac{1}{2}$$

Rejection region: With $n = 25$, $p = \frac{1}{2}$, reject H_0 if $y \leqslant 8$ with $\alpha = .054$. See Table 1(e).
Observe $y = 8$; therefore, reject H_0. Paint B is more durable.

2. Let $p = P[\text{dye 1 measurement exceeds dye 2 measurement}]$

$$H_0: p = \frac{1}{2}$$
$$H_a: p > \frac{1}{2}$$

Rejection region: Using $n = 8$ (since there is one tie), the rejection region is $y = 7, 8$ with $\alpha = 1/256 + 8/256 = .035$. From Chapter 9, Exercise 15, $y = 6$. Therefore, do not reject H_0.

3. Rank from smallest to largest and give solvent businesses the top 6 ranks (or equivalently, the average of the top 6 ranks).

With (1)	Without (2)
4	1
7	2
10	3
13	5
15	6
16	8
17	9
18	11
19	12
20	14

H_0: no difference between the two states.

H_a: businesses in state with strict requirements are more likely to succeed.

Rejection region: State with strict regulations should have higher ranks if H_a is true, making $U = n_1 n_2 + 1/2\, n_1 (n_1 + 1) - T_1$, small.

With $\alpha = .056$, using Table 8, reject H_0 if $U \le 28$.
Calculate $U = 10(10) + 1/2(10)(11) - 139 = 16$. Reject H_0.

4. Rank the scores from low to high. Note $n_1 = 7, n_2 = 8$

Executives (1)	Administrators (2)
6(10)	3(6)
10(15)	5(9)
3(6)	2(4)
8(12.5)	0(1.5)
8(12.5)	3(6)
7(11)	1(3)
9(14)	0(1.5)
	4(8)

H_0: no difference in the distributions.

H_a: scores are higher for executives.

Rejection region: Executives should have higher ranks if H_a is true, making $U = n_1 n_2 + 1/2\, n_1 (n_1 + 1) - T_1$ small. Using Table 8, reject H_0 if $U \le 13$ with

Calculate $U = 7(8) + 1/2(7)(8) - 81 = 3$. Reject H_0.

Set 18B

1. $H_0 : p = 1/2$ where $p = P[\text{Appr. A exceeds Appr. B}]$.

$H_a : p \ne 1/2$

With $\alpha = .022$ from Table 1, reject H_0 if $y = 0, 1, 9, 10$. Since y = number of plus signs = 8, do not reject H_0. We cannot detect a difference between appraisers A and B.

2. H_0: no difference in distributions of appraisals for A and B.
H_a: appraisals different for appraisers A and B.
Rank the absolute differences from smallest to largest and calculate T, the smaller of the two (positive and negative) rank sums.

Property	1	2	3	4	5	6	7	8	9	10
d_i	1860	1380	3490	1200	-80	920	2190	390	-320	520
Rank $|d_i|$	8	7	10	6	1	5	9	3	2	4

Rejection region: With $\alpha = .02$ and a two-sided test, reject H_0 if $T \le 5$.
Since $T - 1 + 2 = 3$, reject H_0. There is a difference between A and B.

3.

Sample	d_i	Rank $|d_i|$
1	2	6.5
2	1	2
3	-1	2
4	2	6.5
5	3	8
6	-1	2
7	0	*
8	2	6.5
9	2	6.5

H_0: no difference in brightness scores.

H_a: difference in brightness scores.

Rejection region: With $\alpha = .05$ and a two-sided test, reject H_0 if $T \le 4$ ($n = 8$, Table 9)

Since $T = 2 + 2 = 4$, H_0 is rejected. There is a difference in mean brightness scores for the two dyes.

4. $H_0: p = \frac{1}{2}$ where $p = P[\text{positive difference}]$ and $n = 24$.

$H_a: p > \frac{1}{2}$

Using $\alpha = .05$ and the normal approximation, H_0 will be rejected if

$$\frac{y - .5n}{.5\sqrt{n}} > +1.645$$

where y = number of positive differences. Calculate

$$z = \frac{y - 12}{.5\sqrt{24}} = \frac{16 - 12}{2.45} = 1.63. \text{ Do not reject } H_0.$$

5. The ranks of the absolute differences are given below along with their corresponding signs.

−12, 13, 6, −4, −10, 3, 14.5, 20, 8, 16, −9, −1, 22, 17, 11, 18, 19, 24, −5, 21, −7, 14.5, −2, 23.

With $\alpha = .05$ and a one-sided test, reject H_0 if $T \leq 92$. Since $T = 50$, reject H_0. Note that the sign test is computationally simple, but the Wilcoxon test is more efficient since it allows us to reject H_0 while the sign test did not.

Set 18C

1. H_0: advertising has no effect on sales.
   H_a: advertising increases sales of advertised model.
   Rejection region: With $n_1 = 13, n_2 = 14$ the normal approximation is used and H_0 is rejected if

$$z = \frac{R - E(R)}{\sigma_R} < -1.645$$

Calculate

$$E(R) = 1 + \frac{2(13)(14)}{27} = 14.48$$

$$\sigma_R^2 = \frac{364(337)}{27^2(26)} = \frac{122668}{18963} = 6.4688$$

$$z = \frac{9 - 14.48}{\sqrt{6.4688}} = \frac{-5.48}{2.54} = -2.16 \qquad \text{Reject } H_0.$$

2. The sequence of runs is AAAAAAEAAEEEEEE or AAAAEAAAAEEEEEE or AAAAAEAAAEEEEEE, depending on how the three observations with rank 6 are arranged. In any case, $R = 4$. The rejecton region, with $n_1 = 7, n_2 = 8$ and $\alpha = .051$ is to reject H_0 if $R \leqslant 5$. Hence, H_0 is rejected and we conclude that status-frustration scores are higher among corporate executives.

3. Rank the examination scores, and note that the interview scores are already in rank order.

Interview Rank (x_i)	Exam Rank (y_i)
4	3
7	2
5	5
3	4
6	1
2	6
1	7

$n = 7$ $\Sigma x_i^2 = 140$

$\Sigma x_i = 28$ $\Sigma y_i^2 = 140$

$\Sigma y_i = 28$ $\Sigma x_i y_i = 88$

$$r_s = \frac{88 - \dfrac{(28)^2}{7}}{140 - \dfrac{(28)^2}{7}} = \frac{88 - 112}{140 - 112} = -.857$$

To test $H_0: \rho_s = 0$; $H_a: \rho_s < 0$, the rejection region is $r_s < -.714$. Hence, H_0 is rejected with $\alpha = .05$.

4. $n = 9$

$\Sigma x_i = \Sigma y_i = 45$

$\Sigma x_i^2 = \Sigma y_i^2 = 285$

$\Sigma x_i y_i = 173$

$H_0: \rho_s = 0$

$H_a: \rho_s < 0$

$$r_s = \frac{173 - \dfrac{45^2}{9}}{285 - \dfrac{45^2}{9}} = \frac{-52}{60} = -.87$$

With $\alpha = .05$, reject H_0 if $r_s < -.600$. Reject H_0.

ANSWERS TO EXERCISES

Chapter 2 Answers

1. 11
2. -2; 14
3. 1; 24
4. 25
5. u
6. $3a^3 - 2a$
7. 2; 2/9
8. 26/27
9. 40
10. 30

11. $x_3 + x_4 + x_5 + x_6 - 4a$

12. $\displaystyle\sum_{i=3}^{6} (x_i - m)^2$

13. $9x + 9$
14. 1
15. 32
16. 60

17. 25
18. 1750
19. $2/x^2 - 3/x + 5$
20. $2/v^2 - 3v$
21. 3
22. 97
23. -15
24. 317
25. .30
26. 16
27. 96.1

Chapter 3 Answers

1. a. Range = 6.8; c. 80; 55; e. median = 19.5; f. 10; g. 75 (upper quartile); h. $\bar{y}$ = 19.03; s^2 = 2.7937; s = 1.67; i. Yes, since 70%, 95% and 100% of the measurements lie in the intervals $\bar{y} \pm ks$, k = 1, 2, 3, respectively; j. Yes (see i).

2. a. Range = 7; b. 2; c. bimodal (0 and 2); d. $\bar{y}$ = 1.96; s^2 = 3.1233; s = 1.77; f. .44; .32; g. No, not bell-shaped.

3. Bar heights for each year represent total sales volume (cash + credit).

4. *Receipts chart:* Individual income taxes — 151 degrees; Corporation income taxes — 58 degrees; Social insurance receipts — 100 degrees; Excise taxes — 22 degrees; Borrowing — 11 degrees; Other — 18 degrees. *Expenditures chart:* Benefit payments — 133 degrees; Grants — 61 degrees; National defense — 105 degrees; Net interest — 25 degrees; Other — 36 degrees.

5. *1960 chart:* Common stock — 180 degrees; Preferred stock — 36 degrees; Industrial bonds — 36 degrees; Government bonds — 90 degrees; Mortgages — 18 degrees.

1970 chart: Common stock — 118 degrees; Preferred stock — 18 degrees; Industrial bonds — 54 degrees; Government bonds — 118 degrees; Mortgages — 72 degrees.

6. Bar height for each year represents total dollar volume (Australia and Great Britain and W. Germany).

7. a. At least zero, 3/4 and 8/9 of the measurements lie in the intervals 41.7 to 43.3, 40.9 to 44.1, 40.1 to 44.9, respectively.

   b. Approximately 68%, 95%, and 99.7% of the measurements lie in the intervals 41.7 to 43.3, 40.9 to 44.1, 40.1 to 44.9, respectively.

8. a. 16%; b. 81.5%

9. a. 4; b. 4; c. 1.7, 1.0, 1.25; e. $s = 1.58$ and is approximated as $\dfrac{6-2}{2.5} = 1.6$.

10. a. 8; b. 8.45 to 9.05; 12.05 to 12.45

11. $\mu = 6.6$ oz

12. a. s is approximated as 16.

    b. $\bar{y} = 136.07$; $s^2 = 292.4952$; $s = 17.1$

    c. $a = 101.82$; $b = 170.27$

    d. Yes, for *approximate* calculations.

    e. No.

13. s is approximated as .8; $\bar{y} = 5$; $s^2 = .5$; $s = .71$

14. $\bar{y} = 1.4$; $s^2 = 2.27$; $s = 1.5$

    At least zero, 3/4 and 8/9 of the measurements lie in the intervals –1 to 2.9, –1.6 to 4.4, and –3.1 to 5.9, respectively.

15. a. At least zero.

    b. Approximately .95 (95%).

16. a. Approximately 97.4%.

    b. Approximately 16.0%.

17. Approximately .025.

18. $\bar{x} = 14.9$; $s_x^2 = 5.88$; $s_x = 2.42$

19. a. $\bar{y} = 4.9$; $s_y^2 = 5.88$; $s_y = 2.42$

    b. Yes.

    c. Yes.

    d. Yes.

20. Mean = 21.45 degrees centigrade, variance = 8.47 degrees centigrade (sq.)
    Mean = 70.61 degrees Fahrenheit, variance = 27.44 degrees Fahrenheit (sq.)

Chapter 4 Answers

1. Sum of the probabilities for all sample points in A.

2. $0 \leqslant P(E_i) \leqslant 1$; $\Sigma P(E_i) = 1$

3. a. Independent if and only if $P(A|B) = P(A)$.

   b. Mutually exclusive if and only if $P(AB) = 0$.

4. a. *ABC; ACB* b. *CAB; ACB;*
   c. *ABC; ACB; CAB;* d. *ACB;*
   e. $P(A) = 1/3$; $P(A|B) = 1/2$; dependent.
5. a. .12; b. .38; c. .88
6. .77
7. a. 1/5; b. 2/5; c. No
8. a. 1/8; b. 0
9. 11/24
10. If independent, $P(AB) > 0$; if disjoint, $P(AB) = 0$.
11. a. 1/2; b. 1/2; c. 5/6
12.

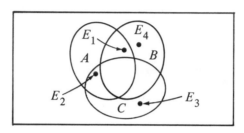

13. a. $\dfrac{1}{6}$; b. $\dfrac{2}{3}$; $\dfrac{1}{3}$; c. $\dfrac{2}{3}$; $\dfrac{2}{3}$; d. $\dfrac{5}{6}$; $\dfrac{5}{6}$

14. a. *B* and *C;* b. *A* and *B;* *A* and *C*
15. a. .25; b. .383; c. .617; d. .558; e. .692; f. .058; g. .13;
    h. .80; i. .583
16. $1 - .59 = .41$
17. No, .5563 is the correct answer.
18. a. $\dfrac{1}{720}$; b. $\dfrac{17}{24}$
19. a. .328; b. .263
20. .0256
21. a. .128; b. .488
22. a. .2; b. .4
23. a. *P*[erroneous indication of tuberculosis]; b. .01089; c. Approxi-
    mately 8% of those with positive x-rays have tuberculosis.
24. 59/64
25. 15/24

Chapter 5 Answers

1.

y	$p(y)$
0	1/6
1	2/3
2	1/6

3. The histogram would approach the probability histogram of Exercise 2.

4. $0 \leqslant p(y) \leqslant 1$, $y = 0, 1, 2$; $\Sigma_{y=0}^{2} p(y) = 1$.

5.

y	$p(y)$
0	1/27
1	6/27
2	12/27
3	8/27

6. $0 \leqslant p(y) \leqslant 1$, $y = 0, 1, 2, 3$; $\displaystyle\sum_{y=0}^{3} p(y) = 1$.

7.

y	$p(y)$
0	.2
1	.6
2	.2

8. a. $\dfrac{1}{4}$; b. $\dfrac{3}{16}$; c. $\dfrac{9}{64}$; d. $p(y) = \left(\dfrac{3}{4}\right)^{y-1}\left(\dfrac{1}{4}\right)$; e. Yes.

9. The mean is approximately 2; Range/4 = (3 − 1)/4 approximates σ; $\sigma \approx .5$

10. $E(y) = \dfrac{17}{8}$; $\sigma = .60$

11. $E(y) = 2$; $\sigma^2 = 5$

12. $E(y) = 2$

13.

y	$p(y)$
0	8/27
1	4/9
2	2/9
3	1/27

14. $E(y) = 1$; $\sigma^2 = \dfrac{2}{3}$

15. $E(y) = \$2800$

16. Premium = \$6.50

18. $E(y) = 1$; $\sigma^2 = \dfrac{1}{3}$; $\sigma = .58$

19. $E(y) = 1.3$; $\sigma^2 = .61$

20. .3

21. \$2.70

Chapter 6 Answers

2. $C_y^n \, p^y \, q^{n-y}$, $y = 0, 1, \ldots, n$

3. a. Not binomial. The number of trials is a random variable and y is not the number of successes.

b. $C_y^5 (1/15)^y (14/15)^{5-y}$, $y = 0, 1, \ldots, 5$

c. Not binomial. p is not a constant and the trials are dependent.

d. $C_y^5 (.6)^y (.4)^{5-y}$, $y = 0, 1, \ldots, 5$

4. a.

y	$p(y)$
0	q
1	p

b. $\mu = \displaystyle\sum_{y=0}^{1} y\, C_y^1\, p^y\, q^{1-y} = p;$

$\sigma^2 = \displaystyle\sum_{y=0}^{1} (y-p)^2\, C_y^1\, p^y\, q^{1-y} = pq$

5. a. $p(y) = C_y^4 (1/2)^4$, $y = 0, 1, \ldots, 4$

b.

y	$p(y)$
0	1/16
1	4/16
2	6/16
3	4/16
4	1/16

c. 2;   d. 1;   e. $np = 2$; $npq = 1$

6. $A = 81$; $B = 99$

7. 130;   170

8. 1202;   1246

9. a. 5/32;   b. 31/32

10. a. .328;   b. .942

11. a. 1/32;   b. .812

12. a. .122;   b. .957

13. a. 82;   b. 76

14. .083

15. a. .214; .214

b. .316; .211

16. a. .9801;   b. .6400

17. a. $a = 1$;   b. .069;   c. P [accept|p low] is higher and P [reject |p high] is lower; more costly.

18. $\alpha = .001$; $\beta = .05$

19. a. $H_0: p = .4$;   b. .166;   c. $H_a: p > .4$;   d. .367

20. a. Declaration that the cheeses differ when they are equally desirable.

b. Failure to declare that a difference exists when one of the cheeses is more desirable.

c. .022; d. .952; e. .264; f. .004; g. When p is close to the value specified in H_0.

21. a. .629; b. 6
22. a. .110803; b. .012; c. .119
23. a. $44; b. $2200
24. .0758
25. a. 1.0, 1.0   c. .537, .736   e. .000, .011
     b. .873, .914   d. .092, .376   f. .000, .000

Chapter 7 Answers

1. No, since the probability that the boy has randomly selected the three balls is .0006.
2. a. .9713; b. .1009; c. .7257; d. .9706; e. .8925; f. .5917
3. a. $z_0 = 0.7$; b. $z_0 = -1.5$; c. $z_0 = 1.55$; d. $z_0 = -1.1$
4. a. $z_0 = 2.13$; b. $z_0 = 1.645$
5. a. .8413; b. .8944; c. .9876; d. .0401
6. No.
7. a. .2743; b. .9452
8. a. .0475; b. .0475; c. .5788
9. a. .0139; b. .0668; c. .5764
10. a. .876; b. .875
11. a. .608; b. 595
12. a. .9838; b. .0000; c. .8686
13. a. .1635; b. .0192; c. Yes, since $P[y \leqslant 60/p = .2] = .0192$
14. a. .6826; b. .1574
15. $\mu = 10.071$
16. .0548
17. .3520
18. 87.48
19. .0516
20. a. $H_0: p = .2$; $H_a: p < .2$; b. $\alpha = .1292$; c. $\beta = .0336$
21. a. .0548; b. $(.0548)^3 = .0002$

Chapter 8 Answers

1. The inference; measure of goodness.
2. Unbiasedness; minimum variance.
3. 61.23 ± 1.50
4. $.06 \pm .07$
5. $.030 \pm .033$
6. $2.705 \pm .012$
7. 38 ± 25

8. 22 ± 1
9. Approximately 256.
10. Approximately 100.
11. Approximately 100.
12. Approximately 41.
13. .1151 (use correction for continuity).
15. $z = 2.5$; yes.
16. $z = -5.2$; reject the claim.
17. $z = .65$; no.
18. $z = -3.40$; yes.
19. a. $z = 5.8$; yes. b. $3.0 \pm .85$
20. a. $(\hat{p} - .2)\Big/\sqrt{\dfrac{(.2)(.8)}{400}}$; b. $z > 2.33$; c. $|z| > 2.58$; d. $.20 \pm .03$
21. Approximately 3600.
22. $z = 1.25$; no.
23. $19.1 \pm .64$
24. $z = 5$; yes.
25. $.06 \pm .04$
26. $z = -1.67$; no.
27. $.07 \pm .08$
28. $z = -2.67$; yes.
29. .01
30. $z = .91$; no.
31. Approximately 40,000.
32. Approximately 400.

Chapter 9 Answers

1. According to the Central Limit Theorem, these statistics will be approximately normally distributed for large n.
2. i. The parent population has a normal distribution.
   ii. The sample is a random sample.
3. The number of degrees of freedom associated with a t-statistic is the denominator of the estimator of σ^2.
4. a. 2.365; b. 2.947; c. 2.920; d. 1.315; e. 1.796
5. Do not reject H_0, since $t = -.6$.
6. $2.48 < \mu < 4.92$
7. Reject H_0, since $t = 3.2$.
8. $12.70 < \mu < 13.70$
9. Reject H_0, since $t = -2.12$.
10. Do not reject H_0, since $t = 1.09$.
11. i. The parent populations have normal distributions.
    ii. The population variances are equal.
    iii. The samples are independent random samples.
12. Reject H_0, since $t = 3.68$.

13. $.86 < \mu_1 - \mu_2 < 2.34$
14. Reject H_0, since $t = 2.92$.
15. Do not reject H_0, since $t = 2.29$.
16. Do not reject H_0, since $t = 1.03$.
17. a. 24.7690; b. 10.8649; c. 20.2777; d. 16.0471; e. 45.7222
18. Do not reject H_0, since $\chi^2 = 8.19$.
19. $.214 < \sigma^2 < 4.387$
20. Do not reject H_0, since $\chi^2 = 2.816$.
21. $2.275 < \sigma^2 < 52.326$
22. a. 2.23; b. 2.34; c. 3.43; d. 6.63
23. Do not reject H_0, since $F = 1.796$.
24. a. Yes, since the variances have not been shown to be significantly different.
    b. Do not reject H_0, since $t = 2.65$.
25. Reject H_0, since $F = 2.06$.

Chapter 10 Answers

2. a. **Profit Table**

	Demand			
Inventory	27	28	29	30
27	5.40	5.40	5.40	5.40
28	5.10	5.60	5.60	5.60
29	4.80	5.30	5.80	5.80
30	4.50	5.00	5.50	6.00

b. **Opportunity Loss Table**

	Demand			
Inventory	27	28	29	30
27	0.00	0.20	0.40	0.60
28	0.30	0.00	0.20	0.40
29	0.60	0.30	0.00	0.20
30	0.90	0.60	0.30	0.00

c. Minimax level is 28.
d. 28 with expected opportunity loss of $0.17.

3. Invest in the savings account; expected return for drilling = $0; expected return for savings = $120.
4. Greater than .212.
5. a. **Profit Table**

	Rain	No Rain
Insurance	−2000	18,000
No Insurance	−5000	20,000

b. Do not buy insurance; expected profit for insuring = $13,000; expected profit for not insuring = $13,750.
6. Up to $1250.
7. a. $p = .1429$; b. $0.
8. Expected return given A = $9400; expected return given B = $11,000.
   a. Contract B; b. Contract B
9. a.

Cakes Pre-pared	Demand				
	0	1	2	3	4
0	0	2	4	6	8
1	2	0	2	4	6
2	4	2	0	2	4
3	6	4	2	0	2
4	8	6	4	2	0

b. Minimax decision = 2; c. 2 cakes
10. a.

Sales volume	Alternative		
	Do not manufacture	Buy $1000 machine	Buy $2000 machine
1000	0	0	500
2000	0	1000	1000
5000	0	4000	5500

b. Buy the $2000 machine; c. Buy the $2000 machine.
11. a. $9000. b. 5/41. c. 0
12. a. $E(L_{acc}) = \$4.00$; $E(L_{rej}) = \$9.20$; accept the lot.
    b. $E(L_{acc}) = \$12.25$; $E(L_{rej}) = \$2.57$; reject the lot.
       Revised probabilities are .02, .33, .40, .25.

    c. $E(L_{acc}) = \$15.60$; $E(L_{rej}) = \$2.06$; reject the lot.
       Revised probabilities are .04, .22, .29, .45.

    d. $1.43; e. $1.94
13. a. Let x be the basic cost of the domestic lot.
       $E(\text{domestic cost}) = \$100 + x$
       $E(\text{foreign cost}) = \$120 + x$; buy domestic lot.
    b. $E(\text{domestic cost}) = \$100$
       $E(\text{foreign cost}) = \$128.60 + x$; buy domestic lot.
       Revised probabilities are .297, .553, .151.
14. Contract B.

Chapter 11 Answers

1.

	y-intercept	slope
a.	−2	3
b.	0	2
c.	−0.5	−1
d.	2.5	−1.5
e.	2	0

2. a. $\hat{y} = .86 + .71x$

   c. $SSE = 4/7 = .5714$; $s^2 = .1143$;

     SSE will be zero only if all of the observed points were to lie on the fitted line.

   d. Reject $H_0: \beta_1 = 0$, since $t = 11.11$.

   e. $.56 < \beta_1 < .86$

   f. $r = .98$

   g. Since $r^2 = .96$, the use of the linear model rather than $\bar{y}$ as a predictor for y reduced the sum of squares for error by 96%.

   h. $.82 < y_p < 2.32$

   i. Reject $H_0: \beta_0 = 0$, since $t = 6.7$.

3. a. $\hat{y} = 8.86 - 1.27x$

   c. $SSE = 2.34$; $s^2 = .5857$; $s = .76$

   d. Reject $H_0: \beta_1 = 0$, since $t = -13.9$.

   e. $r^2 = .98$; see problem 2g.

   f. 2.51 ± 1.27; $1.24 < y_p < 3.78$

   g. $2.51 \pm .48$; $2.03 < E(y|x = 5) < 2.99$

4. If $r = 1$, the observed points all lie on the fitted line having a positive slope and if $r = -1$, the observed points all lie on the fitted line having a negative slope.

5. a. $\hat{y} = 2 - .875x$.

   c. $SSE = .25$; $s^2 = .0833$; $s = .289$

   d. Reject $H_0: \beta_1 = 0$, since $t = 12.12$.

   e. $2.525 < E(y|x = -1) < 3.225$

   f. $r^2 = .98$; see problem 2g.

   g. $-.345 < y_p < 2.595$

   h. $\bar{x}$.

6. The fitted line may not adequately describe the relationship between x and y outside the experimental region.

7. The error will be a maximum for the values of x at the extremes of the experimental region.

8. a. $\hat{y} = 7.0 + 15.4x$.

   b. $SSE = 50.4$; $s^2 = 8.4$.

   c. Reject $H_0: \beta_1 = 0$, since $t = 16.7$.

   d. $43.0 < E(y|x = 2.5) < 48.0$.

   e. $13.6 < \beta_1 < 17.2$.

   f. $r^2 = .979$; see problem 2g.

9. a. $\hat{y} = 6.96 + 2.31x$

   c. $SSE = .9751$; $s^2 = .1219$

   d. Reject $H_0: \beta_1 = 0$, since $t = 19.25$.

   e. $r = .99$

   f. $r^2 = .979$

   g. Do not reject H_0; $t = 1.67$.

   h. $9.27 \pm .69$; $8.58 < y_p < 9.96$

10. a. $\hat{y} = 20.47 - .76x$

   b. $SSE = 4.658$; $s^2 = .5822$

   c. Reject $H_0: \beta_1 = 0$, since $t = -22.3$.

   d. $-.86 < \beta_1 < -.66$

e. $9.83 \pm .55; 9.28 < E(y|x = 14) < 10.38$

f. $r^2 = .984$; see problem 2g.

Chapter 12 Answers

1. a. $\hat{y} = -28.391 + 1.463x_1 + 3.845x_2$

   b.

Source	d.f.	SS	MS	F
Regression	2	884.7946	442.3973	1470.8
Residual	7	2.1054	.3001	
Total	9	886.9000		

   c. $R^2 = .9976$

2. b. $\hat{y} = .1964 - .1000x + .0619x^2$

3. a. 99.85%; b. yes; $F = 1682.3214$; c. Yes; $F = 7.0359$;

   d. Yes; $F = 227.9363$; e. Linear term contributes .21%; It should be deleted from the model.

4. a. $y = \beta_0 + \beta_1 x_1 + \beta_2 x_2 + \beta_3 x_3 + \beta_4 x_4 + \epsilon$

   b. $\hat{y} = -1.5887 - .0078x_1 + .6753x_2 + 28.0134x_3 + 3.4889x_4$

   c. $\hat{y} = 26.4564$ or 27 days.

7. Do not reject H_0. $F = .904$

8. Reject H_0. $F = 11.739$. Variables x_3 and x_4 contribute significant information.

Chapter 13 Answers

1. a. Completely randomized design.

   b.

		ANOVA		
Source	d.f.	SS	MS	F
Chemicals	2	25.1667	12.5834	2.59
Error	9	43.75	4.8611	
Total	11	68.9167		

   c. no; d. -2.25 ± 3.53; e. 39; f. 43.75; g. 11 ± 2.02

2. a. Randomized block design.

   b.

		ANOVA		
Source	d.f.	SS	MS	F
Applications	3	18.9167	6.3056	9.87
Chemicals	2	62.1667	31.0833	48.65
Error	6	3.8333	0.6388	
Total	11	84.9167		

   c. $F = 48.65$; reject H_0; yes; d. 5.25 ± 1.38; e. 21; f. Yes.

3. a. Randomized block design.

   b.

		ANOVA		
Source	*d.f.*	*SS*	*MS*	*F*
Lines	2	102.2	51.1	11.53
Days	9	474.3	52.7	11.89
Error	18	79.8	4.43	
Total	29	656.3		

   c. $F = 11.5$; yes.
   d. $F = 11.9$; yes.
   e. 4.4 ± 1.98

4. a. Completely randomized design.

   b.

		ANOVA		
Source	*d.f.*	*SS*	*MS*	*F*
Treatments	3	1052.68	350.89	1.76
Error	15	2997.95	199.86	
Total	18	4050.63		

   c. $F = 1.76$; no.
   d. -12.6 ± 19.06
   e. i. If possible, form five blocks based upon academic achievement as measured by college grade point average, whereby those five graduates within each block would have similar GPA's.
      ii. When there is no effect of GPA upon performance measured by the examination.

5. a.

		ANOVA		
Source	*d.f.*	*SS*	*MS*	*F*
Programs	2	25817.49	12908.74	4.43
Error	13	37851.51	2911.65	
Total	15			

   $F = 4.43$; yes.
   b. -63.1 ± 59.9

6. a.

		ANOVA		
Source	*d.f.*	*SS*	*MS*	*F*
Autos	4	489.80	122.45	7.55
Additive	3	154.15	51.38	3.17
Error	12	194.60	16.22	
Total	19	838.55		

   b. $F = 3.17$; no.   c. $F = 7.55$; yes; yes.

Chapter 16 Answers

4. a. $130.25 ± $6.12
   b. $13,025 ± $612
5. .15 ± .15
6. 15 ± 15
7. $n = 175$
8. .68 ± .05
9. $n = 189$
10. a. 37.9 ± 5.2 miles
    b. .29 ± .07
11. a. $\hat{R} = .8925$
    b. $\hat{\tau}_y = \hat{R}\tau_x = \$31,166.10$
    c. $\tau_y = N\bar{y} = \$32,364$
12. a. $n = 100$
    b. Select a number between 1 and 100 at random. The sample will include the account corresponding to that random number and every 100th account on the list thereafter.

Chapter 17 Answers

2. a. Yes.
   b. No. Since p_i, $i = 1, 2, 3$ changes from trial to trial.
   c. Yes.
3. a. 8.4; b. 18.0; c. 75.6
4. Reject H_0, $X^2 = 16.535$.
5. Do not reject H_0, $X^2 = 2.300$
6. Reject H_0, $X^2 = 7.97$.
7. Do not reject H_0: $p_1 = p_2 = p_3 = p_4$, $X^2 = 1.709$.
8. Reject H_0, $X^2 = 9.333$.
9. Do not reject the model, $X^2 = 6.156$.

Chapter 18 Answers

1. Sign test: both; Mann-Whitney U test: independent; Wilcoxon test: related; runs test: independent.
2. $z = -2.54 < -1.645$. Reject H_0.
3. Reject H_0 when $R \leqslant 7$. For $R = 10$, do not reject H_0. The runs test is less efficient for detecting a difference in population means.
4. Reject H_0 when $T \leqslant 8$. For $T = 11$, do not reject H_0.
5. Reject H_0 if $y \leqslant 2$ with $\alpha = .055$. When $y = 1$, reject H_0.
6. $r_s = 1$. While $r = 1$ only when the data points all lie on the same straight line, r_s will be 1 whenever y increases steadily with x.
7. a. .738; b. .738 $\geqslant$ .643; reject H_0.
8. With $\alpha = .032$, reject H_0 when $R \geqslant 13$. Observe $R = 13$; reject H_0.